Some Common Elements

Element	Symbol	Atomic number	Approximate atomic weight	Electron arrangement
Aluminum	Al	13	27	•2)8)3
Bromine	Br	35	80	•2)8)18)7
Calcium	Ca	20	40	•2)8)8)2
Carbon	C	6	12	•2)4
Chlorine	Cl	17	35.5	•2)8)7
Copper	Cu	29	63.5	•2)8)18)1
Fluorine	F	9	19	•2)7
Helium	He	2	4	•2
Hydrogen	H	1	1	•1
Iodine	I	53	127	•2)8)18)18)7
Iron	Fe	26	56	•2)8)14)2
Lead	Pb	82	207	•2)8)18)32)18)4
Magnesium	Mg	12	24	•2)8)2
Mercury	Hg	80	201	•2)8)18)32)18)2
Nitrogen	N	7	14	•2)5
Oxygen	O	8	16	•2)6
Phosphorus	P	15	31	•2)8)5
Potassium	K	19	39	•2)8)8)1
Silicon	Si	14	28	•2)8)4
Silver	Ag	47	108	•2)8)18)18)1
Sodium	Na	11	23	•2)8)1
Sulfur	S	16	32	•2)8)6
Tin	Sn	50	119	•2)8)18)18)4
Titanium	Ti	22	48	•2)8)10)2
Zinc	Zn	30	65	•2)8)18)2

USING CHEMISTRY

About the Author

Oscar E. Lanford has worked as a research chemist, a teaching assistant in chemistry, an instructor in chemistry, a professor of chemistry, and as Chairman of the Chemistry Department at the State University of New York College for Teachers, Albany. Since 1952 he has been Dean of this College.

He has served as a member of the Committee of Physical Science Syllabi of the New York State Science Teachers Association and as a member of the Chemistry Syllabus Revision Committee of the New York State Department of Education.

Dr. Lanford and his family apply modern practical chemistry in the operation of a successful Hudson River Valley farm.

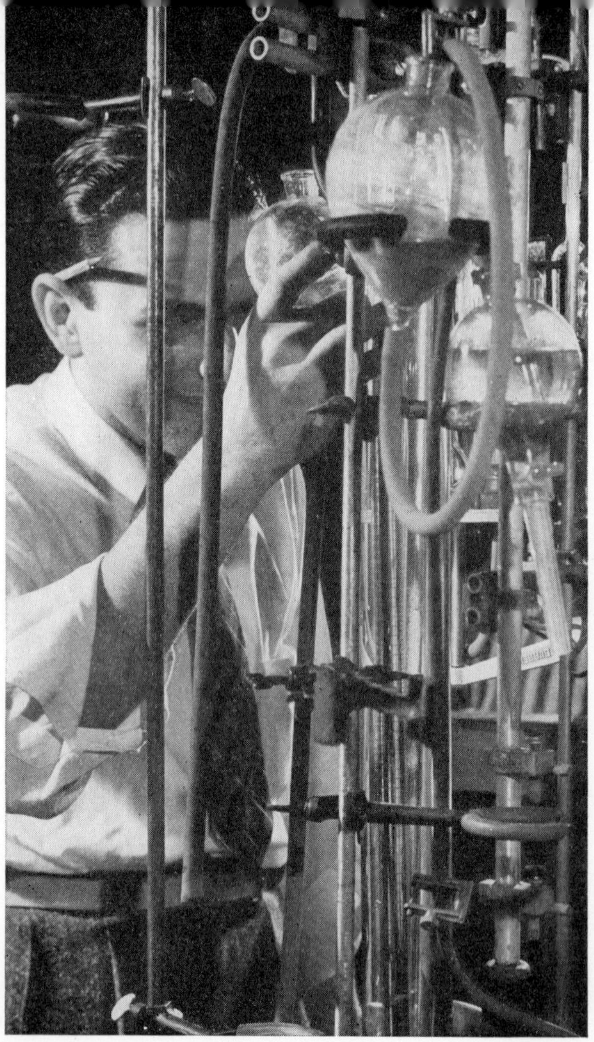

McGraw-Hill Book Company, Inc.   New York   Toronto   London

Using Chemistry

OSCAR E. LANFORD
1959 Edition

drawings by **THEODORE R. MILLER**

USING CHEMISTRY

Copyright © 1959 by the McGraw-Hill Book Company, Inc.

Copyright © 1955 by the McGraw-Hill Book Company, Inc. Printed in the United States of America. All rights reserved. This book, or parts thereof, may not be reproduced in any form without permission of the publishers.

Library of Congress Catalog Card Number: 58-14355

Photographs on the title page of this book used by permission of the Standard Oil Company of New Jersey, Revere Copper and Brass Incorporated, Wide World Photos, and U.S. Navy.

PREFACE

The educational demands in science for this nuclear and space age have brought into sharp focus the need for science instruction that emphasizes basic scientific principles. The scientific developments of the last twenty years demonstrate the fact that although the applications of scientific principles do change, the principles themselves are essentially unchanging.

The revised edition of *Using Chemistry* follows the same philosophy as the earlier edition. The primary emphasis is on the basic principles upon which the science of chemistry is built. In *Using Chemistry* the reader will find as much emphasis on *why* certain reactions occur as on *what* reactions do occur. Scientific principles are of prime importance because they give man the ability to understand and correlate natural phenomena. For this reason, principles cannot be learned and appreciated without constant application to specific cases of chemical change. Therefore, in *Using Chemistry* the specific physical and chemical facts and the principles are woven together.

In placing primary emphasis on basic principles, the author has de-emphasized industrial process and technology. It has been his experience, based on twenty years of teaching, that details of industrial processes are generally not worth teaching in a beginning course except as they may be used to illustrate a basic principle, such as in the Haber process for ammonia synthesis.

The revised edition of *Using Chemistry* contains an extensive section on nuclear energy and nuclear reactions. This section was written while keeping in mind the most recent developments in this rapidly developing branch of science. A new self-explanatory Nuclear Power Plant transvision follows page 210. Emphasis has been placed on constructive applications of atomic energy.

Man-made satellites and rockets have created new interest in highly energetic chemical reactions and the reader will find reference to rocket fuels in appropriate sections of this book.

As a result of the suggestion of many users of the first edition and the increased concern for the more able student, this revised edition contains over 250 additional questions and problems. The problems are intended primarily for the better student and for that reason have been grouped together following the Appendix. However, their range of difficulty is such that by proper selection they will challenge but not discourage classes with a wide range of ability.

Similarly the text material is so arranged that, by careful selection of material, a course can be presented that is meaningful and challenging to the student of average ability. At the same time, inclusion of the entire text will result in a course of such scope and depth as to challenge the best college-bound student.

One important outcome of a course in chemistry is that the students derive some understanding of how science develops and the way in which the work of each succeeding generation of scientists builds upon that of the preceding generations. For this reason, *Using Chemistry* is arranged so that the student is introduced to the evidence for a theory and the need for a theory to correlate the facts before the theory is presented. This results in the absence of dogmatic statements unsupported by evidence.

Throughout *Using Chemistry*, considerable emphasis has been placed on the relationship between the forces that hold together atoms and molecules and the resulting physical and chemical properties of the compound. These principles are among the most important developments in twentieth-century science. Without such principles one can only teach that while carbon dioxide is a gas, silicon dioxide is a solid. With the inclusion of these principles, the student can readily see why these two oxides have such different physical properties.

The extensive section on organic chemistry that appeared in the earlier edition has been brought up to date. This section meets the desires expressed by many teachers for more material on organic chemistry. It includes sections on fuel resources, substitutes for petroleum, plastics and rubbers, as well as on the various classes of organic compounds.

Using Chemistry includes nutrition because good nutrition is everybody's business. Many Americans live on an inadequate diet, not because of their limited income but because of ignorance. The chapter on "Chemistry and Nutrition" includes the latest dietary recommendations of the Food and Nutrition Board of the National Research Council. The chapter points out the advantages of a superior diet over a merely adequate one. The chapter presents evidence on the relation of diet to longevity. While most of the emphasis is placed on human nutrition, some mention is made of practical animal feeding since the basic principles are the same.

Using Chemistry brings a realization of the ways in which the chemical elements, in all their forms, influence man's life and his standard of living. The student is made aware that conservation starts with chemistry. This book emphasizes the fact that known deposits of petroleum and iron and copper ore are definitely limited. Natural resources, such as those that are obtained from sea water or from the atmosphere, are nearly limitless. Accelerated use of the world's natural resources calls for a wise policy, which would ensure that the world's demands for food, fiber, and metal continue to be met. Perhaps the generation now in high school will contribute eventually to the formulation of such a policy.

The unit on the metals begins with a chapter that surveys the general properties and metallurgical methods of the metallic elements. The metallurgy of each metal is given in the chapter dealing with that metal, but many teachers may want to require the student to know only the general metallurgical methods as given in Chapter 43.

The general method for balancing oxidation-reduction equations is taken up along with cells and batteries in Unit Twelve because these topics are closely related. However, *Using Chemistry* is so arranged that the section on oxidation-reduction reactions can be taken up at any time after Chapter 27.

Illustrations, teaching materials, and all of the drawings in *Using Chemistry* have been made especially for this textbook. Visual explanations of processes and procedures have been carefully integrated with the text. The photographs have been selected for their interest and value in illustrating the influence that modern chemistry has on the lives of all of us. Following page 20 there are eight pages of four-color illustrations that convey a little of the beauty as well as the utility of modern science.

Special teaching aids at chapter ends include *Key Words*, *Highlights* of the major facts and principles of the chapter, and *Questions* for discussion. At the end of each unit there are a number of individual and group projects. These *Suggested Projects* range from additional experiments to be performed in the laboratory to conferences with leaders in the community who are concerned with chemical manufacturing and applications of chemistry to health and living in general. The interest and difficulty range of these projects is broad enough to include all students who may be enrolled in high school chemistry.

No other generation of young people has ever found high school chemistry more related to daily living or richer in vocational opportunities than the one now in the high schools. *Using Chemistry*, the author believes, will help the students benefit fully from the challenge offered by the course and will assist the teacher in meeting the varied needs of the students.

OSCAR E. LANFORD

ACKNOWLEDGMENTS

The author owes many thanks to his associates and friends for advice and guidance in the preparation of this textbook. Dr. Walter S. Lapp, Chairman of the Science Department, Overbrook High School, Philadelphia, has made many helpful suggestions based on his thirty years' experience as a high school chemistry teacher. The author also wishes to acknowledge the assistance of Dr. Derk V. Tieszen and Miss Jean S. Moore of the Chemistry Department Staff of the New York State College for Teachers in reading the manuscript and making valuable suggestions, and of his many former students who have contributed much to this book. Assistance from Mrs. Madeleine F. Coutant, Assistant in Secondary Curriculum, State Education Department, Albany, is gratefully acknowledged. He particularly expresses gratitude to his wife, Caroline Sherman Lanford, without whose generous help this book could not have been written. For the 1959 edition, the author is indebted to many users for their suggestions. He is especially indebted to Mr. Daniel Corr, Chairman of the Science Department, Columbia High School, East Greenbush, New York, and to Mr. Raymond Byrne, Chairman of the Science Department, Batavia Junior-Senior High School, Batavia, New York.

Oscar E. Lanford

CONTENTS

Preface   v
List of Tables   xii

UNIT ONE: *The Fundamental Tools of the Chemist*

1. Chemistry and You   1
2. The Materials Used by the Chemist   4
3. The Scientific Method   12
4. Atoms and Molecules   16
5. Chemical Shorthand and Transcription   25

UNIT TWO: *Two Common Elements*

6. Oxygen   45
7. The Reactions of Oxygen: Combustions and Respiration   53
8. Hydrogen   63

UNIT THREE: *Gases*

9. The Properties of Gases   78
10. The Structure of Gases and the Kinetic Molecular Theory   90
11. The Liquefaction of Gases   97

UNIT FOUR: *Water and Solutions*

12. Water and the Properties of Liquids   107
13. The Purification of Water and Its Chemical Properties   132
14. Solutions   146
15. Some Quantitative Properties of Solutions   159

UNIT FIVE: *Atomic Structure and Nuclear Energy*

16. The Periodic Table — 169
17. Radioactivity — 181
18. The Nucleus of the Atom — 195
19. The Uranium Bomb — 208
20. The Uranium Reactor: Constructive Applications of Nuclear Energy — 216
21. The Planetary Electrons: Chemical Properties and Atomic Number — 224
22. The Halogen Family — 235

UNIT SIX: *Some Theoretical Chemistry*

23. Some Quantitative Chemistry: Avogadro's Law and Chemical Calculations — 256
24. Energy and Chemical Change — 266
25. The Factors Which Affect the Speed of Chemical Reactions — 273
26. Chemical Equilibrium — 282
27. Solutions of Acids, Bases, and Salts — 292

UNIT SEVEN: *Sulfur, Nitrogen, and Phosphorus*

28. Sulfur and Hydrogen Sulfide — 314
29. The Oxygen Compounds of Sulfur — 326
30. The Atmosphere and the Inert Gases — 337
31. Nitrogen and Ammonia — 343
32. The Oxygen Compounds of Nitrogen — 357
33. Phosphorus — 367

UNIT EIGHT: *King Carbon*

34. The Forms of Carbon — 380
35. Some Simple Carbon Compounds — 395
36. The Hydrocarbons, Fuels, and Petroleum — 411
37. Some Other Organic Compounds — 432
38. Some Giant Molecules Made by Nature — 460

39. Some Man-made Giant Molecules: Synthetic Plastics and Rubbers	473
40. Chemistry and Nutrition	489

UNIT NINE: *The Mineral Realm*

41. Silicon	509

UNIT TEN: *Between Solutions and Mixtures*

42. Colloids	526

UNIT ELEVEN: *Metals*

43. The Metals	539
44. The Alkali Metals	552
45. The Alkaline Earth Metals	566
46. Copper, Silver, and Gold	588
47. Aluminum	606
48. Zinc, Cadmium, and Mercury	621
49. Iron, Cobalt, and Nickel	633
50. Tin, Lead, and Titanium	649

UNIT TWELVE: *Electrochemistry*

51. Oxidation-Reduction Reactions	661
52. Cells and Batteries	669

Appendix	681
Atomic Weights	682
Properties of Some Inorganic Substances	685
Electron Structures of Atoms	688
Molarities and Normalities of Commercial Reagents	689
Vapor Pressure of Water in Millimeters of Mercury	689
Weights and Measures	690
Large and Small Numbers	690
Additional Questions and Problems	691
Index	707

Nuclear Power Plant transvision following page 212

LIST OF TABLES

5–1.	Valences of common elements and radicals	39
8–1.	The activity series	75
11–1.	Critical constants	98
16–1.	Predicted and actual properties of element number 32	171
21–1.	The electron structures of the inert gases	226
22–1.	Properties of the halogens	253
23–1.	Molar volumes of some gases at STP	258
23–2.	Densities of some gases	259
24–1.	Heats of formation per mole at 25°C	268
27–1.	Common strong and weak acids	300
27–2.	Some pH values	304
27–3.	Hydrolysis of some salts	307
27–4.	Weights of common substances for $1N$ solutions	309
30–1.	Composition of dry air at sea level	337
30–2.	Properties of the inert gases	338
33–1.	Properties of red and white phosphorus	371
34–1.	Fuel values of common fuels	391
34–2.	Products formed by distillation of one ton of average bituminous coal	392
36–1.	Some normal paraffin hydrocarbons	413
36–2.	Products from distillation of petroleum	421
36–3.	Estimated cost of gasoline synthesized from various raw materials, relative to cost of gasoline from natural petroleum	429
37–1.	Some organic acids of fruits and vegetables	443
37–2.	Some esters of fruits	445
37–3.	The main glycerides of natural fats and oils	446
37–4.	Approximate compositions of some fats and oils, in percent	447
39–1.	Tensile strength of some textile fibers	484
39–2.	Comparative resistance of natural and synthetic rubbers	487
40–1.	Recommended daily dietary allowances	493

40–2.	Composition of foods: nutrients per 100 grams edible portion	505
41–1.	Composition of various glasses, in percent	520
42–1.	Classification of colloids	527
43–1.	Comparison of metals and nonmetals	540
43–2.	Approximate tensile strengths of metallic elements after drawing into wire	542
43–3.	Physical constants of the metals	543
43–4.	Ores of the common metals	545
44–1.	Properties of the alkali metals	553
44–2.	Occurrence of the alkali metals in nature	554
44–3.	The Solvay process	559
44–4.	Amounts of potassium removed from the soil by crops	560
45–1.	Properties of the alkaline earth elements	567
45–2.	Occurrence of the alkaline earth elements in nature	568
45–3.	Composition of a Dow metal	573
46–1.	Properties of copper, silver, and gold	588
47–1.	Properties of aluminum, Al	611
48–1.	The elements zinc, cadmium, and mercury	621
49–1.	Alloy steels	644
50–1.	Properties of tin, Sn	650
50–2.	Properties of lead, Pb	652
50–3.	Alloys containing tin or lead	654
50–4.	Properties of titanium, Ti	658
Atomic Weights		682–684
Properties of Some Inorganic Substances		685–687
Electron Structure of Atoms		688
Molarities and Normalities of Commercial Reagents		689
Vapor Pressure of Water in Millimeters of Mercury		689
Weights and Measures		690
Large and Small Numbers		690

UNIT ONE: The Fundamental Tools of the Chemist

CHAPTER 1

chemistry and you

As you read this, it is possible that somewhere in the world a group of scientists, engineers, and technicians crouch in a control room waiting out the count-down for the launching of another earth satellite or possibly a rocket to the moon. The success or failure of any such launching can depend upon the accuracy with which an analytical chemist, working in a quiet laboratory, perhaps hundreds of miles away from the scene of the launching, carried out an analysis of certain components of the fuel mixture. If this chemist's analytical results are not correct, the fuel in the missile will not fire as planned and the entire launching will fail.

At the same moment in another laboratory another chemist is examining a sample of water taken from the water mains of a large city. The health of every man, woman, and child in that city depends upon the safety of this water supply. It is the job of this chemist to maintain a constant scientific vigil on this water and give instructions for whatever treatment is necessary to keep it safe.

At the same moment in a research laboratory another chemist may be crystallizing a new compound, one which has never been made before. He does not know what practical value, if any, it will have for him and his fellow man. He knows that not all new compounds are immediately useful to man although each new one does fill one more square in the scientific jigsaw puzzle he calls *understanding Nature*. He also knows that only by preparing new compounds and studying their properties were those compounds of great practical value to man discovered. He knows, for example, that the one, commonly called *DDT*, was first made in 1847 by a research chemist who never knew of its value to man as an insecticide (see page 453). He also knows that the new drugs, herbicides, plastics, and textiles came about in the same way.

Iron ore is found in reddish rocks such as these. The ore is valuable because of its chemical properties. (American Museum of Natural History)

Simultaneously, in a classroom another chemist is engaged in instructing young people in that branch of science known as chemistry. His job is to pass on to the younger generation the most significant things that all past generations of chemists have learned by experimentation and reasoning. He knows that each generation of man for the past two hundred years has become more dependent upon the chemist for food, shelter, clothing, cleanliness, and health, and that coming generations will be even more dependent upon their chemists. This chemist's work will be done carefully and efficiently because the well-being of future generations depends upon an adequate supply of well-trained chemists.

As you take up the study of this new subject, you may have these two questions in mind: What is chemistry? and Of what importance is chemistry to me?

What is chemistry? **Chemistry** is the science that deals with the properties of **matter** and the changes that matter undergoes.

Properties are the characteristics of a material by means of which it may be recognized and described. They are also the characteristics that determine the uses to which the material may be put.

You are already familiar with many changes that matter undergoes. For example, the value of coal is due to the fact that when mixed with hot oxygen, it liberates heat as it is converted into carbon dioxide. In certain sections of Minnesota and Michigan, great quantities of a reddish rock (hematite) are dug from the ground each year. The value of this material lies in the fact that when it is heated with coke, it is changed into other materials, one of which is the metal iron.

The study of chemistry is, therefore, a study of the various materials found on the earth and the changes that all these different forms of matter undergo. Incidentally, chemistry also includes a study of how the results of these changes influence the life of man.

Of what importance is chemistry to you? As has been noted above, chemistry is important to everyone whether or not he has any knowledge of the subject. Since modern man is so highly dependent upon the chemist, it is essential that each generation train an adequate number of professional chemists. There are many openings for chemists in industry, government, and education. Even though you do not expect to become a professional chemist, you may find that a knowledge of chemistry is essential in your chosen profession. This would certainly be true if you are going into medicine, pharmacy, nursing, engineering, or agriculture.

Perhaps a knowledge of chemistry can be of most direct practical value to the greatest number of people through the homemaker. The homemaker is responsible for the diet and health of the family. The diet has a great influence on the individual's health, disposition, mental health, and ability to work. A homemaker is much better prepared to give her family the benefits of the newer knowledge of nutrition if she has an understanding of chemistry.

Disregarding all the practical reasons cited above for studying chemistry, there is still another reason. The study of chemistry is, as you will see, an exciting intellectual adventure in itself, for through it one can gain a much better understanding of Nature and of one's own place in the scheme of Nature.

KEY WORDS

chemistry   matter   properties

QUESTIONS

1. Make a list of all the properties of water of which you can think.
2. What are some important occupations in which a knowledge of chemistry is essential?
3. List as many ways as you can in which applied chemistry influences modern transportation methods.
4. Why should a housewife have some knowledge of chemistry?
5. Make a list of things that you enjoy today because of chemistry, but that were unknown to your grandparents.

CHAPTER 2

the materials used by the chemist

In Chap. 1 you read that chemistry deals with all the various materials found on the earth, with the properties of these materials, and with the changes which these materials can undergo. It may seem that it would be impossible for any one person to become even moderately well acquainted with such a wide variety of materials. As a matter of fact, however, chemistry is not difficult, provided you use the right approach. One thing to keep in mind throughout the study of chemistry is this: Instead of attempting to remember isolated facts, try to classify and, if possible, to relate the various facts. To a considerable extent the ability to classify and to relate facts that seem isolated is the secret to the successful study of chemistry. This ability is one of the important "tools" of the scientist. Before the use of this tool can be illustrated, however, it will be necessary for you to learn the meaning of a few new terms.

Properties of substances and mixtures

The *physical properties* most used to describe and identify materials are color, odor, taste, density (weight per unit volume), freezing point, boiling point, hardness, and solubility or nonsolubility in water and other liquids. All these properties are independent of the size and shape of a sample and hence are distinguishing characteristics.

Substance is the term used by chemists to apply to **homogeneous** forms of matter, that is, those which are the same in all their parts. Thus iron, sulfur, salt, and sugar are substances. Milk, river water,

A piece of granite. Granite is a mixture of several different substances including quartz and feldspar. (American Museum of Natural History)

wood, and granite, on the other hand, are not substances because they are not homogeneous. If a piece of granite, for instance, is examined closely, you will see that it consists of several different substances, some of which you may be able to identify. You will find quartz, feldspar, and other less common substances.

A mixture can be separated into its components

All the various materials with which you come in contact are grouped as either *pure substances* or *mixtures of two or more pure substances*. The properties of a **mixture** depend on the properties of the pure substances of which it is made up. For, in a mixture, each component substance keeps its own characteristic set of physical and chemical properties.

For example, if you form a mixture of iron and sulfur by grinding them together in a mortar, you change the properties of neither the iron nor the sulfur. Each particle of iron retains its identity just as if the sulfur were not present, and the sulfur is not affected by the presence of the iron. You can demonstrate this fact for one specific property by testing iron and sulfur separately, and then the mixture, with a magnet. Whether pure or in a mixture, the iron is magnetic and the sulfur is nonmagnetic. Therefore, if you apply a magnet to the mixture of iron and sulfur, the iron can be separated from the mixture (Fig. 2–2).

Differences in solubilities separate mixtures

Another test that shows that each component of a mixture keeps its identity is the test of solubility.

Although neither the iron nor the sulfur can be dissolved in water, the sulfur is readily soluble in another liquid, carbon disulfide. Thus,

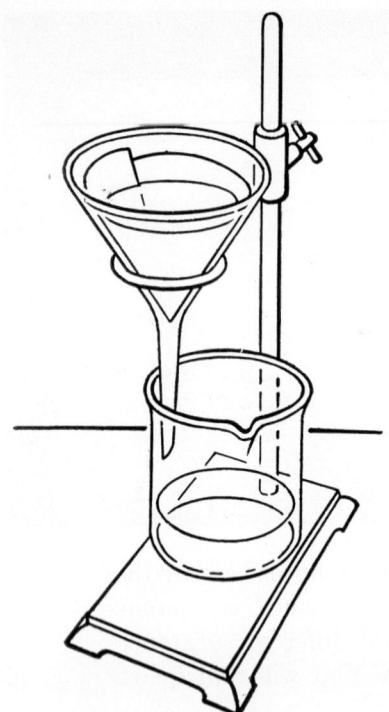

Fig. 2–1. Iron and sulfur can be separated by dissolving the sulfur in carbon disulfide and filtering. The iron will remain on the filter paper and the carbon disulfide solution of sulfur will pass through it.

if a small amount of the sulfur is added to some carbon disulfide in a test tube, some of the sulfur will dissolve. You can show that it does dissolve by filtering some of the liquid onto a watch glass. **Filtration** is a process used to separate solids from liquids and involves pouring the mixture onto filter paper or a similar material through which the liquid but not the solid can pass (see Fig. 2–1). After a few minutes the carbon disulfide will evaporate and a deposit of sulfur will be found on the watch glass. (This procedure is generally a good method for finding out whether or not a solid is soluble in a given liquid.) If enough carbon disulfide is used, all the sulfur will dissolve. On the other hand, if this test is applied to iron, you will find that the iron is not dissolved by the carbon disulfide and is entirely unchanged by the liquid. That is, after you filter the iron and carbon disulfide mixture, all the iron will be found in the **residue** (that portion which does not pass through the filter paper). Also, after you evaporate the **filtrate** (the liquid

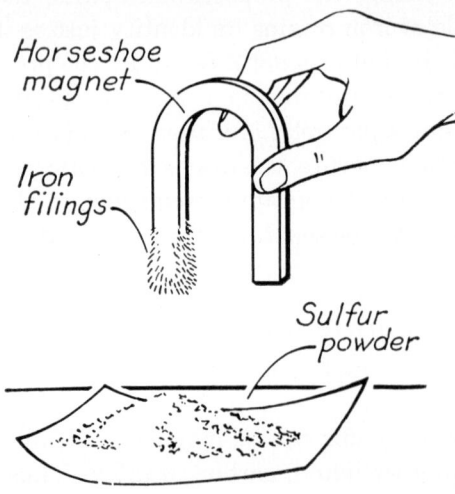

Fig. 2–2. Iron can be separated from sulfur by use of a magnet. The iron filings will be attracted to the magnet and the sulfur powder will remain unaffected.

The refining of sugar depends upon differences in solubility of the sugar and its impurities. Sugar juice, extracted from the sugar cane or the sugar beet, is evaporated in huge vacuum pans until sugar crystals begin to form. The impurities in the sugar juice stay in solution and are separated from the sugar crystals by being strained off in a machine called a centrifuge. (Sugar Information, Inc.)

which passes through the filter paper), no deposit of iron will appear.

Now if you add carbon disulfide to the iron-sulfur mixture, filter the mixture, and evaporate the filtrate, you will find that it is still possible to dissolve all the sulfur and none of the iron of the mixture. Thus in the mixture of sulfur and iron each substance retains its individual solubility properties.

By testing other specific properties of iron and sulfur separately and when mixed together in a similar manner, you can show that in the mixture each component retains all its individual characteristic properties.

Mixtures can, in general, be separated by taking advantage of the differences in the physical properties of the components. Separations, such as the one illustrated, based on difference in solubility, are particularly important because they are widely used in the laboratory and in industry for purifying substances. Thus difference in solubility is used in the refining of crude sugar (the process of separating the sugar from the other substances with which it is mixed in nature). This process is carried out by taking advantage of the difference in solubility in water of the sugar and the other substances originally present. Crude salt is purified in the same manner. Even silver is removed from crude lead by this principle.

Physical change and chemical change

The chemist is concerned with two types of changes: (1) physical changes and (2) chemical changes.

1. Physical change. Everyone is familiar with the fact that many substances can exist in three different forms—solid, liquid, and gas. Thus water which is a liquid, on being cooled sufficiently, changes to ice which is a solid. When liquid water is heated, it changes to water vapor which is a gas.

This type of change is called physical change. **The characteristic of physical change is that the substance still retains its identity.** Also, a physical change is generally readily *reversible*. In the case of water which was described above, the change was accomplished by a change in temperature. However, changes in pressure, as well as in other factors, can also produce physical changes.

2. Chemical change. **In a chemical change or chemical reaction the substance loses its identity and one or more new substances appear in its place.** A piece of coal, on being heated in air, burns, forming a colorless gas, carbon dioxide, which has no similarity to the original material. A sample of iron, on exposure to air, slowly turns to a reddish-brown scaly mixture. The iron has disappeared, and in its place there are several new substances which together are called *rust*. The formation of rust is due to a chemical change.

Chemical changes are distinguished from physical changes by another fact. *Generally chemical changes are difficult or impossible to reverse*, whereas many physical changes are easily reversed by changing external conditions such as temperature and pressure. Thus if the housewife finds, on opening the back door some morning, that her milk is frozen, she is not likely to be particularly upset, but if she finds the milk has soured—that there has been a chemical change of milk sugar into lactic acid—you may be sure the milkman will hear about it without delay!

Elements and compounds

Many common substances can be converted by chemical changes into two or more other substances. For example, if direct-current electricity is passed through water containing a small amount of sulfuric acid, the water is converted into two gases, oxygen and hydrogen. Oxygen appears at the positive electrode,[1] and hydrogen appears at the negative electrode (Fig. 2-3, left). This process is called *electrolysis*.

Another sort of treatment—heating—changes the red powder

[1] An electrode is a terminal, usually a plate or rod, by which an electric current enters or leaves a material. The positive electrode is known as the anode, the negative electrode as the cathode.

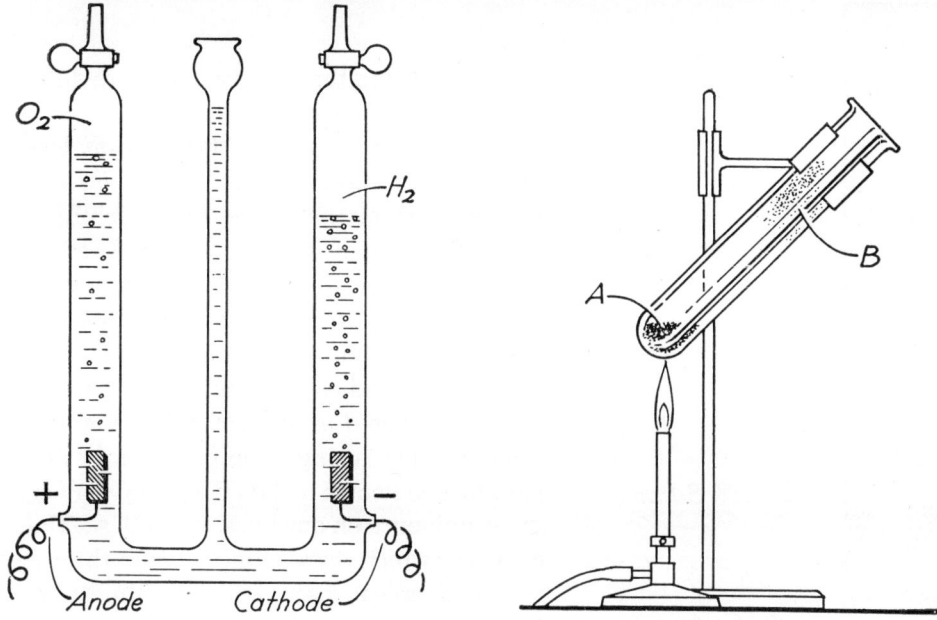

Fig. 2–3. Left, water is chemically changed into two new substances, hydrogen and oxygen, by passing direct-current electricity through it. Right, mercuric oxide (A) is chemically changed into mercury (B) and oxygen by heating.

known to the chemist as *mecuric oxide* into a colorless gas, oxygen, and a gray liquid metal known as *mercury* or *quicksilver* (Fig. 2–3, right).

Many other substances also can be decomposed (broken down) into two or more different substances. The question arises: Can all substances be decomposed by these or similar methods? It has been found that, although a great many substances are similarly decomposable, there are some which are not. For example, iron, sulfur, mercury, copper, and oxygen cannot be decomposed into other substances by ordinary chemical methods. This difference makes it possible to classify all substances into two groups: (1) Substances, such as mercuric oxide or water, which are made up of two or more simpler substances and are called **compounds** and (2) substances which cannot be decomposed by ordinary chemical methods. These substances are evidently in their most elementary chemical form and are therefore called **elements**. Of course, all compounds consist of two or more elements united chemically. In other words, all the materials on the earth are made up of either elements in the uncombined state or compounds, which consist of two or more of these elements chemically combined.

Elements are the building blocks of all matter

The elements may be considered as building blocks, each element being a building block of somewhat different type from any other element. From these building blocks all the known compounds are

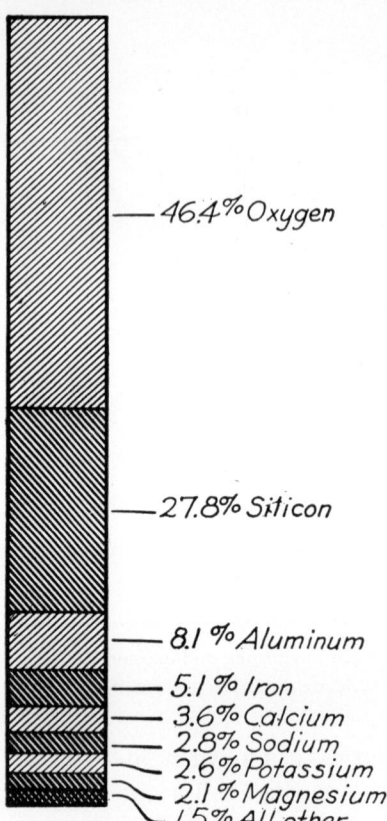

Fig. 2–4. The composition of the earth's crust.

made by fitting together two or more different kinds of blocks in a definite way.

It is known now that there are at least one hundred and two elements. Every time two or more of the elements are combined in a different way a new compound results. The number of different compounds which are possible is almost unlimited. More than five hundred thousand compounds have already been studied and many new ones are being discovered each year. When you consider that just a single compound, for example, the one known as DDT, can have a very great influence on our lives, you will see that changes which can come about through future chemical discoveries are almost unlimited in number.

The *abundance in nature* of the various elements differs widely. Figure 2–4 shows the relative abundance of the elements in the earth's crust and atmosphere. You can see that the two elements oxygen and silicon make up about three-quarters of the earth's crust.

The object of a course in chemistry

The object of a course in chemistry is for you to learn all you can about each of the elements. Your study will include (1) the sources of the elements, (2) their physical properties, (3) the conditions under which they combine with other elements, (4) the properties of the resulting compounds, and (5) the uses of the elements and their compounds. Finally, by studying the uses of the elements and their compounds, you should come to realize some of the ways in which chemistry, as applied by man, and chemical processes, as we find them in nature, influence your life.

KEY WORDS

chemical change	element	homogeneous	residue
chemical reaction	filtrate	mixture	substance
compound	filtration	physical change	

HIGHLIGHTS

Substances are of two kinds: **elements** and **compounds.** An element cannot be resolved into a simpler substance by ordinary chemical methods. A compound consists of two or more elements combined in definite proportions by weight. There are at least ninety-eight elements, natural or man-made. The number of compounds possible is almost unlimited.

Mixtures may be separated by procedures based upon a knowledge of the properties of the substances in the mixture. Differences in solubility or magnetism, for instance, may be the basis of separating a mixture of finely divided iron and sulfur.

Matter undergoes two types of change: **physical change** and **chemical change.** In general, chemical changes are more difficult to reverse than physical changes.

QUESTIONS

1. Make a list of six pure substances.
2. Make a list of six materials which are mixtures and state what substances are contained in each.
3. If you were given some crude salt which contained some sand, how might you separate pure salt from this mixture?
4. Into what two groups does the chemist classify all matter?
5. List all the physical properties of iron which you can think of.
6. List all the physical properties of sulfur which you know.
7. Explain why sulfur is a substance while granite is not.
8. What is the essential difference between a physical change and a chemical change?
9. Give two illustrations of a physical change and show why you classify each as a physical change.
10. Give two illustrations of a chemical change and show why you classify each as a chemical change.
11. Classify the following as physical or chemical changes: (*a*) freezing of water, (*b*) souring of milk, (*c*) rusting of iron, (*d*) burning of wood, (*e*) evaporation of water, (*f*) formation of a cloud (*g*) dissolving of sulfur.
12. Define: (*a*) element, (*b*) compound.
13. Give three examples of an element.
14. How many elements are known to man?
15. Name the five most abundant elements in nature. List these in the order of their abundance.
16. Give three examples of a compound.

CHAPTER 3

the scientific method

It is a remarkable fact that although men have, consciously and unconsciously, carried out chemical changes for many hundreds of years, most of the important chemical discoveries have been made within the last 150 years. In fact, we may say that the science of chemistry as we know it today came into existence about the beginning of the nineteenth century. In 1805 an English schoolmaster named John Dalton set forth a theory which has come to be known as *Dalton's atomic theory*. This theory has formed the cornerstone of modern chemistry.

Astronomy has been called the *mother of the science of physics*. This is because it was from study and speculation about the planets and stars that certain rules regarding their motion were learned and tested. These rules eventually led to the development of all the various branches of physics.

Man's earliest interest in chemistry was, as his chief interest in it is today, purely practical. Chemical changes provided early man with his only source of artificial heat and illumination, with his food, and with his clothing. Almost as soon as he learned to write, man discovered how to obtain metals from certain rocks, how to extract dyes from certain plants, and how to make alcoholic drinks by the fermentation of fruits and grains.

Some of these discoveries proved to be of great economic importance. Many of them in the early years of history formed the bases of flourishing industries. It is interesting to note, however, that in most cases centuries of practice of a process based upon these discoveries brought practically no improvement in the methods of carrying out the process. No improvement of the methods was possible, except by accidental discovery, because the nature of the processes was not understood.

What are scientific facts, laws, and theories?

Since you will meet the terms fact, law, and theory many times in your study of this book, you should be able to distinguish clearly between them. Many misunderstandings will occur unless you are clearly aware of the differences in meaning of these terms.

Facts are scientific observations collected and tested by experiment. A comparison and classification of many experimentally established facts may lead to some generalization regarding the behavior of a certain **system**[1] under a given set of conditions. Such a *generalized statement*, which is in accord with many experimental facts and which is not contrary to any known fact, is called a **law.**

Scientists are, without exception, inquisitive, or else they would not be scientists. The existence of a law always raises the question: Why does the system behave in this way? If a set of circumstances can be imagined about the make-up of the system which, if true, would explain the law and which agrees with all known facts about the system, it is called a **theory.** If the theory is correct and complete, it is in accord with all that is now known about the system in question. This theory also will generally make possible predictions about some other properties of the system that are as yet unknown. If these predictions are proved true by further experiment, the theory is greatly strengthened. If the predictions are not verified, then the theory is shown to be incorrect and must be discarded.

Students beginning the study of science (and some who are not just beginning) meet many unnecessary difficulties through failure to distinguish between law and theory. A law is merely a condensed statement of many experimental results which any scientist could verify if he would take the necessary time and trouble. A theory is a possible explanation for the law which may or may not be the correct explanation. However, as long as the theory is in accord with all known facts in the case and contrary to none, it is exceedingly useful in correlating, understanding, and remembering experimental results.

An illustration

A very much oversimplified illustration may be helpful in grasping the relationship between fact, law, and theory. Suppose you were to conduct an experiment which consisted of counting the number of cars passing a certain intersection in a given city. You might find that on Monday morning between the hours of eight and nine o'clock 506 cars passed this intersection going east and 57 passed it going west.

---

[1] The scientist uses the term system to refer to all the material and/or apparatus which is part of his experiment.

Use of the scientific method has resulted in the great advances science has made in the last hundred years. In research laboratories, chemists determine the facts upon which scientific laws are based. (U.S. Public Health Service)

In the afternoon of the same day, between the hours of five and six o'clock, you might find there were 657 cars going west past the same point and 67 going east. During the middle of the day you might find the number of cars passing this point in both directions was about the same. Assume that a similar count was made on many different days and that the results for each weekday were substantially the same as those given above. You could then make a general statement about the movement of traffic past this point which would summarize all the data collected. This statement would say that on weekdays in the morning from eight to nine the majority of cars passing the point was eastbound, whereas from five to six o'clock in the afternoons on the same days the majority of cars was westbound. Such a statement which is in accord with all the known facts relating to the system and contrary to none is an oversimplified analogy to a law of science.

Now if you had really made the study just described, you would certainly want to know why the majority of cars in the morning moved east and in the afternoon moved west. If one of the residential sections of the city was west of the point of observation and the principal business section was east of this point, you probably could imagine one explanation for the observed traffic movement. Such an explanation is analogous to a scientific theory. This theory immediately suggests methods by which its correctness could be verified. Once the correct explanation for the facts has been established, it is much easier to remember the facts involved. It is also easier to make additional predictions about the system which have a good chance of being correct.

The many accomplishments of modern chemistry and its tremendous influence over our way of living are largely the result of the method of approach you have just seen illustrated. That is, progress is made (1) by accumulation of facts, (2) by classification of the facts and eventually deriving laws from them, (3) by proposing and testing theories to explain these laws, and (4) by making new and useful predictions from the theories. This sequence is what is meant by the **scientific method.**

In the next chapter you will see how this method led to the establishment of a theory without which chemistry could hardly have developed to its present state.

KEY WORDS

| fact | scientific method | theory |
| law | system | |

HIGHLIGHTS

From primitive times man has observed and applied certain isolated facts relating to matter and its behavior. **Facts** are truths learned by experiment and observation. A **law** is a statement derived by the correlation of related facts. A **theory** is a proposed explanation of a law or laws.

The remarkable progress in chemistry and other sciences dates back 150 years to the time when Dalton published his atomic theory. Since then there has been more progress in practically all scientific fields than during all previous time. The reason for this remarkable development is the fact that the scientific method has been applied by research workers everywhere.

QUESTIONS

1. Mention a few of the ways in which primitive man applied chemistry.
2. What is the meaning of the term *system* as it is used by the scientist?
3. State the meaning of the words *fact, law,* and *theory* as they are used by the scientist.
4. How are scientific laws discovered?
5. What is the relation of a scientific law to a scientific theory?
6. Compare a scientific law with a governmental law.
7. Do scientists *enforce* laws of science as policemen enforce governmental laws?
8. What is largely responsible for the many accomplishments of modern chemistry?

CHAPTER 4

atoms and molecules

At the beginning of the nineteenth century, **John Dalton,** on the basis of evidence which follows, set forth the **atomic theory** which has served as the foundation of modern chemistry. In his theory Dalton supposed the following to be true:

1. All matter is made up of minute particles called **atoms** (from the Greek word meaning *indivisible*, or *not cut*).

2. All the atoms of any one element are exactly alike in size and weight[1] but differ from atoms of other elements in this respect.

3. Atoms of one element may combine with atoms of another element. The result is a **chemical compound.** The atoms making up the compound are held together by "forces of chemical affinity."

4. Atoms cannot be divided[1] and therefore only whole atoms unite with other atoms.

Dalton's theory is important because it helps you see a mental picture of the nature of matter and of chemical change. Such a mental picture is very useful in understanding chemical changes or reactions.

When you look at a sample of copper, even with the best microscope available, it seems to be completely continuous. However, according to the atomic theory, you can imagine this element to be made up of minute spheres (atoms) each of which is exactly alike (Fig. 4–1). Similarly every other element is made up of minute spheres. The atoms of each element are different in size and weight from the atoms of other elements. A chemical reaction between two elements, such as copper and sulfur, is a process by which atoms of copper pair off with atoms of sulfur in a regular and orderly fashion to form a new substance. In this case the new substance contains one atom of copper combined with one atom of sulfur.

[1] See exceptions to this given later in this chapter.

The laws upon which the atomic theory was based

The principal basis of Dalton's atomic theory consisted of two laws relative to chemical reactions which had been established before 1800. These are the law of definite composition and the law of multiple proportions. The **law of definite composition** is as follows: **The proportion by weight of the elements which combine to form a certain compound is always the same.** That is, the composition of all samples of a given compound is always the same, regardless of the source of the particular sample.

There are two general ways to learn the composition of a compound. The composition may be determined by building up the compound from its elements and noting the weight ratio in which the elements combine. This is known as the method of **synthesis.** Or the composition may be determined by starting with the compound and decomposing it into its constituent elements. This is known as the method of **analysis.**

How the composition of a compound is determined

The method of synthesis may be illustrated by the following experiment which you might make to determine the composition of nickel sulfide. Dry a clean porcelain crucible and weigh it empty. Add a sample of powdered nickel and weigh the crucible again. Then add an excess of powdered sulfur. (To add a material **in excess** is to use more than that required to react completely with the other components of the system.) Mix the nickel and the sulfur thoroughly; then place the crucible over a bunsen flame and heat. Under the influence of heat, nickel and sulfur combine to form nickel sulfide, which is not volatile. (This means that nickel sulfide does not vaporize.) The excess sulfur melts and vaporizes, so that at the end of the heating only nickel sulfide remains in the crucible.

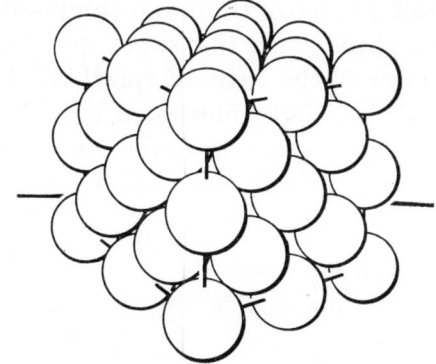

Fig. 4–1. A drawing showing the structure of copper. Most metals are made up of crystals in which the metal atoms are arranged as shown here.

The data obtained in such an experiment are as follows:

1. Weight of crucible empty   15.67 grams (g)
2. Weight of crucible + nickel   19.29 g
3. Weight of crucible + contents
   after heating 30 min   21.27 g
4. Weight of crucible + contents
   after heating 5 min more   21.27 g
5. Weight of nickel (step 2 −
   step 1)   3.62 g
6. Weight of nickel
   sulfide (step 4 − step 1)   5.60 g
7. Weight of combined
   sulfur (step 6 − step 5)   1.98 g

Percentage of sulfur in nickel sulfide:

$$\frac{1.98}{5.60} \times 100 = 35.3\%$$

Percentage of nickel in nickel sulfide:
$$100 - 35.3 = 64.7\%$$

When you determine the composition of a compound by the method of analysis, a weighed sample of the compound is decomposed and the weights of the products are determined. From this information you can calculate the percentage of each of the elements present in the compound.

Laws of multiple proportions and definite composition

Certain pairs of elements combine under different conditions to form more than one compound. Of course, the compositions of the different compounds of the same two elements will not be the same. But there is always a striking relationship between them. According to the **law of multiple proportions: When two elements combine to form more than one compound, the quantities of one which combine with the same quantity of the other stand to each other in the ratio of small whole numbers.**

This may be illustrated by the oxides of carbon. Two such compounds, carbon monoxide and carbon dioxide, are well known to chemists. Their composition may be expressed as follows:

	Ratio of Carbon	*to*	*Oxygen in Compound*
Carbon monoxide	12	to	16
Carbon dioxide	12	to	32 ($= 2 \times 16$)

That is, the different quantities of oxygen which will combine with 12

Plate I. Iron is widely used because steel can have various properties depending upon the other elements present with the iron. Here a chemist uses a special apparatus to analyze steel samples from an open-hearth furnace. (American Iron and Steel Institute)

Plate II. Plastics are important in the life of every American and are used for everything from telephones to food packaging. These kettles are used to carry out the key step in making a plastic. (E. I. du Pont de Nemours & Co.)

Plate III. The first nylon filament ever spun was spun on this tiny laboratory machine. Nylon was first introduced to the public in the form of nylon-tufted toothbrushes. (E. I. du Pont de Nemours & Co.)

Plates IV and V. The production of new colors in the form of pigments and dyes is one of the many contributions of chemistry to modern living. Before new colors are introduced, however, they must be carefully tested for many qualities, including fastness to light and washing. Top, pigments intended for interior paint finishes are being tested for washability. Bottom, pigments intended for stucco coating are being given outdoor weathering tests. (E. I. du Pont de Nemours & Co.)

Plates VI and VII. The high quality of the fruit produced in modern commercial orchards is largely due to careful and regular spraying of the trees to control fungi and insects. Most fungicides and insecticides in use today are synthetic organic compounds which were unknown ten years ago. Chemists have even developed compounds which will prevent apples dropping from the trees before they are ripe. Other synthetic compounds influence the coloring of the fruit. (E. I. du Pont de Nemours & Co.)

Plate VIII. Going in for the kill this FB4F jet has just unleashed a barrage of 24 rockets. Although the design and construction of a plane are the work of aeronautical engineers, such planes would be impossible without the various metals, plastics, and fuels which are made available through chemical research. (American Iron and Steel Institute)

Plate IX. A modern oil refinery at night. (Cities Service Co.)

Plate X. Cellulose by the ton. Cellulose is used in making paper, cellophane, rayon, and smokeless powder. Wood and cotton are our principal sources of cellulose. The photograph shows a stacker-conveyor piling up the gigantic stockpile of logs needed to keep a paper mill going. (American Iron and Steel Institute)

Plate XI. Thanks to modern science, industrial plants of today are a safer and healthier place to work than the factories of 50 years ago. Preventive medicine, a major concern of industrial hygienists, involves sampling the atmosphere for contamination as shown above. (American Iron and Steel Institute)

Plate XII. These stainless steel cones are a spray-drier used for drying a product that might decompose if heated to drive off the water. Its use depends upon spraying the material to be dried into a chamber of heated air. By forming very fine particles the water can be evaporated before the product decomposes. (Union Carbide and Carbon Corp.)

John Dalton (1766–1844), an English schoolmaster, gave us the atomic theory, which has been the cornerstone of modern chemistry. (Fisher Scientific Co.)

parts of carbon stand to each other in the ratio of small whole numbers (1:2).

A similar situation is found in the case of the compounds of hydrogen and oxygen:

	Ratio of Oxygen	to	Hydrogen in Compound
Hydrogen peroxide	16	to	1.008
Water	16	to	2.016 ($= 2 \times 1.008$)

In all other cases where two elements form more than one compound, the situation is similar to those given in the preceding examples. The ratio of the elements is that of small whole numbers.

The law of multiple proportions tells us indirectly that the elements are made up of atoms which are not divided by ordinary chemical reactions. This can be illustrated best by an analogy. Suppose that you go to the grocery store and ask for $\frac{2}{3}$ lb of butter. The grocer replies that he cannot sell you $\frac{2}{3}$ lb of butter but can sell you $\frac{1}{4}$, $\frac{1}{2}$, $\frac{3}{4}$, or 1 lb. You realize at once that the butter in question comes in $\frac{1}{4}$ lb units.

Thus in the combination of carbon and oxygen, a given quantity of carbon can unite with a certain weight of oxygen, or with twice that much, but not with just any quantity of oxygen.

According to the law of definite composition, all samples of a given compound always have the same composition. Therefore, the union of two or more elements to form a compound always involves a combination, or union, of the atoms concerned in the same definite fashion. If this were not true, all samples of the compound would not have the same composition.

Atomic weights

In order to understand more about the **quantitative** aspects of chemical reactions (quantitative aspects are those concerned with amounts, as well as kinds, of products), you should know something about the weights of atoms of the various elements. Thus if you know that atoms of two elements combine in an atomic ratio of 1:1, you can easily calculate the weight ratio in which they combine if you know the weights of the atoms concerned. Or if you have determined the composition of a compound (see pages 17 and 18) and you know the necessary atomic weights, you can calculate the atomic ratio in which the elements exist in the compound (see pages 31 to 33).

The weights of single atoms are now known with great accuracy, but these weights in grams are exceedingly small[1] and consequently very awkward to work with. For this reason a *relative* scale of atomic weights has been set up in which **the weight of one atom of the various elements is given relative to the weight of one oxygen atom, which is arbitrarily assigned a weight of 16 units.** Such a table of atomic weights is given in the Appendix (pages 682 to 684).

Although the values given in this table are commonly called atomic weights, you should be careful to note that these do not represent the absolute weights of the atoms in question but only show the *relative* weights of one atom of the various elements. Thus the atomic weight given for sulfur is 32.06 and for oxygen is 16.00. This means that one atom of sulfur is a little more than twice ($32.06/16.00$) as heavy as one atom of oxygen. Similarly an atom of hydrogen weighs approximately one-sixteenth ($1.008/16.00$) as much as an atom of oxygen.

In setting up the table of atomic weights, it makes no fundamental difference what element is selected as the standard of comparison or what value is assigned to it. However, if oxygen equal to 16 is selected as the standard, all the elements have atomic weights greater than 1. Also, many of the elements have atomic weights which are either whole numbers or very nearly whole numbers. It was mainly for these reasons of convenience that oxygen was selected as the standard.

Atomic and molecular models

Not only have the fundamental features of Dalton's theory been proved true, but also scientists have learned a great deal about the actual weights and sizes of individual atoms and the ways in which different atoms unite to form compounds. It is known that all atoms are essentially spherical and that their radii—though varying somewhat from element to element—are about one **angstrom unit** (Å).

---

[1] The weight of an atom of carbon is 1.99×10^{-23} g, or 0.0000000000000000-000000199 g.

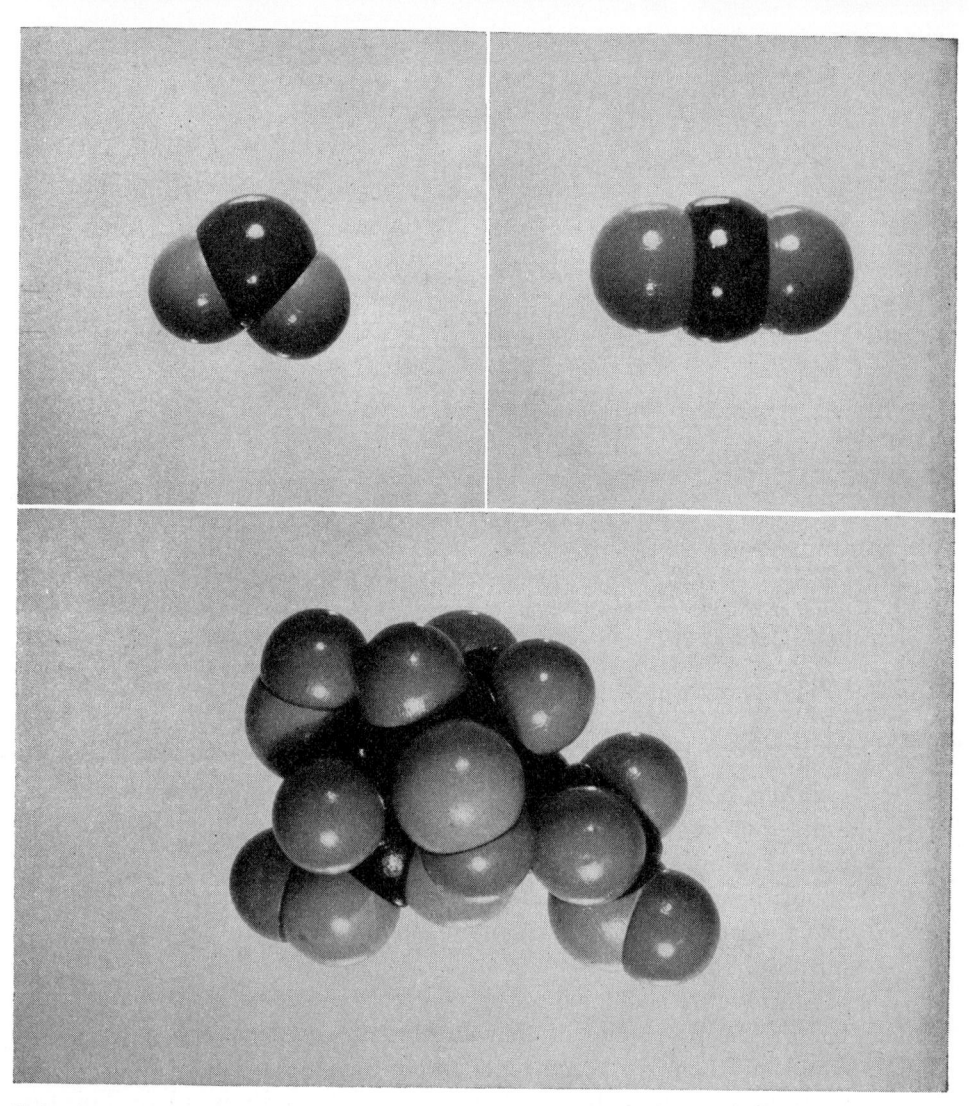

Molecular models. Top left, water; top right, carbon dioxide; bottom, glucose. (Fisher Scientific Co.)

An angstrom unit is equal to $\frac{1}{100,000,000}$ centimeter (cm). Also, where more than two atoms unite to form a compound, it has been possible, in many cases, to measure the angle formed. For example, in the case of the compound carbon dioxide, we know that the two oxygen atoms lie on exactly opposite sides of the carbon atom. In the compound water, the two hydrogen atoms lie on the same side of the oxygen atom, making an angle with it of 105 degrees (deg). Thus it is possible to construct scale models of compounds. These scale models show not only the atomic ratios in which the atoms unite, but also the relative diameters of the atoms and the geometric way in which the atoms arrange themselves to form the compound.

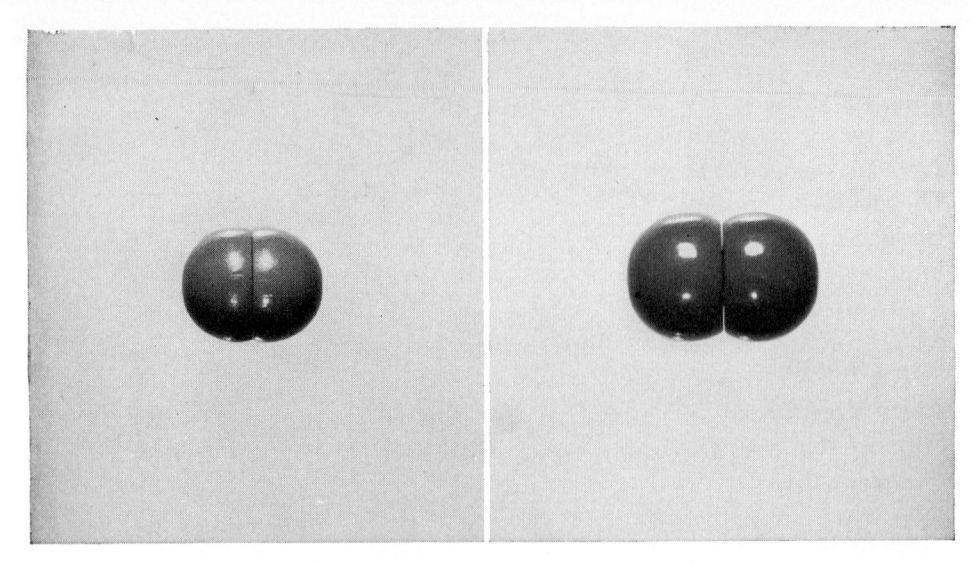

Left, molecule of elementary hydrogen gas. Each hydrogen molecule contains two hydrogen atoms. Right, oxygen molecule. Each oxygen molecule contains two atoms of oxygen. (Fisher Scientific Co.)

The photographs on page 21 show scale models of the compounds water, carbon dioxide, and glucose, grape sugar. The models are intended to show the units of which each compound is built up. For example, a drop of water is made up of a very large number of tiny units, one of which is represented by the model of the compound water. Many interesting and important deductions can be made about the physical and chemical properties of a compound by building and studying such models,[1] and chemists use them frequently for this purpose.

A **molecule** is defined as the smallest quantity of a substance which has all the properties of that substance. Evidently a drop of water could in theory be continually subdivided without changing the properties of the water until only one of the units was left. This unit is the smallest quantity which has the same composition as larger samples. It is the smallest quantity of water which can exist; hence it is a molecule of water. In addition to the model of the molecule of water, the other models in the photograph represent a molecule of carbon dioxide and a molecule of glucose.

You have already read that molecules of compounds are always made up of two or more atoms of elements. In the case of some elements, there is only one atom in the molecule. In the case of other elements, there are more than one atom in the molecule. Therefore, you need to distinguish between atoms and molecules of elements. They are not necessarily the same. In general, an atom of an element in the free

[1] Atom model kits are available commercially from Fisher Scientific Company, Pittsburgh, Pa.

state will unite with other similar atoms to form a molecule which contains two or more atoms. Thus hydrogen in the free state is made up of molecules each containing two atoms. The same is true for oxygen. However, the number of atoms present in a molecule of an element is not necessarily two. It may be one or more. You will learn the number of atoms in a molecule of each element as you meet the element.

An **atom** may be defined as the smallest quantity of an element which can take part in a chemical reaction.

The following example will illustrate the vast number of molecules which are present in a specimen large enough to see and handle. Suppose that you start with 18 milliliters (ml) (about 1.2 tablespoons) of water. Imagine further that by some means you could count the molecules of water at the rate of 1000 per hour. You would need 690 quadrillion years to count them all. In other words, if counting had started when life first appeared on this planet, about two billion years ago, and had continued at the rate of 1000 molecules per hour up to the present time, only about $\frac{1}{350,000,000}$ of the total would have been counted by today.

More recent developments on the nature of matter

Much has been learned about the nature of matter since the Quaker schoolmaster first stated the atomic theory. All this has shown that Dalton was fundamentally correct in his theory but that he was incorrect in two details. Until after 1900 it was generally believed that, as Dalton had stated, "All the atoms of any one element are exactly alike in weight." It is now known, however, that most elements are made up of atoms of two or more different weights. For example, three types of hydrogen atoms, which differ in weight, are found in nature. They weigh approximately one, two, and three on the atomic-weight scale. *These three forms are always present in the same proportions in all occurrences of hydrogen in nature.* The ratio in which they are found in nature is 6400 atoms of hydrogen 1 to one atom of hydrogen 2 with a very, very small amount of hydrogen 3. Atoms of the same element which have different weights are called *isotopes*. An atomic weight is the weighted average of the weights of the isotopes. Such an average takes account of the relative proportions of the isotopes.

The other necessary modification of Dalton's original theory grew out of the discovery of radioactivity in 1896. From this and later discoveries, it was learned that an atom may be split under certain conditions. You will read about this in detail in a later chapter. However, such atom splitting never occurs in ordinary chemical reactions. Therefore, in chemical reactions you may still consider elements as being made up of small, indivisible spheres.

KEY WORDS

analysis	chemical compound	law of multiple
angstrom (Å)	Dalton	proportions
atom	in excess	molecule
atomic theory	isotope	quantitative
atomic weight	law of definite composition	synthesis

HIGHLIGHTS

Dalton based his **atomic theory** largely on the evidence supplied by the laws of **definite composition** and **multiple proportions**. His original theory has been modified in two respects. It has been found that not all **atoms** of the same element have the same weight. Also, in 1896, it was discovered that there are certain elements which disintegrate.

Atoms of an element which have different weights are called **isotopes**. The weighted average of the weights of all of the isotopes of an element is the **atomic weight** of the element. The atomic-weight scale is based upon taking 16 as the atomic weight of oxygen. On this scale all atomic weights are greater than 1.

QUESTIONS

1. Who suggested the atomic theory upon which modern chemistry is built?
2. What are the main points in the atomic theory?
3. In what respects has the atomic theory been modified by more recent discoveries?
4. State the difference between a molecule and an atom.
5. State the law of multiple proportions and explain how this indicates that matter is made up of atoms.
6. State the law of definite composition and explain the relation between this law and the atomic theory.
7. What is the basis of the scale of atomic weights?
8. Explain this statement: The atomic weight of calcium is 40.
9. Why is oxygen used as the standard for atomic weights?
10. In the illustrative experiment involving nickel sulfide, how do the data given show that all the uncombined sulfur has been volatilized?
11. What is an isotope?

CHAPTER 5

chemical shorthand

and transcription

One of the first things you must do in taking up the study of chemistry is to learn to understand and to write the shorthand used by the chemist. This shorthand principally consists of the chemical symbols for the elements. You will use the symbols in writing the formulas of compounds and in writing equations to express chemical changes.

Symbols

Chemists find it convenient to use symbols to represent the various elements. These symbols are given in the table of Atomic Weights in the Appendix (page 682) of this book along with the names of the elements. Consult the list at this time. You will see that the symbol for the element is always one or two letters which are suggested by the name of the element. Thus H is for hydrogen, S is for sulfur, C is for carbon, O is for oxygen. For calcium, Ca is used since C is used for carbon. For the same reason, Cl is used for chlorine.

In writing the symbols, you should note that (1) the first letter in the symbol is always a capital and (2) the second is always a small (uncapitalized) letter. Thus calcium is Ca, *not* CA. This convention is very important and must be observed if the symbol is to mean what it is intended to mean. The reason for this will become clear when you learn to write formulas.

In some cases the symbol of the element comes from the name of the element in a language other than English. Thus Fe for iron comes from its Latin name *ferrum* and the symbol for copper, Cu, comes from

The analytical chemist (left) owes a great deal to Johann Jacob Berzelius (right), who not only introduced the use of modern chemical symbols but also is the father of modern analytical chemistry. (Standard Oil Co. and Fisher Scientific Co.)

the Latin word *cuprum*. The symbols for sodium and potassium come from the German words for the elements, which are *Natrium* (Na) and *Kalium* (K), respectively.

There are several reasons why the symbols are used. The first is that the symbols are easier to write than the names, which, of course, are longer. Also, the symbols have a more precise meaning than the names (see page 27). Finally the symbols are international, whereas the names of the elements may be different in different languages. Thus the element called iron in English is *fer* in French and *Eisen* in German, but the symbol is always Fe.

The set of symbols now used by chemists was originated by the Swedish chemist Berzelius (1779–1848), who was the most distinguished chemist of his period and one of the greatest of all time. However, the idea of using symbols for the elements goes back through the days of the alchemist to the Egyptians and early Greeks. Alchemists used symbols to confuse the public and keep "professional" secrets. Today symbols are used to obtain precision and clarity.

| Mercury | Soap | Phosphorus | Salt | Oil | Sulfur | Zinc |

Fig. 5–1. Some symbols used by the alchemist.

What is the meaning of a symbol?

A symbol stands for more than the name of an element. It stands for one atom or atomic part of the element indicated. Thus, C means one atom of carbon. You have seen that each atom has a definite weight and that the relative weight of one carbon atom is 12. The symbol C, therefore, stands for 12 parts by weight of carbon. Similarly O stands for one atom of oxygen or 16 parts by weight of oxygen.

An important chemical unit of measure

Chemists find it very convenient to use a unit of measure called the **gram-atomic weight. One gram-atomic weight of an element is the atomic weight of that element in grams.** Thus 16 g of oxygen is one gram-atomic weight of oxygen, 32 g of sulfur is one gram-atomic weight of sulfur, and 12 g of carbon is one gram-atomic weight of carbon. The term gram-atomic weight is sometimes abbreviated as *gram atom.*

In order to understand the meaning of the unit gram-atomic weight, reread Chap. 4, page 20, on the meaning of atomic weight. Having done so, you will note that, although the atomic weight is a relative weight only, a gram-atomic weight is a very definite quantity for each element.

The significance of this unit of measure is that **in a gram-atomic weight of any element there are the same number of atoms as in a gram-atomic weight of any other element.** You can see that this is true from the following:

By definition:

$$1 \text{ gram-atomic weight S} = 32 \text{ g}$$
$$1 \text{ gram-atomic weight O} = 16 \text{ g}$$

Let us say that one atom of oxygen weighs y g (y of course would be a *very* small number). Then from our table of atomic weights we see that one atom of sulfur weighs $2y$ g. So in 16 g of oxygen there are $16/y$ atoms of oxygen; in 32 g of sulfur there are $32/2y = 16/y$ atoms of sulfur. Or, without the mathematics, you can see that, since each sulfur atom weighs twice as much as each oxygen atom, then a pile of

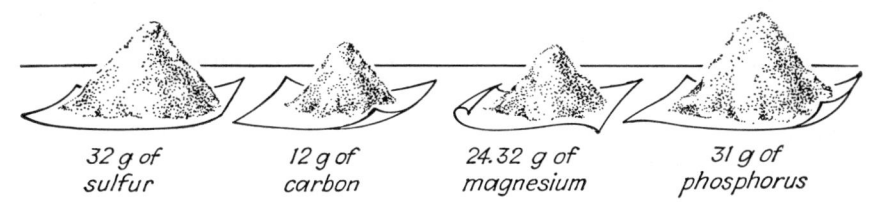

| 32 g of sulfur | 12 g of carbon | 24.32 g of magnesium | 31 g of phosphorus |

Fig. 5-2. There are the same number of atoms in each of the quantities shown above.

27

sulfur will weigh twice as much as a pile of oxygen which contains the same number of atoms.

These facts follow from the fact that the atomic weights are relative weights of one atom of the various elements compared with the weight of an oxygen atom as 16 units. But from the atomic weights you cannot find the actual weight in grams of an atom of oxygen. Therefore, the preceding facts do not tell you how many atoms there are in a gram-atomic weight of an element, even though you know there are the same number in each case. However, from information outside the scope of this book, it is known that there are 6.02×10^{23} atoms in one gram-atomic weight. This is known as **Avogadro's number.** The number is 6.02×1 followed by 23 zeros, or $6.02 \times 100{,}000{,}000{,}000{,}000{,}000{,}000{,}000$. Dividing this number into 16 g, the weight of oxygen which contains this number of atoms, we get

$$\frac{16.0}{6.02 \times 10^{23}} = 2.66 \times 10^{-23} \text{ g (or } 0.0000000000000000000000266 \text{ g)}$$

as the actual weight of one oxygen atom.

The importance of the unit gram-atomic weight is that in a chemical reaction we are concerned with a re-pairing of atoms. Therefore, quantities of the different elements which contain the same number of atoms are of more significance than merely equal weights of different elements which would not contain the same number of atoms.

Although chemists now know the actual weights of atoms in grams, they seldom use these weights. As you have seen, the actual weights are very small numbers and therefore awkward to use. For most purposes, the relative atomic weights serve just as well.

Formulas

The formula for a substance is written by setting down the symbols for each element present in the substance. Thus CO is the formula for carbon monoxide. The formula shows that a molecule of carbon monoxide consists of one atom of carbon combined with one atom of oxygen.

Some molecules contain more than one atom of an element. In this case a small number (subscript) following the symbol for the element is used to show the number of atoms of that element present in one molecule. Thus the formula for water is H_2O. This shows that the molecule contains two atoms of hydrogen and one atom of oxygen. The formula for carbon dioxide, CO_2, tells us that the molecule contains one atom of carbon and two atoms of oxygen. The formula for grape sugar (glucose) is more complex: $C_6H_{12}O_6$. This means that one molecule of glucose contains six atoms of carbon combined with twelve atoms of hydrogen and six atoms of oxygen.

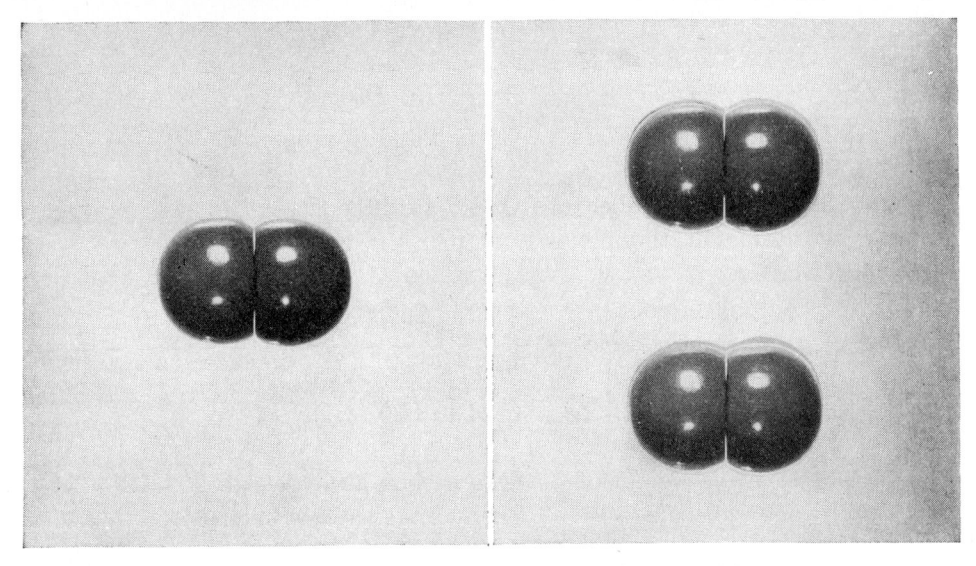

Left, O_2 means one molecule of oxygen consisting of two atoms. **Right,** $2O_2$ means two molecules of oxygen each containing two atoms. (Fisher Scientific Co.)

As you read in Chap. 4, some elements have more than one atom in each molecule. This is true of oxygen, hydrogen, nitrogen, and certain other gases. The formula for an element is written in the same way as that of a compound, except that there is, of course, only one element present. The formula for an element should show the number of atoms present in a molecule and therefore is not necessarily the same as the symbol for the element. Thus

$$\text{Oxygen gas is } O_2$$
$$\text{Nitrogen gas is } N_2$$
$$\text{Hydrogen gas is } H_2$$

The formula O_2 means two oxygen atoms joined together to make a molecule, whereas 2O means two oxygen atoms not joined together. Similarly $2O_2$ means two molecules of oxygen, each consisting of two atoms. That is, a number placed in front of a formula indicates the number of molecules being considered. And $5CO_2$ means five molecules of carbon dioxide, each of which contains one atom of carbon and two atoms of oxygen.

What information is contained in a formula?

To get complete information from a formula you need to know the relative atomic weights of the elements involved. You can find these weights in the table Atomic Weights on page 682 of the Appendix. Now look at the formula for ethane, C_2H_6. You find that the relative atomic weight of carbon is 12 and hydrogen is 1. What does a formula such as C_2H_6 tell us?

	In General	In This Formula
1.	What elements are present	Carbon and hydrogen
2.	Relative number of atoms in the molecule	One C to three H
3.	Actual number of atoms in the molecule	Two C and six H
4.	Weight ratio of the elements	C 24 to H 6 (4:1)
5.	Relative weight of one molecule	Two carbon atoms weigh 2 × 12 = 24 Six hydrogen atoms weigh 6 × 1 = 6 Weight of one molecule = 30
6.	Percentage composition	$24/30 \times 100 = 80\%$ carbon $6/30 \times 100 = 20\%$ hydrogen

In this table (step 5) you have seen how to calculate the relative weight of one molecule. This is called the **molecular weight**. The molecular weight of any compound is calculated in the same way.

Calculate the molecular weight of carbon dioxide, CO_2:

One carbon atom weighs	12
Two oxygen atoms weigh 2 × 16	32
Molecular weight of CO_2	44

Calculate the molecular weight of glucose, $C_6H_{12}O_6$:

Six carbon atoms weigh 6 × 12	72
Twelve hydrogen atoms weigh 12 × 1	12
Six oxygen atoms weigh 6 × 16	96
Molecular weight of glucose	180

What is the meaning of the molecular weight?

The molecular weight of a compound is the relative weight of one molecule of that compound compared with the weight of one oxygen atom equal to 16.

The gram-molecular weight is the molecular weight in grams. Thus one gram-molecular weight of glucose is 180 g, and one gram-molecular weight of carbon dioxide is 44 g. The term **gram-molecular weight** is commonly abbreviated **mole**. The significance of the term is that one mole of any compound contains the same number of molecules as a mole of any other compound. This number of molecules is the same as the number of atoms in one gram atom of any element. Thus, there are

6.02×10^{23} molecules of glucose in 180 g of glucose
6.02×10^{23} molecules of carbon dioxide in 44 g of carbon dioxide
6.02×10^{23} molecules of water in 18 g of water
6.02×10^{23} molecules of oxygen (O_2) in 32 g of oxygen
6.02×10^{23} molecules of hydrogen (H_2) in 2.016 g of hydrogen

There is one important bit of information about a compound which is not contained in its formula—how the compound is prepared.

How are formulas determined?

Formulas for compounds do not just suddenly appear from nowhere. When each new compound is discovered, chemists must determine its formula by laboratory measurements. The percentage composition is determined by analysis or synthesis of the compound (see Chap. 4, pages 17 to 18). From the percentage composition it is possible to calculate the formula, as you will now see.

In Chap. 4, page 18, one method of finding out the composition of a compound was shown with the data for nickel sulfide (NiS). It was found that the composition of nickel sulfide is as follows:

$$S = 35.3 \text{ percent}$$
$$Ni = 64.7 \text{ percent}$$

From this we may calculate its formula.

Before starting the calculation, we must have clearly in mind what is meant by **percent**. Percent means parts per 100 parts of the whole. Thus if we say a class is 60 percent boys and 40 percent girls, we mean that for every 100 students there are 60 boys and 40 girls. We do not necessarily mean that there are 100 students but only that the ratio of boys to girls is 60 to 40. For instance in a class of 30 there would be 18 boys and 12 girls.

In the compound of sulfur and nickel, in 100 parts by weight of nickel sulfide there are 35.3 parts by weight of sulfur and 64.7 parts by weight of nickel. To write the formula we must convert this *weight* ratio to an *atomic* ratio of atoms of nickel to atoms of sulfur, since a formula is essentially an atomic ratio. Divide the parts by weight of each element by the relative weight of one atom of that element.

Atomic Ratio

$$\text{Atoms of Ni} = \frac{64.7 \text{ parts by weight Ni}}{58.69 \; (= \text{relative weight one atom Ni})} \quad 1.10$$

$$\text{Atoms of S} = \frac{35.3 \text{ parts by weight S}}{32.06 \; (= \text{relative weight one atom S})} \quad 1.10$$

Now the formula, of course, must show a whole number of atoms of each element, so the ratio of atoms of nickel to atoms of sulfur is converted to the same whole number ratio, that is, 1.1:1.1 = 1:1. Therefore, we see that for each atom of nickel there is one atom of sulfur. The simplest formula possible for the compound is NiS.

To avoid mistakes in solving problems of this type, you should set up a table similar to the ones below.

Calculate the formula of the compound which has the following composition:

$$\text{Hydrogen} = 11.19 \text{ percent}$$
$$\text{Oxygen} = 88.81 \text{ percent}$$

Element	Percent composition		Atomic weight		Quotient: atomic ratio	Whole number atomic ratio
Hydrogen	11.19	÷	1	=	11.19 ⎫ convert to whole num- ber ratio by dividing both by 5.55	2
Oxygen	88.81	÷	16	=	5.55 ⎭	1

The compound contains two atoms of hydrogen to one atom of oxygen. Therefore, the formula is H_2O.

Calculate the formula of a compound having the following composition:

$$\text{Sodium} = 32.38 \text{ percent}$$
$$\text{Sulfur} = 22.57 \text{ percent}$$
$$\text{Oxygen} = 45.05 \text{ percent}$$

Element	Percent composition		Atomic weight		Quotient: atomic ratio	Whole number atomic ratio
Sodium	32.38	÷	23	=	1.408 ÷ 0.705	2
Sulfur	22.57	÷	32	=	0.705 ÷ 0.705	1
Oxygen	45.05	÷	16	=	2.816 ÷ 0.705	4

Therefore, the formula is Na_2SO_4.

When a formula is calculated from the percentage in this way, the result is called an **empirical formula**. This is the simplest possible formula which the compound could have. It is not necessarily the **molecular formula.** The molecular formula shows the exact number of atoms of each kind in one molecule. That is, it has been calculated that the simplest formula possible for water is H_2O, but so far as we can tell, water could have *any* formula in which there are two hydrogen atoms to one oxygen atom, for example, H_4O_2 or H_6O_3. In order to tell which multiple of the empirical formula is the molecular formula, we must know the molecular weight of the compound. You will learn later how this can be determined in the laboratory. It has been found that the molecular weight of water is 18 and therefore its molecular formula as well as its empirical formula is H_2O.

Calculate the molecular formula of a compound which has a molecular weight of 34 and which has the following composition:

$$\text{Hydrogen} = 5.89 \text{ percent}$$
$$\text{Oxygen} = 94.11 \text{ percent}$$

First, calculate the empirical formula as shown in the preceding examples.

Element	Percent composition		Atomic weight	Quotient: atomic ratio	Whole number atomic ratio
Oxygen	94.11	÷	16	5.88	1
Hydrogen	5.89	÷	1	5.89	1

The empirical formula is HO.

If the molecular formula also were HO, the compound would have a molecular weight of 17. Actually the problem states that the molecular weight of the compound is 34. Therefore, you must multiply the empirical formula by $34/17$ (=2) to get the molecular formula.

The molecular formula is, therefore, H_2O_2. (The compound is hydrogen peroxide.) Check: Calculate the molecular weight of H_2O_2.

$$2H = 2 \times 1 = 2$$
$$2O = 2 \times 16 = 32$$
$$\text{Molecular weight} \quad \overline{34}$$

Chemical equations

Chemical changes, or reactions, are conveniently and precisely described by means of chemical **equations.** Of course, before you can describe a chemical change, you must know the following:

1. Whether or not the reaction does occur.
2. The substances which react to produce the products, and their formulas. A substance that reacts is called a **reactant.**
3. The products formed by the reaction and their formulas.

We may illustrate the writing of an equation by the reaction of nickel and sulfur to form nickel sulfide.

$$Ni + S \rightarrow NiS$$

The equation says that one atom of nickel reacts with one atom of sulfur to yield one molecule of the compound nickel sulfide, NiS.

$$HgO \rightarrow Hg + O_2 \quad \text{impossible}$$

This equation says that one molecule of mercuric oxide (HgO) reacts to give one atom of mercury (Hg) and one molecule, consisting of two atoms, of oxygen. *It is wrong* because one molecule of mercuric oxide contains only one atom of oxygen and could not possibly produce two atoms of oxygen as shown on the right side of the equation. An equation, to be correct, must show the same number of each kind of atom on both sides. A **balanced equation** is one which meets this test. Since the formula for oxygen gas is O_2, we shall have to start with two molecules of mercuric oxide to produce one molecule of oxygen.

$$\text{Corrected} \quad 2HgO \xrightarrow{\text{heat}} 2Hg + O_2$$

In words, this equation says that two molecules of mercuric oxide break down when heated to form two atoms of mercury and one molecule of oxygen containing two atoms. The correct equation always shows the same number of atoms of mercury and oxygen on both sides of the equation. We balance an equation by adjusting the coefficients in front of the formulas, *never* by changing the formulas.

$$2H_2O \rightarrow 2H_2 + O_2 \quad \text{balanced}$$

Remember that the 2 in front of the H_2O means two molecules of water, or a total of four atoms of hydrogen and two atoms of oxygen.

The equation $C + O_2 \rightarrow CO_2$ describes the burning of carbon to form carbon dioxide.

The necessary steps in writing an equation

In making an equation, carry out the following steps in the order given:

1. Write on the left the formula of each substance entering into the reaction and join the formulas by plus signs.
2. Follow these by an arrow, which is interpreted as "yields."
3. Write on the right side of the arrow the formula for each of the products.
4. If necessary, correct the right side by increasing the number of molecules until you use all the atoms shown on the left.

5. If necessary, correct the left side by increasing the number of molecules so as to supply all the atoms shown on the right.

6. Check to make sure that there are the same number of each kind of atom on each side.

Let us illustrate each step by writing the equation for the burning of magnesium, Mg, in oxygen to form magnesium oxide, MgO.

Step 1: $Mg + O_2$
Step 2: $Mg + O_2 \rightarrow$
Step 3: $Mg + O_2 \rightarrow MgO$
Step 4: $Mg + O_2 \rightarrow 2MgO$
Step 5: $2Mg + O_2 \rightarrow 2MgO$

Step 6: There are two atoms of magnesium shown on the left and two molecules of magnesium oxide each containing one atom of magnesium on the right. There are two atoms of oxygen in the form of one molecule on the left and two atoms of oxygen in two molecules of magnesium oxide on the right. The equation is therefore balanced.

WARNING: Be sure to use molecular formulas for gases.

What an equation does not show

Generally an equation does not show what conditions, such as temperature, are necessary in order to bring about the reaction. Thus the preceding equation does not show that the magnesium must be heated before the reaction will occur. And the equation for the decomposition of water does not show what conditions are necessary to cause water to decompose into hydrogen and oxygen. Sometimes you will need to indicate these conditions. When the reactants must be heated, this can be written in above the arrow:

$$2Mg + O_2 \xrightarrow{\text{heat}} 2MgO$$

$$Ni + S \xrightarrow{\text{heat}} NiS$$

Or the electrolytic breakdown of water may be written:

$$2H_2O \xrightarrow{\text{electrolysis}} 2H_2 + O_2$$

Also, generally, an equation does not show what energy change is involved in the reaction. All reactions involve either giving off energy to the surroundings or taking up energy from the surroundings. The former type is the most common, as, for example, the burning of coal:

$$C + O_2 \rightarrow CO_2$$

Although this reaction liberates heat, this fact is not shown by the ordinary chemical equation.

The types of chemical reactions

The chemical reactions most commonly met are of four types: (1) combination or synthesis, (2) simple decomposition, (3) simple replacement, and (4) double replacement.

1. A **combination** type of reaction involves the direct combination of two substances. The following are examples:

$$C + O_2 \rightarrow CO_2$$
$$2Hg + O_2 \rightarrow 2HgO$$
$$Ni + S \rightarrow NiS$$
$$2H_2 + O_2 \rightarrow 2H_2O$$

2. Simple **decomposition** is just the reverse of combination as shown by the following equations:

$$2HgO \rightarrow 2Hg + O_2$$
$$2H_2O \rightarrow 2H_2 + O_2$$

3. The simple **replacement** type of reaction is the type in which one element replaces another. For example,

$$\underset{\text{sulfuric acid}}{H_2SO_4} + Zn \rightarrow \underset{\text{zinc sulfate}}{ZnSO_4} + H_2 \uparrow$$

[An arrow pointing upward (↑) indicates that a gas is given off.]

$$\underset{\text{copper sulfate}}{CuSO_4} + Fe \rightarrow \underset{\text{ferrous sulfate}}{FeSO_4} + Cu$$

4. **Double replacement** involves the decomposition of the two reactants and the formation of two new compounds. That is, there is an exchange of "partners."

$$AgNO_3 + NaCl \rightarrow AgCl \downarrow + NaNO_3$$
$$CuSO_4 + Ca(OH)_2 \rightarrow Cu(OH)_2 \downarrow + CaSO_4 \downarrow$$

Two new forms of chemical shorthand appear in the preceding equations. An arrow pointing downward indicates a solid product. Thus AgCl, $Cu(OH)_2$, and $CaSO_4$ as formed above are solids. Arrows are not always used where solids are formed, but are generally used where solids are formed by the reaction of solutions, as in the examples shown here. A solid formed by the reaction of solutions or other liquids is called a **precipitate**. A group of symbols enclosed in parentheses as in $Ca(OH)_2$ indicates a **radical**. A radical is a group of atoms which acts as a unit, that is, as a single atom. In the formula $Ca(OH)_2$, the 2 means two OH radicals. Therefore, a total of two hydrogen atoms and two oxygen atoms are contained in one molecule of $Ca(OH)_2$.

The classification of reactions into four types is sometimes useful, but the important thing is to be able to write correct equations to describe the chemical changes that you study. This means that, at first, you will need to memorize equations as you meet them.

Valence

How can you learn to write correct formulas for all the compounds you will meet? How can you ever remember that the formula for water is H_2O; for carbon dioxide, CO_2; for mercuric oxide, HgO; and for ferric oxide, Fe_2O_3? Questions like these are probably uppermost in your mind at this point.

Chemists have a scheme which is very helpful in remembering and predicting the formulas of compounds. This scheme depends on the use of a quantity called valence. **The valence of an element is a number equal to the number of hydrogen atoms with which one atom of the element can combine.**

Consider the following formulas:

$$HCl \qquad H_2O \qquad NH_3 \qquad CH_4$$

According to the definition of valence, we see that

$$\text{Valence of Cl} = 1$$
$$\text{Valence of O} = 2$$
$$\text{Valence of N} = 3$$
$$\text{Valence of C} = 4$$

Now when two elements combine, they always do so in such a ratio that the *total* valence of each element is the same. For example, suppose you wish to write the formula for a compound of carbon and chlorine. Since the valence of one carbon atom is 4 and the valence of one chlorine atom is 1, it will require four chlorine atoms to have the same total valence that one carbon atom has. Hence the formula is

$$CCl_4$$

However, for carbon and oxygen, the formula is

$$CO_2$$

because each oxygen atom has a valence of 2. Only two oxygen atoms are needed to have the same total valence as one carbon atom.

In writing formulas, the symbol for the metal is written before the symbol for the nonmetal, that is, Fe_2O_3, *not* O_3Fe_2; AgCl, *not* ClAg; and NaBr, *not* BrNa.

What is the correct picture of valence?

Early chemists considered that each atom had a certain number of hooks on it by means of which it could hook onto other atoms. The valence of the element was equal to the number of hooks on it. Thus

$$H_2 + Cl_2 \rightarrow 2(H\text{—}Cl)$$

$$2H_2 + O_2 \rightarrow 2(H\text{—}O\text{—}H)$$

The idea is that in the compound all the hooks on each atom must be occupied.

From these pictures it is an easy step to the present-day **structural formulas**

H—Cl   H—O—H
$$\begin{array}{c} H \quad H \\ \diagdown \diagup \\ N \\ | \\ H \end{array}$$
$$\begin{array}{c} H \\ | \\ H-C-H \\ | \\ H \end{array}$$

in which each line represents one pair of the earlier chemist's hooks. The total valence for each atom is the same as the number of lines joining it to the molecule.

$$\begin{array}{c} Cl \\ | \\ Cl-C-Cl \\ | \\ Cl \end{array} \qquad O=C=O$$

These structural formulas are not to be taken literally. Scientists do not believe that molecules of these substances look as these pictures suggest. However, modern research has shown that each atom does have a certain number of hooks on it which is equal to its valence— only the hooks are electrical instead of mechanical. We shall learn more about this in a later chapter. In any case these structural formulas are very useful to the beginner in applying the idea of valence to the writing of compounds.

Valence of common elements and radicals

You can write the formula for a compound if you know the valence of the elements. Therefore, at this time you should learn the valences of the common elements and radicals.

TABLE 5–1. Valences of common elements and radicals[a]

Univalent (Valence is 1)	Bivalent (Valence is 2)	Trivalent (Valence is 3)	Tetravalent (Valence is 4)
H	O	Al	C
Cl	S	Fe	Si
Br	(CO$_3$)	(PO$_4$)	
I	(SO$_4$)	N	
Ag	Ca		
(NO$_3$)	Mg		
(OH)	Fe		
(NH$_4$)	Cu		
Na			
K			
Cu			

[a]Those symbols enclosed in parentheses are radicals which act as a single unit in many chemical reactions and can be so treated in writing formulas.

If you memorize this list, you will have very little trouble with formulas.

What is the formula for the compound of silver and chlorine?
Since both are univalent, it must be AgCl.

What is the formula for the compound between H and the (SO$_4$) radical?
Since (SO$_4$) is bivalent, it is H$_2$SO$_4$.

What is the formula for the compound between Al and O?
A structural formula will help here:

$$O=Al-O-Al=O$$

Since Al is trivalent and O bivalent, the correct formula is Al$_2$O$_3$. You will notice in the above formula that each oxygen atom has two valence bonds and each aluminum atom has three valence bonds. The center oxygen has one valence bond directed toward each aluminum atom.

Variable valence

The scheme of valence—useful as it is—has certain shortcomings. Most important of these is that for certain elements the valence is not always the same. For example, iron forms two series of compounds as shown by the chlorides

$$FeCl_2$$
$$FeCl_3$$

In the first compound the iron has a valence of 2 and in the second compound, 3. The conditions of the reaction determine which compound will be formed. A similar situation exists for copper, which may be either univalent or bivalent. There are also other elements which have variable valence.

The element carbon is peculiar. It is practically always tetravalent. However, the compound CO (carbon monoxide) is well known. In this case we must say either that the valence of carbon is 2 or that the valence of oxygen is 4. No other compounds are known in which oxygen is anything but bivalent, so we generally consider carbon to be bivalent in CO. This will not present any difficulties for you because in all the other carbon compounds the valence of carbon is 4.

For practice, it is suggested that you prepare a ruled table, such as the one shown below, on a separate piece of paper and fill in the proper formula in each square.

Do not write in this book.

	Cl	Br	I	O	CO_3	SO_4	NO_3
H							
Na							
K							
Ag							
Fe(II)[a]							
Fe(III)[a]							
Al							
Ca							
Mg							
Cu(I)							
Cu(II)							

[a] The Roman numeral refers to valence, that is, Fe(II) is bivalent iron and Fe(III) is trivalent iron.

How is a compound named?

Although chemists write formulas, they generally use the names rather than the formulas when they speak. It is, therefore, important for you to be able to name a compound from its formula. By learning a few simple rules given below, you will be able to name nearly all the compounds you will meet. Usually the elements present in a compound are named in the order in which their symbols appear.

The alchemist did not use the same symbols for the elements or the same system for naming compounds as the modern chemist does. (Fisher Scientific Co.)

Rule I. Binary compounds are given a name ending in *-ide*. (**Binary** compounds are those containing two elements.)

EXAMPLES:

NaCl	Sodium chlor*ide*	ZnCl$_2$	Zinc chlor*ide*
K$_2$O	Potassium ox*ide*	Ca$_3$P$_2$	?
MgS	Magnesium sulf*ide*	KI	?
Ca$_3$N$_2$	Calcium nitr*ide*	NaF	?

Rule II. If the same two nonmetallic elements (see page 176) form more than one binary compound, the prefixes *mono-, di-, tri-, tetra-,* and *penta-* are used to differentiate the compounds.

CO	Carbon *mono*xide	P$_2$O$_3$	Phosphorus *tri*oxide
CO$_2$	Carbon *di*oxide	P$_2$O$_5$	Phosphorus *pent*oxide

Rule III. If a metal forms two series of compounds, these are distinguished by endings. The ending *-ic* is used for compounds in which the metal has the higher valence. The ending *-ous* is used for those having the lower valence. A Roman numeral[1] may also be used to indicate the valence of a metal in a series of compounds.

[1] The latter is the form preferred by the Committee for the Reform of Inorganic Chemical Nomenclature; see "Rules for Naming Inorganic Chemicals," *The Journal of the American Chemical Society*, vol. 63, 1941, pp. 889–897.

Note that *-ic* means a valence of 2 in the case of copper and 3 for iron but always indicates the *higher* valence of the element concerned.

FeO	Ferr*ous* oxide [or iron(II) oxide]
Fe$_2$O$_3$	Ferr*ic* oxide [or iron(III) oxide]
Cu$_2$S	Cupr*ous* sulfide [or copper(I) sulfide]
CuS	Cupr*ic* sulfide [or copper(II) sulfide]

Rule IV. The names of ternary compounds containing oxygen end in *-ate* if there is only one such compound. (**Ternary** compounds are those containing three elements.) If there are two compounds, differing only in their oxygen content, the one containing the more oxygen ends in *-ate*, the other, in *-ite*.

NaNO$_3$	Sodium nitr*ate*	K$_2$CO$_3$		Potassium carbon*ate*
NaNO$_2$	Sodium nitr*ite*	Ca$_3$(PO$_4$)$_2$		Calcium phosph*ate*
Na$_2$SO$_4$	Sodium sulf*ate*	KClO$_3$		Potassium chlor*ate*
Na$_2$SO$_3$	Sodium sulf*ite*	KClO$_2$		Potassium chlor*ite*

The prefix *hypo-* means less than; *per-* means more than. Thus

KClO	Potassium *hypo*chlorite
KClO$_4$	Potassium *per*chlorate

Acids all contain the hydrogen atom. They may be named by the preceding rules but generally are given special names.

Binary acids are named by adding the prefix *hydro-* and the suffix *-ic* to the name of the second element:

HCl	*Hydro*chlor*ic* acid
HBr	*Hydro*brom*ic* acid
HI	?

Ternary acids are also named on the basis of the second element but do not use the prefix *hydro-*:

H$_2$SO$_4$	Sulfur*ic* acid
H$_2$SO$_3$	Sulfur*ous* acid
HNO$_3$	Nitr*ic* acid
H$_3$PO$_4$	?
H$_2$CO$_3$	?

Bases all contain the OH radical and are named as **hydroxides.**

NaOH	Sodium *hydroxide*
Ca(OH)$_2$	Calcium *hydroxide*
Cu(OH)$_2$	?
Al(OH)$_3$	?

KEY WORDS

Avogadro's number	gram-molecular weight	radical
binary	hydroxide	reactant
decomposition	mole	replacement
empirical formula	molecular formula	structural formula
equation	molecular weight	symbol
formula	percent	ternary
gram-atomic weight	precipitate	valence

HIGHLIGHTS

The **symbol** represents one atom of an element. The **gram-atomic weight** of an element is its atomic weight in grams.

The **formula** represents one molecule of a substance. The formula of an element may or may not be the same as the symbol. Some common gaseous elements have two atoms per molecule.

The **(molecular) formula** of a compound indicates how many atoms of each kind of element are in one molecule of the compound. **Gram-molecular weight** is a compound's **molecular weight** in grams.

By calculation from the percentage composition, you can find the **empirical formula** of a compound, that is, the simplest expression in small whole numbers of the relative numbers of atoms of the different elements in the compound. The molecular formula is the same as the empirical formula for some compounds. For other compounds the molecular formula is a multiple of the empirical formula.

From a knowledge of the **valences** of the atoms and **radicals** composing a compound, you can predict the formula of a compound.

There are definite rules for naming many chemical compounds.

An **equation** is a shorthand method of representing a chemical change. It must be balanced if it is to show correctly the relative numbers of atoms and molecules of the various sorts that are involved.

QUESTIONS

1. Why did the alchemist use symbols?
2. Why do chemists use symbols?
3. Why do we write the symbol for calcium as Ca rather than CA?
4. Define the term *gram-atomic weight*.
5. Why is the gram-atomic weight an important unit of measure?
6. Explain why gram-atomic weights of all elements contain the same number of atoms.

7. Do the letters SN suggest a compound or an element? Sn?
8. What information is given by the formula for a compound?
9. What is meant by the term *molecular weight*?
10. What is meant by the term *gram-molecular weight*?
11. What is there in common about a gram-molecular weight of all substances?
12. Calculate the empirical formula of a compound with the following composition: Sodium = 39.5 percent, chlorine = 60.5 percent.
13. Calculate the empirical formula of a compound with the following composition: Magnesium = 60.3 percent, oxygen = 39.7 percent.
14. From the data given in Chap. 4, page 18, on the composition of nickel sulfide, calculate the formula of this compound.
15. Balance the following equations: (a) $KClO_3 \rightarrow KCl + O_2$, (b) $Zn + HCl \rightarrow ZnCl_2 + H_2$, (c) $Al + O_2 \rightarrow Al_2O_3$.
16. What important facts about a chemical reaction are not ordinarily shown by the equation for the reaction?
17. What ending is given to the name of a binary compound?
18. What ending is given to the name of a ternary compound containing oxygen if there is only one such compound? What name endings are used if there are two ternary compounds containing the same three elements?
19. What is a hydroxide?

Suggested Projects for Unit One

1. Learn one fact directly from some element or chemical compound. Describe what you learned and how you went about it.
2. Examine an issue of a large city newspaper and make up lists taken from it of (a) elements, (b) compounds, (c) references to chemical research, and (d) references to chemical industries.
3. See if you can devise a method for separating each of the following mixtures: (a) sawdust and sugar, (b) charcoal and coal dust, (c) sand and sulfur, (d) salt and sand, and (e) iron powder and charcoal powder.
4. Make a list of labels (from bottles or boxes) which contain the names of elements or compounds. *Suggestion:* Look around kitchen, medicine cabinet, tool shed, garage, and garden supply shelf.
5. List five symbols which do not come from the English names of the elements for which they stand. Explain their origin.
6. Name three elements which the ancients used and explain how they used them.

UNIT TWO: Two Common Elements

CHAPTER 6

oxygen

It will be helpful for you to keep in mind the plan to be used in taking up the study of each element. You should note the following items:
1. *History* of the element.
2. *Occurrence* of the element, that is, where and in what chemical forms it is found in nature and whether it is rare or plentiful.
3. *Laboratory preparation* of the element—a method by which samples of the free element may be obtained in the laboratory.
4. *Physical properties* of the element.
5. *Chemical properties* of the element—the important chemical reactions which the element undergoes.
6. *Test* for the element—one particular chemical reaction by means of which the presence of the element can be proved.
7. *Uses* of the element. The practical use of an element outside the laboratory depends chiefly on its physical and chemical properties so that consideration of uses will emphasize certain physical and chemical properties. Some of the uses described will be for man-made articles of *industrial importance*. But many elements have great *biological importance*. Life would be impossible or very difficult without them. Therefore, you will study the biological uses of the elements as well as the industrial uses.

History of oxygen

The famous Italian artist and scientist Leonardo da Vinci (1452–1519) was the first European to point out that the atmosphere contained two different gases. Mayow (1669) measured the proportion of oxygen in the air and discussed its relation to combustion, respiration, rusting, and vinegar making. Hales (1731) made oxygen by heating saltpeter (KNO_3); and in 1771 **Scheele**, a Swedish apothecary, produced samples of oxygen from several different sources.

Credit for the discovery of oxygen is, however, generally given to **Joseph Priestley** (1733–1804), an English clergyman who experimented with chemistry in his leisure time.[1] In 1774 he obtained oxygen by heating a compound now known as *mercuric oxide* (HgO). He accidentally discovered its relation to combustion by idly thrusting a lighted candle into a bottle of the gas which he had prepared. He found that the candle burned with extreme brilliance.

Priestley communicated his discoveries to his fellow scientists in 1774 and is therefore generally credited with the discovery of oxygen because Scheele did not publish an account of his experiments on the preparation of oxygen until 1777.

Occurrence of oxygen

Oxygen makes up approximately one-half of the earth's crust including the atmosphere. Dry air contains about twenty percent oxygen (the remainder being mostly nitrogen). In the air the oxygen is present in the uncombined state as O_2 molecules. Free oxygen is also found dissolved in natural waters, where its presence makes life possible for aquatic, or water-dwelling, animals.

The most abundant compound of oxygen is water, which contains 88.8 percent of this element. Most of the rocks and minerals found on or near the surface of the earth contain combined oxygen. Common sand is mainly quartz, which is SiO_2. Clay is $H_4Al_2Si_2O_9$. Many metal ores are oxides, such as those of iron (Fe_2O_3), tin (SnO_2), zinc (ZnO), and aluminum ($Al_2O_3 \cdot 2H_2O$).

The human body contains 60 percent oxygen. Almost all organic compounds, such as carbohydrates (sugars, starches, and cellulose), fats, and proteins, contain oxygen.

Preparation of oxygen

Oxygen is found in nature in both the free and the combined states. Thus it can be prepared either by separation from the other components with which it is mixed in the atmosphere or by liberation from a compound.

Most of the oxygen sold in industry is obtained from the atmosphere. The oxygen is separated from the other constituents of the air by first liquefying the air. This is accomplished by compression and cooling (see Chap. 11, pages 103 to 105). The liquid "air" is mainly nitrogen and oxygen [with boiling points (bp) −196°C and −183°C,

---

[1] Because of religious persecutions in England, Priestley came to America in 1794, where he lived, and was buried, in Northumberland, Pa. The burning glass which he used to heat the mercuric oxide in his historic experiment is now preserved on the campus of Dickinson College in nearby Carlisle, Pa.

Oxygen is forced into cylinders, such as those shown here, under pressures as high as 2000 lb/in.² In this form pure oxygen can be stored and shipped most economically. (Linde Air Products Co.)

respectively]. Because of this difference in boiling points, the two elements can be separated by distillation (see Chap. 13, pages 136 to 138). Pure oxygen in gaseous form is stored and shipped industrially in stout steel cylinders at pressures up to 2000 pounds per square inch (lb/in.²).

If much oxygen is to be used in the laboratory, the cheapest and easiest way to get it is to buy a cylinder of the gas. Commercial oxygen is now widely available at a very low cost. Small cylinders only 3 in. long can be purchased.

Another laboratory source of oxygen is any compound that easily liberates oxygen and that is readily available at not too great a cost. The compound used by Priestley meets the first requirement nicely. When mercuric oxide is gently heated in a flame, it breaks down into oxygen and mercury:

$$2HgO \xrightarrow{\text{heat}} 2Hg + O_2 \uparrow$$

The liquid mercury generally collects as droplets inside the test tube. However, since mercuric oxide is a rather expensive compound, it is not suitable for preparing a great quantity of oxygen.

Potassium chlorate ($KClO_3$) is the most practical compound to use for the laboratory preparation of oxygen. When this white solid is heated, it melts at 368°C (centigrade) and slightly above its melting point begins to decompose. As the potassium chlorate decomposes, oxygen is liberated.

$$2KClO_3 \xrightarrow[368°C]{\text{heat above}} 2KCl + 3O_2 \uparrow$$

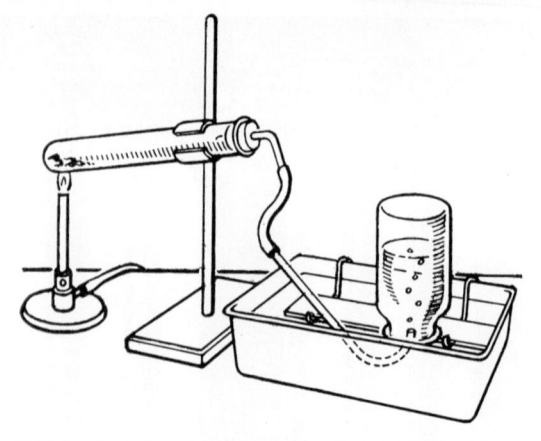

Fig. 6-1. Heating potassium chlorate is a convenient method of preparing oxygen in the laboratory. The oxygen may be collected by displacement of water, as shown in this drawing.

The other product, potassium chloride, is normally a white solid and remains behind in the tube.

If the potassium chlorate is first mixed with manganese dioxide (MnO_2), the desired reaction occurs at much lower temperatures (below 200°C).

$$2KClO_3 \xrightarrow[200°C]{MnO_2 \text{ heat}} 2KCl + 3O_2 \uparrow$$

Yet careful study of this last reaction shows that the manganese dioxide is not changed in the process. *Its mere presence* in the test tube causes the reaction to take place *more rapidly* than it would otherwise take place under the same conditions. Such an agent is known as a **catalyst.** Catalysts increase the rate of a chemical reaction without being permanently affected by the reaction. Some catalysts are of great practical importance and you will learn more about them in later chapters.

Water, the most common compound containing oxygen, cannot be broken down by heating. However, it is easily decomposed by passing direct-current electricity through it. The name given to this process is **electrolysis.**

$$2H_2O \xrightarrow{\text{electrolysis}} 2H_2 \uparrow + O_2 \uparrow$$

The process is easily carried out as shown in Fig. 2-3, page 9.

Although pure water may be used in the electrolysis, a small amount of sulfuric acid or sodium hydroxide (lye) dissolved in the water makes the process more efficient in terms of the electric energy consumed. The presence of sulfuric acid or sodium hydroxide in the water lowers the electrical resistance of the water, so that less electric energy is wasted in heating the water. Consequently a greater percentage of the electric energy is used to bring about the desired reaction. The reaction is the same whether or not the sulfuric acid or sodium hydroxide is added. The electrolysis of water produces two gases. Oxygen is liberated at the positive electrode and hydrogen at the negative electrode.

Physical properties of oxygen

Oxygen is an odorless, colorless gas. Its normal boiling point is −183°C. This is the highest temperature at which it can exist as a liquid under atmospheric pressure.[1] Under higher pressures, oxygen may exist as a liquid at higher temperatures. But no matter how great the pressure is, oxygen can never exist as a liquid at temperatures higher than −118°C. This is known as its **critical temperature.** The critical temperature is the highest temperature at which a substance can exist as a liquid. Each gas has a characteristic critical temperature.

Since oxygen is only slightly soluble in water (5 volumes of oxygen in 100 volumes of water at 0°C), it is conveniently collected by the displacement of water from a bottle (Fig. 6–1). Although the solubility of oxygen in water is low, all aquatic organisms are dependent upon this dissolved oxygen for carrying on their life processes. A lake, 1 mile in diameter and with an average depth of 20 ft, exposed to the atmosphere, will contain approximately 1100 *tons* of dissolved oxygen.

The chemical properties and uses of oxygen are discussed in the next chapter.

Ozone

Occasionally after a flash of lightning you may notice a peculiar sharp odor in the atmosphere. This odor may be due to the presence of a small amount of ozone formed by the action of the electric energy on oxygen. Ozone is a form of the element oxygen containing three atoms to the molecule, O_3.

In the laboratory, ozone is prepared by passing a stream of oxygen through an electric discharge as shown in Fig. 6–2.

$$3O_2 + \text{electric energy} \rightleftarrows^* 2O_3$$
oxygen   ozone

* A double arrow $\rightleftarrows$ indicates that the reaction is reversible, that is, that it can proceed either from left to right as it is written or from right to left.

Ozone is a pale blue gas which boils at −112°C. It is more soluble in water than is oxygen. It has a striking odor rather similar to chlorine but not quite so intense. The name *ozone* comes from the Greek word meaning *to smell.*

In chemical behavior, ozone is similar to oxygen; but since ozone

[1] Atmospheric pressure at sea level is 14.7 lb/in.²

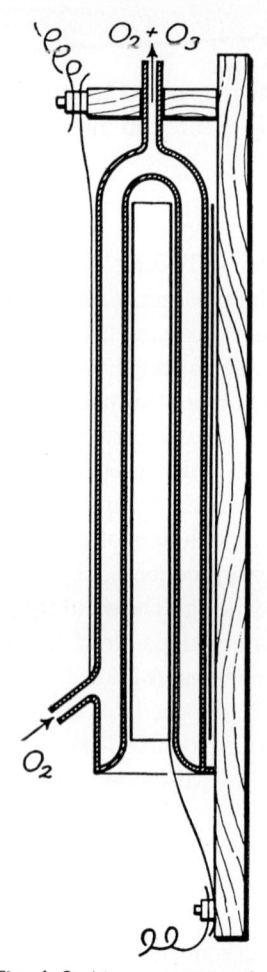

Fig. 6–2. A cross section of a laboratory-type ozone generator is shown in the drawing above. In this generator ozone can be prepared by passing a stream of oxygen through an electric discharge.

contains more energy, its reactions are more vigorous than the corresponding reactions of oxygen.

Ozone is unstable and slowly changes back into oxygen by reversing the above reaction. (The energy is liberated as heat.) Hence ozone cannot be stored but must be made as it is to be used.

It is believed that at altitudes of 12 to 15 miles above the earth's surface, the atmosphere contains a high proportion of ozone. There it is formed by a reaction similar to that performed in the laboratory except that **ultraviolet radiant energy**[1] from the sun takes the place of electric energy.

$$3O_2 + \text{ultraviolet rays} \rightleftarrows 2O_3$$

The ozone so formed breaks down again into oxygen and in so doing gives off energy in the form of heat. Thus there is always some oxygen available to absorb part of the ultraviolet rays of the sun. This formation of ozone absorbs much of the ultraviolet radiation which otherwise would reach the earth's surface. That is, the ozone layer 12 to 15 miles above the earth's surface absorbs most of the ultraviolet radiation in the same way that a blue glass absorbs red light.[2] If the ozone layer did not exist, life on this planet would surely be very different if not altogether impossible.

Ozone is sometimes used to sterilize water and to remove odors in air. It is used also for bleaching ivory, flour, waxes, and oils.

Oxygen is not the only element which can exist in more than one molecular form. Later you will see that, among others, carbon, sulfur, and phosphorus can exist in more than one molecular form, also. The various forms of an element are called **allotropic** modifications. That is, ozone is an allotropic modification of the element oxygen.

[1] Ultraviolet radiant energy is radiant energy of a wave length just shorter than that of visible light.

[2] If you are not familiar with this effect, you should look at objects of different colors through a blue glass.

In these large-size commercial ozone generators large quantities of ozone are prepared for industrial use. The ozone from this plant is used to purify water. (Ozone Processes Division, The Welsbach Corp.)

KEY WORDS

allotropic	electrolysis	Scheele
catalyst	ozone	ultraviolet radiant energy
critical temperature	Priestley	

HIGHLIGHTS

Priestley is credited with the discovery of oxygen because he was the first to publish an account of preparing the pure gas. Oxygen is abundant in the earth's crust, in the waters of the earth, and in the air. It occurs both in the free state and combined with other elements.

The most practical method for the laboratory preparation of pure oxygen is by heating a mixture of potassium chlorate and manganese dioxide. The former material supplies the oxygen and the latter serves as the **catalyst.** Industrially oxygen is prepared by separating it from air.

Oxygen is a colorless, odorless, and tasteless gas, slightly heavier than air, and only very slightly soluble in water. Its normal boiling point is $-183°C$ and its **critical temperature** is $-118°C$.

Ozone is an **allotropic** form of oxygen.

QUESTIONS

1. Why was Priestley given credit for the discovery of oxygen, although Scheele, the Swedish apothecary, was the first to prepare it?
2. How did Priestley first prepare oxygen?
3. Approximately what proportion of the earth's crust and atmosphere is oxygen?
4. Approximately what percentage of the atmosphere is oxygen? What element makes up most of the remaining part of the atmosphere?
5. What is the most abundant compound containing oxygen?
6. List several common oxygen-containing compounds other than the one you named in question 5.
7. From what source do we obtain most of the pure oxygen used in industry? By what means is it purified?
8. Give three methods for preparing oxygen in the laboratory. Write balanced equations for each.
9. Define critical temperature.
10. If a flask open to the atmosphere contained liquid oxygen, what would be the temperature of the oxygen?
11. Of what importance to man is the ozone layer?
12. Explain how the ozone layer transforms ultraviolet radiation into heat.
13. List two uses for ozone.
14. What is meant by the term *allotropic modification?* Illustrate.

CHAPTER 7

the reactions of oxygen: combustions and respiration

Our civilization is distinguished from earlier civilizations in the numerous ways in which we use controlled **energy**. We heat our houses in winter and cool them in summer through our intelligent use of energy. All our modern methods of transportation and communication are possible because we have learned to produce and control vast amounts of energy. The useful work accomplished per man-hour in the factories and on the farms of America has risen steadily for the last hundred years. This has been possible because of the increased use of machines, the operation of which requires energy. Thus the increased use of energy has, in large measure, been responsible for continually shortening the American working day and at the same time improving our standard of living.

From what sources is this energy obtained? Disregarding atomic energy, which at present is just becoming important as a practical source of energy, energy for industrial purposes and home use is obtained from water power or from coal and oil. Coal and oil, which are by far our most important sources of energy, do not release energy until they are burned. As you know, oxygen is necessary for the production of energy from coal and oil. Yet because oxygen is freely available and costs us nothing, we are inclined to lose sight of its importance.

Energy to run machines is obtained by burning coal and petroleum products. This generating station uses many tons of oxygen every 24 hours. (Consolidated Edison Co.)

The phlogiston theory

Most of you have known of the role of oxygen in **combustion** (burning) from childhood. Therefore, it is difficult for you to realize that men have understood this only since the latter part of the eighteenth century. In the early seventeenth century a theory of combustion was developed in Germany by Stahl and Becher. This theory stated that every combustible substance was composed of *calx* (ash) and an imaginary fluid called **phlogiston.** According to the phlogiston theory, combustion consisted of the loss of phlogiston, whereas the calx remained. Since some substances left more ash than others, it was assumed that they contained more calx. The theory seems rather ridiculous when you realize that the ash from the burning of wood weighs less than the wood, whereas the ash from the burning of a metal, such as aluminum or magnesium, weighs more than the metal. Thus according to Stahl and Becher's theory, it was necessary to assume that phlogiston under certain circumstances had real weight and under other conditions had a negative weight. Yet the phlogiston theory was generally accepted for over one hundred and fifty years.

Lavoisier and the nature of combustion

The great French scientist **Antoine Laurent Lavoisier** (1743–1794) sounded the death knell of the phlogiston theory. Lavoisier showed that oxygen is necessary for combustion and that combustion consists of the combination of oxygen with the substance concerned. For 12 days Lavoisier heated mercury in a retort. The neck of the retort projected into the air in a jar enclosed over mercury (Fig. 7–1). As the heating progressed, the mercury in the retort became covered with a red powder, and at the end of 12 days the air in the jar had lost one-fifth of its volume. This loss in volume was indicated by the fact that the mercury rose in the jar. The remaining air in the jar would not support combustion. This experiment proved that air contains something which is needed for combustion. The red powder which had formed on the surface of the mercury was collected and heated. From it was collected a gas equal in volume to the shrinkage of the air in the earlier portion of the experiment. This gas was very active in supporting combustion and was identical with the element previously discovered by Priestley and called *dephlogisticated air* by him. Lavoisier also showed that if you collect *all* the products of a combustion reaction, these products *always* weigh more than the substance before burning. Hence he stated that combustion consists of the combination of the substance with a certain component of the atmosphere. In the mistaken belief that this new element was an essential ingredient of all sour substances, Lavoisier named it *oxygen* from the Greek word for *acid-former*.

BIOGRAPHICAL NOTE: Lavoisier, "the father of modern chemistry," was a member of the aristocracy and a former government official. He was brought to trial in Paris during the French Revolution and sentenced to die within twenty-four hours. When the presiding judge was asked to delay the execution in order that Lavoisier might finish some of his work, the judge replied, "The Republic has no need for scientists." Ironically, only a few years later, the French Republic, ringed around with enemies, was almost on the point of collapse because of lack of chemicals for carrying on war. Common substances like soda and saltpeter (for gunpowder) were difficult to produce. A man like Lavoisier might have been of greater service to his country at this time than a man like Napoleon.

Fig. 7–1. Lavoisier, with an apparatus similar to the one shown here, proved that oxygen is necessary for combustion.

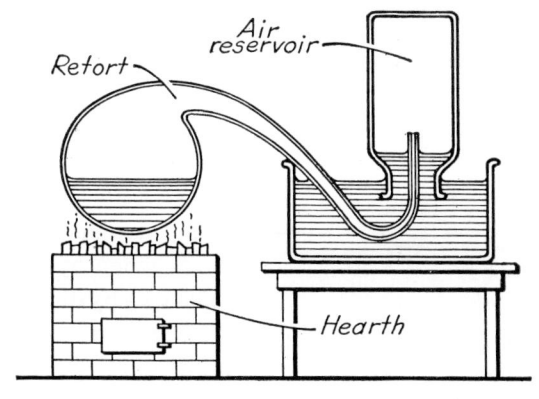

Chemical reaction of oxygen with other elements

When heated, oxygen combines directly with all the elements except the following: the inert gases (see Group Zero of the periodic table), gold, silver, chlorine, bromine, iodine, and certain members of the platinum family. With some elements oxygen reacts much more vigorously than with others. Thus magnesium and aluminum, when burned in pure oxygen, produce a light of great intensity.

$$2Mg + O_2 \rightarrow 2MgO$$
$$4Al + 3O_2 \rightarrow 2Al_2O_3$$

The metals magnesium and aluminum are used in signal flares. The second reaction (that of aluminum with oxygen) is the source of light in the modern photoflash bulb, which contains aluminum foil in pure oxygen.

With iron, oxygen reacts less vigorously. But finely divided iron (or steel wool) will burn when heated in pure oxygen, and the heat of the reaction is great enough to melt some of the unburned iron.

$$3Fe + 2O_2 \rightarrow Fe_3O_4$$
$$(Fe_2O_3 \cdot FeO)$$

At room temperature iron combines with oxygen, but more slowly. The familiar brown iron rust is largely, but not entirely, Fe_2O_3.

$$4Fe + 3O_2 \rightarrow 2Fe_2O_3$$

Many of the nonmetallic elements also unite directly with oxygen. White phosphorus, on exposure to air, ignites itself, or spontaneously, and forms P_2O_5.

$$4P + 5O_2 \rightarrow 2P_2O_5$$
(white)   phosphorus pentoxide

Sulfur and carbon must be heated to start the combustion.

$$S + O_2 \rightarrow SO_2$$
sulfur dioxide

$$C + O_2 \rightarrow CO_2$$
carbon dioxide

Hydrogen and oxygen react with great vigor and produce large quantities of heat.

$$2H_2 + O_2 \rightarrow 2H_2O$$

For this reason a very high temperature results when hydrogen burns in pure oxygen. The **oxyhydrogen** torch (oxygen + hydrogen) was at one time widely used for welding and cutting through metal. This torch

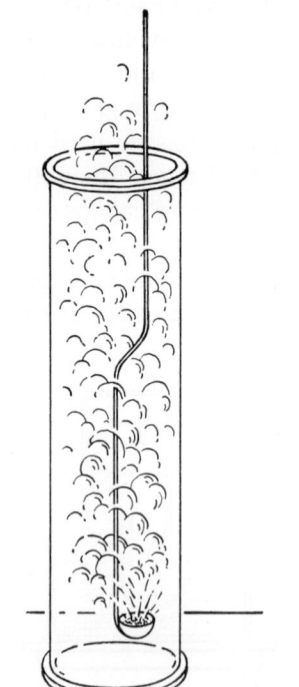

Fig. 7-2. Finely divided iron burns in pure oxygen.

now has been largely replaced by the **oxyacetylene** torch (oxygen + acetylene, C_2H_2), which gives an even higher temperature.

Oxides of the metals are all solids with very high melting points. Some metallic oxides are almost impossible to melt [Al_2O_3, melting point (mp) 2050°C]. On the other hand, oxides of the nonmetals are mainly gases at room temperature.

Reaction of oxygen with compounds

A simple rule enables you to predict what will be formed by the burning of a compound: **When a compound is burned, the products are the oxides of the elements in the original compound, if those oxides are stable.** Thus methane or marsh gas, CH_4, when burned in an excess of oxygen would yield water and carbon dioxide.

$$CH_4 + 2O_2 \rightarrow CO_2 + 2H_2O$$

Any other **hydrocarbon,** that is, a compound containing carbon and hydrogen only, when burned in a plentiful supply of oxygen will also yield carbon dioxide and water. Gasoline is a mixture of several hydrocarbons. A typical component of gasoline is octane (C_8H_{18}), which, when burned completely, yields the same products.

$$2C_8H_{18} + 25O_2 \rightarrow 16CO_2 + 18H_2O$$

If a carbon-containing compound is burned in a limited supply of oxygen, carbon monoxide (CO) is formed.

$$2C_8H_{18} + 17O_2 \rightarrow 16CO + 18H_2O$$

If more oxygen is available than that required to form the monoxide of carbon, some monoxide may be burned to form carbon dioxide.

$$2CO + O_2 \rightarrow 2CO_2$$

In the cylinders of an automobile engine, the oxygen supply is limited, so that part of the gasoline is burned to produce carbon dioxide and water, and part is burned to produce carbon monoxide and water. Carbon monoxide is a very poisonous gas; therefore, it is very dangerous to breathe automobile exhaust fumes. Every year many people are killed by carbon monoxide. They are poisoned as a result of carelessly running an automobile engine in an improperly ventilated building. If you have noticed automobile exhaust gases on a very cold day, you know that water is one of the products of the combustion of gasoline. When an automobile engine has just been started on a cold day, you may see water drip out of the exhaust pipe. The cold has caused the water vapor to change to a liquid, or condense, before it escapes from the exhaust. The track left by an aircraft engine at high altitudes is also condensed or frozen water vapor formed by burning the fuel.

Coal is largely carbon and carbon-hydrogen compounds. On complete combustion it yields carbon dioxide and water.

Wood, paper, starches, and sugars are all very similar chemically, and all belong to the class of substances known as **carbohydrates.** All carbohydrates contain carbon plus hydrogen and oxygen in the ratio of two atoms of hydrogen to one atom of oxygen. On combustion they yield the expected products.

$$C_6H_{12}O_6 + 6O_2 \rightarrow 6CO_2 + 6H_2O$$
glucose or dextrose

The same products, carbon dioxide and water, are formed whether the glucose is burned in a flame or consumed as food and oxidized in the human body. This is also true for fats, which are organic compounds of carbon, hydrogen, and oxygen.

When a metal sulfide is heated in air, you can predict the products (see page 57). Zinc sulfide yields zinc oxide and sulfur dioxide.

$$2ZnS + 3O_2 \rightarrow 2ZnO + 2SO_2 \uparrow$$

This type of reaction is not important as a source of heat. However, it is very important in producing certain metals from their sulfide ores. Mercuric sulfide, on being heated in air, yields sulfur dioxide and mercury. You do not obtain mercuric oxide under these conditions since (as you saw in Chap. 6, pages 46 and 47) this substance is unstable at high temperatures. Instead you obtain the products into which mercuric oxide would decompose.[1]

$$HgS + O_2 \rightarrow Hg + SO_2 \uparrow$$

Substances which do not burn

Substances which are not affected by oxygen are grouped in two classes: (1) those elements which have a very slight affinity or no affinity for oxygen, such as gold, platinum, and the inert gases, and (2) those substances which are already fully oxidized. Most fireproof substances fall into the second class. Brick, cement, and asbestos are

---

[1] This equation can be gotten by adding the two equations.

$$2HgS + 3O_2 \rightarrow 2HgO \text{ (unstable)} + 2SO_2$$
$$\underline{2HgO \quad\quad \rightarrow 2Hg + O_2}$$
$$2HgS + 3O_2 \rightarrow 2Hg + 2SO_2 + O_2$$
or
$$HgS + O_2 \rightarrow Hg + SO_2$$

Since asbestos is made of fully oxidized elements, an asbestos suit does not burn and thus protects a man from fire. (Johns-Manville).

the most important materials used in fireproof construction. These materials do not burn for the same reason that carbon dioxide and water do not burn—they consist of substances which are already fully oxidized. Bricks are made of sand (SiO_2) and clay ($H_4Al_2Si_2O_9$). Asbestos is $Mg_3Si_2O_7 \cdot H_2O$. Portland cement is largely Ca_2SiO_4 and $Ca_3(AlO_3)_2$. Steel, although actually not inert to oxygen, does not rapidly combine with it unless in the finely divided form. Wood, rubber, and paper, containing carbon and hydrogen, which are capable of combining with oxygen, are therefore combustible.

Test for oxygen

Oxygen is recognized by the fact that substances which burn in air burn more brilliantly in oxygen. A wood splint, smoldering in air, bursts into flame when placed in pure oxygen. This is a good test for the element.

Uses of oxygen

Every year we use millions of tons of oxygen, as air, for the burning of coal, oil, gasoline, and wood. Many millions more are used by man and other animals for the oxidation of foodstuffs in the body. This oxidation supplies the energy to keep the body warm and to carry on the life processes. The energy requirement of the human body varies greatly with the degree of activity of the individual and with his size and development. Girls of high school age need, on the average, 2500 large Calories (1 large Calorie = 1000 small calories[1]) of energy per day. Boys of the same age require approximately 3800 large Calories per day. In the oxidation of foods to supply this energy, about 1 liter of oxygen is used per 5 large Calories of energy produced. Thus girls of high school age will consume about 500 liters (approximately 130 gal) of oxygen per day, whereas boys of the same age will consume 760 liters (approximately 200 gal) of oxygen per day. The oxygen required for these processes enters the body by way of the lungs. It is then picked up by the *hemoglobin*, a substance in the red blood cells, and is carried by the blood to the tissues, where it is released. The car-

[1] The calorie is defined in Chap. 12, page 109.

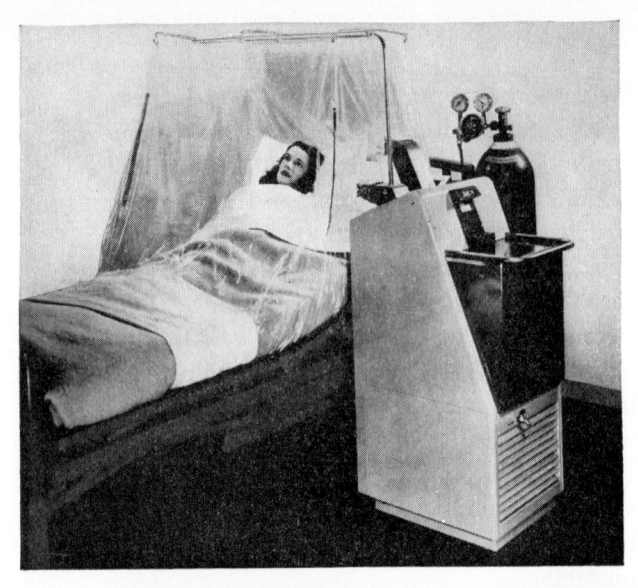

When a person is ill, an oxygen tent may be used to supply him with a higher percentage of oxygen than is normally found in the air. (Linde Air Products Co.)

bon dioxide produced by the oxidation is taken up by the blood in the tissues and returned to the lungs, where it is discharged. This exchange of gases through the lungs is known as **respiration**.

If the lungs are damaged by harmful gases or by disease, such as pneumonia, the oxygen of the air usually cannot be transferred to the blood at the proper rate. The patient may be aided by being placed in an oxygen tent or by using an oxygen mask. Aviators must have supplies of pure oxygen to breathe at high altitudes where the pressure of oxygen in the atmosphere is too low for human requirements. High-altitude rockets and jets are unable to obtain enough oxygen for fuel combustion from the atmosphere because the oxygen pressure is too low at the altitudes at which they travel. Consequently such vehicles must carry not only their fuel but also the oxygen with which to oxidize it if the fuel requires combustion. This necessary increase in the fuel load reduces the "pay load." It is reported that the X-1 jet rocket plane is driven by a mixture of liquid oxygen and alcohol (C_2H_5OH). This plane is said to burn 600 gal of liquid oxygen and alcohol in 2.5 min. In this time it attains speeds exceeding 1000 miles per hour (miles/hr). Planes propelled by atomic energy would have a range much greater than the range of planes whose fuel requires combustion.

Much of the energy of an ordinary gas flame is used in heating the nitrogen of the air to the flame temperature. As you know, any substance burns more rapidly in oxygen than in air. Therefore, a higher flame temperature can be obtained by supplying the oxygen for combustion as pure oxygen rather than as air. This fact explains the higher temperature of the **oxygas** (oxygen and illuminating gas) flame, which is used for working pyrex glass. The oxyhydrogen and oxy-

This rocket is being prepared for launching. Rockets travel at very high altitudes where the pressure of the oxygen in the atmosphere is low. For this reason, rockets must carry not only their fuel, but also the oxygen to burn it. (U.S. Army Signal Corps)

acetylene torches, which depend upon the same principle, are used for welding steel and iron and for cutting steel beams and plates. In cutting steel, the metal is first heated to white heat; then pure oxygen is directed onto the hot steel. At this temperature the oxygen causes the iron to burn away. The temperature of the oxyacetylene torch is so high that it can be used for cutting steel even under water.

There are other, slower oxidation processes which, although not so spectacular, are very important. Thus the drying of linseed-oil paint is a process in which oxygen combines with the linseed oil to form a tough, hard film. The decay of wood is largely an oxidative process by which the wood is finally converted to the usual products, carbon dioxide and water.

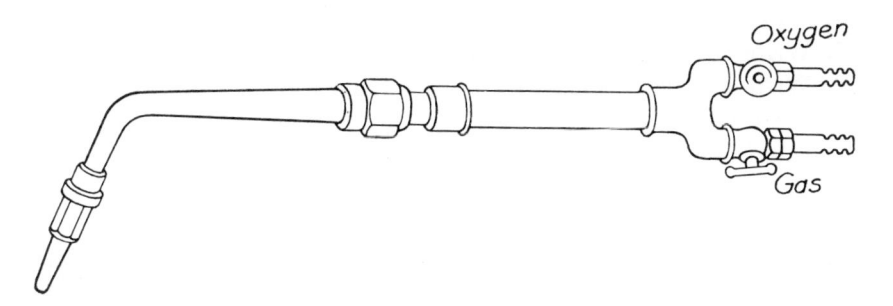

Fig. 7-3. The oxygas torch. This torch is used for working pyrex glass and for other purposes that require a very high temperature.

KEY WORDS

carbohydrate	hydrocarbon	oxyacetylene	phlogiston
combustion	Lavoisier	oxygas	respiration
energy	oxide	oxyhydrogen	

HIGHLIGHTS

Man's remarkable progress during the past two centuries has been largely due to his intelligent use of different forms of **energy**.

The **phlogiston** theory of **combustion** was overthrown by **Lavoisier**. His explanation of the real nature of combustion was based on quantitative experiments.

At high temperatures, oxygen reacts with many elements and compounds. Pure oxygen reacts with some substances so vigorously that very high temperatures are produced. Ordinary combustion is combination with oxygen accompanied by the liberation of heat and light.

Some fireproof materials are substances which already contain all the combined oxygen they are capable of holding.

Oxygen is important in industry as well as in natural processes, such as combustion and respiration. Jet rocket fuel may contain liquid oxygen in addition to the combustible material, such as alcohol.

QUESTIONS

1. List five fuels which supply energy by reacting with oxygen.
2. What sources of energy used on earth do not require oxygen?
3. Cite five cases in which machines now do the work formerly done by man or animal power.
4. Explain how Lavoisier showed that a certain component of the atmosphere was necessary for combustion.
5. Why did Lavoisier name the element needed for combustion oxygen?
6. Which elements do not unite directly with oxygen?
7. Write two oxidation reactions used as a source of light.
8. Write two oxidations used as a source of energy for heat.
9. State the rule which predicts what is formed when a compound is burned. Illustrate the rule by writing equations for burning of a hydrocarbon, a carbohydrate, and mercuric sulfide (HgS).
10. List five substances which will not burn.
11. If the average student requires 3000 large Calories per day, how many liters of oxygen are consumed in 1 hr by a class of 20?
12. Why does an oxygas flame produce a higher temperature than is produced when the same gas is mixed with air and burned?

CHAPTER **8**

hydrogen

Although hydrogen has been known to scientists for a long time, the public first became aware of the outstanding chemical property of free hydrogen on May 6, 1937. On that day the great German airship *Hindenburg* arrived over Lakehurst, N. J., on a flight from Ludwigshafen, Germany. As it was approaching its mooring mast, the ship suddenly burst into flame. The intense heat of the blaze melted the metal framework of the ship, and in almost less time than it takes to tell, all that remained of the enormous ship was a mass of wreckage on the ground. The ship had been filled with hydrogen as the buoying agent. Either by leakage or in some other way this hydrogen became mixed with air. It is believed that a spark from static electricity ignited this mixture and led to the resulting fire. The product of the combustion, water vapor, condensed and fell to the ground as a small local rainstorm.

The combustion of hydrogen on a large scale. The airship *Hindenburg* was destroyed by fire on May 6, 1937, when the hydrogen with which it was filled was ignited by accident. (Wide World)

Lord Henry Cavendish was the discoverer of hydrogen. He also made several other important discoveries, such as determining the freezing point of mercury and isolating argon. (Fisher Scientific Co.)

History of hydrogen

Hydrogen was discovered in 1766 by the Englishman **Lord Henry Cavendish,** who called it *inflammable air*. He also proved that this "inflammable air" would unite with Priestley's "dephlogisticated air" (which we know as oxygen) to produce only ordinary water. Lavoisier accordingly named Cavendish's inflammable air *hydrogen*, (from the Greek word meaning *water producer*).

Henry Cavendish (1731–1810) was a wealthy English nobleman who had but one interest in life—scientific study and research. He had a strange personality and a dislike and fear of people, which made him avoid them. He is said to have ordered his dinner by writing a note so that he would not need to see the servants in his own house. In addition to his work on hydrogen and water, Cavendish determined the composition of nitric acid, isolated argon for the first time (although he did not realize what he had done), and measured the freezing point of mercury. In order to obtain the necessary low temperature, the latter experiment was conducted in North America by the Hudson's Bay Company under Cavendish's direction and at his expense. He also made measurements which enabled him to calculate the mass and average density of the earth.

Occurrence of hydrogen

Hydrogen is never found free in nature in any great quantity. You can see that this must be true because, if hydrogen occurred free in nature, it would be mixed with oxygen in the atmosphere. Such a mixture would surely have become ignited, and long before now the world would have witnessed an explosion beside which the *Hindenburg* disaster would seem inconsequential. A very small amount of free hydrogen is found in some natural gas and also in gases from volcanoes and in some meteorites.

Hydrogen compounds, however, are abundant in nature. Water, which contains 11.2 percent by weight of hydrogen, is the most plentiful hydrogen compound. Natural gas and petroleum are chiefly compounds of carbon and hydrogen. All living cells are made up of compounds containing hydrogen. Hydrogen is also present in the combined form in almost all products of living things, such as fats, vegetable oils, proteins, starches, sugars, wood, cotton, and alcohol.

Acids

All acids are hydrogen-containing compounds. The name acid is applied to a group of compounds, all members of which have certain properties in common. Thus all acids (1) contain hydrogen, (2) in water solution have a characteristic sour taste, (3) in water solution react with certain metals to produce free hydrogen, and (4) in water solution change the color of certain dyes or indicators. For example, an acid will change the color of blue litmus to pink and cause pink phenolphthalein to become colorless.

You will consider the properties of acids more completely in a later chapter. The following are examples of common acids:

Acetic acid present in vinegar
Citric acid present in oranges, grapefruit, and other *citrus* fruits
Sulfuric acid, H_2SO_4, sometimes known as oil of vitriol
Hydrochloric acid, HCl, the muriatic acid used by the plumber and tinsmith

Preparation of hydrogen

Hydrogen is one of the easiest elements to prepare from its compounds. It is readily liberated from (1) water, (2) acids, or (3) alkalis.

1. From water

a. Hydrogen is produced from water by electrolysis, at the same time as oxygen (see Fig. 2–3, page 9).

$$2H_2O \xrightarrow{\text{electrolysis}} 2H_2 \uparrow + O_2 \uparrow$$

b. Certain active metals, such as calcium, sodium, and potassium, liberate hydrogen from water.

$$Ca + 2H_2O \rightarrow Ca(OH)_2 + H_2 \uparrow$$
$$2Na + 2H_2O \rightarrow 2NaOH + H_2 \uparrow$$
$$2K + 2H_2O \rightarrow 2KOH + H_2 \uparrow$$

In each case only half of the hydrogen is liberated. The other half remains with the oxygen to form the OH group (called the **hydroxyl radical**), which combines with the metal.

The preparation of hydrogen by the reaction of calcium and water is accomplished by dropping shavings of calcium into a pyrex bottle filled with water and inverting the bottle so that its mouth is under water as shown in Fig. 8–1.

Pieces of sodium the size of a pea, dropped on water, react so vigorously with the water to produce hydrogen that the sodium is heated to melting.

The reaction of potassium is even more vigorous; the hydrogen liberated is so hot that it burns at the surface of the water where it makes contact with oxygen in the air. Both sodium and potassium float on the surface of the water because they are less dense than water.

The reactions of sodium and potassium with water are quite dangerous. You should always use the greatest care in performing these experiments. Use only small pieces of the metal and protect your eyes with goggles, since the solutions of sodium hydroxide (NaOH) and potassium hydroxide (KOH) which are formed are very corrosive.

c. Magnesium and iron react with cold water to form hydrogen. However, the reaction takes place so slowly that the process is not useful for the preparation of hydrogen. If hot water or steam is used, the reaction is much more rapid.

$$Mg + H_2O \rightarrow MgO + H_2 \uparrow$$
$$\text{(steam)}$$

$$3Fe + 4H_2O \rightarrow Fe_3O_4 + 4H_2 \uparrow$$
$$\text{(steam)} \quad \text{magnetic oxide of iron}$$

Fe_3O_4 is really a compound between FeO and Fe_2O_3. It is sometimes written $FeO \cdot Fe_2O_3$.

In the laboratory you can prepare hydrogen easily by passing steam over hot steel wool in a pyrex tube (see Fig. 8–2).

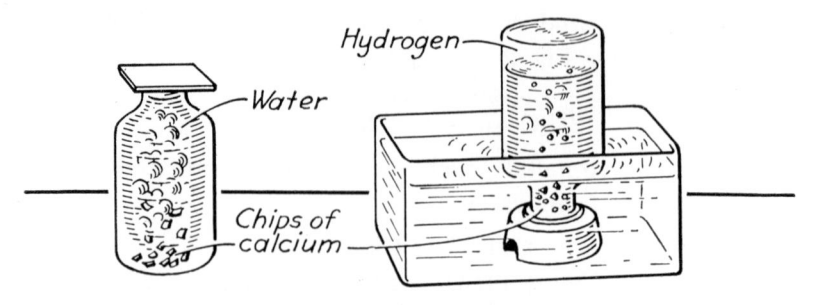

Fig. 8–1. Active calcium replaces part of the hydrogen in water, liberating hydrogen gas.

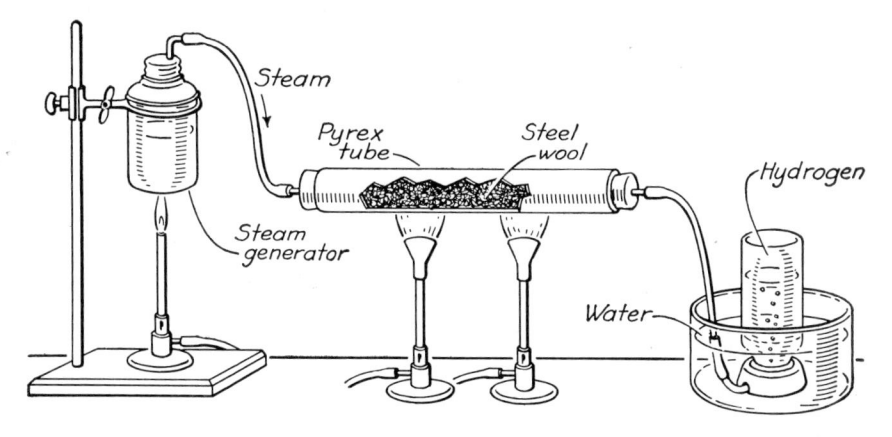

Fig. 8–2. Steam reacts with hot iron to produce hydrogen. A useful setup is shown above.

d. Hydrogen can also be prepared by heating carbon red hot and passing steam over it. The hot carbon reacts with the oxygen of the water and the hydrogen is freed.

$$\underset{\text{(red hot)}}{C} + \underset{\text{(steam)}}{H_2O} \rightarrow \underbrace{CO \uparrow + H_2 \uparrow}_{\text{water gas}}$$

The product, known as *water gas*, is a mixture of carbon monoxide and hydrogen. Both are combustible and when burned liberate large quantities of heat. Water gas is frequently used in city fuel gas because of its high heat value.

To obtain pure hydrogen, the water gas is mixed with more water and passed over a suitable catalyst at 500°C.

$$CO + H_2O \xrightarrow[500°C]{\text{catalyst}} CO_2 \uparrow + H_2 \uparrow$$

Thus additional hydrogen is produced, and the other product, carbon dioxide, is easily separated by passing the gas over suitable absorbents. This method is one of the chief sources of industrial hydrogen. Coke is used as the source of the carbon needed for the process. Most of the remainder of the industrial hydrogen is prepared by the action of steam on iron and from natural gas (which is largely CH_4).

$$CH_4 + H_2O \rightarrow CO \uparrow + 3H_2 \uparrow$$

2. *Hydrogen from acids.* In producing hydrogen in the laboratory, dilute solutions of acids are used almost exclusively.[1] Although you may use any of the metals mentioned on page 66 (carbon is not a metal) which liberate hydrogen from water or steam, zinc is most commonly used. Dilute hydrochloric or sulfuric acid solutions are generally employed. When either dilute hydrochloric acid or sulfuric

---

[1] Commonly the concentration of acid used is about three molar. See Chap. 15, page 159, for a definition of molarity.

acid solution is poured onto zinc, hydrogen is liberated at a rapid (but not a dangerous) rate.

$$Zn + H_2SO_4 \rightarrow ZnSO_4 + H_2 \uparrow$$
$$Zn + 2HCl \rightarrow ZnCl_2 + H_2 \uparrow$$

Sometimes iron nails are used in place of zinc, but in this case the hydrogen produced is contaminated with carbon-and-hydrogen containing compounds because nails are not pure iron.

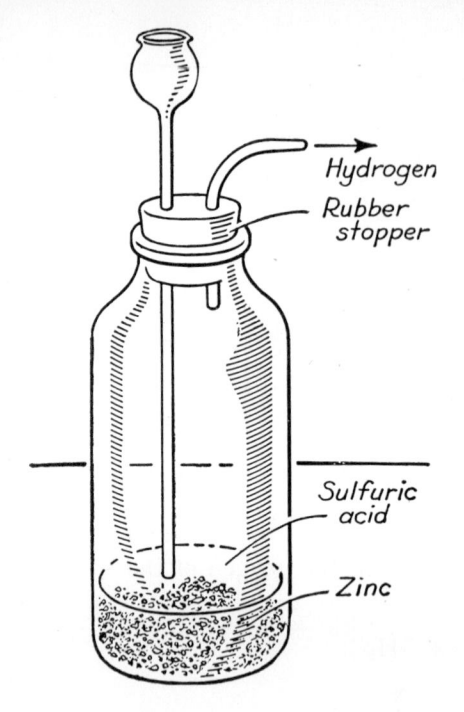

$$Fe + H_2SO_4 \rightarrow \underset{\text{ferrous sulfate}}{FeSO_4} + H_2 \uparrow$$

$$Fe + 2HCl \rightarrow \underset{\text{ferrous chloride}}{FeCl_2} + H_2 \uparrow$$

Fig. 8–3. A convenient method of generating hydrogen in the laboratory.

3. *Hydrogen from alkalis.* Zinc, aluminum, and silicon will react vigorously with water solutions of **alkalis**,[1] such as sodium hydroxide (NaOH) or potassium hydroxide (KOH), to liberate hydrogen.

$$2H_2O + 2Al + 2NaOH \rightarrow 3H_2 \uparrow + 2NaAlO_2$$

You should be careful in carrying out this reaction in a test tube. The reaction may be slow at first but, once started, is likely to proceed very rapidly and the alkali solution may be blown out of the tube. This reaction is the basis of some commercial products used for unplugging drainpipes. The hydrogen produced, when a mixture of sodium hydroxide and aluminum is added to the water in a clogged pipe, tends to remove the obstruction as a result of the gas pressure developed. The sodium hydroxide also tends to make grease in the pipeline water-soluble.

Physical properties of hydrogen

Hydrogen is unique in that it has the lowest density of any known substance. It is colorless, odorless, and tasteless. Its boiling point is $-252.8°C$, which is the lowest of any known substance except helium. When liquid hydrogen is allowed to evaporate under reduced pressure, it freezes to a colorless solid (mp $-259.1°C$).

[1] The hydroxides of the alkali metals (see page 177) are commonly called alkalis.

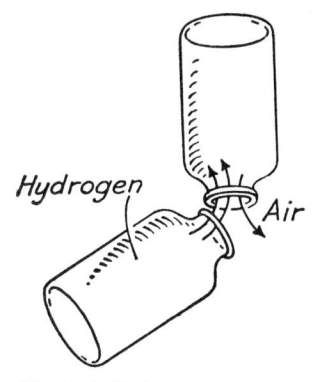

Fig. 8-4. Hydrogen gas pours upward.

A certain volume of hydrogen weighs only about 0.07 as much as the same volume of air at the same pressure and temperature. A body immersed in a fluid is buoyed up with a force equal to the weight of the fluid displaced. This principle is known as Archimedes' principle and it may be applied to gases as well as liquids. If a balloon is filled with 7 g of hydrogen at room temperature and pressure, it will displace a volume of air weighing 100 g. Therefore, the balloon will be buoyed up by a net force of 93 g (weight of air displaced minus weight of hydrogen), and it can lift any weight up to this amount. This fact is responsible for the use of hydrogen in filling balloons such as those used for making weather observations, and for its former use in dirigibles such as the *Hindenburg*.

If you wish to pour hydrogen from one container into another filled with air, the hydrogen must be poured upward (Fig. 8-4). Soap bubbles blown with hydrogen rise in the air. They explode when touched with a burning taper. The low density of hydrogen relative to air can be observed by pouring hydrogen *upward* into an inverted beaker fastened to a balance.

Chemical properties of hydrogen

A jet of hydrogen burns in air or oxygen with a bluish, almost colorless, flame. The temperature of the flame is very high and may reach 2500°C. The sole product of this reaction is water. You can show the presence of water by holding a cold beaker above the flame. You will see water vapor condense on the walls of the beaker (Fig. 8-5).

WARNING: Never light the hydrogen from a generator until you are sure

Fig. 8-5. When hydrogen burns, water is produced. This can be proved by the experiment shown. The moisture formed by burning the hydrogen is condensed as droplets on the cold beaker.

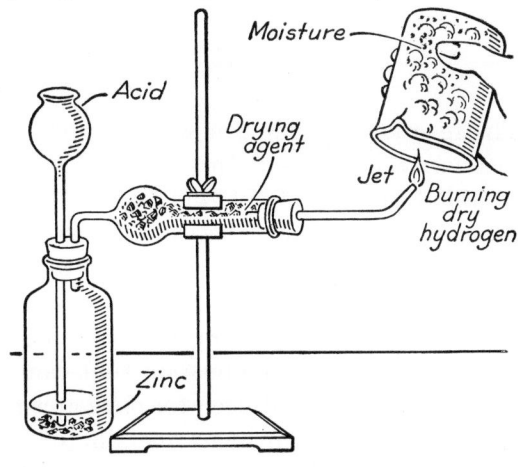

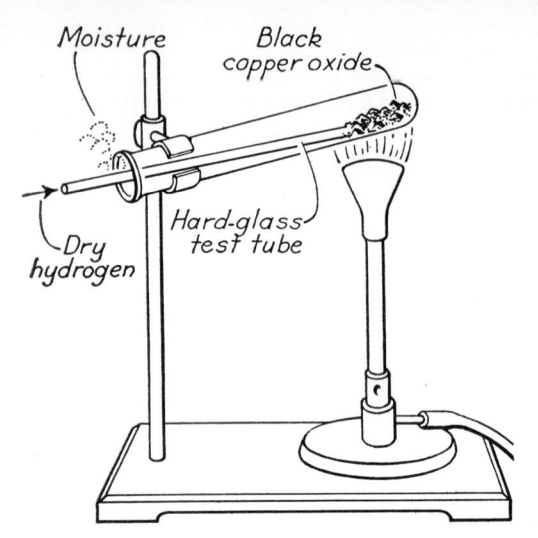

Fig. 8–6. When a stream of dry hydrogen is passed over hot copper oxide, the black copper oxide is reduced to pink copper metal.

all the air has been swept out of the generator. If you light the hydrogen without taking this precaution, a violent explosion may occur in the generator. An even better safeguard is to put a trap between the generator and the jet to be lighted.

When mixed with air, hydrogen is very explosive. This can be demonstrated as follows:

Fill a stout bottle, such as a milk bottle, two-thirds full of hydrogen. Fill the remaining third of the bottle with oxygen by collecting the gases over water. Hold your face well away from the bottle and place a lighted taper in the mouth of the bottle. A loud explosion will result.

WARNING: The bottle should be enclosed in a wire basket as it sometimes breaks.

Hydrogen also combines directly with many other nonmetals such as chlorine, bromine, and sulfur.

$$H_2 + \underset{\text{chlorine}}{Cl_2} \rightarrow \underset{\text{hydrogen chloride}}{2HCl}$$

$$H_2 + \underset{\text{sulfur}}{S} \rightarrow \underset{\text{hydrogen sulfide}}{H_2S}$$

The reaction of hydrogen with chlorine is almost as vigorous as the reaction with oxygen. In fact a jet of hydrogen lighted in air will continue to burn in chlorine, and hydrogen chloride will be formed. The flame is greenish. This example shows you that there are reactions other than those involving oxygen which proceed rapidly with the liberation of heat and light. Since all reactions which take place rapidly with the liberation of heat and light are called *combustion*, this is one type of combustion that can take place without oxygen.

The affinity of hydrogen for oxygen is so strong that hydrogen will remove oxygen from many metallic oxides. Thus when hydrogen is passed over hot copper oxide it removes the oxygen. Water is formed and metallic copper is left behind (Fig. 8–6).

$$\text{CuO} + \text{H}_2 \xrightarrow{\text{heated}} \text{Cu} + \text{H}_2\text{O}$$
copper oxide → copper

Metallic tungsten[1] (wolfram) is also made this way.

$$\text{WO}_3 + 3\text{H}_2 \xrightarrow{\text{heated}} \text{W} + 3\text{H}_2\text{O}$$
tungsten oxide (wolfram oxide) → tungsten (wolfram)

The removal of oxygen from a compound is called *reduction*.[2] Since hydrogen can be used effectively in reduction, hydrogen is said to be a good *reducing agent*.

Although hydrogen burns, it does not support combustion. (Oxygen supports combustion.) If you light a wax taper and insert it in a bottle of hydrogen held mouth down, the taper will ignite the hydrogen where it meets the air at the mouth of the bottle. As you insert the taper further, its flame will go out since the hydrogen in the bottle will not support combustion. The flame at the mouth of the bottle will continue to burn and re-ignite the taper when it is slowly withdrawn (Fig. 8–7).

With the active metals hydrogen forms metal hydrides.

$$2\text{Na} + \text{H}_2 \rightarrow 2\text{NaH}$$
sodium hydride

$$2\text{Cs} + \text{H}_2 \rightarrow 2\text{CsH}$$
cesium → cesium hydride

$$\text{Ca} + \text{H}_2 \rightarrow \text{CaH}_2$$
calcium hydride

[1] The Committee on Nomenclature of the International Union of Chemistry in 1950 officially adopted the name *wolfram* for the element formerly called *tungsten*. There has been some resistance to the acceptance of the name wolfram in America. The American Chemical Society has decided to retain the name tungsten.

[2] For a complete definition see Chap. 51, page 662.

Fig. 8–7. Hydrogen burns but does not support combustion. A lighted taper will ignite the top of a bottle filled with hydrogen where the gas meets the air. As the taper is inserted into the bottle, it goes out, but it is re-ignited as it is withdrawn.

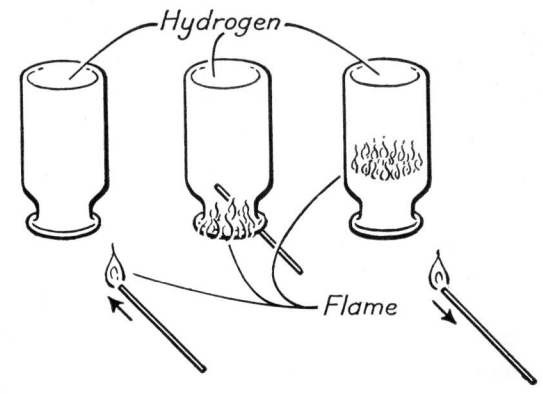

Hydrogen is of great importance in maintaining our food supply because it is used in making ammonia. Ammonia is essential to the manufacture of nitrogen fertilizers for crops and recently ammonia has been applied directly to the soil, as shown in this farm scene.

These metal hydrides are white solids. Sodium hydride is used in industry to remove the iron oxide scale from steel plates. Cesium hydride is the light-sensitive substance in many photoelectric cells, such as those used in the motion picture industry.

Uses of hydrogen

Although hydrogen is very important in maintaining our standard of living, its uses are not obvious. The most important industrial use of hydrogen is in the manufacture of ammonia (NH_3), which is made by the direct combination of hydrogen and nitrogen. This compound is essential to the manufacture of nitrogen fertilizers. Sometimes you feel that your grocery bill is too high. You can take some consolation in the fact that the quality and quantity of foods would be much lower and the prices much higher if American chemists and engineers were not able to supply farmers with nitrogen fertilizers at a low cost. The compound ammonia has another important use. That is its use in the production of explosives.

Hydrogen under pressure (and in the presence of nickel or palladium as catalyst) will react with many vegetable oils, such as soybean, peanut, and cottonseed oils. The result is to "harden," or raise the melting point of, the oil. This process is called **hydrogenation**. By controlling the extent of hydrogenation of the oil, the melting point of the product can be controlled. To make a lard substitute for cooking purposes, the hydrogenation is stopped before completion. If hydrogenation is completed, a material comparable to tallow is obtained. Great quantities of hydrogen are used for preparing vegetable shortenings and for making oleomargarines. The latter contain partly hydrogenated vegetable oils which resemble butter in consistency.

Hydrogen is used in the preparation of many foods. For example, it is used in the making of the vegetable shortenings that are so common in the American kitchens today.

As you have read, hydrogen in water gas is used for fuel. Another use of hydrogen is to hydrogenate coal. In this process a liquid similar to natural petroleum is formed. This process was employed extensively in Germany during World War II to supply much needed motor fuel and lubricating oil (see Chap. 36, page 429). Hydrogen is also used in the manufacture of methanol (see page 434). Because of its low density, hydrogen is used to fill weather-observation balloons.

The activity series

You have seen that hydrogen may be liberated from certain of its compounds (water and acids) by certain metals. You have seen also that this reaction is much more vigorous with a metal such as sodium than with one such as iron. This raises the question: Is it possible for every metal to replace hydrogen from its compounds? A simple test will show you that it is not. A wire of copper, silver, or platinum in a beaker of hydrochloric acid gives no observable reaction (Fig. 8–8).

$$HCl + Cu \rightarrow \text{no reaction}$$

Fig. 8–8. A copper wire in hydrochloric acid shows no reaction.

Whether or not a given metal will liberate hydrogen from an acid depends on a property which chemists call **activity.** The activity of an element is a measure of its tendency to enter into chemical reaction. Each element has a different activity, and it is possible to compare the activities of the various metallic elements. The actual method of comparison cannot be given here, but you can get an approximate idea of the relative activities by noting the vigor with which the elements react with water under the same conditions. As you know, potassium reacts very vigorously with cold water, sodium reacts somewhat less vigorously, and magnesium reacts scarcely at all (with *cold* water). This is also their order of activity. A more complete list is the **activity series** given in Table 8–1. Although hydrogen is not a metal, its activity can be compared with the metals because it forms the same types of compounds (such as oxide, chloride, and sulfate).

Table 8–1 lists the elements in order of their decreasing tendency to form any given compound. For example, magnesium is listed above hydrogen. This means that free magnesium has a greater tendency to combine with chlorine to form magnesium chloride than hydrogen has to form the corresponding compound hydrochloric acid. Therefore, magnesium will rob hydrochloric acid of its chlorine, forming magnesium chloride and free hydrogen.

$$Mg + 2HCl \rightarrow H_2 \uparrow + \underset{\text{magnesium chloride}}{MgCl_2}$$

Any metal above hydrogen in the list will liberate hydrogen from an acid or, more slowly, from water. Any metal listed below hydrogen will not liberate hydrogen from an acid or from water.

In the same way, any element in the activity series will replace any other element below it. Thus an iron nail dipped into a solution of copper sulfate becomes coated with pink metallic copper.

$$\underset{\text{copper sulfate}}{CuSO_4} + Fe \rightarrow \underset{\text{ferrous sulfate}}{FeSO_4} + Cu$$

This is the reason why solutions of copper sulfate quickly corrode iron or galvanized (zinc-coated) tanks.

The activity series is useful in predicting the relative stability of compounds. The series says, in effect, that potassium has a greater tendency to form an oxide than mercury does. This fact means that the oxide of potassium will have greater **stability,** that is, have *less* tendency to decompose (the reverse process) than mercuric oxide will. You have already learned that mercuric oxide is easily decomposed by gentle heating. No amount of heating will decompose potassium oxide.

TABLE 8–1. The activity series[a]

Potassium	A	B	C	D		
Sodium	A	B	C	D		
Calcium	A	B	C	D		
Magnesium		B	C	D		
Aluminum		B	C	D		
Manganese		B	C	D		
Zinc		B	C	D		
Iron		B	C	D	E	
Nickel			C	D	E	
Tin			C	D	E	
Lead			C	D	E	
Hydrogen				D		
Copper				D	E	F
Mercury				D	E	F
Silver					E	F
Platinum					E	F
Gold					E	F

A = elements displacing hydrogen from cold water
B = elements displacing hydrogen from water at elevated temperatures
C = elements displacing hydrogen from acids
D = elements combining directly with oxygen
E = oxides reduced to free metal by hydrogen
F = metals occurring free in nature; oxides decomposed by heat

[a] In water solutions calcium is more active than sodium. In the absence of water, sodium is more active than calcium.

Thus *stability* of oxides decreases from top to bottom of series. Also, ease of reduction with hydrogen increases toward bottom of series.

The metals which are found free in nature are at the bottom of the list below hydrogen. The metals known to have been first used by the human race were gold and silver. Later a method was discovered for liberating copper from its compounds, leading to the Age of Bronze. Tin, lead, and iron came still later. Aluminum has been available commercially for only about forty years, and magnesium has been produced in quantity only since about 1935. The list read from bottom to top gives us roughly the historical order in which the metals have come into use. Some of the important relationships contained in the activity series are shown in the columns of Table 8–1.

KEY WORDS

acid	activity series	Cavendish	hydroxyl radical
activity	alkali	hydrogenation	stability

HIGHLIGHTS

As a result of the *Hindenburg* disaster, the use of hydrogen in dirigibles was discontinued.

Hydrogen was discovered by **Cavendish** about eight years before Priestley discovered oxygen.

Water, the most abundant source of hydrogen, contains approximately eleven percent of the element. All **acids** contain hydrogen, which may be replaced by certain metals.

Hydrogen can be prepared from water, acids, and **alkalis** by the reaction of appropriate metals. It can also be made by the electrolysis of water.

Hydrogen has the lowest density of any known substance, being only about one-fourteenth as heavy as air. It burns with an intense heat, forming water. It is also an excellent reducing agent.

Hydrogen is used in the synthesis of ammonia and in the manufacture of vegetable shortenings.

QUESTIONS

1. Explain why you would not expect to find large quantities of hydrogen free in nature.
2. Name five natural substances which contain hydrogen.
3. List four properties common to all acids.
4. List two acids found in nature.
5. Write balanced equations for the reactions of three different metals with cold water.
6. Give two commercial sources of hydrogen.
7. Give one method suitable for generating hydrogen in the laboratory.
8. List 10 metals more active than hydrogen in order of their decreasing activity.
9. List five metals below hydrogen in activity.
10. Which would you expect to be more stable, mercuric oxide or iron oxide? Explain.
11. Explain the relation between the activity of a metal and whether or not the metal is found free in nature.
12. What relation exists between the activity of a metal and its tendency to combine directly with free oxygen?
13. List the advantages and disadvantages of hydrogen gas as a lifting agent.
14. Will hydrogen support combustion? Explain.

15. Write five reactions in which hydrogen acts as a reducing agent. (*Hint:* See the activity series.)
16. List as many ways as you can in which industrial hydrogen influences the way you live.

Suggested Projects for Unit Two

1. Prepare some manganese dioxide from an old dry cell. Work out your own method.
2. Learn how to prepare oxygen from hydrogen peroxide. What else is needed and why?
3. Predict what will be formed when each of these substances is burned: CS_2, C_2H_6, and $C_6H_{12}O_6$. See if you can write correctly balanced equations for each, assuming there is sufficient oxygen available for complete combustion.
4. See if you can find several illustrations of combustions which do not involve oxygen.
5. Obtain all the information you can concerning one serious dust explosion. Write an account of it and bring out the cause.
6. Find out why highly concentrated hydrogen peroxide is a very dangerous material.
7. Why is shortening so called?

UNIT THREE: Gases

CHAPTER 9

the properties of gases[1]

Substances exist in three physical forms: *solid, liquid,* and *gas.* You have already studied two common gases, oxygen and hydrogen. Chemistry deals with many gases. Many properties are common to all gases. If you know these, you can predict many of the properties of any specific gas. In this chapter you will learn some of the *facts* about the properties of gases. You will see also how some of these facts have been built into *laws.* In the following chapter you will see how these facts and laws are explained by a *theory* concerning the make-up of a gas.

The properties of gases

Gases are characterized, and distinguished from solids and liquids, by the following properties:

1. Gases exert a pressure equally in all directions. If a solid, such as a book, is lying on a table, the pressure of the book is entirely on the top of the table. But a gas exerts pressure equally in all directions. You know that a toy balloon tends to become spherical when inflated. If the gas exerted its pressure only in certain directions, the balloon would tend to stretch only in those directions. Moreover, in a balloon or other container, if no leaks occur and if its temperature is constant, a gas will exert its pressure forever. It is true that an automobile tire occasionally has to be blown up to keep it from going flat, but this is due to leakage and perhaps to a reaction of the air with the rubber inside the tube.

---

[1] At the discretion of the teacher, this chapter may be omitted without loss of continuity in the subject matter of this book.

2. *Low density.* One **milliliter** (ml)[1] of oxygen, at 0°C and a pressure of 1 atmosphere, weighs 0.001429 g. The same volume of water under these conditions weighs 0.9998 g.

3. *Diffusibility.* Unconfined gases are able to move from one place to another with no outside help. This action is called **diffusion.** A bottle of perfume, when opened, quickly makes its presence known all over the room. A small sample of a gas placed in a container quickly spreads itself uniformly through the container. This shows that gases have the property of diffusibility.

4. *Permeability.* Gases can diffuse into a space already occupied by another gas as well as into a vacuum.[2] If a few drops of liquid bromine are poured into a flask which is quickly stoppered, the bromine rapidly evaporates, forming a brown gas which you can easily see. Although the gas is formed at the bottom of the flask and its density is greater than that of air, the bromine will quickly spread uniformly through the entire flask. It will do so even though the flask is "full" of air. That is, the bromine spreads itself throughout the flask by diffusion. In so doing it shows that the air is **permeable.** Gases are readily permeated by other gases.

5. *Compressibility and expansibility.* You think of solids and liquids as occupying fixed volumes (actually, they are slightly, but only very slightly, compressible). Gases, on the other hand, are compressible almost without limit. The volume of a certain sample of gas depends only on its temperature and the pressure exerted upon it. In the same way, gases can expand without limit. That is, any gas will fill what volume is available to it.

The barometer

The pressure of the atmosphere is measured with a barometer. A simple form of barometer is shown in Fig. 9–1. A glass tube about one meter (m) long is sealed at one end by heating and rotating it in a bunsen flame. The tube is then completely filled with mercury. A small open dish is filled about one-quarter full with mercury. The tube is then carefully inverted with the open end beneath the surface of the mercury in the open dish. The column of mercury in the tube falls, leaving a vacuum at the top, until the pressure of the mercury column inside the tube just balances the atmospheric pressure which is pushing

---

[1] A milliliter is 1/1000 of a liter. The liter is defined as the volume (amount of space occupied) of 1000 g of water at 4.02°C. The cubic centimeter is almost but not exactly the same as the milliliter. The difference is so slight that milliliters and cubic centimeters are sometimes used interchangeably. The cubic centimeter is by definition the volume of a cube 1 cm on edge.

[2] A vacuum is a space which contains no matter. A perfect vacuum cannot be obtained for laboratory experiments but can only be approximated.

on the mercury in the open dish. Thus the height of the mercury column is a measure of the atmospheric pressure. We usually indicate the atmospheric pressure in terms of the height of this column of mercury. In chemistry this height is generally expressed in millimeters (mm). Other measures of pressure are sometimes used for other purposes.

The actual atmospheric pressure varies with the altitude and the weather. At sea level and 45 deg latitude, the average atmospheric pressure is equivalent to a column of mercury about 760 mm high. A unit of pressure commonly used is the **atmosphere. One atmosphere pressure is the same as 760 mm of mercury,** or 29.9 in. of mercury. This is also equivalent to 14.7 lb/in.² Since the density of mercury is 13.6 times the density of water, a pressure of 1 atmosphere will support a column of water which is 13.6 times 760 mm in height.

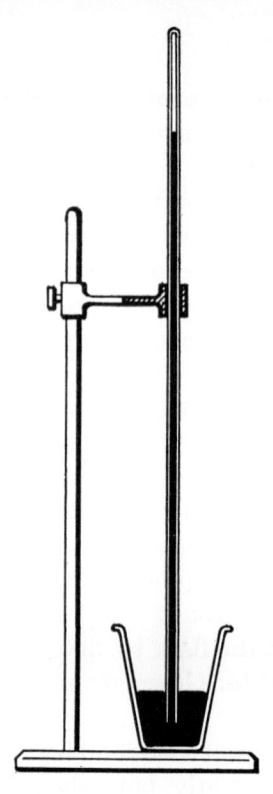

Fig. 9-1. A simple mercury barometer.

How do we measure the quantity of a gas?

Chemists often have to work quantitatively with gases as well as with solids and liquids. In general chemical experiments are either qualitative or quantitative. Qualitative experiments are concerned with what products are formed. Quantitative experiments are concerned not only with what products are formed but also with the quantities of products as well. To measure a solid, chemists can weigh the material on a balance. To measure a liquid, they can weigh it, or they can measure its volume with a **graduated cylinder,** a **burette,** or a **pipette** (see Fig. 9-2). Then the weight of the liquid can be calculated by multiplying its volume by its density (= weight per unit volume).

Weight of liquid in grams = volume in milliliters × weight in grams of 1 ml

But measuring a gas brings special problems. If you try to weigh the gas, you find the process awkward because the gas escapes if it is not completely confined. You also find that the container necessarily weighs much more than the gas, and this fact makes it difficult to get an accurate weight for the gas. The best procedure is to measure the volume of the gas and then, if necessary, the weight of the gas can be

Fig. 9–2. Common laboratory apparatus for measuring volume. From left to right: A 100-ml graduated cylinder graduated in milliliters, a 50-ml burette graduated in tenths of milliliters, a 0.1-ml pipette graduated in hundredths of milliliters, a 1-ml pipette graduated in tenths of milliliters, a 5-ml pipette graduated in tenths of milliliters, and a 10-ml pipette graduated in tenths of milliliters. Note that all the apparatus is graduated for 20°C since the volume of most substances varies with change in temperature. (Fisher Scientific Co.)

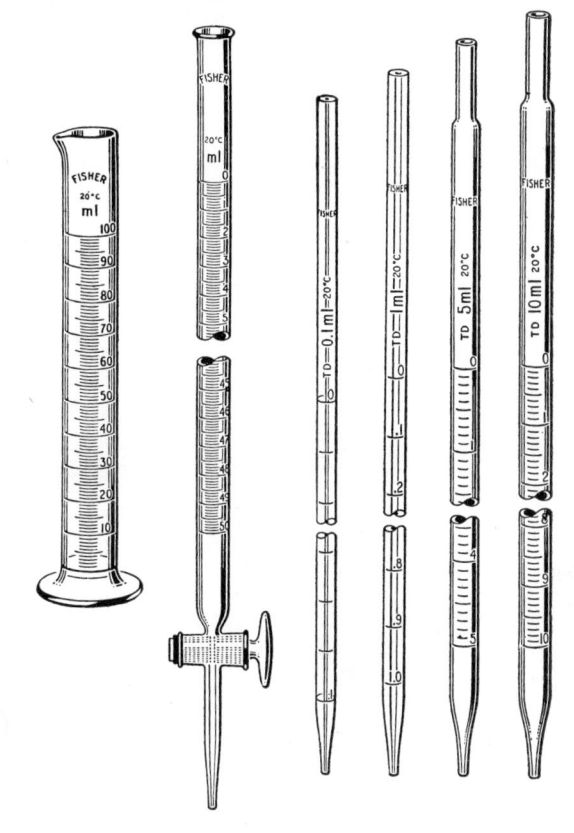

calculated by multiplying its volume by its density. (In a later chapter you will learn a simple relationship between the density of a gas and its formula.) But since the volume of a gas depends on its pressure and temperature, you must measure these, also.

A simple way to measure gas volume is to collect the gas by the displacement of water (see Fig. 6–1, page 48), or other liquid, from a graduated cylinder. The temperature of the gas will be the same as the temperature of the confining water, which is easily determined with a thermometer. The pressure of the gas can be made equal to atmospheric pressure by moving the cylinder up or down until the levels of the water outside and inside the cylinder are the same (Fig. 9–3). The volume of the gas at this pressure and temperature is read directly from the cylinder. By consulting the barometer, you can find the atmospheric pressure and hence the *total* pressure of the gas in the cylinder. If water is used as the confining liquid it will evaporate into the cylinder as water vapor, which contributes to the total pressure. To get the pressure of the gas being collected, you must subtract the pressure due to the water vapor. This will depend only on the temperature. The value can be read in the table Vapor Pressure of Water in Millimeters of Mercury on page 689 in the Appendix. If mercury is used, no

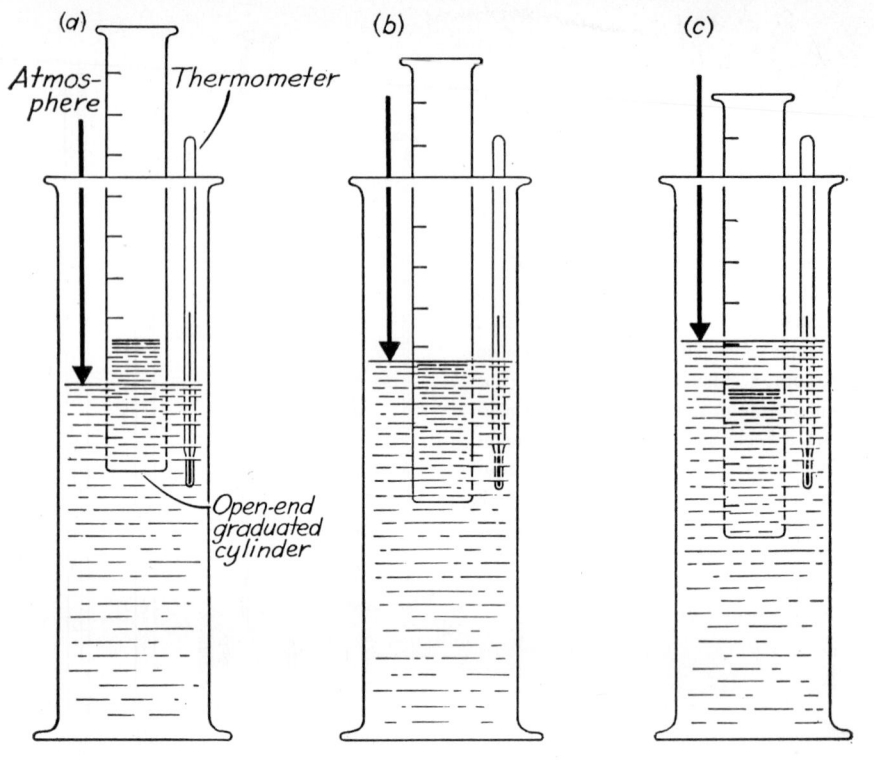

Fig. 9–3. A good method of measuring the pressure, volume, and temperature of a gas. Move the graduated cylinder up or down until the levels of water inside and outside are equal (b). The gas is now at atmospheric pressure and the same temperature as that of the water. Read the volume of the gas on the graduated cylinder. In (a) the gas pressure is less than atmospheric. In (c) the gas pressure is greater than atmospheric.

correction is necessary. Mercury does not evaporate enough to produce appreciable pressure at room temperature.

Boyle's law

If the temperature of a certain mass of gas is kept constant and the pressure on the gas is changed, the volume is inversely proportional to the pressure. By this is meant that the volume *decreases* in the same proportion as the pressure *increases*. Figure 9–4 shows this relationship. Algebraically stated

$$\frac{P_1}{P_2} = \frac{V_2}{V_1} \quad \text{(temperature being constant)}$$

or $\quad P_1 V_1 = P_2 V_2$

Where V_1 = volume of gas at pressure P_1
V_2 = volume of gas at pressure P_2

The units of P and V do not matter if the same units are used in both cases.

EXAMPLE

An automobile tire having a volume of 2.5 cubic feet (ft³) is inflated to a pressure of 45 lb/in.² This would be 30.3 lb/in.² on the gauge at the service station, as such gauges give the difference between the pressure in the tire and atmospheric pressure. What volume of air at 14.7 lb/in.² was used if the temperature was constant?

SOLUTION

$$\frac{P_1}{P_2} = \frac{V_2}{V_1}$$

$P_1 = 14.7$ lb/in.²
$P_2 = 45$
$V_1 =$ unknown
$V_2 = 2.5$ ft³

$$\frac{14.7}{45} = \frac{2.5}{V_1}$$

$$V_1 = \frac{2.5 \times 45}{14.7} = 7.65 \text{ ft}^3 \text{ air at } 14.7 \text{ lb/in.}^2 \text{ required to fill tire}$$

The effect of temperature change

You probably know that if gas is heated in a confined space, the pressure of the gas increases. This fact is the most common cause of blowouts of automobile tires which become overheated by high-speed driving or by other causes. As the temperature of the air in the tire increases, the pressure of the confined air may increase enough to burst the tire. **At constant volume the pressure of a gas is directly proportional to the temperature measured on the absolute**

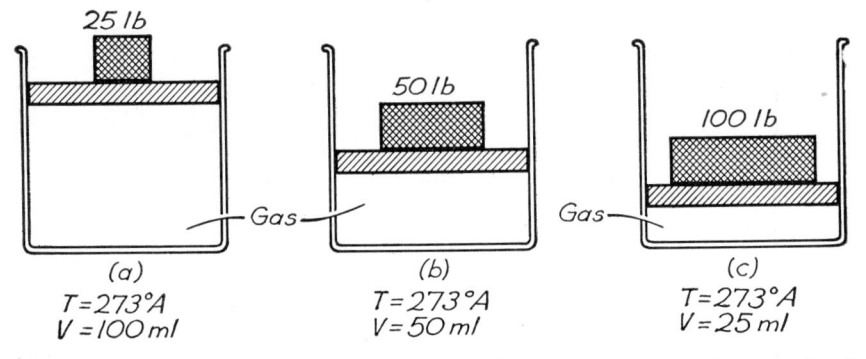

(a) 25 lb — Gas — $T = 273°A$, $V = 100$ ml

(b) 50 lb — Gas — $T = 273°A$, $V = 50$ ml

(c) 100 lb — Gas — $T = 273°A$, $V = 25$ ml

Fig. 9–4. Boyle's law. At constant temperature the volume of a gas is inversely proportional to its pressure. The volume of a gas (a) is cut to one-half (b) by twice the pressure and to one-quarter (c) by four times the pressure.

scale. [The temperature on the absolute (A) scale is obtained by adding 273 to the centigrade temperature (see Fig. 9–5).]

The relationship just described is known as **Gay-Lussac's law.** It may be stated algebraically as:

$$\frac{P_1}{P_2} = \frac{T_1}{T_2} \quad \text{(volume being constant)}$$

or
$$P_1 T_2 = P_2 T_1$$

Where P_1 = pressure of gas at absolute temperature T_1
P_2 = pressure of gas at absolute temperature T_2

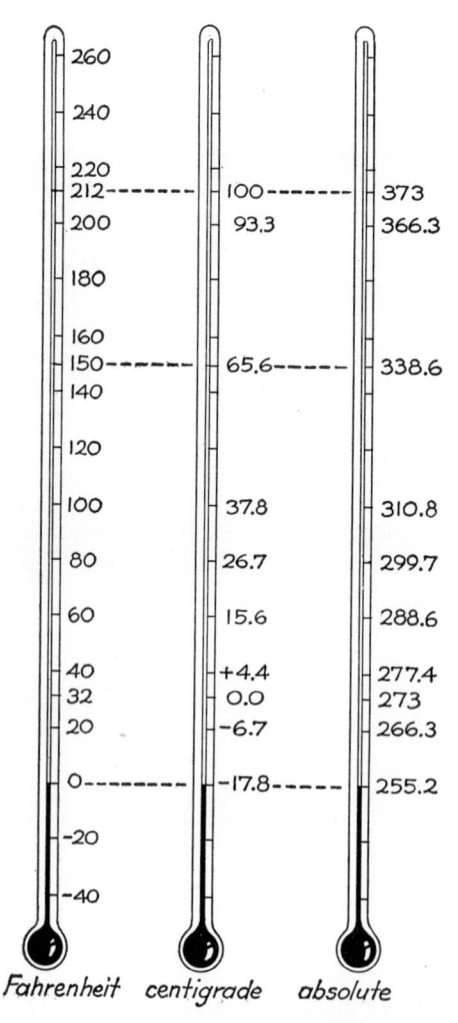

Example

An automobile tire is inflated with air at 5°C to a pressure of 40 lb/in.² If as a result of fast driving the temperature of the tire rises to 60°C, what is the pressure in the tire if its volume does not change?

Solution

$$\frac{P_1}{P_2} = \frac{T_1}{T_2}$$

$P_1 = 40$ lb/in.²
$T_1 = (5 + 273) = 278°$A
$T_2 = (60 + 273) = 333°$A
$P_2 = $ unknown

$$\frac{40}{P_2} = \frac{278}{333}$$

$$P_2 = \frac{333 \times 40}{278} = 47.9 \text{ lb/in.}^2$$

Some automobile manufacturers take these facts into consideration in the instruction book which goes with the new automobile. For example, one automobile manual says the tires should be inflated to 28 lb/in.² (gauge pressure) if cold or 30 lb/in.² if the tires have been warmed by driving.

Fig. 9–5. The temperature scales most commonly used.

Fig. 9-6. Charles's law. If the pressure of a sample of gas is held constant, its volume is directly proportional to its absolute temperature. Doubling the temperature of the gas (a) doubles its volume (b) at the same pressure.

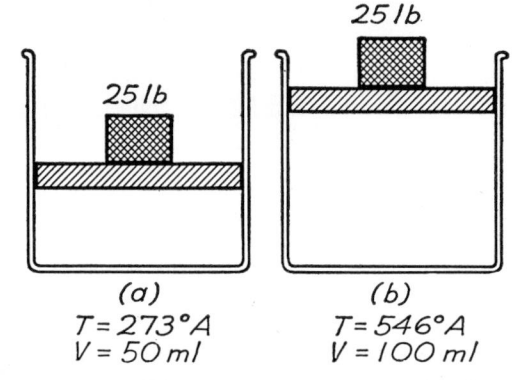

(a)
$T = 273°A$
$V = 50 \text{ ml}$

(b)
$T = 546°A$
$V = 100 \text{ ml}$

A similar law relates temperature and volume of a gas at constant pressure. **The volume of a given mass of gas is directly proportional to the absolute temperature at constant pressure.** This law is illustrated in Fig. 9-6. This is known as **Charles's law.** Or algebraically:

$$\frac{V_1}{V_2} = \frac{T_1}{T_2} \quad \text{(pressure being constant)}$$

Where V = volume
T = absolute temperature

EXAMPLE

A sample of hydrogen collected at 25°C and 1 atmosphere pressure has a volume of 93 ml. What will be its volume at 0°C and 1 atmosphere? *Be sure to use absolute temperature.*

SOLUTION

$$\frac{V_1}{V_2} = \frac{T_1}{T_2}$$

$V_1 = 93$ ml
$V_2 =$ unknown
$T_1 = 25 + 273 = 298°A$
$T_2 = 0 + 273 = 273°A$

$$\frac{93}{V_2} = \frac{298}{273}$$

$$V_2 = \frac{273 \times 93}{298} = 85.2 \text{ ml}$$

You will notice that as the temperature decreases the volume (or pressure) decreases. Perhaps you wonder what will happen at −273°C. This is 0°A. Substitution in the equation would give a volume or pressure of zero at this temperature. From this you might infer that the gas would completely disappear at −273°C. There are, however, two good reasons why this need not bother you. In the first place, absolute zero has not been reached, although it has been approached to within 0.1°A. In the second place, all gases liquefy before reaching absolute zero. These laws apply only to gases and are not intended to describe the behavior of liquids.

Standard temperature and pressure

As you have seen, it is necessary to specify the pressure and temperature at which a certain volume of gas is measured. Most frequently chemists are interested in the volume of a gas at 0°C (= 273°A) and 1 atmosphere. These conditions are known as standard temperature and pressure, which is abbreviated STP. Thus STP means 0°C and 1 atmosphere.

Graham's law of diffusion

One gas diffuses readily into a space already occupied by another gas until both are uniformly distributed throughout the space. Nor do the relative densities of the two gases make any difference in the final result (see Fig. 9–7). You can show this by placing mouth to mouth two bottles, one containing hydrogen, the other oxygen. Place the bottle containing the hydrogen on top. Since the density of hydrogen is only one-sixteenth as great as that of oxygen, you might expect the hydrogen to remain on top. Actually both gases are distributed throughout both bottles in a few minutes. You will see this by removing the bottles and passing a lighted taper across the mouth of each. A loud report results in both bottles, showing that each contains both hydrogen and oxygen.

However, the rates of diffusion of different gases depend on their densities. Hydrogen, being the lightest gas, diffuses most rapidly, helium next most rapidly, and so on. The exact relationship was discovered in 1829 by the Englishman Thomas Graham and is known as **Graham's law: The rates of diffusion of two gases at the same temperature are inversely proportional to the square roots of their densities.**

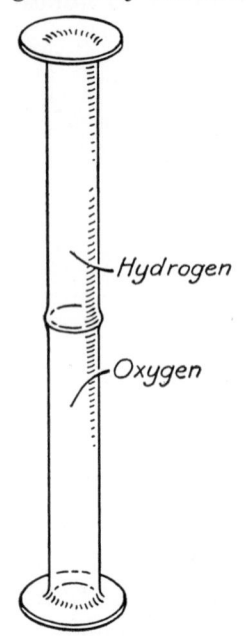

Fig. 9–7. Hydrogen and oxygen will mix by diffusion.

Or

$$\frac{r_1}{r_2} = \sqrt{\frac{d_2}{d_1}}$$

Where r_1 = rate of diffusion of gas 1
r_2 = rate of diffusion of gas 2
d_1 = density of gas 1
d_2 = density of gas 2

As applied to hydrogen and oxygen, since the density of oxygen is sixteen times as great as that of hydrogen:

$$\frac{r_H}{r_O} = \sqrt{\frac{d_O}{d_H}} = \sqrt{\frac{16}{1}} = 4$$

Thus hydrogen diffuses four times as rapidly as oxygen.

To illustrate Graham's law, you can carry out two simple experiments:

Place a beaker over a porous cup of unglazed porcelain connected as shown in Fig. 9–8. Pass a stream of hydrogen into the beaker. This forces water out of the jet tube, creating a small fountain. The explanation is that the hydrogen diffuses into the porous cup faster than the air diffuses out of it. This creates the extra pressure which ejects the water. When the beaker containing hydrogen is removed, the hydrogen diffuses out of the cup faster than the air can diffuse back in. The escape of the hydrogen creates a partial vacuum which causes air to be forced back through the jet tube.

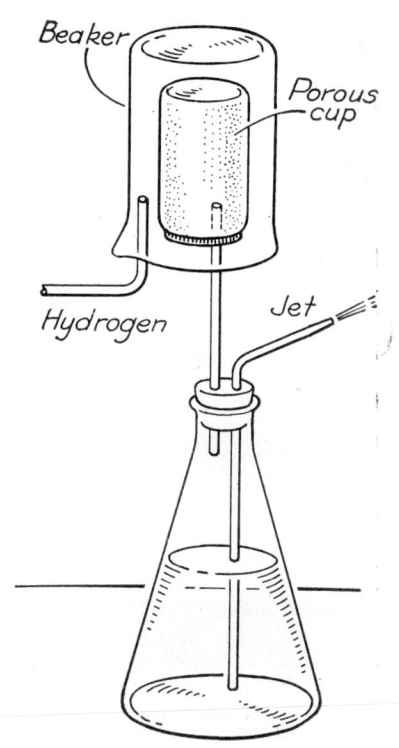

Fig. 9–8. An illustration of Graham's law.

There is an even simpler way to demonstrate Graham's law. Withdraw the stoppers from a bottle of concentrated hydrochloric acid and a bottle of concentrated ammonium hydroxide. When you hold the stoppers about two feet apart, a white smoke appears around the stopper from the hydrochloric acid but not around the other stopper. The small amounts of solutions on the stoppers give off the colorless gases ammonia (NH_3) and hydrogen chloride (HCl). The density of the ammonia is less than half that of the hydrogen chloride. On contact, these gases react to form a white solid:

$$NH_3 + HCl \rightarrow NH_4Cl$$
(gas) (gas) (white solid)
ammonium chloride

The smoke that you see consists of fine particles of this solid. Since the ammonia diffuses more rapidly than the hydrogen chloride, it reaches the stopper from the hydrochloric acid bottle before the hydrogen chloride can reach the ammonium hydroxide stopper.

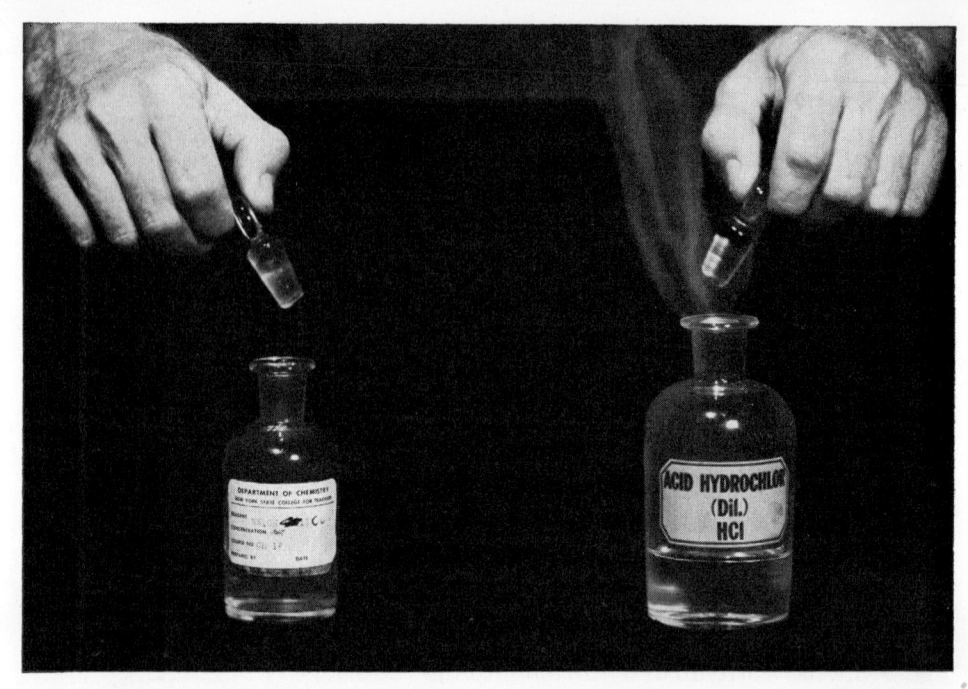

Ammonia gas from the stopper of the ammonium hydroxide bottle reacts with hydrogen chloride gas from the stopper of the hydrochloric acid bottle to form solid ammonium chloride. Judging from the place where the smoke is formed, which gas is more dense?

KEY WORDS

atmosphere	burette	Gay-Lussac's law	milliliter (ml)
barometer	Charles's law	graduated cylinder	permeable
Boyle's law	diffusion	Graham's law	pipette

standard temperature and pressure (STP)

HIGHLIGHTS

The growth of our knowledge concerning the nature of gases is a good example of the relations between facts, laws, and theories.

All gases exert pressure in all directions. All have a low density compared to liquids. All diffuse into or mix with other gases. All can expand and be compressed.

The weight of gas is most readily determined by multiplying its density by its volume. The **barometer** is an instrument used to determine the pressure of the **atmosphere.**

Boyle's law relates volume and pressure of gases at constant temperature. **Gay-Lussac's law** relates pressure and temperature of gases at constant volume. **Charles's law** relates volume and temperature of gases at constant pressure. **Graham's law** refers to the rates of **diffusion** of two gases.

QUESTIONS

1. Explain how you would collect a sample of gas in order to measure its pressure, temperature, and volume.
2. In collecting a gas over water, what correction must be made in measuring the pressure of the gas? Is the same correction necessary when the gas is collected over mercury?
3. What is meant by STP?
4. Why is it advisable to use mercury rather than water for making a barometer? Do you think a barometer could be made by using water? Explain.
5. A 100-ml sample of gas is collected at 0°C and 1.5 atmospheres. What is the volume of the gas at STP?
6. What would be the volume at STP of a sample of gas which occupies 59 ml at 0°C and a pressure of 700 mm of mercury?
7. One liter of a gas is heated at constant pressure from 0 to 100°C. What is the resulting volume of the gas?
8. If the air in a certain airplane tire has a pressure of 30 lb/in.^{2} at 25°C, what pressure will it have if cooled in flight to -30°C if its volume stays constant?
9. If the air in an automobile tire has a pressure of 43 lb/in.^{2} at 20°C, to what temperature must the tire be heated to raise the pressure to 50 lb/in.^{2} if the volume of the tire stays constant?
10. Give some common observations which show that air is permeable to other gases.
11. Examine the reagent bottles on the laboratory side shelf and note the "white dust," or ammonium chloride, which accumulates when ammonium hydroxide and hydrochloric acid are near each other on the shelf. Which of these two bottles collects most of the "dust"? Explain.

CHAPTER 10

the structure of gases and the kinetic molecular theory

In Chap. 9 you learned some properties of gases. The facts stated in that chapter apply not only to certain gases but to *all* gases. In this chapter you will learn the explanation for these properties, which are characteristic of all gases. The development of an understanding of the nature of gases is a good illustration of the scientific method. The statements made in the preceding chapter are all based upon experiments; that is, they are experimental facts which have been consolidated into laws. No assumptions or theories are involved in these laws. You will now see how these facts lead to a description of the make-up of gases. This description is known as the **kinetic molecular theory**. Thus science grows from facts to laws to theory.

The kinetic molecular theory

The question to be answered is this: What can be imagined about the make-up of all gases which would result in their having the properties that we have just learned? Just to see where it will lead you, imagine the following:

1. A gas is made up of minute particles all of which are exactly alike. Call these particles *molecules*.

2. The molecules are widely separated from each other, in comparison with their size, so that the distance between molecules is many million times their diameter. That is, gases are mostly empty space.

Gas molecules striking the pistons in an automobile engine force them down, thus furnishing the force which drives the car. (Mercury Division of Ford Motor Company)

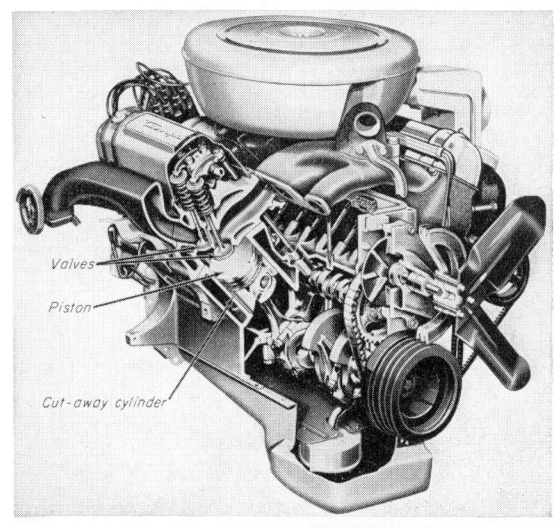

3. The molecules are in a state of rapid, random motion, so that there are molecules moving in all possible directions. Consider a gas to be like a swarm of angry bees, with each bee as a molecule. Since the molecules are moving, they have energy of motion which is called **kinetic energy.**

4. When the molecules collide with the wall of the container or with another molecule (as they must do often), no energy of motion is lost. That is, the molecules are moving as fast after the collision as they were before the collision. However, they are moving in another direction. In other words, gas molecules have perfect elasticity.

5. The average velocity (rate of motion) of the gas molecules increases as the absolute temperature increases, but it does not change unless the temperature changes.

You will see that these assumptions explain the properties of gases. This picture of the nature of gases is called the kinetic molecular theory from the two main parts of it, namely, that the gas is made up of molecules and that the molecules possess kinetic energy. It is one of the most useful and important theories of all science.

You have never seen a molecule of gas nor has anyone else. Molecules are so small that neither you nor anyone else may ever see one. Yet the five assumptions you have just read explain the properties of gases so well that there can be no doubt about their essential correctness. Scientists are just as sure that gases are made up of molecules and that molecules have kinetic energy as they are of the make of automobile which they own. In fact, scientists can measure the size and shape of many gaseous molecules.

Since, however, you cannot see the gaseous molecules, you must make full use of your imagination in order to understand the kinetic molecular theory.

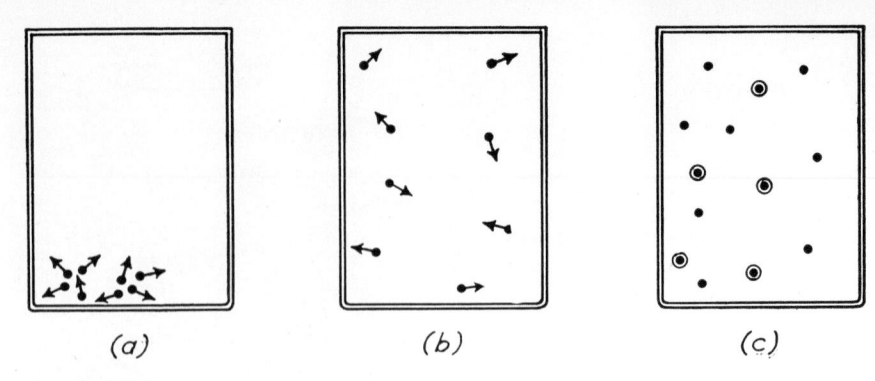

Fig. 10–1. Diffusion of gases. A sample of gas released in the bottom of a container (a) spreads by diffusion throughout the container (b) whether or not another gas is present in the container (c).

How does the kinetic molecular theory explain the properties of gases?

1. Pressure. **Pressure** measures force per unit area. In an automobile tire the pressure of the air may be 40 lb/in.² This means that the gas is pressing on each square inch of the tire with a force of 40 lb. We know that gases exert a pressure on all sides of their container, and that, without leakage and temperature changes, this pressure is forever constant. How is this explained? The pressure of the gas is the result of molecules bombarding the wall of the container. Since the molecular motion is completely random, you would expect the same number of molecules per second to strike each square inch of the container. Thus you would expect the pressure to be the same on all the walls of the container, just as it actually is found to be. Also, the theory states that the molecular velocity is constant as long as the temperature is constant. Therefore, you would expect the pressure to be maintained forever if no molecules leaked out and the temperature did not change.

2. Diffusion. How do we explain the ability of a gas to move from one place to another, that is, diffusion? Diffusion is the natural consequence of the random motion of the molecules.

Figure 10–1(a) shows a few molecules of a gas which have been released in the bottom of a container. Some of the molecules will start to move in all directions. Those moving downward will soon strike the bottom of the container and be reflected back. Those which start straight upward may be able to move all the way to the top before striking anything. The result will be a uniform distribution of the molecules through the entire container as shown in Fig. 10–1(b).

One gas diffuses into a space already occupied by another gas because gas molecules are very far apart in comparison with their size. There is plenty of room for molecules of a different type to get in between those already present as shown in Fig. 10–1(c). (The drawings are not to scale as the molecules are relatively very much too large.)

3. *Dalton's law.* Another law relating to gases known as **Dalton's law** says that **the total pressure of a mixture of two or more gases is equal to the sum of the pressures of each individual gas.** You can easily understand this law from Fig. 10–1(c). Each gas behaves as though the other or others were not there, and the total pressure on the container is the sum of the pressures from each gas.

4. *Boyle's law.* How do we explain the fact that the pressure of a gas increases as the volume decreases at constant temperature (Boyle's law)? You can understand this law from Fig. 10–2. In Fig. 10–2(a) the molecules are exerting a pressure such that the gas can just support the 25-lb weight. In Fig. 10–2(b) the gas is shown compressed into half its former volume. All the molecules have been squeezed into half the volume they occupied before. Consequently each molecule will hit the wall of the container twice as many times per second. This will produce a pressure twice as great as before, although the velocity of the molecules has not been changed.

5. *Charles's and Gay-Lussac's laws.* The kinetic molecular theory states that the kinetic energy of the gas molecules depends only on the temperature and that it is proportional to the absolute temperature. Suppose a certain number of molecules of a gas are confined as in Fig. 10–3(a) at a temperature of 273°A and a pressure of 1 atmosphere. Assume the temperature is raised to 546°A as shown in Fig. 10–3(b). This means that the kinetic energy of the molecules will be doubled. But if the molecules move faster, they will hit the wall more often and also harder. In other words the pressure of the gas will increase as the absolute temperature increases if the volume is kept constant. Or suppose that the gas at first is confined by a movable piston with a 25-lb weight as shown in Fig. 10–3(c). Then as the temperature is raised, the increased activity of the molecules will push the weight up until the increased activity of the molecules has been counterbalanced by their being less concentrated [Fig. 10–3(d)]. This is Charles's law:

$$\frac{V_1}{V_2} = \frac{T_1}{T_2} \quad \text{at constant pressure}$$

Fig. 10–2. Boyle's law and the kinetic molecular theory. If the volume of a gas is reduced to one-half, the concentration of molecules is doubled. This doubles the pressure of the gas.

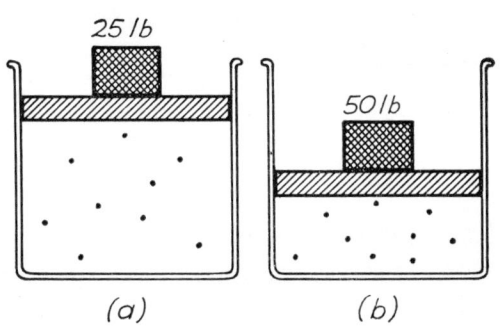

(a)	(b)	(c)	(d)
T=273°A	T=546°A	T=273°A	T is higher than 273°A

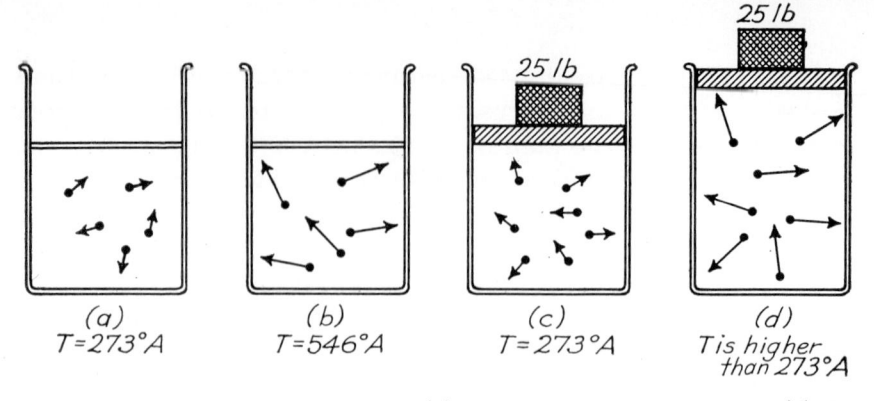

Fig. 10-3. Pressure equals 1 atmosphere (a); pressure equals 2 atmospheres (b). The kinetic theory explains Gay-Lussac's and Charles's laws. Increasing the temperature of a gas really is an increasing of the kinetic energy of the molecules of the gas. If the volume remains constant as in (b), a greater pressure results. But if the pressure is constant as in (c) and (d), an increase in volume occurs.

Figure 10-3(a) and 10-3(b) represent Gay-Lussac's law:

$$\frac{P_1}{P_2} = \frac{T_1}{T_2} \quad \text{at constant volume}$$

Where V = volume
T = absolute temperature
P = pressure

Heat and temperature

The relationship between Charles's law, the absolute-temperature scale, and heat needs a little more consideration. Many people confuse heat and temperature by wrongly thinking they are the same thing. Yet you will realize that there is more heat in a bathtub full of warm water than in a teacup of boiling water, although the temperature of the former may be only 40°C while that of the latter is 100°C. So you see that the temperature does not measure the amount of heat contained in a body. What, then, does temperature measure? To answer this, consider the purpose for which you use a thermometer. If the thermometer outside your window reads 0°F, you know that if you go out unprotected by heavy clothing, heat will flow from your body to the surroundings. As a result, you will get the sensation of being cold. If the outside temperature is 110°F, you will expect just the opposite sensation. If two bodies at different temperatures are placed in *thermal* contact,[1] the result can always be predicted: heat will flow from the hotter body to the colder one. As a result of this the temperature of the hotter body falls and that of the colder one rises.

---

[1] To place bodies in thermal contact is to place them so that it is possible for heat to flow from one to the other.

You can now see that **temperature** measures only one thing, namely, the **direction of flow of heat**. Or returning to the kinetic molecular theory, you see that temperature measures the **average kinetic energy of the molecules**. This latter statement is true, whether the substance is a gas or a liquid or a solid. In all three cases molecular motion exists, and the higher the temperature, the greater the degree of molecular motion.

Heat, on the other hand, is a **form of energy.** It is the kinetic energy of the molecules. The total heat contained in a body is the **sum of the kinetic energy possessed by all the individual molecules.** Thus in a cupful of water at 100°C the average kinetic energy of the individual molecules is higher than the average kinetic energy of the molecules in a bathtub of water at 40°C. However, the total kinetic energy (heat) of all the molecules in the bathtub is greater because there are so many more molecules. That is, heat *is* molecular motion. Temperature measures the intensity of this motion *per molecule*.

You can now understand how heat flows by **conduction** from one body to another. Molecules of the hot body collide with molecules of the cold body and in so doing give the molecules of the cold body some of their kinetic energy. This happens just as a fast moving billiard ball may strike a slower moving ball and transfer some of its energy to the slower ball. The result will be that the molecules of both bodies will come to have the same average kinetic energy (temperature).

You can now see why a **vacuum,**[1] as in a thermos bottle, is such a good insulator. In a perfect vacuum, which is unobtainable, there would be *no* molecules to transfer the kinetic energy—heat—from the outside to the inside or vice versa. Since there are always some molecules left in even the best vacuum obtainable, there is always some heat flow by conduction. But, in general, the fewer molecules there are in the space, the better the insulator.

The significance of absolute zero ($= -273.16$°C) is that at such a temperature, if it could be obtained, all molecular motion would cease. At this temperature all the molecules would be stationary. At this temperature, and this temperature only, the heat energy contained in a body would be zero. This temperature has never been attained. You can now easily see why. To reach the absolute zero, you would have to remove all kinetic energy of motion (heat) from the body. But heat will flow out of a body only if it can flow into a colder body (one of lower kinetic energy). Thus to cool a body to absolute zero, we should have to have one that is already colder than absolute zero. This is not only impossible but ridiculous. Scientists have, however, approached the absolute zero to within one-tenth of a degree.

[1] See Chap. 9, page 79.

KEY WORDS

conduction heat kinetic molecular theory temperature
Dalton's law kinetic energy pressure vacuum

HIGHLIGHTS

The development of the **kinetic molecular theory** illustrates the application of the scientific method.

According to the kinetic molecular theory, a gas is made up of minute particles called *molecules*. The molecules of a gas are separated from each other by distances which are large compared with the size of the molecule. The molecules of gases are always in rapid and random motion. Gas molecules are perfectly elastic and do not lose energy when colliding with other molecules. The higher the **temperature,** the more rapidly the molecules of a gas move.

The kinetic molecular theory explains the laws of Boyle, Gay-Lussac, Charles, and Graham.

Dalton's law relates to the total **pressure** of a mixture of gases.

Heat can flow only from a hotter to a colder body. Temperature is a measure of the direction of flow of heat. It also is a measure of the average **kinetic energy** of molecules.

QUESTIONS

1. State the main points in the kinetic molecular theory.
2. Show how the kinetic molecular theory explains Boyle's law.
3. Show how the kinetic molecular theory explains Charles's law.
4. Do you think it would be possible to explain all the known properties of gases by a set of assumptions entirely different from the kinetic molecular theory? Explain.
5. What is the difference between a law and a theory?
6. How does the kinetic molecular theory explain pressure?
7. How does the kinetic molecular theory explain diffusibility?
8. How does the kinetic molecular theory explain permeability?
9. What is meant by absolute zero? What can you say about molecular motion at absolute zero?
10. Do you expect that scientists will ever cool an object to absolute zero? Explain.
11. If one end of a copper wire is held in a flame, the other end also will become warm. Explain how the heat gets to the other end of the wire.
12. What is the difference between heat and temperature?

CHAPTER 11

the liquefaction of gases

One fact about gases which was not stated in the previous chapters is that all gases can be liquefied under the proper conditions of temperature and pressure. The **liquefaction** of gases, that is, the changing of a gas to a **liquid** by cooling and compressing it, is important in everyday life in many ways. Pyrofax, Essotane, and others, which are known as *canned gases,* are used in many homes for cooking and heating. These are hydrocarbons which are normally gases. They are kept in liquid form by being confined in steel cylinders. Many substances, such as ammonia, sulfur dioxide, and chlorine, which normally are gaseous, are stored and shipped as liquids in the same way. Carbon dioxide is liquefied in the process of changing it to dry ice (solid carbon dioxide). You have learned in Chap. 6, page 46, that liquefaction of air is the first step in separating oxygen and nitrogen from air. Also, all mechanical refrigeration is based on the alternate liquefaction of a gas and **vaporization**[1] of the resulting liquid. This cycle is also used in a device called the *heat pump,* about which you will learn later.

How are gases changed into liquids?

Water vapor in the atmosphere may be changed into liquid water by cooling. Thus a pitcher of cold water "sweats" on a humid day because it cools the air in contact with it enough to condense some of the water vapor. Dew, fog, and clouds are also formed in the same way; that is, cooling of the atmosphere causes condensation of some of its water vapor. In the same way, cooling, if carried far enough, will liquefy any gas. The temperature to which any gas must be cooled in order to liquefy it depends upon the pressure of the gas. In every case the greater the pressure of the gas, the higher the temperature at which it will liquefy and vice versa. Thus an increase in pressure and a decrease

[1] Vaporization is the process of formation of a vapor from a liquid or a solid.

in temperature bring about liquefaction. However, **for every gas there is a temperature above which it will not liquefy no matter what pressure is applied.** This temperature is characteristic of the gas and is known as its *critical temperature*. For example, the critical temperature of carbon dioxide is 31°C. This means that at 31°C and lower temperatures carbon dioxide can exist as a liquid if it is confined at a high enough pressure. At temperatures higher than 31°C, carbon dioxide exists only as a gas, no matter what pressure is used. The pressure needed to keep carbon dioxide liquid at 31°C is 73 atmospheres (= 73 × 14.7, or 1073 lb/in.^{2}). The pressure needed to liquefy any gas at its critical temperature is called the **critical pressure.** At lower temperatures, the pressure needed is lower. Since the critical temperature of carbon dioxide is a little above average room temperature, it is commonly stored and shipped in strong steel cylinders as a liquid. Oxygen, however, has a critical temperature of −118.8°C. Therefore, oxygen exists only as a gas at room temperature. It cannot exist as a liquid at room temperature even when under a pressure of 2000 lb/in.^{2}, which is the pressure used in commerce for storing and shipping this gas. Table 11–1 contains the critical constants for some important substances.

TABLE 11–1. Critical constants[a]

Name	Formula	Critical temperature, °C	Critical pressure, atmospheres	Normal boiling point, °C
Helium	He	−267.9	2.26	−268.9
Hydrogen	H$_2$	−239.9	12.8	−252.8
Neon	Ne	−228.7	25.9	−245.9
Nitrogen	N$_2$	−147.1	33.5	−195.8
Carbon monoxide	CO	−139	35	−190
Oxygen	O$_2$	−118.8	49.7	−183
Carbon dioxide	CO$_2$	31.1	73.0	
Hydrogen chloride	HCl	51.4	81.6	−83.7
Hydrogen sulfide	H$_2$S	100.4	88.9	−61.8
Ammonia	NH$_3$	132.4	111.5	−33.3
Chlorine	Cl$_2$	144	76.1	−34.6
Sulfur dioxide	SO$_2$	157.2	77.7	−10
Water	H$_2$O	374.0	217.7	100
Alcohol	C$_2$H$_5$OH	243.1	63.1	78.5
Freon 12	CF$_2$Cl$_2$	112	40.1	−29.8
Freon 21	CHCl$_2$F	178.5	51	8.9
Methyl chloride	CH$_3$Cl	143.1	65.8	−24.2

[a] The data (except for Freons) are from the *Handbook of Chemistry and Physics*, 34th ed., Chemical Rubber Publishing Co., Cleveland, Ohio, 1952. The data on Freons are from Kinetic Chemicals, Inc., Wilmington, Del.

How do liquids differ from gases?

There are two obvious differences between a liquid and a gas. First, the liquid always has a higher density. For example, 18 g of liquid water at 100°C and 1 atmosphere occupies a volume of 19.7 ml. But, 18 g of water vapor at 100°C and 1 atmosphere occupies a volume of 30,600 ml. Second, the liquid occupies a fixed[1] volume, whereas the gas will expand until it has uniformly filled any container in which it is placed. Thus when a drop of water is placed on a glass plate, the molecules cling together and remain there as a coherent unit. However, when a bubble of gas is released in the same way, the molecules scatter and spread until they are distributed all over the room.

Liquids and the kinetic molecular theory

Liquids do not fly apart and scatter in all directions as do gases. Therefore, it is evident that there are forces within liquids which bind each molecule of a liquid to its neighbors and thus bind all the molecules into a coherent drop (or larger quantity). You have already learned in Chap. 10, page 95, that the molecules of all substances are in motion (that is, have kinetic energy) at all temperatures above absolute zero. So we must imagine that the molecules of a liquid are in a state of rapid motion, but that their momentum is not great enough, on the average, to allow a *molecule to escape from its neighbors*. Furthermore, since liquids are nearly incompressible, each molecule must be, in effect, touching its neighbors.[2]

In Chap. 10 you imagined a gas to be like a swarm of angry bees in which each bee is moving rapidly and completely at random with respect to its neighbors. Now, you might imagine a liquid to be like a cluster of quiet bees in which each bee, while still moving slightly, is nevertheless holding on to its neighbor. Perhaps a good biologist could tell you why bees hang on to each other and form a cluster. But chemists still do not completely understand the nature of the forces which hold each molecule to its neighbors in a liquid. Yet these forces exist and are responsible for the very existence of liquids. That is, without these forces there would be no liquids. They are sometimes called **van der Waals' forces,** after a Dutch scientist. The magnitude (intensity) of these forces varies in different substances. This is why

[1] This is not to say that liquids are completely incompressible. Liquids can be compressed slightly by applying very great pressures. But the effect is so slight as to be negligible for most purposes.

[2] The slight compressibility of liquids is probably due to deformation of the molecule. For example, if oranges are packed into a crate in the usual way, only a certain number can be packed into 1 ft³. However, if the oranges are squeezed tightly until they are distorted, a few more can be forced into the same volume.

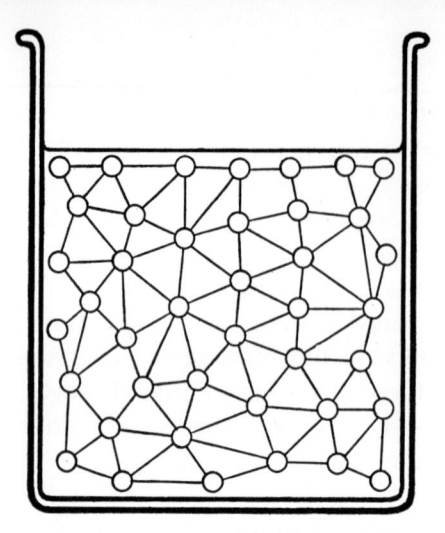

Fig. 11–1. A useful picture of liquid is gotten by drawing circles to represent the molecules and then drawing lines from each molecule to its neighbors to represent the forces which hold the molecules together.

different substances liquefy at different temperatures. For all molecules, however, **these forces become greater the closer the molecules approach each other.**[1]

The same forces of attraction that are present between adjacent molecules of a liquid exist between gaseous molecules. These forces are not generally noticed in a gas because (1) the molecules are so far apart that the forces are very weak and (2) the kinetic energy of the gaseous molecules is so large that by comparison the forces of attraction are almost negligible. Therefore, although these forces of attraction do exist between gaseous molecules, the forces are not normally strong enough to draw the molecules together, that is, liquefy the gas. But you have learned that gases are caused to liquefy by cooling and compression. Compressing a gas brings the molecules closer together. As the molecules are brought closer together, the forces of attraction between neighboring molecules become much greater. Cooling reduces the kinetic energy of the molecules. At the pressure and temperature at which the forces of attraction between neighboring molecules **become great enough to overcome the momentum which the molecules have** as a result of their random motion, the forces draw the molecules all together, that is, the gas then liquefies.

Liquefaction and the critical temperature

The higher the temperature, the greater the pressure required to liquefy a gas. This is because at higher temperatures the gas molecules are moving more rapidly, and hence the forces of attraction between the molecules must be greater in order to pull the molecules together. The forces of attraction between molecules can be increased only by bringing the molecules closer together, that is, by applying greater

[1] These forces are approximately inversely proportional to the seventh power of the distance between the molecules.

pressure. However, for each gas there is a certain temperature above which it will not liquefy no matter what pressure is used. This is true because the forces of attraction between molecules can be increased only by bringing the molecules closer together. These forces can never be made greater than the values which they have when the molecules are as close to each other as they can get, that is, effectively touching each other. Now, at temperatures above the critical temperature, even these maximum forces of attraction are not great enough to overcome the high kinetic energy of the molecules; hence liquefaction does not occur. In other words, the critical temperature is the temperature above which the kinetic energy of the molecules becomes greater than the energy of the maximum forces of attraction which can exist between the molecules.

You might think of liquids as being like a cluster of bees in which each bee is tied to its neighbors by imaginary rubber bands. The individual bees can stretch these bands and so escape from the cluster, but only if the bees become sufficiently active. To make the analogy more nearly correct, you would have to imagine that, as the bees separate from each other, the force with which the elastic bands tend to pull them together becomes less.

Liquid air

Not many years ago liquid air was a rare commodity available only in a very few places in the world. Now more than one hundred plants in this country produce it on an industrial scale. Liquid air is even shipped in commerce. There are few sections of the country where it is not now available on short notice. The principal reasons for the manufacture of liquid air are that it offers a practical means of separating nitrogen and oxygen from the atmosphere and that it provides a convenient method of obtaining a low temperature. Liquid air consists of nitrogen (bp $-195.8°C$) and oxygen (bp $-183°C$). Since the nitrogen is more volatile, when the liquid air boils, the nitrogen boils away

Fig. 11-2. A vacuum flask for holding liquid air is based on the same principle as a thermos bottle, which is a good insulator partly because of the vacuum between its inner and outer walls.

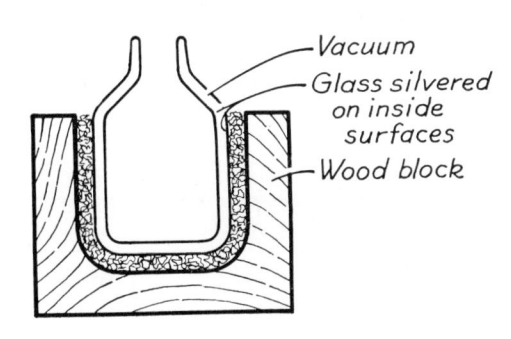

Left top and bottom, flowers and an egg become hard and brittle when dipped into liquid air. Right top, liquid air can be poured from a flask. Right bottom, liquid air is more dense than water and sinks, boiling violently. (Science Service)

first. In this way the nitrogen and oxygen are separated by the process of distillation. You have already learned some of the uses for pure oxygen (see Chap. 7, pages 59 to 61). Most of the nitrogen obtained from liquid air is used in making fertilizers and explosives or in filling electric-light bulbs.

Liquid air may be kept for several days in an efficient vacuum flask where it slowly boils away (Fig. 11–2). The boiling point is at first about $-190°C$; but as the nitrogen boils out, the boiling temperature rises nearer to that of pure oxygen. Liquid air is a nearly colorless liquid, but it turns slightly bluish as the nitrogen boils out.

Liquid air has very peculiar effects on many substances. These effects are due to either (1) its low temperature or (2) the high concentration of oxygen molecules which it contains. The result of the

This photograph shows a commercial distillation column for separating oxygen from nitrogen in liquid air. When the gases are separated, they are pumped into strong steel cylinders under very high pressures. In this way they may be stored and shipped most economically. Both oxygen and nitrogen remain gaseous in the cylinders since the temperatures at which they are stored and shipped are above their critical temperatures.

high concentration of oxygen molecules is to make liquid air a powerful oxidizing agent. Because of its low temperature, flowers, fruits, eggs, meat, rubber, and other more or less elastic materials, when immersed in liquid air, become as brittle as glass. Mercury is frozen to a hard solid. The powerful oxidizing action of liquid air can be shown by soaking a mixture of cotton and charcoal in it and, after the mixture has become saturated with liquid air, igniting the mixture.

CAUTION: These experiments could be dangerous.

The cotton burns almost instantly. A glowing cigarette, dropped into a beaker of liquid air, is completely burned almost instantly. In fact liquid oxygen absorbed by charcoal is used as an explosive. Because of these properties, **no highly combustible substances such as a hydrocarbon or an active metal should ever be added to liquid air or liquid oxygen.** If this is done, a serious explosion may result. There has been at least one case in which aluminum powder added to liquid air produced a disastrous explosion.

How is liquid air made?

In view of the low boiling point of liquid air, you are probably wondering how it is made. The fundamental requirement for liquefying air is the same as that for liquefying any other gas—it must be cooled below its critical temperature and then it can be caused to liquefy by

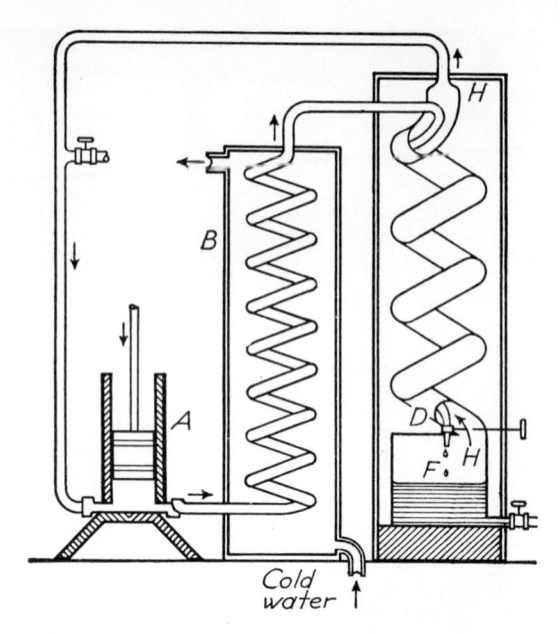

Fig. 11-3. Diagram of a Linde liquid air machine. See the text below for a complete description of the operation of this machine.

sufficient compression. But the critical temperature of oxygen is $-118.8°C$ and that of nitrogen is $-147.1°C$. Since it is not possible to cool the air this much with ordinary mechanical refrigeration, a special method of cooling the air must be used. In the Linde liquid air machine, the method used to cool the air is the same in principle as one of the methods by which clouds are formed in nature. You probably know that a drop in barometric pressure may produce enough cooling of the atmosphere to lead to condensation of some of the water vapor in the atmosphere, that is, to cloud formation. This is because a reduction in atmospheric pressure always involves an expansion of the air. **The expansion of any gas** (except hydrogen and helium under certain conditions) **is a cooling process.** That is, when a gas under pressure is allowed to expand, the gas becomes cooler. You can remember this easily because it is just the opposite of what happens when a gas is compressed. Anyone who has pumped up a bicycle tire with a hand pump has noticed that when the air is compressed it becomes hotter. The cooling which accompanies the expansion of a gas is known as the **Joule-Thomson effect.** It is named after the British scientists who were among the first to study this behavior.

The diagram of the **Linde liquid air machine** is shown in Fig. 11-3. An air compressor, A, supplies air (from which carbon dioxide, moisture, and dust have been removed) under 200 atmospheres pressure to pipe coil, B, which is immersed in cold water. The cold water removes the heat of compression. The air then passes through the expansion valve, D, into region H, where the pressure is 1 atmosphere. As a result of the reduction in pressure, the air is cooled somewhat but not enough for liquefaction. This cooled air passes around the pipe containing the entering compressed air, thus cooling the air still under pressure. The cooled compressed air is then further cooled on expansion. The cooling process continues progressively until the air still under pressure is so cold that on expansion a portion of it liquefies and collects in F. This process continues as long as the machine is in operation.

It can be seen that, aside from the initial cost of the machine, the chief expense involved is the energy to operate the compressor. A Linde machine operating at 200 atmospheres produces about one-half liter of liquid air per kilowatt hour of energy consumed.

Liquefaction of hydrogen and helium

Hydrogen and helium are the most difficult gases to liquefy because of their low boiling point and low critical temperature. Furthermore, when they are allowed to expand at room temperature, they do not become cooler but rather become warmer. However, if hydrogen is first cooled to the temperature of liquid air and then allowed to expand, it does become cooler. In this way hydrogen can be liquefied in a Linde-type machine. Helium must be cooled to the temperature of boiling hydrogen before it can be further cooled by expansion in the Linde machine.

KEY WORDS

critical pressure	liquefaction	van der Waals' forces
Joule-Thomson effect	liquid	vaporization
Linde machine	liquid air	

HIGHLIGHTS

All gases can be liquefied under proper conditions of temperature and pressure. Many gas fuels are sold as **liquids** under pressure.

A Dutch physicist, van der Waals, pointed out that all molecules exert an attraction for each other. The closer together the molecules are, the greater is this attraction. When a gas is cooled and/or compressed sufficiently, these **van der Waals' forces** overcome the kinetic momentum of the molecules and the gas liquefies.

The greater the pressure, the higher is the temperature at which a given gas liquefies. Each gas has its *critical temperature*, above which it will not liquefy regardless of pressure. The pressure required to liquefy a gas at its critical temperature is its **critical pressure.**

The expansion of a gas is accompanied by cooling (the **Joule-**

Thomson effect). Conversely, the compression of a gas is accompanied by a heating effect. Air can be liquefied by expansion of the highly compressed and cooled gas.

Just as natural air is a mixture mainly of nitrogen and oxygen, so **liquid air** is a mixture of these same elements in liquefied form. Because nitrogen is more volatile than oxygen, it tends to vaporize first when liquid air is allowed to boil.

QUESTIONS

1. Mention some ways in which liquefaction of gases serves to influence the American standard of living.
2. By what means are gases liquefied?
3. Define critical temperature.
4. Define critical pressure.
5. Explain how air is caused to liquefy.
6. If the critical temperatures of oxygen and nitrogen were 100°C higher than they actually are, do you think the present method would be used to liquefy air? Explain.
7. Which of the substances listed in Table 11–1 would you expect to be shipped as liquids confined in steel cylinders? Which would you expect to be stored and shipped as gases only?
8. In what ways do liquids differ from gases?
9. What are van der Waals' forces?
10. How is hydrogen liquefied?
11. From the fact that they are practically incompressible, what do you infer about the structure of liquids as compared to gases?

Suggested Projects for Unit Three

1. Find out all you can about industrial gases. Among the things you can do in such a project are:
   a. Make as complete a list of such gases as you can.
   b. Speak to people who use such gases. Write an account of all you learn in this way.
   c. Compile a list of precautions that should be taken in handling canned gases.
   NOTE: Be sure to include the gases used as refrigerants.
2. Learn how to make a "snowball" of dry ice. If you decide to do this, be sure to wear gloves.
3. Suggest a project of your own involving gases in general.

UNIT FOUR: Water and Solutions

CHAPTER 12

water and the properties of liquids

You have already studied two of the most important elements and a few of the properties of liquids. You will now study the most important liquid, water, and many of the properties common to all liquids.

Of all things found in nature, none plays a more varied role than water. It is the substance which transports foodstuffs to, and removes waste products from, all living cells. Hence life—both plant and animal—as we know it on this planet is unthinkable without it. Evaporation of water from the skin cools our bodies. This evaporation is necessary to maintain constant body temperature. Evaporation from the soil, trees and other plants, rivers, lakes, and oceans provides the water vapor in the air. This water vapor condenses as rain. The processes of evaporation and condensation help maintain a reasonably constant and moderate temperature on the surface of the earth which is required for the forms of life on this planet. The moon receives about the same intensity of radiation[1] from the sun as does the earth because its distance from the sun is about the same as the earth's. However, we believe that during the day the temperature on the moon rises to at least 100°C and at night probably drops to −100°C. This temperature change occurs because there is no air and no water on the moon.

Water covers roughly seventy-five percent of the earth's surface. Man has developed many uses for water. He uses it to transfer heat

---

[1] The intensity of radiation means the amount of heat and light per unit of surface area.

Left, a farm planted in strip contours. Right, a badly eroded farm. Contour farming helps to control the utilization of natural waters and to prevent soil erosion. (Standard Oil Co.)

from the furnaces to the rooms of his houses; to transfer the energy released in the combustion of oil to the propellers driving a ship; to trap part of the sun's energy by damming rivers to generate electric energy.

However, man has not yet learned to control fully nature's waters. Every year millions of dollars' worth of property is destroyed by flood. Every day priceless tons of topsoil from our farm lands are washed away and forever lost because of incorrect and irresponsible farming and forestry practices. Engineers have irrigated small areas of fertile land, but we have no control over the amount of rain which falls on most of our farm land. A few inches too much rainfall at a certain time of the year can ruin a crop. A few inches too little rainfall may also ruin a crop. Scientists have shown quite recently how rainfall may be caused by man under certain conditions. This is done by seeding proper types of clouds with dry ice, silver iodide, or other substances. But only a beginning has been made in controlling rainfall. Many people think that aside from the establishment and maintenance of world peace, the control and proper utilization of our natural waters is the most important problem facing mankind today.

Finally most of the chemical reactions which take place in nature or are carried out in the laboratory, occur between substances which are dissolved in water. That is, water must be present in order for a great many reactions to take place, even though water may not appear in the equation. When a metal and an acid produce hydrogen

$$Zn + 2HCl \rightarrow ZnCl_2 + H_2 \uparrow$$

no water is shown in the equation. However, you will see later that the reaction does not occur unless some water is present.

Water is the basis of some of our units of measure

Pure water is odorless and also colorless in small samples. In a large mass, pure water is said to be bluish in color. Anyone who has seen a swimming pool or clear lake in sunlight knows that natural water is bluish in large masses. But natural water is, of course, not pure. It may contain many different substances.

Water in a high state of purity is easily obtained by distillation (see Chap. 13, pages 136 and 137). Because it is readily available, very pure water has been used in defining many of our scientific units of measure.

1. The calorie. The unit of heat is called the **calorie** (cal). It is correctly defined as the amount of heat needed to raise the temperature of one gram of water from 14.5°C to 15.5°C.[1] Engineers usually use a different unit of heat, the British thermal unit (Btu). The Btu is defined as the amount of heat needed to raise the temperature of one pound of water one degree Fahrenheit. One Btu equals 252 cal.

The calorie is inconveniently small for many purposes, for example, for studying the energy requirements of human beings. Hence, another unit, the large Calorie or greater Calorie, is used. The large **Calorie** has a value of 1000 cal and is spelled with a capital C to distinguish it from the smaller unit, calorie.

2. Specific heat. The amount of heat (number of calories) needed to raise the temperature of one gram of any substance one degree centigrade is known as its **specific heat.** Different substances have widely different specific heats. Thus the specific heat of iron is 0.11 calorie per gram (cal/g), and the specific heat of water is 1.0 cal/g. The average specific heat of rock and soil on the surface of the earth is about 0.2 cal/g. This means that it takes five times as much heat to raise the temperature of 1 g of water 1°C as it does to raise the temperature of 1 g of rock 1°C. Or if 1 cal of heat is removed from 1 g of water, the temperature drops 1°C; but if 1 cal of heat is removed from 1 g of rock, the temperature drops 5°C. This fact is part of the explanation of how large bodies of water moderate the climate. Suppose that 1 g of water and 1 g of rock receive the same amounts of energy from the sun's rays. Suppose this radiant energy is all used to raise the temperature of the water and the rock. Then the temperature of the rock will rise *five times* as many degrees as the temperature of the

---

[1] The calorie is sometimes defined as the amount of heat needed to raise the temperature of one gram of water one degree centigrade. Strictly speaking, this is only approximately correct because the exact amount of heat necessary depends somewhat on the temperature interval. That is, not *exactly* the same amount of heat is needed to raise the temperature from 14.5 to 15.5°C as is needed to raise it from 26 to 27°C, for example.

In the desert, extreme temperature changes occur because there is so little water in the land and so little water vapor in the air. (Standard Oil Co.)

water. After sundown if the rock loses the same amount of heat that the water loses, by radiation, the temperature of the rock drops five times as many degrees as does the temperature of the water. Partly for this reason large bodies of water are generally warmer in winter and cooler in summer than the surrounding land. Also, the climate on land that is close to the water will be milder in both summer and winter for this reason.[1] (Another factor which enters into the complete explanation of how water helps control climate is discussed on page 115.

3. *Specific gravity.* As noted earlier, the *density* of a substance is defined as its weight per unit volume. Thus the density of water at 4°C is 1 gram per milliliter (g/ml) or 1 gram per cubic centimeter.[2] In English units the density of water is 62.4 pounds per cubic foot (lb/ft^3).

The **specific gravity** of a substance is defined as the weight of that substance compared with the weight of an equal volume of water. Thus the specific gravity of copper is 8.9, which means that volume for volume copper is 8.9 times as heavy as water. One cubic centimeter of copper therefore weighs 8.9 (8.9 × 1) g and 1 ft^3 of copper weighs (8.9 × 62.4 =)555.36 lb.

The specific gravity of an object may easily be measured by weighing it first in air and then again in water. By Archimedes' principle, the *difference* between the weight of an object in air and its weight in water equals the weight of the water displaced by the object. This

[1] This is illustrated by the following data from the records of the U. S. Weather Bureau. The average July temperature on Long Island is 70°F, whereas at the same latitude in Nebraska the average July temperature is 75°F. The average January temperature on Long Island is 30°F and at the same latitude in Nebraska the average January temperature is 20°F.

[2] See footnote on page 79.

weight is the same as the weight of a volume of water equal to the volume of the object. That is,

Weight in air − weight in water = weight of volume of water equal to volume of object

Hence

$$\text{Specific gravity of object} = \frac{\text{weight of object in air}}{\text{weight in air} - \text{weight in water}}$$

Since different substances have different specific gravities, you can easily tell whether an object, such as a spoon, is "solid" (sterling) silver or silver plate. The specific gravity of sterling silver is 10.3. If the object is silver-plated, its specific gravity will be lower and will depend on what metal is present. If the object is silver-plated on brass (an alloy of copper and zinc), its specific gravity will be about 8.8. If plated on steel, its specific gravity will be about 7.8.

4. *Temperature scales.* The centigrade and Fahrenheit (F) temperature scales also are based upon the physical properties of water. A mercury thermometer consists of a glass bulb filled with mercury sealed to a tube of uniform bore, that is, of uniform width inside. When the bulb is placed in a well-stirred mixture of ice and water, the point on the tube to which the mercury falls is called 0°C, or 32°F. When the bulb is placed in water boiling at 1 atmosphere, the point on the tube to which the mercury rises is called 100°C, or 212°F. The space between these two points is divided into 100 parts for the **centigrade** scale or 180 parts for the **Fahrenheit** scale to obtain 1°C or 1°F. Some less expensive thermometers are filled with alcohol or toluene colored with a red dye to make the liquid easily visible, but otherwise they are constructed as the mercury-filled ones.

Sometimes we wish to convert Fahrenheit temperature into centigrade temperature or centigrade into Fahrenheit. To do this, you must remember that there are 180° on the Fahrenheit scale between the freezing point and the boiling point of water, and 100° on the centigrade scale between the same points. Therefore,

$$\frac{C}{F - 32} = \frac{100}{180} = \frac{5}{9}$$

or solving for C, $$C = 5/9(F - 32)$$

If you wish to convert centigrade temperature into Fahrenheit temperature, you must solve for F. Thus

$$F = 9/5 C + 32$$

You will also recall that degrees **absolute** equals degrees centigrade plus 273.

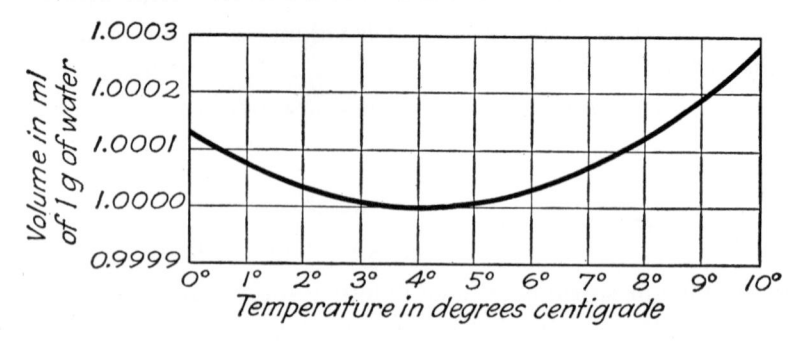

Fig. 12–1. This graph shows the dependence of volume of liquid water on temperature.

Water has a maximum density at 4°C

Most liquids contract regularly on cooling. Indeed, the use of mercury or alcohol in thermometers is based upon this fact. Water, however, behaves very differently when cooled. For this reason you would find that water would not make a satisfactory liquid for filling thermometers even aside from the fact that it solidifies at 0°C. To illustrate the peculiarity in the way water acts, suppose you make a thermometer in which the liquid is water. As the thermometer is cooled from room temperature downward, you would find that the water contracts until 4°C is reached. When the thermometer is cooled below this temperature, you would find that the water begins to *expand* again. That is, a certain weight of water occupies a smaller volume at 4°C than at temperatures either above or below this point. Since the volume of water is a minimum at 4°C, the density of water is a maximum at this temperature. This phenomenon is usually described by saying that water has its maximum density at 4°C.

The behavior of water is not only unusual for a liquid since most liquids contract regularly when cooled until the freezing point is reached, but it is also very important in nature in helping to prevent ponds from freezing solid. Thus the water on the surface of a quiet pond on a cold night when cooled below 4°C becomes less dense than the warmer water below it. Therefore, the cold water remains on the surface and soon forms ice crystals. Since water expands on solidification (as anyone who has had a water-filled radiator freeze well knows), ice that forms on a pond remains floating at the surface. This layer of ice greatly slows the cooling of the water below by the cold air. If very cold weather continues long enough, the pond can freeze solid. But this happens much more seldom than would be the case if water—like most liquids—were to contract on solidification. If this contraction took place, the ice would sink to the bottom as it formed. Unfrozen water would be forced to the surface to be quickly chilled and frozen. Thus most aquatic life remains alive in cold climates because of the

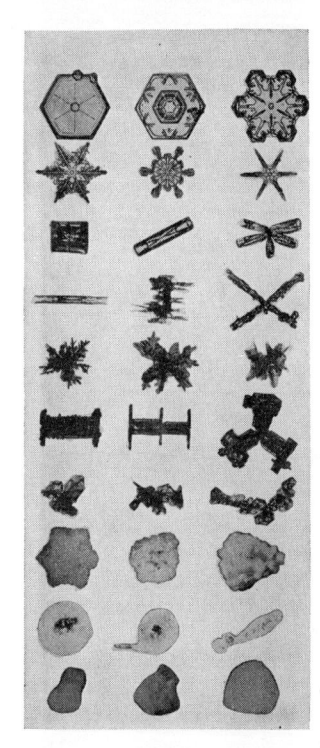

Snow crystals. Top to bottom, plates, stellars, columns, needles, spatial dendrites, capped columns, irregular crystals, graupel, sleet, and hail.

peculiar volume changes of water on cooling and solidification. This is only one of many illustrations of the remarkable, unique combination of chemical and physical properties that water has. Without these special properties, no life, as we know it, could exist on this planet.

Ice

You have seen that the removal of 1 cal of heat from 1 g of liquid water reduces its temperature by 1°C. Thus if you have 1 g of water at 5°C and remove from it 5 cal, its temperature will drop to 0°C. *However, none of the water will freeze unless you remove more heat from it.* You find that, in order to freeze this gram of water at 0°C to ice at 0°C, you must remove from it 80 cal of heat. The specific heat of ice is different from that of liquid water. It is 0.5 cal. If 1 g of ice at -5°C is heated slowly, it is found that 2.5 cal are needed to raise its temperature to 0°C. But to melt the ice into water at 0°C, 80 cal of heat must be supplied per gram of ice melted. This is known as the **heat of fusion** of ice. Every solid has a characteristic heat of fusion. When water, or any liquid, freezes, heat is given off to the surroundings. When ice, or any solid, melts, heat is consumed from the surroundings. For a certain substance the amount of heat removed to freeze it and the amount of heat consumed to melt it is the same. This heat of fusion is sometimes called *latent heat of fusion* because the term *latent* means hidden. In a sense this heat is hidden since it does not cause a change in temperature. It is important to realize that the magnitude of this heat of fusion of ice is great as compared with the specific heat of water. It requires as much heat to melt a quantity of ice at 0°C into water at 0°C as it does to raise the temperature of the same amount of water from 0 to 80°C. This is the most important fact that explains why the refrigeration machinery for a quick-freeze unit must have a much greater capacity for cooling than the refrigeration machinery for an ordinary refrigerator of the same size. Suppose that 1 kilogram (= 1000 g, or 2.2 lb, and abbreviated kg) of a vegetable at 25°C (= 77°F) is placed in a quick-freeze unit operating at -20°C (= -4°F). The freezer must (1) cool the vegetable to 0°C, (2) freeze

113

it, and (3) cool the frozen product from 0 to −20°C. You can calculate the total heat which must be removed from the food if you assume the vegetable is pure water (actually it is only about 90 percent water).

1. To cool 1000 g of water from 25 to 0°C
$$\text{Remove } 1000 \times 25 \times 1 = 25{,}000 \text{ cal}$$
2. To freeze 1000 g of water into ice at 0°C
$$\text{Remove } 1000 \times 80 = 80{,}000 \text{ cal}$$
3. To cool 1000 g of ice from 0 to −20°C
$$\text{Remove } 1000 \times 20 \times 0.5 = \underline{10{,}000 \text{ cal}}$$
$$\text{Total heat to be removed } \quad 115{,}000 \text{ cal}$$

Of the total heat to be removed, 80,000 cal or about 70 percent is for the freezing; only about 30 percent is for the actual cooling.

Evaporation and condensation

It is known that water evaporates at all temperatures. The wet laundry hung on the line dries when the water in it evaporates. Wet streets dry after a rain as a result of evaporation. Ice and snow slowly disappear even when the temperature does not reach their melting point. Of course, in all these cases the water molecules have escaped from the liquid or solid into the atmosphere. That is, the liquid or solid has changed into a gas. In the case of liquids, we call this evaporation. The changing of a solid (such as ice) directly into a gas is known as **sublimation.** Like melting, evaporation is a heat-consuming process. Its opposite, **condensation,** the change of gas into liquid, is a process which always involves giving off heat to the surroundings.

The evaporation of 1 g of water at 100°C consumes 540 cal of heat. This is known as the latent **heat of vaporization.** The condensation of 1 g of steam at 100°C liberates 540 cal of heat to the surroundings. At temperatures lower than the boiling point, liquids evaporate less rapidly, yet the heat of vaporization must be supplied regardless of the temperature at which the vaporization occurs.

This is the way the temperature of our bodies is maintained constant even though the atmospheric temperature and the amount of energy that is liberated in our bodies may vary widely. Moisture escapes through the skin to the surface as perspiration. When this moisture evaporates from the skin, the heat of vaporization is supplied from the body. Supplying the heat of vaporization cools the body and thus prevents a temperature rise. The sweat glands in the skin control the rate of perspiration according to the amount of cooling needed by the body.

It is important to realize that the magnitude of the heat of vaporization of water is great compared with its specific heat. Thus the heat consumed in the evaporation of 1 g of water (540 cal) is enough to raise the temperature of 5.4 g of water from its freezing point to its boiling point (provided none of it evaporates).

The more rapidly a liquid evaporates, the greater the cooling effect. Therefore, an alcohol bath is more effective in reducing the temperature of a feverish patient than a water bath—because the alcohol is more volatile. Ether spilled on the hand produces an even greater cooling effect. Ethyl chloride (C_2H_5Cl) is so volatile that it freezes the surface tissue when sprayed on the skin. For this reason it is used as a local anesthetic.

The intense cooling produced by evaporation of ether can be demonstrated by freezing a few drops of water by this means. Wet the bottom of a watch glass with a few drops of water and place it on a small piece of wood (or another good insulator). Then pour a few cubic centimeters of ether into the watch glass. Fan the ether with a sheet of paper to make it evaporate rapidly. In about a minute the watch glass will be frozen solidly to the block of wood.

Condensation, as you read earlier, is the reverse of evaporation. It is a process in which heat is given off to the surroundings. Steam heating of buildings is possible because liquid water absorbs the heat of vaporization from the furnace as steam is formed. The steam, when it condenses in the radiators, gives off to the room the same amount of heat that the liquid water had absorbed to form steam. Because steam gives off heat when it condenses, steam burns are much worse than water burns even though the water and steam are at the same temperature.

The alternate evaporation and condensation of water in nature is an important factor in preventing wide variations in atmospheric temperature. Thus if water and rock receive the same amount of heat from the sun, the temperature of the rock will rise more for two reasons. The first reason is that the specific heat of the water is higher. This fact has already been discussed (see page 109). The second reason is that all the heat received by the rock will be used to raise its temperature. Water, being volatile, will partly evaporate. Evaporation consumes heat, so that only part of the heat received by the water will be used to raise its temperature. At night, as the earth loses its

Fig. 12–2. Water can be frozen when ether is evaporated very rapidly.

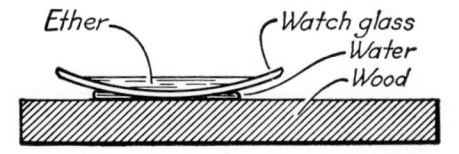

heat by radiation, some of the water vapor formed by evaporation during the day condenses as clouds or dew. This condensation gives off heat which tends to prevent a drop in temperature. You probably know that the greatest extremes of temperature between night and day are found in the desert, where there is the least water.

Evaporation and the kinetic theory

In Chap. 11, page 101, you read that a given liquid exists only under certain conditions of temperature and pressure. These conditions must be such that the attractive forces between adjacent molecules are greater than the average kinetic energy of the molecules. In evaporation the molecules leave the surface of the liquid and, by doing this, become gaseous. The question is raised: How is it possible for them to do so if the preceding statement about liquids is correct? The answer lies in the word *average* in the statement. In a liquid or a gas not every molecule is moving with exactly the same speed. At any instant some are moving rapidly, some more slowly, and others, in the act of rebounding, may be momentarily stationary. However, the *average* velocity of all the molecules is always the same at the same temperature, although there is a wide distribution of individual velocities.

Figure 12-3 represents the molecules of liquid water. Molecule A may be struck simultaneously by several molecules, B, C, D, and thereby acquire a high kinetic energy. The average kinetic energy of the lot would not change, however, because B, C, and D would lose a corresponding amount of energy in the process. This particular molecule A may acquire enough momentum to overcome the attractive forces of its neighbors and move into the space above the liquid. According to the kinetic theory, this is the way evaporation of a liquid takes place. **Evaporation involves the selective removal from the surface of the fastest-moving molecules.** You can see why evaporation is a cooling process. Naturally taking away the fastest-moving molecules of the liquid will reduce the average velocity of those left behind. This is the same as saying that the temperature of the liquid will drop.[1] Or if the temperature of the liquid is to be kept constant, heat from outside must flow into the liquid to speed up the lazier molecules left behind. Adding heat will bring the average velocity up to what it was before the fastest-moving molecules escaped. In the case of water 540 cal/g is needed.

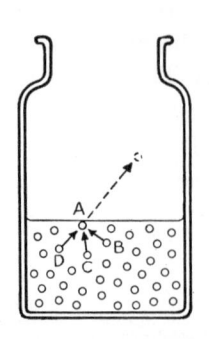

Fig. 12-3. Schematic diagram of evaporation of a liquid.

[1] See Chap. 10, pages 94 and 95.

The vapor pressure of water

The tendency of a liquid to evaporate is indicated by what is called its **vapor pressure.** You can measure the vapor pressure of a liquid easily by inserting a small amount of the liquid into the open end of a barometer tube (Fig. 12–4). The liquid rises to the top of the mercury in the tube. There part of the liquid evaporates until the space is saturated with the vapor (see page 122). This vapor, or gas, exerts a pressure that depends upon its concentration. The level of the mercury is thereby forced down by this vapor pressure until the pressure of the vapor plus the pressure due to the mercury remaining in the tube becomes equal to the atmospheric pressure. The vapor pressure is generally stated in terms of the length of the column of mercury to which it is equivalent. Thus in Fig. 12–4 the tube on the left shows the original height of the mercury, that on the right the height after the space has become saturated with vapor. The difference in the two heights gives the pressure due to the vapor. The value of the vapor pressure depends upon the liquid—the more volatile the liquid the greater its vapor pressure. The vapor pressure also depends upon the temperature. It increases as the temperature increases. It is possible to have a vapor pressure less than the characteristic value for a certain liquid at a certain temperature if not enough liquid is added to saturate the space. It is never possible to have a pressure greater than this characteristic value. If, for example, the vapor is compressed in an attempt to increase its pressure, some of the vapor condenses until the pressure decreases to its initial value. The vapor pressure of water at various temperatures is shown in Fig. 12–5. A more complete table entitled Vapor Pressure of Water in Millimeters of Mercury is given in the Appendix on page 689. These values represent the maximum pressure which water vapor can exert at these temperatures. Since the pressure of a gas depends on its concentration, these pressures correspond to the greatest concentration of water vapor which is possible at these temperatures.

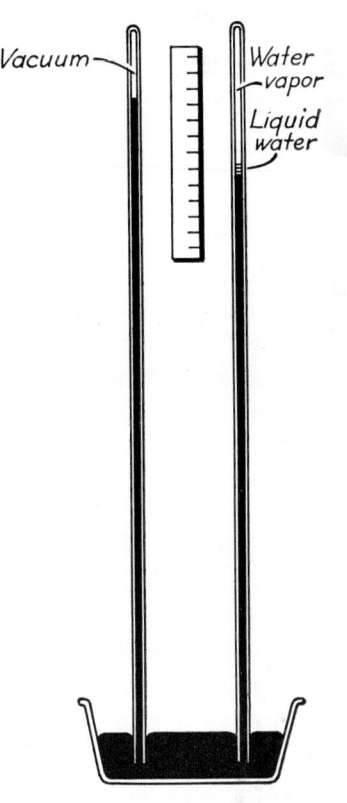

Fig. 12–4. The pressure of the water vapor is measured by the amount by which the mercury is forced down in the barometer tube.

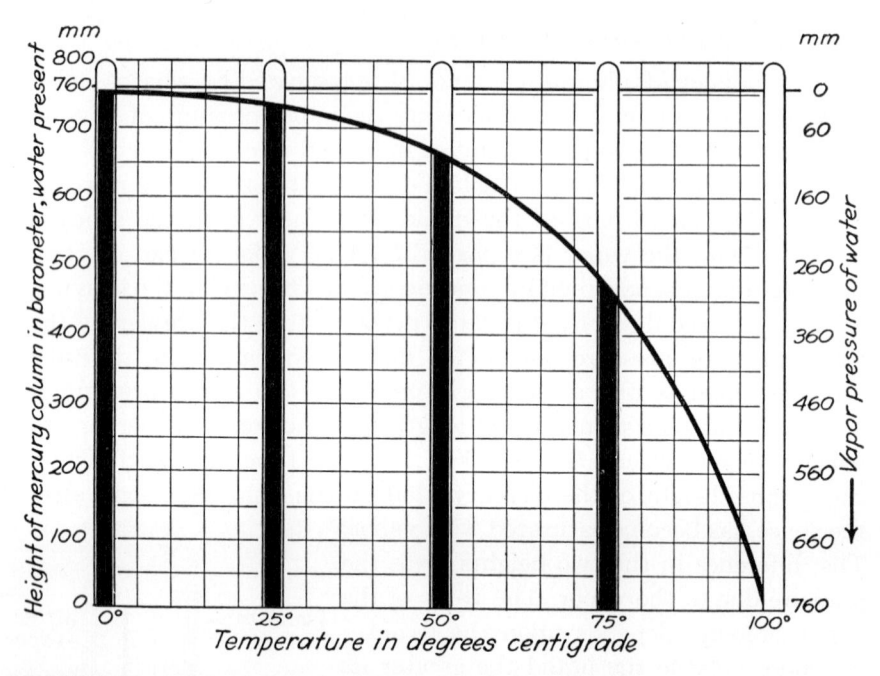

Fig. 12–5. The vapor pressure of water from 0 to 100°C. The vapor pressure increases with temperature. At 100°C the vapor pressure is equal to 760 mm of mercury. The barometer tubes emphasize the significance of the curve.

Boiling

Boiling point means the temperature at which bubbles of vapor form beneath the surface of a liquid and, being less dense than the liquid, rise to the top and escape. You will understand this process better if you first consider the conditions under which the bubbles will form. The bubble shown in Fig. 12–6 will not form and cannot exist unless the pressure of the vapor in this bubble is at least as great as the external pressure. Now the atmosphere is pressing on the surface of the liquid, so that the pressure tending to cause the bubble to collapse is equal to the atmospheric pressure plus the pressure due to the column of liquid directly above the bubble. The pressure of the liquid, however, is so slight as to be negligible. **A liquid boils in an open vessel when its vapor pressure becomes equal to atmospheric pressure.** Since atmospheric pressure can vary, the boiling point of a liquid can also vary. The *normal* boiling point of a liquid is the temperature at which its vapor pressure becomes equal to 1 atmosphere.

Reference to Fig. 12–5 will show that the vapor pressure of water becomes equal to the pressure of 760 mm of mercury at 100°C. That is, the normal boiling point of water is 100°C. However, if the atmospheric pressure is lower than 760 mm, water will boil at a lower temperature. In Fig. 12–5, it can be seen that the vapor pressure of water

Pressure cookers allow water to be heated above 100°C because they prevent the escape of the vapor, thereby increasing the pressure on the liquid.

is 600 mm at 93.5°C. Thus in a region where the atmospheric pressure is 600 mm, water will boil at 93.5°C.

It is not possible to heat a liquid in an open vessel above its boiling point because as the liquid boils all the heat which flows into the liquid is used to vaporize it.

Since the barometric pressure is less at high altitude, the cooking of foods on high mountains and in airplanes presents special problems. It is not the act of boiling but the temperature to which the food is heated that cooks it. If potatoes, for example, are to be cooked in an open vessel at an altitude where the pressure is 600 mm, it will require nearly twice as long to cook the potatoes because of the lower temperature to which they are subjected. At sea level potatoes would cook faster if the water in which they were cooked could be heated above 100°C. But we have already seen that *this is not possible unless the external pressure on the water is greater than 1 atmosphere.* This is the principle behind the use of pressure cookers.

In a pressure cooker the water vapor above the liquid is not allowed to expand as the cooker is heated. Hence the pressure on the water

Fig. 12–6. For a liquid to boil, bubbles of vapor must form down in the body of the liquid. Thus the vapor pressure of the liquid must be at least as great as the pressure of the atmosphere which tends to collapse the bubble.

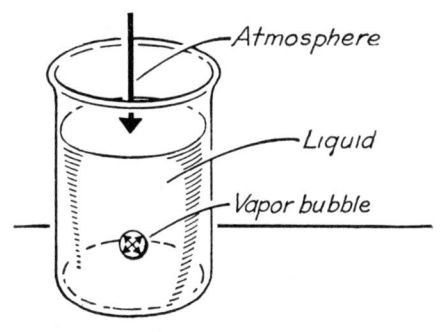

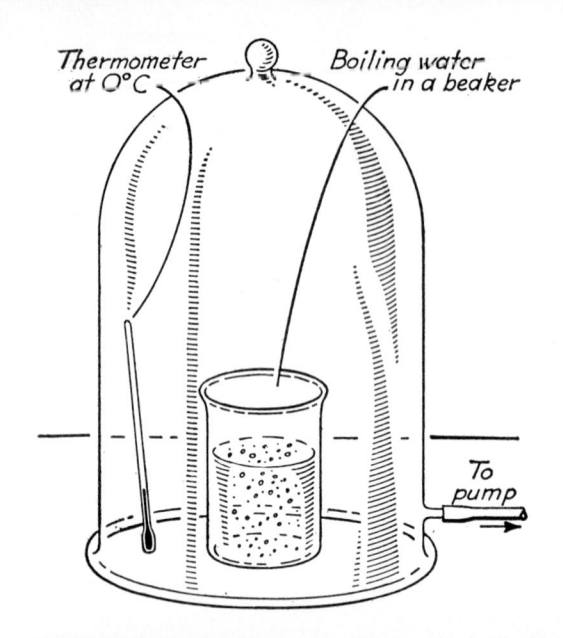

Fig. 12–7. Boiling water under a bell jar. If the pressure is low enough, the water in the beaker will begin to boil even though the temperature is 0°C. Some of the water may be frozen because of the heat absorbed by evaporation.

increases as the temperature of the water increases. So instead of boiling at 100°C, the temperature of the liquid continues to rise. This is the important factor in shortening the time needed for cooking. The small pressure cookers now marketed for home use in cooking foods generally work at pressures of 10 to 15 lb/in.^{2} *greater* than atmospheric pressure. This is done by providing valves which open only when the vapor pressure exceeds these values. Remember that 1 atmosphere equals 760 mm of mercury, or 14.7 lb/in.^{2} You can see that 10 lb/in.^{2} is equivalent to 517 mm of mercury, and 15 lb/in.^{2} is equivalent to 775 mm. This means that these cookers operate at a total pressure of roughly $1\frac{2}{3}$ to 2 atmospheres. The vapor pressure of water is 2 atmospheres at 121°C (= 248°F). When the water in the pressure cooker reaches this temperature, the vapor pressure is sufficient to open the valve; boiling begins and no further rise in temperature occurs. The increase in cooking temperature from the boiling point of 100°C in an ordinary pot to 121°C in the pressure cooker greatly shortens the needed cooking time. Pressure cookers are particularly good in decreasing cooking time on mountains and in airplanes.

The effect of reduced external pressure on boiling point can be demonstrated by placing a beaker of liquid under a bell jar and pumping out part of the air (Fig. 12–7). If enough air is pumped out, water may be caused to boil even at 0°C. As a result of the heat absorbed by evaporation, some of the water freezes to ice. This is the way in which liquid helium is frozen at −272.2°C.

Dry ice, which is solid carbon dioxide, is manufactured in a similar way. Carbon dioxide gas is pumped into a cylinder maintained at room temperature but below 31°C until the pressure of the gas in the cylinder causes liquefaction. Then the cylinder of liquid carbon dioxide is inverted, the valve opened, and the liquid sprayed out into the atmosphere. At room pressure the liquid, being far above its boiling point, boils rapidly. The heat absorbed by its vaporization cools some of the carbon dioxide to $-78.5°C$, at which temperature it freezes and forms a miniature snowstorm of solid carbon dioxide. If the mouth of the cylinder is covered with a loose canvas bag, the solid carbon dioxide may be collected (Fig. 12–8). These flakes are then pressed into cakes to give the familiar slabs of dry ice.

An interesting and simple experiment to show the relation of external pressure to boiling point is illustrated in Fig. 12–9. Fill

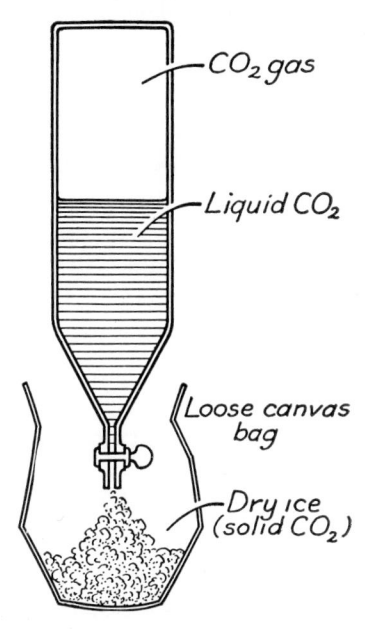

Fig. 12–8. Dry ice is produced by the evaporation of liquid carbon dioxide.

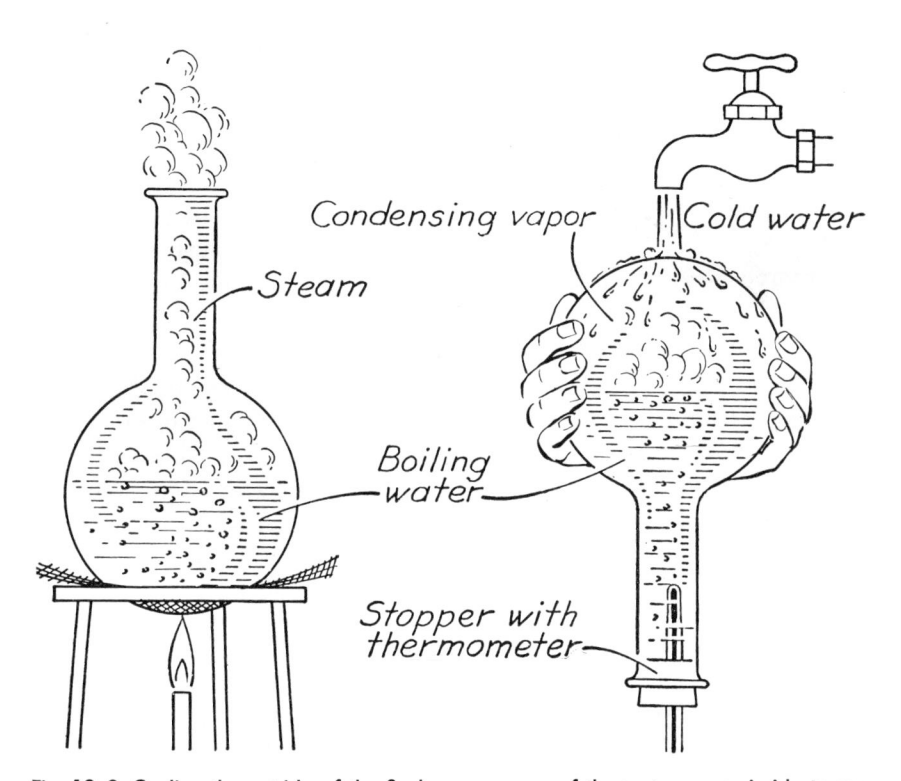

Fig. 12–9. Cooling the outside of the flask causes some of the water vapor inside to condense. This reduces the pressure and allows the water to boil at a lower temperature.

an ordinary pyrex flask half-full of water. Heat the water to boiling and boil for a few minutes to expel the air. Stopper the flask; then invert it and pour cold water over it. As the flask cools, the water begins to boil again.

There are times when boiling under reduced pressure is desirable, for example, in the evaporation of water from a sugar solution to cause crystallization of the sugar. If the boiling takes place at atmospheric pressure, the high temperature needed will cause decomposition (caramelization) of some of the sugar. Under reduced pressure the water boils away at lower temperatures and in this way pure white granulated sugar is obtained.

The pressure of a vapor above a liquid is limited

You have learned that for each temperature there is a maximum vapor pressure which can exist above a liquid. Thus, as shown in Fig. 12–10 the liquid evaporates into the closed space above it until the vapor pressure reaches a certain value above which it cannot go. Why do not all the molecules evaporate into the closed space since some do, and all the molecules are alike? The answer lies in the fact that the evaporation of water is a *reversible* change. That is, the reverse reaction, condensation, can and does occur. As noted in Chap. 6, page 49, a reversible change is represented by a double arrow, thus:

$$H_2O \rightleftharpoons H_2O$$
$$\text{(liquid)} \quad \text{(vapor)}$$

At the instant the liquid water is placed in the closed space, only one of these changes, namely, evaporation, can occur because there is no water vapor present. However, as soon as some vapor has formed above the liquid, some of the molecules in the vapor strike the surface of the liquid in their random motion and thereby condense. The greater the concentration of vapor molecules, the more molecules there will be striking the surface per second. Therefore, the number of molecules of vapor that condense per second increases as their concentration increases. So as evaporation continues, the concentration of vapor

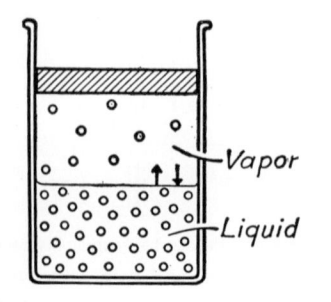

Fig. 12–10. Evaporation is a reversible process in which vapor molecules may condense back into the liquid.

molecules increases, and the rate of condensation increases, until the *rate of condensation becomes equal to the rate of evaporation.* The space is then said to be *saturated* with the vapor. After these two rates become equal, there can be no further increase in the concentration of vapor. Evaporation is still occurring, but for every molecule that evaporates one also condenses so that the number of molecules in the vapor state does not change. Thus if you could see the individual vapor and liquid molecules in a stoppered flask standing at room temperature, you would note that, although the individual molecules are first in the liquid and then in the vapor, the total number of molecules in either form does not change.

The condition described is referred to as a state of **dynamic equilibrium.** It is very important for you to understand clearly the simple picture involved since it is a condition very often met in chemistry. Dynamic equilibrium always has the following characteristics:

1. The change in question (which may be physical or chemical) is a reversible one.

2. The products of the change accumulate in the system (in our example the water vapor is not allowed to escape).

3. The reactions do not stop when equilibrium is reached. They proceed at equal rates. Therefore, one reaction is nullifying the effect of the other.

It would be possible to change the proportions of vapor to liquid for the equilibrium described between liquid water and water vapor in one of the following ways:

1. By opening the flask so that the vapor can escape. In this case the vapor molecules diffuse out of the flask. The rate of condensation is thereby reduced. However, the rate of evaporation remains unchanged until all the liquid has evaporated.

2. By increasing the temperature. This increases the rate of evaporation. According to the kinetic molecular theory, an increase in temperature gives more of the liquid molecules the kinetic energy necessary to escape. When the rate of evaporation is greater, equilibrium will be reached only when the rate of condensation is also greater. This means equilibrium will be reached when the concentration of vapor is greater. Thus as you have already learned, the *vapor pressure increases with the temperature.*

3. By reducing the volume of the vapor above the liquid. Suppose the vapor which has come to equilibrium with the liquid [Fig. 12-11(*a*)] is suddenly compressed into one-half its former volume [Fig. 12-11(*b*)]. As a result of crowding the vapor molecules, there will be more of them striking the surface per second than before. Hence the rate of condensation will *temporarily* be greater than the rate of

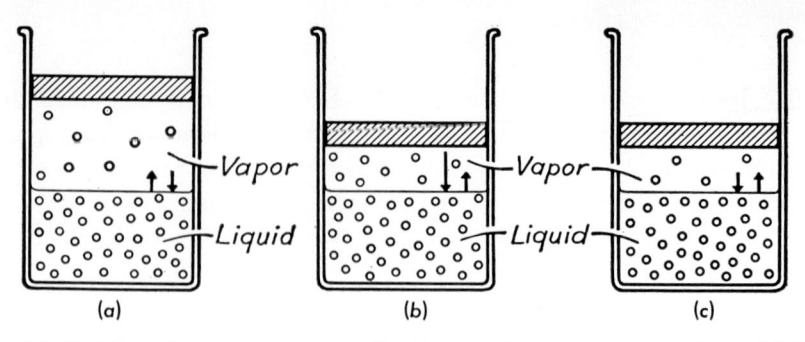

Fig. 12–11. Effect of compressing vapor. The liquid and vapor are in equilibrium (a). The vapor has been compressed to one-half its former volume (b). This temporarily increases the rate of condensation, as explained in the text, but does not change the rate of evaporation, and eventually equilibrium is again reached (c), with the concentration and pressure of vapor the same as before compression.

evaporation. This will lead to a reduction in the concentration of vapor molecules until the two rates again become equal. Then the concentration of vapor (and hence its pressure) will be just the same as it was before compression [Fig. 12–11(c)].

The presence or absence of air in the space occupied by a vapor has no influence on the equilibrium pressure of the vapor. Statements sometimes are seen about the "ability of air to hold water vapor." Such statements are entirely meaningless because the only thing which determines the greatest concentration of water vapor which can exist in air, or in a vacuum, is the temperature.

A fan directed on the surface of a dish of water in the atmosphere hastens the evaporation of the water. The reason is that even in an open dish some of the water-vapor molecules condense. This condensation is a result of water-vapor molecules colliding with other vapor, or air, molecules. The water-vapor molecules are then "batted" back down onto the surface of the water, where they condense. Now the rate at which the water disappears from the dish is equal to the difference between the rate of escape of molecules from the liquid and the rate at which the vapor molecules condense. The function of the air blast is to sweep the vapor molecules away as soon as they are formed. This reduces the rate of condensation and thereby increases the actual rate at which the water disappears. A blast of air has no effect on the absolute rate with which the water molecules escape from the surface of the liquid.

Humidity

Everyone agrees that a high atmospheric temperature is more agreeable if the humidity is low. The word humidity refers to the amount of water vapor in the atmosphere. Humidity is generally stated in terms of the percentage saturation of the atmosphere. The percentage saturation, that is, the **relative humidity,** is the actual vapor pressure of water compared to the maximum vapor pressure possible at the temperature of the vapor. Thus if the actual vapor pressure of water in the atmosphere is 10 mm at 25°C and the maximum vapor pressure possible at this temperature is 23.5 mm, the percentage saturation or relative humidity is $10/23.5 \times 100 = 42.5$ percent.

Humidity is an important factor in determining whether air is comfortable or uncomfortable. The reason, as you have just seen, is that evaporation of liquid water is a reversible process. The *net* rate at which the liquid disappears is equal to the difference between the rate of evaporation and the rate of condensation. Since increasing humidity increases the rate of condensation, it decreases the net rate at which perspiration evaporates from our skin. High humidity thus lessens the effectiveness of evaporation of perspiration in cooling our bodies. Therefore, a high temperature is more uncomfortable when accompanied by high humidity. (Probably a psychological factor also is involved when the clothing becomes wet and sticky from lack of evaporation.)

On the other hand, if the humidity is too low, evaporation of moisture from the body proceeds very rapidly. Too rapid evaporation results in the drying out of the membranes of the nose and throat, which also is objectionable. Low humidity is most apt to occur in heated buildings in the wintertime. If the outside temperature is very low, the amount of moisture in the air is low even though the air may be saturated. When this cold air is brought inside and warmed, the amount of moisture needed to saturate it increases enormously. Therefore, the heated air has a very low relative humidity. Unless such air is artificially humidified, that is, has moisture added to it, objects in the building such as flowers, food, furniture, and people will "dry out" to an undesirable degree. For average room temperatures a relative humidity of 30 to 40 percent is considered ideal.

Air conditioning

Air conditioning involves three main factors: (1) ventilation—changing the air to remove the excess carbon dioxide, smoke, dust, odorous vapors, and other objectionable materials; (2) heating or cooling the fresh air as needed; and (3) adjusting the humidity of the fresh air as needed.

In winter the fresh air admitted is heated by the usual heating devices, after which it is humidified. This may be done by passing the hot air over wicks saturated with water or by spraying steam into the hot air. It is better, however, to pass the air through a fine spray of liquid water droplets. The main consideration is that the evaporating surface should be large enough to add the proper amount of moisture to the air. Some of the humidifying devices provided for dwellings are entirely inadequate in this respect.

In summer the air may be hot and moist. It must, therefore, be cooled and its moisture content reduced. It may be cooled by being passed through a cold-water spray, over ice, or over the coils of a mechanical refrigerator. When air is passed over refrigeration coils, some of the excess moisture may be condensed or frozen and thereby removed. If, in this process, the air is cooled below the final temperature desired and then warmed, the humidity may be maintained at the desired percentage. Otherwise after cooling to the desired temperature, the excess water vapor may be removed by passing the air over such drying agents as calcium chloride, silica gel, or activated alumina.

If a sterile atmosphere is necessary, most of the air-borne microorganisms may be destroyed by exposing the air to ultraviolet radiation from mercury lamps.

The conditioning of air is not only important for homes, theaters, and restaurants, but it also is absolutely essential in certain types of factories where a high degree of uniformity in the products is necessary. Some examples of industries that need air conditioning are those that manufacture textiles and matches and those that do very precise machine-tool work, such as in the manufacturing of aircraft engines.

Mechanical refrigeration

It is hard to estimate the impact of the development of mechanical refrigeration on our lives. If grandfather who lived in the country had any ice in the summertime for cooling his tea, the chances are that it was ice cut from the pond during the last winter and carefully stored in leaves, straw, or sawdust to keep it from melting. In grandfather's day, ice cream was made the hard way at home by freezing the custard with a mixture of salt and ice in a hand-turned freezer. It was a rare treat. Mechanical air conditioning and quick-freezing were unknown.

The principle involved in all mechanical refrigeration is that a liquid can be made to evaporate under reduced pressure. In so doing the liquid consumes heat from the surroundings.

A diagram of a mechanical refrigerator is shown in Fig. 12–12. The essential parts are (1) a compressor, C, generally operated by an electric motor in a small refrigerator; (2) the evaporating coils, A; and (3) the condensing coils, B. The coils contain a substance known as the *refrigerating liquid*. This liquid is capable of being alternately vaporized and condensed, depending on the pressure to which it is subjected. In operation the compressor, C, maintains a low pressure

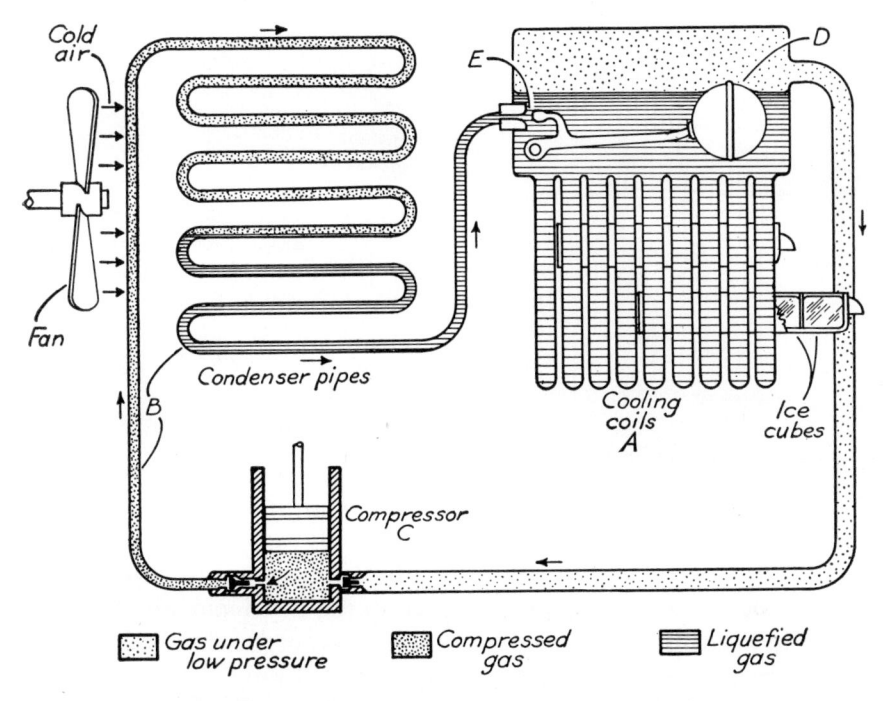

Fig. 12–12. A schematic diagram showing how the household electric refrigerator operates. A, evaporating coils; B, condensing coils; C, compressor; D, valve float; E, expansion valve.

in the evaporating coils, A, which contain the refrigeration liquid. As a result of the low pressure in A, the liquid boils. In so doing it absorbs the necessary heat of vaporization from the space around the coils. This space is thereby cooled. The compressor pumps the gas produced by vaporization of the liquid into the condensing coils, B, where the pressure is high enough to liquefy the gas. The heat of condensation of the vapor is given off to the area surrounding the condensing coils, B. These coils are located somewhere outside the refrigerator itself. The net result is to transfer heat from the refrigerator compartment to the outside. The liquid in B then passes through an expansion valve, E, (which is really just a very small hole) into the evaporating coils, A, where it again evaporates. The entire cycle is repeated over and over. In order to take off the heat of condensation from the condensing coils, B, a fan may be used to blow air over them. In large refrigeration units, the condensing coils, B, may be cooled by running water. In home refrigerators, however, the heat is usually given off to the room by conduction. The refrigerating liquid used in domestic refrigerators is generally either Freon 12 (CF_2Cl_2) or methyl chloride (CH_3Cl). In large cold-storage units, ammonia (NH_3) is commonly used or sometimes carbon dioxide.

This photograph shows a heat pump installed in a home. The evaporation coils of this unit are located somewhere outside the house.

The heat pump

The heat pump is an application of "refrigeration in reverse" for heating purposes, which, although still in the developmental stage, is likely to become widely adopted as a method of heating buildings in regions where electric energy is cheap and plentiful.

Consider the electric refrigerator in the kitchen at home. You will notice that somewhere on the outside there is a series of coils. (Possibly these coils are enclosed in fins much the same as an automobile radiator.) These are the condensing coils corresponding to B in Fig. 12–12. If the refrigerator has been running recently, you will find the coils are warm. What is the source of the heat in the coils? It really comes from two sources. Mainly it is the heat the refrigeration machinery has pumped out of the box in the process of cooling the contents. That is, it is the heat removed from the steak, butter, milk, and other foods in the process of cooling them. Some of the heat in the coils comes from the electric energy used in the process of running the refrigerator compressor. (This is due to the fact that gases heat up when compressed, just as in pumping up a bicycle tire.) The heat produced by the electric energy, however, is generally only about one-fifth of all the heat in the coils, and it is only for this one-fifth that you will pay in the next bill from the power company. The other four-fifths of the heat in the coils costs nothing. That is, by running the electricity through the refrigerator, you have produced in the coils five times as much heat as an electric heater would have produced.

The preceding paragraph explains the principle of the heat pump. Obviously, there is not enough heat in a refrigerator to heat your house. Outdoors, however, there is plenty of heat, particularly underground, even though the temperature there is not very high.

The heat pump is merely a large refrigeration machine in which the evaporation coils are located outdoors and the condensing coils indoors in the various places where heat is desired. Under good conditions a heat pump may give off five units of heat into the house for every unit of electric energy used. The other four units of heat come from outdoors.

The heat-absorbing (evaporation) coils may be located outside in the air, but this causes some difficulty because of icing. A better plan is to locate the coils in a deep well or a lake if such is available.

Tests show that such a method of heating is practical even in a climate as severe as New York State and Michigan. It is claimed that a well-insulated house in the latitude of central Indiana can be heated as cheaply with a heat pump when electricity costs 1.5 cents per kilowatthour as it can be with an oil burner when oil is 11 cents per gallon.

The heat pump has many advantages over conventional heating methods. No burning is involved; hence there is no dirt or soot from coal or oil. There is no need for a chimney or flue. Thus the initial cost of the home is reduced. Best of all, by reversing a few valves on the heat pump, the direction of refrigeration can be reversed. In this way the house can be cooled in summer and warmed in winter with the same piece of equipment.

KEY WORDS

absolute
boiling point
Calorie
calorie
centigrade

condensation
dynamic equilibrium
Fahrenheit
heat of fusion
heat of vaporization

relative humidity
specific gravity
specific heat
sublimation
vapor pressure

HIGHLIGHTS

Water is the most abundant and important of all liquids. All living things depend upon it. It covers three-fourths of the earth's surface. Water is also the medium in which a great many chemical reactions take place.

Water is the basis of the **calorie,** the unit used in measuring the quantity of heat. The **specific gravity** of a substance is its density relative to that of water. The freezing and boiling points of water are used as reference points on both the **Fahrenheit** and the **centigrade** temperature scales.

Water is at its maximum density at 4°C. That is, it expands at higher and lower temperatures. Water also expands on freezing, which is unusual for a liquid. It is for this reason that ice floats, a very important fact in nature.

The **heat of fusion** of water is 80 cal/g and its **heat of vaporization** is 540 cal/g.

The evaporation of a liquid is an effect of kinetic molecular motion. The rate of evaporation increases as the temperature increases. When the **vapor pressure** of a liquid becomes equal to the atmospheric pressure, we say the liquid boils. Water, for instance, boils at 100°C under 1 atmosphere pressure, and at this temperature its vapor pressure is 760 mm. The pressure cooker is based on this principle: By increasing the pressure, a higher temperature of boiling is obtained and the food cooks in less time.

The relation between evaporation and **condensation** of a liquid in a closed system at a given temperature is an example of what is spoken of as a **dynamic equilibrium.** Molecules of the liquid are evaporating at the same rate as the molecules of vapor are condensing.

Relative humidity is the ratio (expressed in percentage) between the actual vapor pressure of the atmosphere and the maximum vapor pressure possible at that temperature.

Air conditioning is a system of controlling the circulation, the temperature, and the humidity of the air within buildings in order to provide more healthful and more comfortable living conditions.

Mechanical refrigeration is based upon the principle that on evaporation a liquid absorbs heat from its surroundings. The **heat pump** is a special case of refrigeration in which heat is pumped from outdoors into a space to be heated.

QUESTIONS

1. List all the ways you can think of in which water is essential for human life.
2. List as many man-made uses for water as you can.
3. Why is the control and utilization of natural water so important to man?
4. Define the calorie. What is a large Calorie?
5. Define the Btu.
6. What is specific heat?
7. How does the specific heat of rock and earth materials compare with that of water? What relation do these facts have to climate?
8. What is the difference between specific gravity and density?
9. Explain how you would determine the specific gravity of a supposedly pure nugget of gold.

10. Express the following in degrees Fahrenheit: (*a*) 0°C, (*b*) 20°C, (*c*) 80°C, (*d*) 300°A, and (*e*) −40°C.
11. Express the following in degrees centigrade: (*a*) 0°F, (*b*) −30°F, and (*c*) 200°F.
12. Explain why the fact that water has a maximum density at 4°C tends to keep ponds and lakes from freezing solid in winter.
13. What is heat of fusion?
14. How much heat is given off by the freezing of 1 kg (= 1000 g) of water at 0°C?
15. Explain why quick-freeze cabinets intended for freezing foods must have greater refrigeration capacity than those intended merely for storing already frozen foods.
16. What is heat of vaporization?
17. If 1500 g of steam at 100°C in a radiator condenses to liquid water at 100°C, how much heat is given off?
18. How many calories are used in a boiler in converting 1 kg of water at 25°C into steam at 100°C?
19. Explain the relation of heat of vaporization of water to climate.
20. Explain, in terms of the kinetic molecular theory, the process of evaporation of a liquid.
21. Continue your answer to question 20 to include an explanation of heat of vaporization.
22. What is sublimation?
23. What is meant by the vapor pressure of water? How is vapor pressure measured?
24. What is the vapor pressure of water at 100°C?
25. Define boiling point.
26. Explain why food cooks more rapidly in a pressure cooker than in an open pan.
27. Why should pressure cookers always be equipped with a safety valve which opens when a certain predetermined temperature is reached?
28. Explain how you could cause water to boil at 25°C.
29. Explain what is meant by the statement: The evaporation of a liquid is a reversible process.
30. What are the three functions of air conditioning?
31. Draw a diagram and use it to explain the principle of mechanical refrigeration.
32. What is a heat pump? Explain the principle involved.
33. What are the advantages of the heat pump over a conventional method of heating a building?
34. In the experiment described on page 121, why does the water boil as the flask is cooled? How long will boiling continue?

CHAPTER 13

the purification of water and its chemical properties

The well-known English poet, Lord Byron, once wrote,

>'Til taught by pain
>Men really know not what good water's worth.

There are many communities in America today in which the people can be thankful and proud that this quotation does not apply to them. Unfortunately, it is still true in some parts of America. Just what is "good water," and what is it worth?

Pure water, to the chemist, means water unmixed with anything else, that is, water which contains no significant amount of any other substance. To the city water official, pure water means water that is safe and suitable for drinking, bathing, laundering, and steam making, since these are the main uses for the municipal water supply. The public-health value of good water for municipal use has been shown many times. In many cities the death rate from typhoid fever alone was cut 75 percent when the water supply was properly purified.

Natural water

From the chemical point of view, all natural waters are impure. Rain, which is the purest form of natural water, contains dissolved gases from the atmosphere (oxygen, nitrogen, and carbon dioxide), suspended dust particles, and a small amount of ammonium nitrate.

Natural water, such as that shown in the small waterfall in the photograph, generally has many impurities. These impurities may be dissolved in the water or suspended in it. Natural water must be purified before you can be sure that it is safe to drink. (The American Museum of Natural History)

The most impure form of natural water is sea water, which contains a total of about 3.6 percent solid matter in solution. Sea water contains at least a small amount of practically every known element.[1] However, the solid present in greatest quantity is common salt.

Most people get their water from springs, wells, rivers, or lakes. The impurities in such natural water fall into three classes.

1. Dissolved matter. In addition to dissolved gases, calcium sulfate ($CaSO_4$), calcium bicarbonate [$Ca(HCO_3)_2$], and the corresponding compounds of magnesium and iron are commonly found dissolved in natural waters. These substances act chemically upon soaps (see Chap. 45, page 581). The water in which they are found is called **hard water.** For drinking purposes, the presence of these substances in water is not harmful. Indeed, the presence of these minerals may even be beneficial to the animal or human being who drinks the water. When hard water is used for laundry and steam making, however, the presence of the calcium, magnesium, and iron salts listed above *is* objectionable. They waste soap, discolor garments, and form boiler scale.

As long as the water supply does not contain appreciable amounts of fluorides, selenium, arsenic, or copper compounds, or organic matter resulting from decay of plants or animals, it is probably safe for drinking *so far as dissolved matter is concerned.*

2. Suspended matter. Suspended matter consists of solid particles so small that they settle out of water slowly or not at all. However, the

---

[1] For example, it is estimated that there are more than two tons of gold in each cubic mile of sea water.

particles are usually large enough to be seen with a microscope. Clay and sand are commonly present in water in this way, causing the water to be turbid, or muddy. A certain amount of partially decayed organic matter may also be carried in water in suspension.

3. *Bacteria.* The presence or absence of harmful types of bacteria is the principal factor in determining whether water is safe to drink. If silt is present, the bacteria are mostly attached to the suspended clay particles. However, *bacteria may be present in water which is sparklingly clear.* Appearance is no guide in the selection of safe drinking water.

The most common types of water-borne diseases in this country are typhoid and paratyphoid fevers, dysentery, and cholera. The organisms that cause these diseases always get into the water supply from contamination by sewage. The only safe way of testing the **potability,** that is, the safety and suitability for drinking, of water is by chemical and bacterial analysis.

The presence of ammonia (NH_3) or ammonium salts in water may indicate recent contamination by sewage. The ammonia and ammonium salts in the sewage are gradually converted from ammonia into nitrites, that is, salts containing the NO_2^- radical, and finally into nitrates, that is, salts containing the NO_3^- radical. Therefore the relative amounts of these substances present in the water indicate how long ago the sewage was added. Raw sewage, of course, is the most dangerous. A rule commonly used is that drinking water is safe when it contains less than $1/100$ part of nitrogen from nitrite per million parts of water. This, of course, is not because this amount of nitrite is toxic, but because it indicates too recent contamination with sewage. Also, fresh water normally contains practically no sodium chloride. Since all higher animals excrete large amounts of sodium chloride, its presence in water is also a good indication of recent contamination.

A direct bacterial analysis is, on the whole, more reliable than the indirect chemical tests just described. Generally the bacteriologist, instead of looking directly for harmful bacteria, looks for a harmless variety, *Escherichia coli*, which is always present in sewage from man and higher animals. If this organism is present in quantities greater than 1 per 50 ml, the bacteriologist considers the water unsafe for drinking.

Purification of municipal water supplies

Purification of municipal water supplies has two main objectives: (1) to remove suspended matter to clarify the water and (2) to remove or kill all harmful bacteria.

The first objective is accomplished by filtration. You know that a screen wire keeps out flies but allows small gnats to come through.

Fig. 13-1. A schematic drawing of a sand filter. Sand filters are commonly used to help purify municipal water supplies.

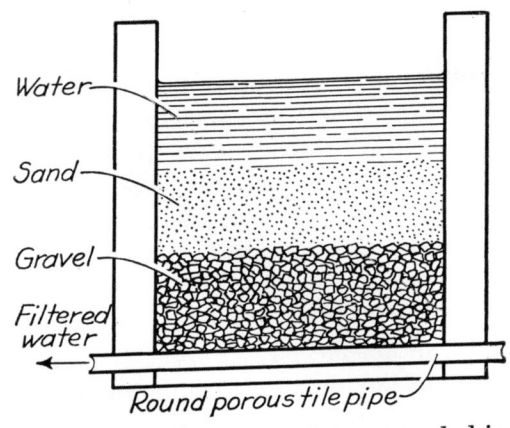

In the same way, it is possible to remove sand particles suspended in water by passing the water through a filter. This is a medium containing holes of a size that will keep out the solid matter but allow the water to flow through. You have seen that you can do this in the laboratory by lining a funnel with paper similar to blotting paper. Municipal water supplies are clarified by filtering the water through beds of sand. Two types of filters are in use, a slow type and a rapid one. In Fig. 13-1 you see the cross section of a slow filter. Water seeps through the bed of sand and gravel which holds back most of the suspended matter. In rapid filtration, aluminum sulfate and lime are added to the water before it is filtered. The reaction is

$$Al_2(SO_4)_3 + 3Ca(OH)_2 \rightarrow 2Al(OH)_3 \downarrow + 3CaSO_4 \downarrow$$

The precipitated aluminum hydroxide [$Al(OH)_3$] is a slimy, gelatinous solid to which much of the silt adheres. The aluminum hydroxide settles rapidly and carries with it the adhering silt. The water is then filtered through a bed of coarse gravel to remove the rest of the suspended matter.

The filtration process removes some, but not all, of the bacteria. It is always necessary to add some agent that will kill the bacteria that remain. Chlorine is the substance most widely used for this purpose. When added in the proper amount, it kills all the bacteria present without producing an objectionable taste or odor in the water. Never are more than about 0.8 parts per million required. (This means 0.8 lb of chlorine per million pounds of water.) Ammonia (NH_3) is generally added, too, because its presence increases the effectiveness of the chlorine.

It is hard to overestimate the importance of the development of this method of sterilizing water. First used in about 1913, it was developed by the U.S. Army to purify water for an army in the field. It was soon evident that the method could be applied to city water supplies, and its use spread quickly. It has resulted in wide reductions in death rates.

Superchlorination is now beginning to replace ordinary chlorination. In this new process, chlorine is added in excess of the amount needed to kill all bacteria in the water. The object of this method is to destroy all organic matter present that might serve as nutrient for bacteria which get into the water later. This excess chlorine is then converted into harmless chlorides by the addition of sulfur dioxide.

Other methods of purifying water

In an emergency, almost any natural water can be made safe to drink by boiling it for 10 min. Boiling kills all harmful bacteria present. Of course, it does not remove any dissolved materials except air and other gases, nor does it clarify the water.

A small amount of sodium hypochlorite (NaClO) added to water will destroy all harmful bacteria. In water, sodium hypochlorite has the same germicidal properties as chlorine,[1] but it has the additional advantage of being a white solid that is easily kept and transported. Small tablets of this chemical are available commercially to campers, hikers, and others for sterilizing water. When properly used, sodium hypochlorite tablets effectively sterilize water, but they are likely to produce a rather unpleasant taste.

Ozone (see Chap. 6, page 50) is sometimes used in place of chlorine to disinfect water. Ultraviolet radiation also is claimed to sterilize water when properly used. Both these methods are more expensive than chlorination except where electric energy is very cheap.

Chemically pure water: distillation

The only practical way to make chemically pure water is by **distillation.** The laboratory apparatus used is shown in Fig. 13-2.

The impure water in the flask is boiled to produce vapor which condenses and drips into the receiver. The material which collects in the receiver is known as the **distillate.** If the impurity in the water is a nonvolatile solid, it can be completely separated by distillation since it remains behind in the flask.

However, if the impurity in the water is a volatile liquid, it cannot be completely separated by one simple distillation. Suppose the material to be distilled contains methyl alcohol, CH_3OH, (bp 64.5°C) and water. On being heated, the liquid starts to boil at a temperature somewhere between the boiling point of pure water and that of pure methyl alcohol. The vapor coming over will contain both water and methyl alcohol since both are volatile. However, since the methyl

---

[1] This is because, when put in water, chlorine produces hypochlorous acid (see Chap. 12, page 239) and hypochlorous acid and its salts are very good germicidal agents.

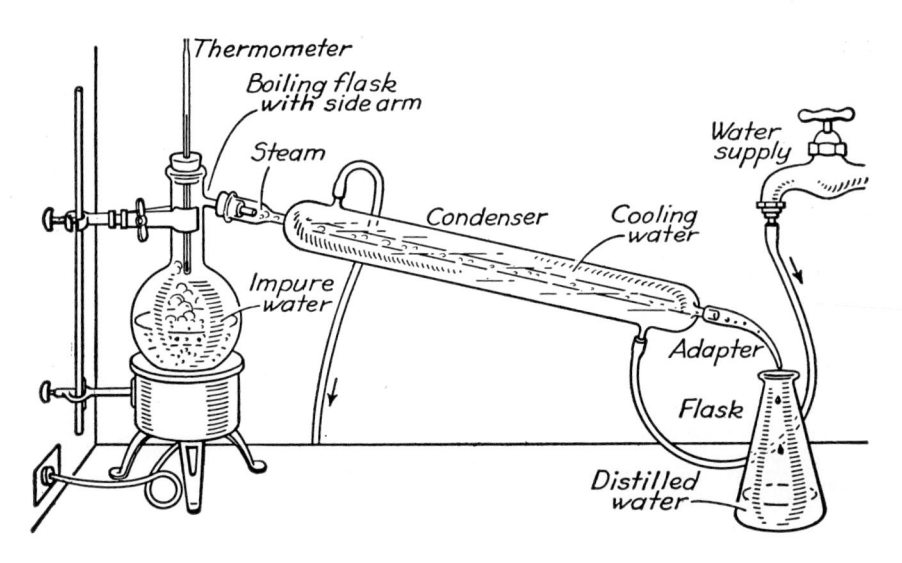

Fig. 13-2. Water and other liquids can be purified by distillation. A common type of laboratory still is shown above.

alcohol is more volatile (its boiling point is lower) than the water, the vapor coming off will contain a higher percentage of methyl alcohol than the solution from which it is being distilled contains. That is, the first bit of distillate will be richer in methyl alcohol than the original solution. If you redistill this first bit of distillate, further enrichment will result. By several such redistillations, you could produce some pure methyl alcohol. This is known as **fractional distillation.**

Distillation is an important procedure both in the laboratory and in industry for separating a liquid from a solid or for separating two liquids. Of course, the most important example of distillation is found in nature in the production of rainfall. It is by distillation also that gasoline, kerosene, and other materials are separated from crude oil (see Chap. 36, page 421). You have already seen how distillation is used to separate oxygen and nitrogen.

In some cases ordinary distillation cannot be used for a separation because the substances involved decompose before the normal boiling point of the solution is reached. This is true in the separation of a sugar-water solution by distillation. If the solution is heated to its normal boiling point to vaporize the water, the sugar partially decomposes at this temperature. To avoid such decomposition, the solution is distilled in a partial vacuum to lower the boiling temperature. This process is known as **vacuum distillation.** It is extensively employed with organic chemicals. Vacuum distillation reached the peak of development in the distillation of vitamin A from fish liver oils. Vitamin A is present along with many other substances in these oils. Although it is slightly volatile, it cannot be distilled out under normal

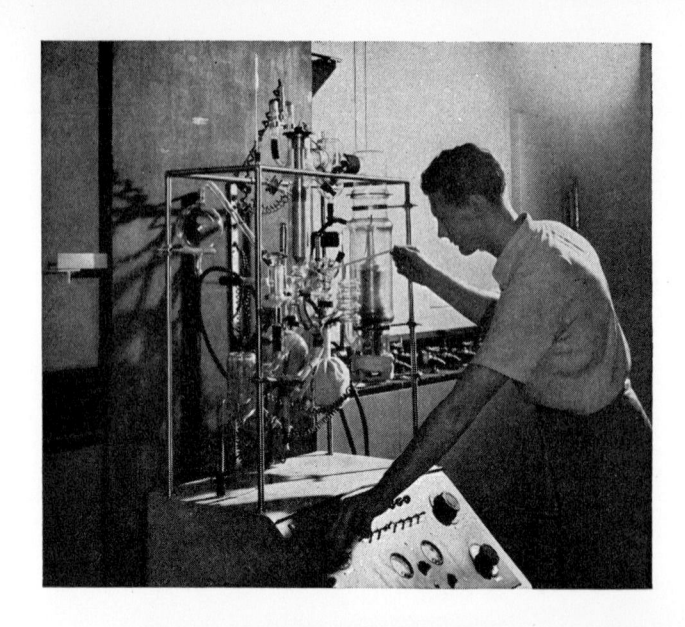

A laboratory-size molecular distillation unit is shown in this photograph. It is being used in a research project for the petroleum industry. (Standard Oil Co.)

conditions because the temperature required causes decomposition. By using exceedingly low pressures, the vitamin A is distilled and separated in almost pure form without significant decomposition. It requires very special vacuum pumps, stills, and techniques to maintain the extremely low pressures needed for vitamin A distillation. The procedure has consequently come to be known by the special term **molecular distillation.** On the average, several tank-car loads of fish oils are distilled in this way every day. Molecular distillation is also used to separate vitamin E from cottonseed oil.

Hydrates

If copper sulfate ($CuSO_4$), which is a white powder, is added to water, it dissolves, and the solution turns blue. Now if the water is evaporated from this solution, a deposit of blue crystals forms. These blue crystals are commonly known as *blue vitriol.* In addition to copper sulfate, the crystals also contain water, having a formula $CuSO_4 \cdot 5H_2O$. However, the water present is not ordinary liquid water; it is combined with the copper sulfate. Substances of this type are known as hydrates (a general term that indicates a compound between water and something else). Other common examples are Glauber's salt ($Na_2SO_4 \cdot 10H_2O$), washing soda ($Na_2CO_3 \cdot 10H_2O$), epsom salts ($MgSO_4 \cdot 7H_2O$), photographer's hypo ($Na_2S_2O_3 \cdot 5H_2O$), and common soda alum [$NaAl(SO_4)_2 \cdot 12H_2O$].

You can see that the number of combined water molecules is not always the same. When heated sufficiently, hydrates give off their water as vapor. This gives you a good test for a hydrate. You can carry the test out by heating some of the crystals in a test tube held horizontally. If the substance is a hydrate, water vapor will condense on the cool end of the tube (Fig. 13–3).

$$\underset{\text{(blue)}}{CuSO_4 \cdot 5H_2O} \xrightarrow{\text{heat}} \underset{\text{(white)}}{CuSO_4} + \underset{\text{(vapor)}}{5H_2O \uparrow}$$

Some hydrates lose their water more easily than others. Copper sulfate pentahydrate ($CuSO_4 \cdot 5H_2O$) must be heated to about 100°C before it begins to **dehydrate** (lose water). However, sodium carbonate decahydrate, commonly known as washing soda ($Na_2CO_3 \cdot 10H_2O$), will lose its water of hydration at room temperature if placed in even a moderately dry atmosphere. This process of loss of water of hydration at room temperature is known as **efflorescence** (literally, this term means *blooming*). Hence, washing soda is efflorescent under certain atmospheric conditions. However, if the atmospheric humidity is very high, washing soda will not effloresce. For a hydrate to be efflorescent, its tendency to give off water vapor (its vapor pressure) must be greater than the vapor pressure of water in the atmosphere. Of course, no hydrate will be efflorescent in a closed bottle for the same reason that liquid water will not completely evaporate in a closed bottle (see Chap. 12, pages 122 and 123). That is, the dehydration of a hydrate is a reversible reaction.

Hydrates frequently crystallize from solution and form large symmetrical crystals. You can see this happen by growing an alum crystal. Dissolve some powdered potash alum [$KAl(SO_4)_2 \cdot 12H_2O$] in the minimum amount of hot water and set the solution aside in an uncovered beaker. In a few days you will see that large and sometimes perfectly shaped crystals of the alum are formed.

Certain hydrates have a color different from the anhydrous salt. You have seen that this is true for copper sulfate pentahydrate

Fig. 13–3. Testing crystals for water of hydration. The formation of droplets of water in the cool end of the tube shows that the crystals contain water.

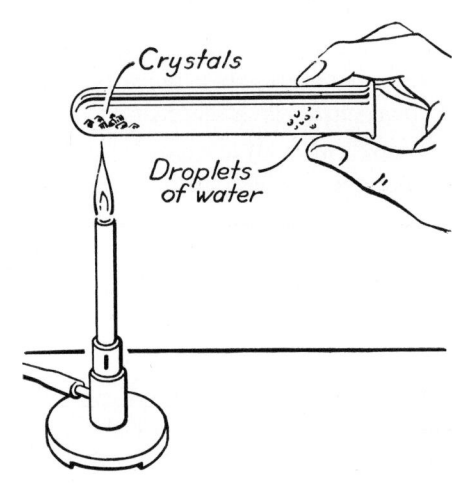

($CuSO_4 \cdot 5H_2O$). The anhydrous white copper sulfate ($CuSO_4$), therefore, serves as a good test for water. When it is added to a liquid containing even a small amount of water, the crystals turn blue because of the formation of the pentahydrate.

$$CuSO_4 + 5H_2O \rightarrow CuSO_4 \cdot 5H_2O$$
(white) \qquad\qquad\qquad (blue)

Cobalt chloride hexahydrate ($CoCl_2 \cdot 6H_2O$) behaves in a similar way. This substance is a flesh-pink solid. The anhydrous cobalt chloride ($CoCl_2$) is dark blue. You can also use cobalt chloride as a test for moisture.

$$CoCl_2 + 6H_2O \rightleftharpoons CoCl_2 \cdot 6H_2O$$
(dark blue) \qquad heat \qquad (light pink)

This reaction is the basis of the so-called *sympathetic ink*. If you use a solution of cobalt chloride in writing on a piece of paper, the "ink" is practically invisible after it has dried because of the light color of the cobalt chloride hexahydrate ($CoCl_2 \cdot 6H_2O$). However, if you warm the writing gently over a flame, dehydration of the hydrate occurs by reversal of the above reaction, and the writing turns intensely blue. If you blow your breath over the writing, it again becomes invisible because of the rehydration of the cobalt chloride.

A piece of paper, dipped into a solution of this salt, dried, and hung in the atmosphere, is a rough indication of humidity. If the air is quite dry, the hydrate will effloresce and color the paper dark blue. As the humidity increases, the salt rehydrates and the blue color disappears. This reaction is sometimes claimed to be an indicator of approaching rain because, of course, atmospheric humidity increases before a rainstorm. However, it is not a reliable "weather forecaster."

Desiccators

When chemists wish to remove moisture from a substance and keep it in a dry state, they place the substance in a desiccator (Fig. 13–4). A desiccator is a container of glass, or sometimes of aluminum, equipped with an airtight top. In the bottom of the desiccator is put a drying agent which absorbs the water vapor present in the air or given off by the substance being dried. The drying agent is generally some substance that absorbs moisture by forming a hydrate. Anhydrous calcium chloride ($CaCl_2$) is commonly used. It reacts with water vapor to form calcium chloride hexahydrate ($CaCl_2 \cdot 6H_2O$). Most gases can be dried by passing the gas through a tube containing granular calcium chloride. Some gases, such as ammonia (NH_3), cannot be dried in this way because they react with the calcium chloride. For such gases there are other drying agents which can be used.

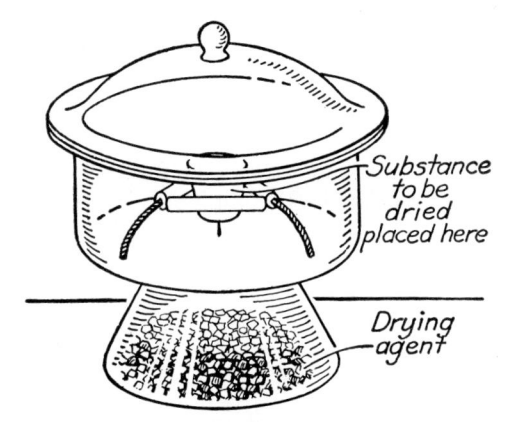

Fig. 13-4. A desiccator. Substances which need to be dried are placed in the desiccator as shown.

Reaction of water with oxides

Oxides of the nonmetals all react with water to form acids. The word acid refers to a group of compounds, all members of which have certain properties in common (see Chap. 8, page 65). Thus

$$SO_2 + H_2O \rightarrow H_2SO_3$$
sulfur dioxide → sulfurous acid

$$SO_3 + H_2O \rightarrow H_2SO_4$$
sulfur trioxide → sulfuric acid

$$CO_2 + H_2O \rightarrow H_2CO_3$$
carbon dioxide → carbonic acid

$$P_2O_5 + 3H_2O \rightarrow 2H_3PO_4$$
phosphorus pentoxide → phosphoric acid

$$N_2O_5 + H_2O \rightarrow 2HNO_3$$
nitrogen pentoxide → nitric acid

Because of their relation to acids, oxides of the nonmetals are called *acidic oxides* or *acid anhydrides*. (The name **anhydride** comes from a Greek word meaning *lacking water*.)

Oxides which react with water to form bases are sometimes called *basic oxides*. Calcium oxide (CaO) reacts with water very vigorously.

$$CaO + H_2O \rightarrow Ca(OH)_2$$
calcium oxide or quicklime → calcium hydroxide or slaked lime

This reaction is commonly known as the *slaking of lime*.

In the same way, sodium oxide reacts very violently with water.

$$Na_2O + H_2O \rightarrow 2NaOH$$
sodium oxide → sodium hydroxide or caustic soda

Both of these products form water solutions which have a soapy feel, a bitter taste (test cautiously), turn red litmus (a vegetable extract) blue, and possess other properties characteristic of a group of compounds which chemists call *bases*. You will learn more later about bases. The above reactions are typical of any oxide of a metal. **All metal oxides react with water to form bases.** Sometimes the reaction is very slow, as with ferric oxide to form ferric hydroxide.

$$Fe_2O_3 + 3H_2O \xrightarrow{slowly} 2Fe(OH)_3$$

Yet even ferric oxide in the presence of water has basic properties.

You can derive the formula for the anhydride of an acid or base very easily by using the following procedure: Write down the formula for the acid or base and subtract from it *all* the hydrogen as water (H_2O). In order to do this, you must, of course, also subtract some oxygen. The remainder is the formula for the anhydride. If there are an odd number of hydrogen atoms in the formula, it is necessary to double the formula in order to subtract all the hydrogen *as water*. For example,

H_2SO_4 *minus* $1H_2O$ *leaves* SO_3
                                              sulfur trioxide or
                                              sulfuric anhydride

H_2SO_3 *minus* $1H_2O$ *leaves* SO_2
                                              sulfur dioxide or
                                              sulfurous anhydride

HNO_3 must be *doubled*. $H_2N_2O_6$ *minus* $1H_2O$ *leaves* N_2O_5
                                                                                     nitrogen pentoxide or nitric anhydride

H_3PO_4 ?
phosphoric acid

HNO_2 ?
nitrous acid

$Mg(OH)_2$ *minus* $1H_2O$ *leaves* MgO
magnesium   magnesium
hydroxide   oxide

KOH *doubled*. $K_2O_2H_2$ *minus* $1H_2O$ *leaves* K_2O
potassium   potassium
hydroxide   oxide

With almost no exceptions, the oxides arrived at by this method do react with water to give the acid or base in question.

Heavy water

Heavy water refers to water in which all the hydrogen atoms are **deuterium,** the isotope of hydrogen with a mass of 2. Chemically, heavy water is the same as ordinary water. Physically, the properties of heavy water are slightly different as you can see in Table 13–1.

Heavy water has become a valuable laboratory tool in recent years. It is available commercially and costs about fifty cents per gram. (Brookhaven National Laboratories)

Heavy water is found in natural water to the extent of about 1 part in 6400 parts of ordinary water. Heavy water can be separated from natural water by taking advantage of the slight differences in physical properties. The details of the procedure are beyond the scope of this book. Since the discovery of heavy water in 1932 by Urey and Murphy of Columbia University and Brickwedde of the U.S. Bureau of Standards, it has been used as a valuable laboratory tool. Heavy water also is used in connection with the production of atomic energy.

TABLE 13–1. Physical properties of water and heavy water

	H_2O	D_2O (heavy water)
Molecular weight	18.016	20.002
Melting point	0.00°C	3.82°C
Boiling point	100.00°C	101.42°C
Relative density, 25°	1.000	1.1076
Heat of fusion	79.7 cal/g	75.5 cal/g

Hydrogen peroxide

Hydrogen peroxide, another compound of hydrogen and oxygen, has the formula H_2O_2. At first sight it may appear to you that this formula violates the rules of valence. Actually it does not. This formula results from the fact that the two oxygen atoms are attached to each other:

H—O—O—H   H—O—H
hydrogen peroxide   water

Any compound in which the two oxygen atoms are joined together in this way is called a **peroxide.**

Hydrogen peroxide is made by the electrolysis of a solution containing ammonium sulfate [$(NH_4)_2SO_4$] and sulfuric acid. The common drugstore variety of hydrogen peroxide is a 3 percent solution in water.

The compound is unstable, decomposing into water and oxygen, sometimes violently.

$$2H_2O_2 \rightarrow 2H_2O + O_2 \uparrow$$

For this reason, the pure compound and even concentrated solutions of it are dangerous explosives. The decomposition of hydrogen peroxide is speeded up (catalyzed) by manganese dioxide and slowed down by certain organic compounds, such as acetanilide ($C_6H_5NHCOCH_3$). Acetanilide is usually added to the commercial 3 percent solution of hydrogen peroxide to improve its stability.

Hydrogen peroxide is used commercially to bleach hair, wool, and feathers. It dissolves dried, caked blood and hence is used by doctors to loosen old bandages. It is also a mild antiseptic.

KEY WORDS

anhydride	distillation	molecular distillation
dehydrate	efflorescence	peroxide
desiccator	fractional distillation	potability
deuterium	hard water	superchlorination
distillate	hydrate	vacuum distillation

HIGHLIGHTS

Potable water is both safe and fit to drink. Natural waters may or may not be potable. Among the impurities that may be found in natural waters are dissolved atmospheric gases, dissolved minerals, suspended or colloidal matter, and bacteria or other microorganisms. The presence of even very small quantities of nitrites makes one suspect contamination with sewage.

Natural waters are purified by sand filtration with or without the addition of chemicals to remove suspended matter. Chlorine is then added to kill bacteria. Small amounts of water may be chlorinated by adding a tablet of calcium or sodium hypochlorite.

When a **hydrate,** consisting of water and a salt, is heated, it loses its water of hydration and changes to an anhydrous powder which may or may not be the same color as the hydrate. Anhydrous copper sulfate is used in testing for the presence of water. Anhydrous cobalt chloride may also be used in this way.

Water reacts with metallic oxides (basic anhydrides) to form bases. Water also reacts with the oxides of nonmetals (acid anhydrides) to form acids.

Heavy water is **deuterium** oxide and is like ordinary water in chemical properties but slightly different in physical properties.

Hydrogen peroxide is manufactured on a large scale by the electrolysis of sulfates.

Water is made chemically pure by **distillation.** Ordinary distillation removes nonvolatile impurities in solution. Volatile impurities must be removed by **fractional distillation. Vacuum distillation** is used to purify substances that would be destroyed by too high a temperature.

QUESTIONS

1. Explain how the term *pure water* has a different meaning to the chemist and to the public health officer.
2. What impurities are commonly present in natural fresh water?
3. What impurities dissolved in water make it unsuitable for drinking?
4. What chemical substances are generally present in natural water which is contaminated with harmful bacteria?
5. Is appearance a guide to the suitability of water for drinking?
6. Explain the two objects to be accomplished in purifying a municipal water supply. How is each accomplished?
7. What is meant by superchlorination?
8. What element, other than chlorine, is sometimes used to purify municipal water?
9. Draw a diagram to explain the process known as *distillation*.
10. What type of impurity is most easily removed by distillation?
11. What is fractional distillation?
12. Why is distillation sometimes carried out under reduced pressure? Cite two such illustrations in industry.
13. Explain how you would test for a hydrate.
14. List three common substances, with formulas, which are hydrates.
15. Explain what is meant by efflorescence.
16. Describe a chemical test for water.
17. How would you remove the water vapor from a small sample of air?
18. Write the reactions of the following substances with water: (a) CaO, (b) Na_2O, (c) SO_2, (d) SO_3, (e) N_2O_5, (f) MgO. Classify the compounds listed as acid or base anhydrides.

CHAPTER 14

solutions

Everyone is familiar with the fact that water will dissolve many substances, such as salt or sugar or automobile antifreeze. The result in each case is called a **solution.** Solutions can be formed not only with water but with many other substances. As a class, solutions are very important, not only in the processes of nature but also in man-made processes. In nature their application ranges from digestion and absorption of foodstuffs, which require that the food first be dissolved, to the formation of vast limestone solution caverns. In industry the application is equally wide, ranging from the refining of cane sugar to the separation of silver from crude zinc. In fact the chemist is dealing with solutions more often than not. In this chapter you will learn something about the formation of solutions and the properties of solutions.

What is a solution?

If a bit of sugar is added to water and stirred, the sugar disappears. Even with the best microscope the sugar can no longer be seen. Yet it has not been lost permanently, because if the water is evaporated, every bit of the original sugar can be recovered. What *has* happened is that the sugar molecules, which make up the sugar crystal, have become separated from each other and distributed uniformly throughout the water molecules. **A solution consists of two** (or more) **components which have intermingled down to molecular proportions.** Solutions are always homogeneous and therefore clear, although they may be colored. You can see this in the case of the solution obtained by adding potassium permanganate to water. Solutions are not to be confused with suspensions, such as that obtained by shaking clay with water. In a suspension the dispersed particles are many thousand times larger than molecules.

Solutions are always clear, but not always colorless. Left, a solution of sugar in water is clear and colorless. Middle, a solution of potassium permanganate in water is clear, but colored purple. Right, a clay suspension in water is cloudy.

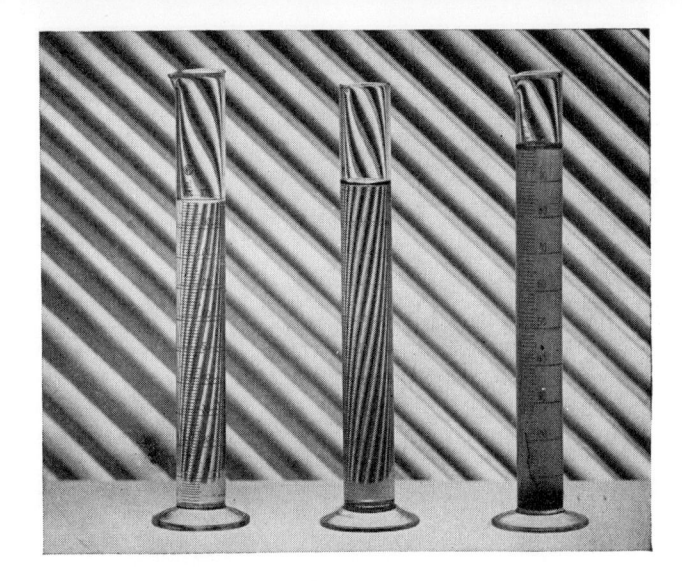

The types of solutions

The two components of a solution are known as the **solute** and the **solvent**. We usually think of the solute as the substance which has been dissolved and of the solvent as the dissolving agent. For example, in a sugar-water solution, the sugar is the solute and the water is the solvent. In some cases the distinction between solvent and solute is not so sharp, however, and must be made arbitrarily. An example of this is in a solution containing alcohol and water.

Although they are the most familiar, liquid solutions are not the only possible type. Solutions in which the solvent or solute may be a gas, a liquid, or a solid also exist. That is, in a solution:

The *solvent* may be:	The *solute* may be:
Gas	Gas
or	or
Liquid	Liquid
or	or
Solid	Solid

Thus there are the following types of solutions:

1. Gas-gas solutions. Example: air or other mixtures of gases.

2. Gas-liquid solutions. Examples: oxygen in natural waters; oxygen, nitrogen, and carbon dioxide in the blood stream; soda water.

3. Gas-solid solutions. Example: hydrogen dissolved in platinum metal. (This type is less common than the others.)

4. Liquid-liquid solutions. Example: an alcohol-water solution such as that used in automobile radiators in the winter.

5. Liquid-solid solutions. Example: sugar in water.

Teflon is a new plastic. It is used for washers, tubes, and tape. One of the reasons that this plastic is so valuable in the laboratory and in industry is because it is insoluble in nearly everything. Teflon even resists those acids which dissolve gold and platinum.

6. *Solid-solid solutions.* Example: brass, a solution of zinc and copper. (This type is quite important in metallurgy, as many alloys are solid-solid solutions.)

In this book we shall be particularly interested in solutions of gases, liquids, or solids dissolved in liquids.

Solubility

The amount of a certain solid which will dissolve in a given amount of liquid is always limited. If one were to take 1000 g of water at 20°C and add a small amount of salt, the salt would dissolve on stirring. Continued addition of salt with stirring would eventually lead to a solution in which no more salt would dissolve. The additional salt would remain apparently unchanged in the bottom of the beaker. The solution would then be **saturated. A saturated solution is one which exists in dynamic equilibrium with excess of the undissolved solute.** When a salt solution becomes saturated at 20°C, it contains 361.5 g of salt per 1000 g of water. This is the solubility of salt in water. One way to express the solubility of a substance is as the amount of the substance contained in a given amount of solvent when the solution is in equilibrium with excess of the solute. Later you will learn other ways to express solubility. In the table Properties of Some Inorganic Substances on page 685 of the Appendix, you will find the solubilities of various compounds.

To the chemist the solubility of a substance is one of its most important properties. It is commonly the basis of his tests for that substance. Solubility also helps to determine the uses to which a substance can be put. For example, if glass were as soluble in water as salt is, it certainly would be of no value to us. On the other hand, if sugar were not fairly soluble in water, man could not digest and absorb it; hence he could not use it as a food.

How may solubility be determined?

You can determine the solubility of a solid in a liquid by preparing a saturated solution of the substance, allowing the excess solid to settle, and carefully removing some of the clear solution with a pipette. Transfer this clear solution to a clean, weighed, evaporating dish. Then weigh the dish and the solution. Evaporate the water by gentle heating (avoid spattering), and determine the weight of the residue. The loss in weight on evaporation represents the water which the solution contained. The weight of the residue represents the amount of solute dissolved in this amount of water.

Soluble and insoluble substances

Inspection of the table Properties of Some Inorganic Substances on page 685 of the Appendix will show that the solubilities of various substances are widely different. Potassium hydroxide has a solubility at 0°C of 970 grams per liter (g/liter) of water, and barium sulfate has a solubility at 18°C of only 0.0022 g/liter of water. Chemists speak of a substance like potassium hydroxide as being *very soluble* in water, of others like sodium chloride as being *soluble*, and of one like barium sulfate as being *insoluble*. The terms are relative only.

That no substance is completely insoluble may be illustrated with glass, which is said to be "insoluble." If you place some powdered glass or fine glass wool in a test tube of distilled water containing a few drops of phenolphthalein, you will find that the phenolphthalein immediately turns pink. This is due to some of the glass dissolving, which produces a basic reaction in water.

Effect of temperature on solubility

In general, increased temperature increases the solubility of a solid in water. This is illustrated by Fig. 14–1. (Note that in this figure the solubilities are expressed in grams per 100 g of water.) There are a few exceptions, however, among which are calcium hydroxide [$Ca(OH)_2$] and sodium sulfate (Na_2SO_4).

You can use Fig. 14–1 to show one important illustration of the application of solutions in the chemical laboratory, namely, the separation of a substance from others mixed with it. Suppose, for example, that you had a mixture of 150 g of potassium nitrate and 150 g of sodium chloride from which you wished to obtain pure sodium chloride and pure potassium nitrate. If you added 100 g of water to the mixture and heated it to 72°C reference to Fig. 14–1, will show that all of the potassium nitrate would dissolve, while only 38 g of the sodium chloride would dissolve. Then by filtering, you could obtain 112 g (150 − 38) of pure sodium chloride.

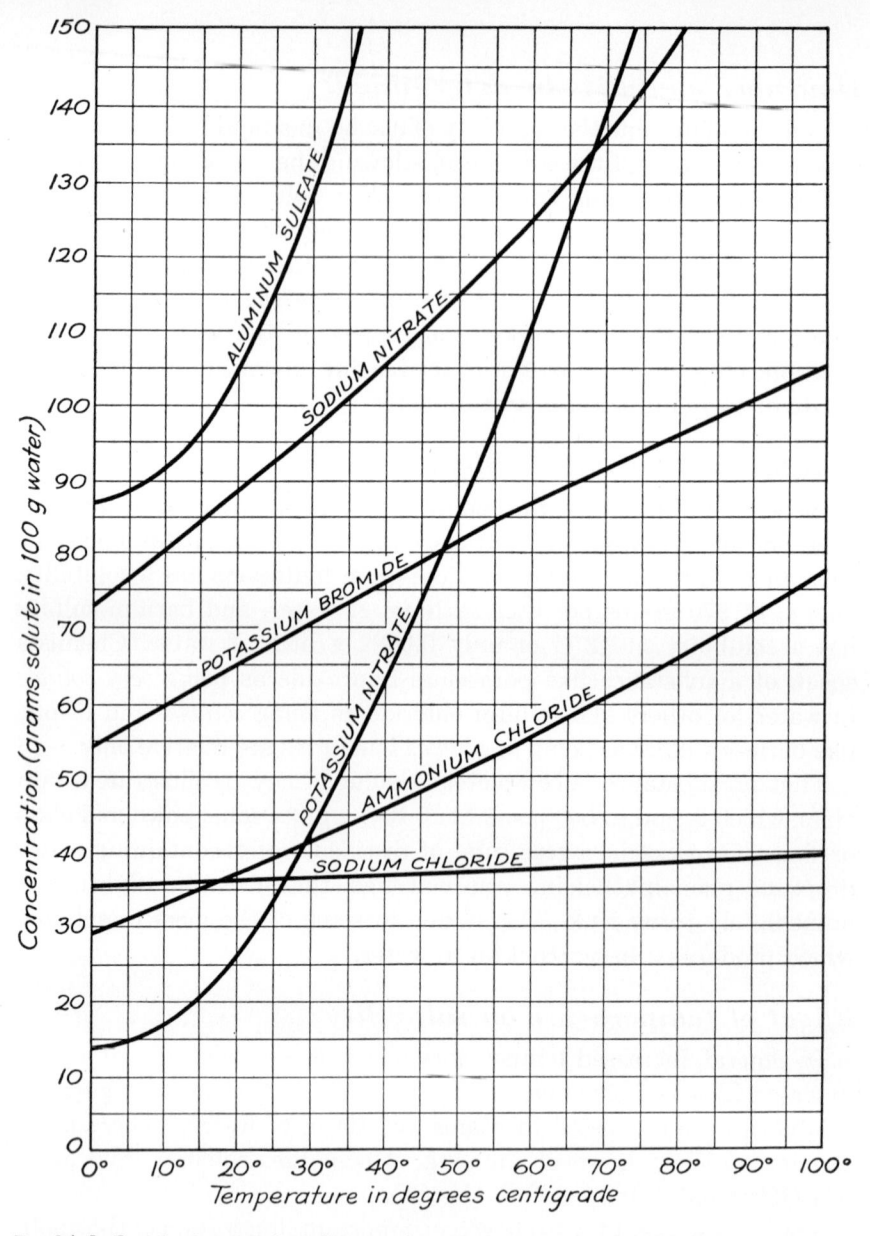

Fig. 14–1. Graphs showing the influence of temperature on the solubility of various salts in water. (Data from Alexander Smith and James Kendall, *Introductory College Chemistry*, Appleton-Century-Crofts, Inc., New York, 1938)

You could obtain pure potassium nitrate from the solution by the following procedure: Cool the solution from 72 to 20°C. At 20°C the solubility of potassium nitrate is only 26 g; hence 124 g (150−26) crystallizes out (that is, separates out of the solution as crystals), while only 2 g (38−36) of sodium chloride crystallizes. These crystals, consisting of 124 g of potassium nitrate and 2 g of sodium chloride, are filtered off and redissolved in the smallest amount of water which will dissolve them at 72°C. On cooling to 20°C, only pure potassium nitrate separates. This is because the 2 g of sodium chloride is not enough to saturate the solution with sodium chloride even at 20°C. This procedure is known as purification by **fractional crystallization** and is one of the most important techniques of the chemical laboratory.

Supersaturated solutions

The fractional crystallization described above is based on the great change in solubility of potassium nitrate with change in temperature. Sometimes when a saturated solution of a substance is prepared at a high temperature and cooled *when there is no undissolved solid present,* there is a delay in the formation of crystals. Such solutions are said to be **supersaturated.** The excess solute always crystallizes out if the supersaturated solution is inoculated with, that is, has added to it, even the tiniest crystal of the substance concerned.

Sodium acetate ($NaC_2H_3O_2$) and sodium thiosulfate ($Na_2S_2O_3 \cdot 5H_2O$) are particularly likely to form supersaturated solutions. This is illustrated by the following: Place about 20 g of either solid in a test tube with 10 ml of water and heat the mixture until all the crystals have dissolved. Allow the stoppered tube to cool to room temperature. Frequently no crystals appear on cooling until the solution is inoculated with a crystal of the solute concerned. At that time the solution may set almost solid with amazing rapidity.

No one completely understands the phenomenon of supersaturation. A crystal consists of a regular geometric arrangement of the atoms (or molecules) present in it. The growth of the crystal consists of adding atoms (or molecules) to it in the same pattern. The spontaneous formation of the crystal pattern from the molecules randomly dis-

Fig. 14–2. Crystallization from a supersaturated solution. Sometimes crystallization is delayed in a carefully prepared supersaturated solution. If the solution is then inoculated with a crystal of the solute, crystals will immediately form.

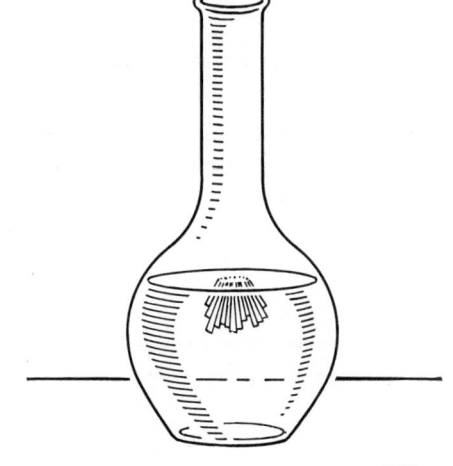

Rain-making machine. Dr. Wallace E. Howell heats silver iodide dissolved in acetone in this machine. This makes a vapor carrying silver iodide crystals rise into the air. These crystals are the right structure to cause crystallization in the clouds.

persed throughout the liquid is the difficult step in crystallization. Because of this difficulty, the crystallization sometimes "can't get started."

Supersaturation is closely parallel to **supercooling.** Many pure liquids, especially water, can be cooled, in the absence of foreign solid particles, many degrees below their normal freezing point. This condition exists in certain clouds which consists of droplets of *liquid* water cooled as low as -35 or $-40°C$. The droplets are so small that they are able to remain suspended in the air indefinitely as long as they remain liquid.[1]

As with a supersaturated solution, if the cloud is inoculated with a crystal of the correct structure, crystallization of the liquid water to snow occurs. These snow crystals start to fall to earth, where they may appear as snow or rain, depending on atmospheric conditions. This is the basis of the rain-making method discovered by Langmuir and Schaefer of the General Electric Company. In rain making, clouds are seeded with dry ice or silver iodide, both of which have the necessary crystal structure to start ice formation. Once this difficult step is past, the process continues unaided.

Honey, certain types of molasses, and some kinds of candy are supersaturated sugar solutions. In candy supersaturation is desirable for smoothness. If crystallization occurs, as it always will with honey when stored long enough, the product becomes grainy because of the sugar crystals which have formed.

[1] For this reason the freezing point of a liquid (or the melting point of a solid) is defined as the temperature of a well-stirred mixture of the solid and the corresponding liquid. The freezing point is not necessarily the temperature at which crystallization first occurs when the liquid is cooled. You will see that this latter temperature is not always the same.

Another look at a saturated solution: equilibrium

The reason for the definition of a saturated solution as given on page 148 can now be made clear. A saturated solution is *not* one which holds in solution the greatest amount of solute—obviously a supersaturated solution holds more. But supersaturated solutions are always unstable and will eventually lose their excess solute and become just saturated.

These questions always arise: When a saturated solution of sugar, let us say, has been formed and no more sugar will dissolve, does the sugar really stop dissolving? If so, why does it, since all sugar crystals are the same? The answer is that even in a saturated solution the solute is still dissolving. However, the solute in solution is crystallizing out at the same rate, so no net change is occurring. A state of equilibrium exists which is quite similar to that between a liquid and its saturated vapor (see Chap. 12, pages 121 to 123).

$$\text{Pure solute} \underset{\text{crystallization}}{\overset{\text{dissolving}}{\rightleftarrows}} \text{solute in solution}$$

It is known from several different lines of evidence that this state of equilibrium exists. One of the most striking experiments concerns the change in crystal shape which may occur in a saturated solution. Suppose a large crystal of sodium chloride has a round hole drilled into it and is then weighed and placed in a saturated solution of sodium chloride. You will find that after standing in the solution the round hole changes to a square one. However, no change in weight of the crystal occurs. This can be explained only by the picture of a saturated solution given here. The salt crystal dissolves and salt particles from the solution take their place on the crystal. But as these crystallize, they arrange themselves in characteristic fashion to make a cubic rather than a round structure. The use of radioactive isotopes also confirms this theory.

Fig. 14-3. A saturated solution is one which is in equilibrium with the undissolved solute. That is, solute dissolves in the solution and crystallizes out of the solution at the same rate.

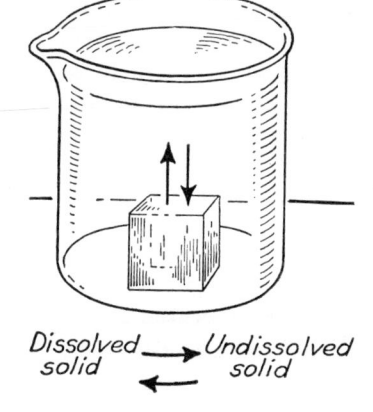

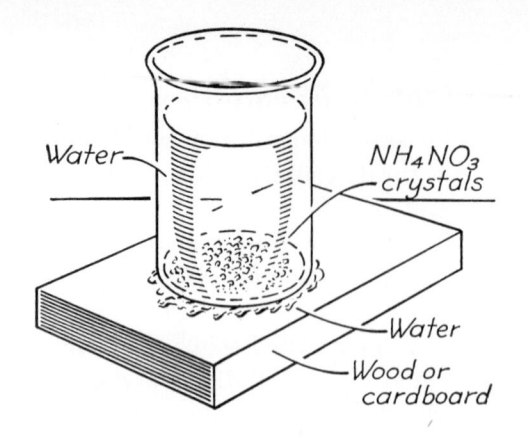

Fig. 14–4. By rapidly dissolving ammonium nitrate (NH$_4$NO$_3$), water on the bottom of the beaker can be frozen. Ammonium nitrate is a good example of a solute which dissolves in water endothermically, that is, with the consumption of heat.

The energy change accompanying solution

When a crystal of sodium acetate is added to a supersaturated solution of sodium acetate, the solution gives off a considerable amount of heat on crystallization. Exactly the same amount of heat was consumed in the process of dissolving this sodium acetate. This heat is known as the **heat of solution.** Some substances consume heat on dissolving, others give it off. An example of the former is ammonium nitrate; of the latter, sulfuric acid.

Dissolving ammonium nitrate in water can actually consume enough heat to freeze water, as the following experiment will show. Pour about 50 g of water from melting ice into a small beaker. Place the beaker on a piece of cellophane or waterproof paper on which there are a few drops of water. The cellophane should rest on a piece of wood or other good heat insulator. If you now add ammonium nitrate (NH$_4$NO$_3$) to the water in the beaker and stir, you will find that the water between the bottom of the beaker and the cellophane is quickly changed to ice. Dissolving ammonium nitrate in water is said to be an **endothermic** process, that is, a process in which heat is absorbed.

The opposite type of heat change is illustrated by dissolving sulfuric acid in water. Carefully pour a few milliliters of sulfuric acid into 50 ml of water in a small beaker, stirring with a thermometer. The solution may reach a temperature over 100°C. This is an **exothermic** process, that is, a process in which heat is given off.

This experiment illustrates another fact of which every chemistry student should be aware. When mixing sulfuric acid and water, you should always pour the acid into the water; never pour the water into into the acid. Whichever way the mixing is done, a large amount of heat is liberated. When the mixing is done correctly, the more dense sulfuric acid flows downward and mixes quickly with the water, thus spreading the liberated heat throughout all the liquid present. If the water is poured into the sulfuric acid, the less dense water will tend to form a layer on top of the acid. This results in a zone of very high temperature where the two layers meet. The temperature may be high enough to cause explosive evolution of steam and acid. Bad acid burns have been caused by disregard of these simple facts.

No useful generalizations can be made about which solutes dissolve exothermically and which dissolve endothermically except the following one: When the formation of the saturated solution is an exothermic process, the solute will be less soluble at high temperatures than at low. When the formation of a saturated solution is an endothermic process, the solute will be more soluble at higher temperatures. Or if you know the effect of temperature on solubility, you can predict whether the dissolving process will be endothermic or exothermic.

Solutions of gases in liquids

The large carbonated beverage industries, ranging all the way from champagne to Coca-Cola, are based on solutions of gases in liquids. In fact, part of the appeal of each of these beverages is based on the tingling sensation they produce on the tongue. Back of this fact is the relationship important to all gas-liquid solutions—Henry's law.

Henry's law is: At constant temperature, the solubility of a gas in a liquid varies directly with its pressure. For example, at 25°C and 1 atmosphere, the solubility of carbon dioxide in water is 1.46 g per 1000 g of water. Now Henry's law says that if the pressure of carbon dioxide is doubled, its solubility will be 2 × 1.46 g per 1000 g of water. The solubility is the weight of gas per unit quantity of liquid.

Carbonated beverages are made by saturating the liquid with carbon dioxide under high pressure. This procedure is used in order to cause a large amount of carbon dioxide to dissolve. When the bottle is opened, the carbon dioxide pressure is reduced, and the liquid fizzes—giving off the excess carbon dioxide. The tingling sensation which such beverages produce is due to the release of carbon dioxide gas bubbles on the tongue.

Henry's law says in effect that the *volume* of gas which will dissolve in a given amount of liquid at a certain temperature is constant—whatever the pressure. This is because as the actual weight of gas which dissolves increases with pressure, the volume of a given weight of this gas decreases with pressure (Boyle's law). Hence in many books, including this one, the solubility of gases is given by stating the volume of gas which dissolves in a certain amount of water. For example, the solubility of sulfur dioxide at 0°C is 80 volumes of the gas in 1 volume of water.

The cause of an occupational disease known as *caisson disease* or *the bends* is another illustration of Henry's law. When air is supplied to men working under high pressure, as in deep-sea diving or tunneling under rivers, the solubility of the oxygen and nitrogen of the atmosphere in their blood stream is increased many times. If the pressure is released too suddenly, as would happen if the diver were brought to the surface too rapidly, the excess gas, particularly nitrogen, would be released in bubbles in the capillaries of the circulatory system. The gas bubbles may clog or even rupture the capillaries, thus reducing circulation and producing "the bends," which may prove fatal. To decrease this danger, the pressure is reduced slowly. This allows the gas to be released slowly so that it can be carried to the lungs and discharged.

Almost always, a rise in temperature decreases the solubility of a gas in a liquid. This is why a glass of water acquires gas bubbles on standing in a warm room and then tastes flat. Everyone has noticed that carbonated beverages fizz more violently if opened when warm.

Solutions of liquids in liquids

When two liquids are mixed, you will observe one of three things. The pair may be:

1. Completely soluble in each other. Methyl alcohol and water are an example. These two can be mixed together in any proportion and they will always dissolve. Such pairs of liquids that have unlimited solubility in each other are said to be completely **miscible**.

2. Partially soluble in each other. Ether and water illustrate this type of liquid in liquid solution. If a few drops of ether are added to 100 ml of water, they will be found to dissolve. Further addition of ether, however, soon produces a saturated solution and the extra ether appears as a separate liquid layer above the water layer.

In this *two-phase* system the bottom layer is a saturated solution of ether in water. You can prove that it contains ether by withdrawing a few milliliters of the bottom layer with a pipette and igniting on a watch glass. The fact that the solution burns proves that it contains ether. The upper layer is a solution of water in ether. That it is mostly ether is evident from its smell. You can prove the presence of water by withdrawing some of the upper layer and testing with anhydrous copper sulfate which you will remember (see Chap. 13,

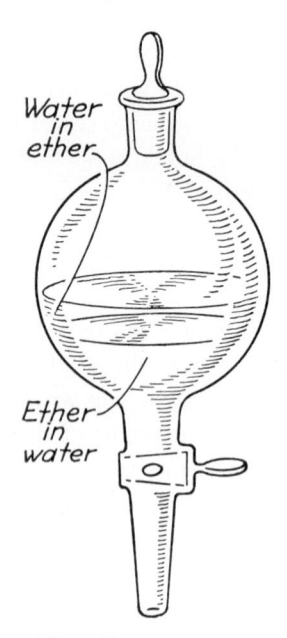

Fig. 14–5. Ether and water form two layers. This is a two-phase system.

pages 139 and 140) is colorless. You will find that the copper sulfate turns blue. This indicates that the hydrated salt, $CuSO_4 \cdot 5H_2O$ has been formed. Water must, therefore, have been present in the ether layer.

$$CuSO_4 + 5H_2O \rightarrow CuSO_4 \cdot 5H_2O$$
$$\text{(white)} \qquad\qquad\qquad \text{(blue)}$$

3. Completely insoluble in each other. Mercury and water are an illustration. Of course one would expect that any two liquids are at least slightly soluble in each other. Mercury and water (or mercury and other common liquids such as ether or alcohol) are so slightly soluble in each other that for all practical purposes we may say that they are completely **immiscible.**

Some generalizations about solubilities

One of the greatest needs of the chemist at present is for a theory to explain and predict solubilities. At present we have no satisfactory theory. All that is known is from experiments measuring solubilities. From these experiments certain generalizations can be drawn. These are as follows:

1. Water is the best solvent that we know of for almost all salts and sugars.
2. Water, in general, is known to be a poor solvent for greases, oils, and fats.
3. Greases, oils, and fats are readily soluble in carbon tetrachloride (CCl_4), carbon disulfide (CS_2), or benzene (C_6H_6).
4. Water is nearly completely immiscible with these good solvents for oils and fats.
5. The good solvents for oils and fats are very poor solvents for the salts and sugars.

Further it is helpful if the student knows certain generalizations regarding the relative solubilities of the different salts in water. These are as follows:

1. All metal *chlorides* are soluble except silver chloride, lead chloride, and mercurous chloride.
2. All metal *sulfates* are soluble except those of calcium, barium, strontium, and lead.
3. All metal *nitrates, chlorates,* and *acetates* are soluble.
4. All salts of *sodium, potassium,* and *ammonium* are soluble.
5. All *carbonates* are insoluble except those of sodium, potassium, and ammonium.
6. All *oxides* and *hydroxides* are insoluble except those of sodium, potassium, ammonium, and barium.

KEY WORDS

endothermic	immiscible	solution
exothermic	miscible	solvent
fractional crystallization	saturated	supercooling
heat of solution	solute	supersaturated
Henry's law		

HIGHLIGHTS

A **solution** is a homogeneous mixture of two or more components. Based on states of matter, there are six types of solutions.

Not all **solutes** are equally soluble in the same **solvent**. **Fractional crystallization** is a method of separating two solutes differing in solubility in the same solvent.

In most cases the solubility of solids in water increases with increasing temperature. **Henry's law** states that for a constant temperature the solubility of a gas in a liquid varies directly with the pressure.

There are several rules or generalizations which enable us to predict the solubility of certain substances.

QUESTIONS

1. List some of the reasons why solutions are of practical importance.
2. Define a solution. How does a solution differ from a suspension?
3. List six different types of solutions and give one illustration of each type.
4. Define a saturated solution.
5. What is a supersaturated solution? Give examples.
6. Classify the following as soluble or insoluble in water: (*a*) NaCl, (*b*) sugar, (*c*) AgCl, (*d*) Na_2CO_3, (*e*) glass, (*f*) $NaNO_3$.
7. What effect on solubility of solids in water is generally produced by raising the temperature?
8. What is the effect of temperature on the solubility of gases in liquids?
9. State Henry's law. Cite two practical applications of it.
10. What is fractional crystallization?
11. In mixing sulfuric acid and water, why should the acid be added to the water rather than the water to the acid?
12. Name one liquid which is completely miscible with water.

CHAPTER 15

some quantitative

properties of solutions

Concentration of solution may be expressed in grams per 1000 g of solvent or in percentage (parts of solute per 100 parts of solution). But often the chemist prefers one of the following methods instead.

Concentration of solutions

1. Molarity. **The molarity of a solution is the number of moles** (gram-molecular weights) **contained per liter of solution.** For example, a 1-molar (M) solution of sodium chloride contains one mole of sodium chloride (= 58.5 g) per liter of *solution*. A 0.5M solution of sugar ($C_{12}H_{22}O_{11}$, molecular weight 342) contains one-half mole ($^{342}\!/_{\!2}$ g) of sugar per liter of solution. To illustrate, let us imagine that the chemist wishes to prepare 1 liter of 0.1M sodium chloride solution. Using the chemical balance, he will weigh out accurately 5.85 g of pure sodium chloride. This material is now carefully transferred to a 1-liter volumetric flask. Water is added slowly with shaking until all the salt is dissolved. Then water is added until the total volume of the solution is just 1 liter. Note that the exact amount of water used is not specified but only the volume of the final solution.

Molar concentration is used by chemists wherever the *volume* of a solution used in an experiment is to be measured. Suppose, for example, that in a certain experiment 200 ml of the 0.1M sodium chloride solution described were used. Since 200 ml is 0.2 of the entire solution which contains 0.1 mole of sodium chloride, this amount of solution contains 0.02 (or 0.1 × 0.2) of a mole of sodium chloride.

To convert molarity to grams of solute per liter, multiply the molarity by the molecular weight of the solute. Thus a 2M solution of

159

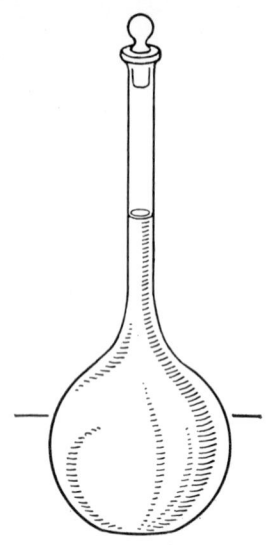

Fig. 15-1. A volumetric flask. To make 1 liter of solution, add enough water to the solute to reach the liter mark.

sulfuric acid (molecular weight 98) contains $2 \times 98 = 196$ g of sulfuric acid per liter. A $0.5M$ solution of sodium hydroxide (molecular weight 40) contains $0.5 \times 40 = 20$ g of sodium hydroxide per liter.

2. *Molality.* **The molality of a solution is the number of moles of solute per 1000 grams of solvent.** For example, a 1-molal (m) sugar solution contains 342 g of sugar in 1000 g of water. In this unit the total weight of solvent and solute is specified. This unit of concentration is used wherever an experiment requires that the *weight* of solution used, rather than its volume, be measured. Since, in general, volumes are more easily measured than weights, molarity is generally used except where the most accurate work is necessary.

3. *Normality.* Normality is defined in Chap. 27, page 309.

The boiling point of solutions

Solutions of nonvolatile solutes always have higher boiling points than the pure solvent. The amount of this **boiling-point increase** depends on the concentration of the solution. This is the basis of the use of the candy thermometer in many home kitchens. Candy is essentially a solution of sugar in water. In cooking it, the object is to boil off just the amount of water necessary to give it the desired consistency when cool. This consistency depends upon the ratio of water to sugar. As the boiling continues, the concentration of the solution increases and its boiling point rises. Hence the point at which to stop the cooking can be indicated by the boiling point. In boiling down maple sap to make maple sugar, the same principle may be used. Determining the correct concentration for candy or maple sugar production is but one of many applications of this important principle.

Let us assume three solutions containing nonvolatile solutes:

Solution	Content	Boiling point at 1 atmosphere, °C
1m sugar ($C_{12}H_{22}O_{11}$)	342 g sugar + 1000 g H_2O	100.51
1m glycerin ($C_3H_8O_3$)	92 g glycerin + 1000 g H_2O	100.51
1m glucose ($C_6H_{12}O_6$)	180 g glucose + 1000 g H_2O	100.51

Measuring the boiling points of these solutions will show that their boiling points are all the same. **The addition of a nonvolatile solute always raises the boiling point of the solvent. The boiling-point increase is directly proportional to the molality. The rate of increase for water is 0.51°C per one molal.** (This is the rate of increase for all substances except acids, bases, and salts, which give a greater increase than this. See Chap. 27, page 311.)

Applications of principle of boiling-point increase

The chemist uses this principle in two ways:

1. To calculate the boiling point of a solution of known concentration. What would be the boiling point at 1 atmosphere of a $2m$ solution of glycerin? The boiling-point increase over that of pure water will be $2 \times 0.51°C = 1.02°C$.

Boiling point of solution = boiling point of water
   + boiling-point increase

Boiling-point increase = molality × molal boiling-point increase

   = 2 × 0.51°C

Boiling point of solution = 100°C + 1.02°C = 101.02°C

2. To determine the molecular weight of an unknown substance. Suppose that 40 g of a substance of unknown molecular weight in 1000 g of water gives a boiling-point increase of 0.255°C. If you recall that one mole per 1000 g of water gives an increase of 0.51°C, you can see that the 40 g must be one-half mole; hence the molecular weight is 80. That is,

$$\frac{\text{Observed increase in boiling point}}{\text{Molal increase in boiling point}} = \frac{\text{grams solute per 1000 g H}_2\text{O}}{\text{molecular weight of solute}}$$

$$\frac{0.255°}{0.51°} = \frac{40}{x}$$

Where x = molecular weight of solute
Solving,
$$x = 40 \times \frac{0.51}{0.255} = 80$$

Qualitatively, the reason for the boiling-point increase is easily understood. In Fig. 15–2, a represents a beaker containing pure solvent. All the molecules on the surface are solvent molecules and thus capable of evaporating. A solution of this solvent containing a nonvolatile solute is represented by b. Part of the surface is now blocked by these

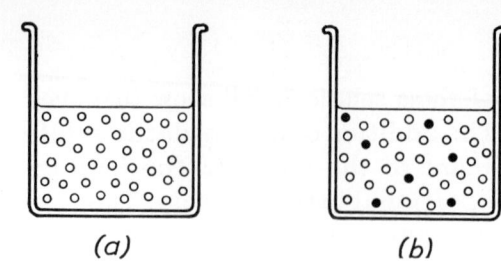

Fig. 15–2. Nonvolatile solutes reduce the evaporation of a solvent by blocking part of the surface from which evaporation occurs. This elevates the boiling point. A beaker of pure water (a); a water solution of a nonvolatile solute (b).

non-evaporating solute particles; hence the vapor pressure of the solution is lower than that of the pure solvent at the same temperature. If you recall the condition necessary for boiling (page 118), you can see that *b* will have a higher boiling point than *a*.

Solutions have lower freezing points than the solvent

Sea water freezes at a lower temperature than fresh water. Alcohol depresses the freezing point of the water in automobile radiators. Both these cases illustrate the same principle. Solutes (except acids, bases, and salts, which are considered in Chap. 27, page 311) all have the same effect in depressing the freezing point when present in the same molal concentration. **The freezing point of water is depressed at the rate of 1.86°C per one molal.** Thus all 1*m* water solutions having a boiling point of 100.51°C will have a freezing point of −1.86°C.

Applications of the freezing-point-depression principle

Radiator **antifreeze** is a common application. The four substances most commonly employed as antifreezes are listed in Table 15–1. To produce a **freezing-point depression** of 10°C, you can see that the solution must be $10/1.86 = 5.38m$. That is, a solution 5.38*m* would have a freezing point of −10°C. Such a solution would contain per 1000 g water:

	5.38 × 32 = 172 g methyl alcohol
or	5.38 × 46 = 247 g ethyl alcohol
or	5.38 × 62 = 333 g ethylene glycol
or	5.38 × 92 = 495 g glycerin

Thus per unit weight, solutes having the lowest molecular weights are the most efficient antifreezes.

Not all substances, however, are equally satisfactory antifreezes, although anything dissolved in water will depress its freezing point. Salt or sugar if used in large enough quantities will prevent the freezing of water *but should never be used in automobile radiators.* Salt is

Radiator antifreeze is an important application of the fact that a solution has a lower freezing point than the pure solvent. Antifreeze protects the water in the automobile radiator from freezing and breaking the radiator.

too corrosive to the cooling system, and sugar will char and clog the system.

Of all the substances that might be chosen for automobile antifreeze, the only ones commonly used are the four listed in Table 15–1. Not all these are equally satisfactory and none of them is entirely satisfactory. Methyl and ethyl alcohols have the disadvantage of low boiling points; hence they evaporate from the radiator and must be replaced periodically. Glycerin and ethylene glycol have such high boiling points that they are considered non-evaporating and make up the commercial "permanent" type of antifreeze. Glycerin, however, forms solutions which are very viscous. Therefore, these solutions do not circulate well in the cooling system. Ethylene glycol solutions have just the opposite fault. These solutions will leak through holes so small that pure water cannot get through them. When ethylene glycol is put into a cooling system, one sometimes discovers holes which otherwise would never have been noticed.

All four compounds tend to change into acids under the conditions of the cooling system and therefore become corrosive. Various corrosion inhibitors are incorporated with these compounds in commercial antifreezes.

TABLE 15–1. Properties of substances used as antifreeze

Name	Boiling point, °C	Formula	Molecular weight	Freezing point of 1 m solution in water, °C
Methyl alcohol	65	CH_3OH	32	−1.86
Ethyl alcohol	78.5	C_2H_5OH	46	−1.86
Ethylene glycol	197.2	$C_2H_4(OH)_2$	62	−1.86
Glycerin	290	$C_3H_8O_3$	92	−1.86

Freezing-point depression and molecular weights

Since the freezing-point depression depends upon the molality, it can be used to determine molecular weights of unknown substances. Suppose, for example, that 100 g of an unknown substance in 1000 g of water produces a freezing point (fp) of −1.25°C. What is the molecular weight of the unknown substance? Proceeding as in the boiling-point problem, page 161:

$$\frac{\text{Observed freezing-point depression}}{\text{Molal freezing-point depression}} = \frac{\text{grams solute per 1000 g H}_2\text{O}}{\text{molecular weight}}$$

$$\frac{1.25°}{1.86°} = \frac{100}{x}$$

Where x = molecular weight
Solving for x,

$$x = 100 \times \frac{1.86}{1.25} = 149$$

The principle of a solute depressing the freezing point is not restricted to solutes that have freezing points below that of water. Thus both methyl alcohol (fp −97.8°C) and sugar (fp 186°C) have the same effect on the freezing point of water. Furthermore, the principle applies to all solvents, although the rate of depression is different for each solvent. Thus when a small amount of one metal is dissolved in another, the melting point of the solution is lower than that of the pure metal. One of the quickest tests of purity for an organic compound is to measure its melting point, since any impurity present will lower its melting point. This test of purity is widely used in the organic chemical industries and in the research laboratory.

Osmosis

Osmosis is particularly important in biological systems. Suppose a funnel tube covered with a piece of cellophane[1] is inverted and immersed in a beaker of water and a sugar solution is placed inside the funnel tube (Fig. 15-3). On standing, the level of the sugar solution in the tube will rise. This happens because the water in the beaker passes through the cellophane into the sugar solution. **Osmosis is the passage of solvent through a semipermeable membrane from a region where the solvent is more concentrated into a region where it is less concentrated.** A semipermeable membrane is one through which the solvent can move but through which the solute

[1] The cellophane must be of the nonmoistureproof variety.

Fig. 15–3. An osmotic cell. When a solution is separated from a pure solvent by a semipermeable membrane, the pure solvent diffuses through the membrane and causes the level of the solution to rise.

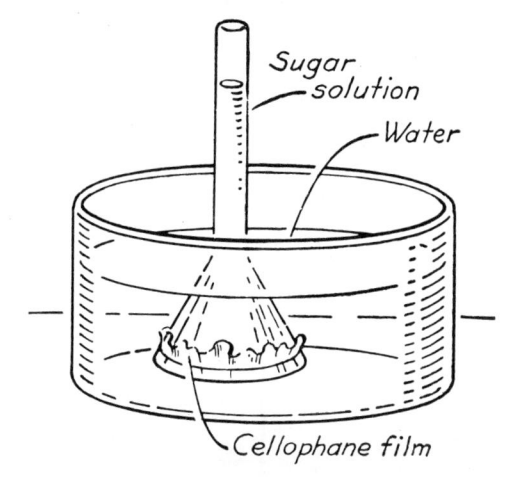

cannot move. Osmosis will always occur whenever pure solvent and solutions (or two solutions of different concentrations) are separated by a semipermeable membrane.

Before considering the application of this process, let us consider its cause. In Fig. 15–4 we have a highly magnified schematic diagram of the osmotic cell. The sugar molecules are shown as spheres too large to get through the pores in the membrane, whereas the water molecules are able to get through the membrane. As a result of their random motion, water molecules will pass through the holes in the membrane in both directions. But since the concentration of water molecules is greater on the pure water side (A), they will move from A to B, the solution side, more rapidly than from B to A. Hence, as a net process, pure water moves into the solution.

The pressure which osmosis can produce (if, for example, an attempt is made to prevent the rise of water in the tube by confining the solution in some way) is surprisingly great. A $1m$ solution of any solute (except an acid, base, or salt), when placed in contact with pure water through a semipermeable membrane, will develop an osmotic pressure of 24.4 atmospheres at 25°C. This is about 359 lb/in.^{2} or great enough to support a column of water 826 ft high.

Scientists believe that osmosis is at least partly responsible for the rise of water from the soil into a tree. Human blood consists essentially of a solution (blood plasma) in which are dispersed the red blood cells. The cells are covered with a semipermeable membrane. Therefore, the solution inside the cells must be in osmotic equilibrium with the plasma. Otherwise, either the cells would burst by osmosis of water into them or they would shrivel as a result of movement of water out of the cells. Normally the human body maintains this osmotic equilibrium without difficulty. However, if any fluid is injected into the blood stream, as sometimes is necessary in illness, it must have the same osmotic pressure as the normal blood plasma to avoid disastrous results.

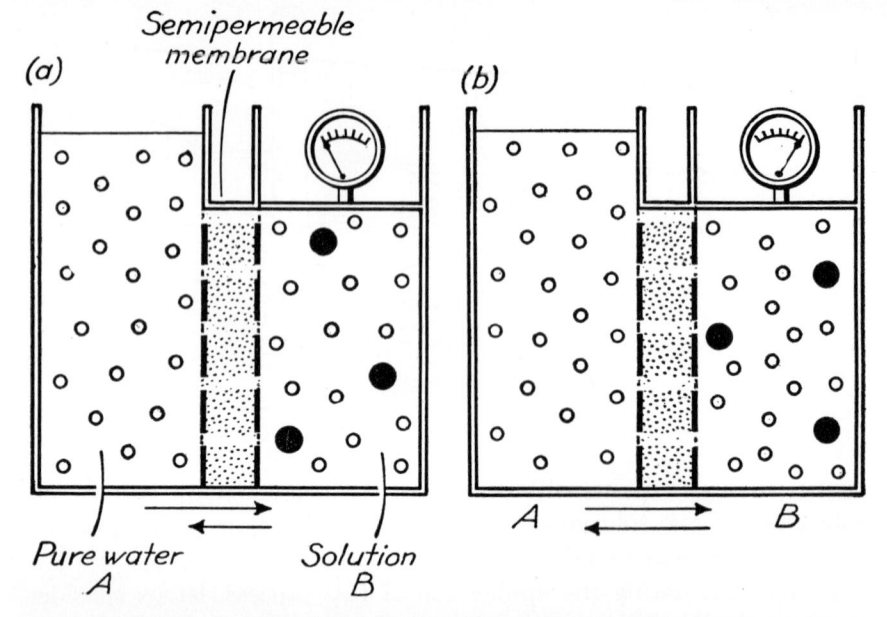

Fig. 15–4. Diagram of osmosis. A solution, B, and the pure solvent, A, are separated by a membrane through which solvent (but not solute) molecules can pass (a). Solvent molecules pass more rapidly from pure solvent to solution. The pressure on the solution necessary to keep its volume constant is known as its osmotic pressure (b).

The osmotic pressure, like freezing or boiling point, depends on the total concentration of solute particles rather than on the exact nature of the solution. Two solutions of the same osmotic pressure will have the same freezing point. The freezing point of human blood plasma is $-0.56°C$. Any solution having this freezing point will have the same osmotic pressure as human blood plasma. The freezing point (and hence the osmotic pressure) of the blood plasma is normally maintained constant by the elimination of excess salts in the urine. If, because of damage to the kidneys, the excess salts are not eliminated, the freezing point of the plasma may drop as low as $-1.04°C$.

When tissues are to be kept for any length of time outside the body for experimental work, they should be bathed in a solution having the same osmotic pressure as normal blood plasma. Such a solution is called a **physiological salt solution**.[1]

An osmotic "flower garden"

An interesting application of osmosis is involved in what has been called an *osmotic "flower garden."* Prepare a solution of sodium silicate (Na_2SiO_3) by diluting commercial water glass with about two volumes of water. Drop crystals of metal salts into this solution. In a few minutes you will see stalks start to "grow" from the crystals and

[1] If, as is common, a sodium chloride solution is used, the concentration should be about 0.9 percent.

quickly reach the surface of the solution. By selecting different-colored metal salts [such as ferric chloride ($FeCl_3$), manganous sulfate ($MnSO_4$), and copper sulfate ($CuSO_4$)], various colors can be produced.

These stalks form and grow as a result of osmosis through a film of insoluble metal silicate which forms around each crystal of a metal salt dropped into the solution. That is, where M is a metal,

$$MSO_4 + Na_2SiO_3 \rightarrow MSiO_3 \downarrow + Na_2SO_4$$

The silicates of all the metals except the alkalis (sodium, potassium, and others) are insoluble.

The precipitated film of metal silicate is permeable to water. The water moves through this film from the sodium silicate side, where the water is *more* concentrated. Eventually, this causes the film to rupture. Then, as the solution on the inside meets the sodium silicate, a new film precipitates and the same thing happens all over again. This is repeated until the "stem" reaches the surface of the solution.

KEY WORDS

antifreeze	freezing-point depression	osmosis
boiling-point increase	molality (m)	physiological salt
concentration	molarity (M)	solution

HIGHLIGHTS

The **concentration** of a solution may be expressed in a number of ways. **Molarity** (moles per liter of solution) is used when it is advantageous to measure by volume. **Molality** (moles per 1000 g of solvent) is used when it is advantageous to measure by weight.

A nonvolatile solute added to a pure solvent raises the boiling point and any solute depresses the freezing point of the solvent. A $1m$ water solution of sugar, for example, has a boiling point of 100.51°C. A $1m$ water solution of sugar (or any solute except acids, bases, or salts) has a freezing point of −1.86°C. The rise of the boiling point and the depression of the freezing point are directly proportional to the molality. It is therefore possible to calculate the boiling point or freezing point of a solution from its concentration. Or from the boiling point or freezing point of a solution, it is possible to determine the molecular weight of the solute.

Osmosis relates to the passage of a solvent through a semipermeable membrane. It is one of the important factors in the life processes of all plants and animals.

QUESTIONS

1. List three ways in which the concentrations of solutions may be expressed.
2. Define a 1m solution.
3. Define a 1M solution. State how a 1M solution differs from a 1m solution.
4. Explain in words how you would prepare a 0.5m solution of glucose ($C_6H_{12}O_6$).
5. How many grams of glycerin ($C_3H_8O_3$) would you add to 1000 g of water in preparing a 2m solution?
6. What would be (a) the boiling point and (b) the freezing point of the solutions mentioned in questions 4 and 5?
7. Methyl alcohol boils at 65°C. Will a solution of methyl alcohol have a boiling point above that of pure water? How will the freezing point of a methyl alcohol solution compare with that of pure water?
8. How much ethyl alcohol (C_2H_5OH) would you add to 2000 g of water in order to form a solution having a freezing point of $-5°C$?
9. How much glycerin ($C_3H_8O_3$) would you add to 2000 g of water in order to form a solution having a freezing point of $-5°C$?
10. Why is sugar unsatisfactory as an automobile radiator antifreeze?
11. Do you think kerosene would make a satisfactory automobile radiator antifreeze? How about sodium chloride? Explain.
12. In this chapter two methods for measuring molecular weights have been given. Explain the basis of each method.
13. Describe a setup in which you would expect osmosis to occur. In which direction will the solvent move? Explain.
14. Describe one biological system in which osmosis is involved.

Suggested Projects for Unit Four

1. It has been stated that ground glass will change phenolphthalein from colorless to red. Find out whether pyrex will have the same effect.
2. Find out what materials are used as corrosion inhibitors in connection with automobile antifreeze solutions.
3. Calculate the quantity of ethylene glycol necessary to protect a 4-gal automobile radiator to 0°F.
4. Visit the waterworks of your city and then write an account of what you have learned.

UNIT FIVE: Atomic Structure and Nuclear Energy

CHAPTER 16

the periodic table

The science of chemistry is important today largely because of its vast number of practical applications which greatly influence our daily lives. These applications always involve specific chemical and physical properties of the elements and their compounds. You have already learned about a few of these specific chemical and physical properties and their applications.

Fundamentally chemical theory is important because it helps you to understand more clearly the specific facts and eventually to predict new, and possibly useful, additional facts. Therefore if you are to acquire a useful working knowledge of chemistry, you must learn many facts about each of the important elements. In doing this, you will find the periodic table a very useful tool. It is like a rack upon which you can hang practically all the important facts about the elements as you learn them. You can then withdraw these facts as you need them. You will do well to learn about the periodic table and the relationships it contains for this reason and because in the development of our knowledge of the structure of the atom it played a leading role. The importance of the periodic table justifies the description which has been given it as "The Great Classification."

The history of the periodic table

The periodic table was developed about the time of the War between the States. This was about half a century after Dalton's atomic theory had been presented and widely, if not universally, accepted. By 1860 the atomic weights of most of the known elements had been accurately determined. Enough was known about the chemistry of many of the elements to suggest that certain elements very closely resemble others. This is well illustrated by the group called the *halogen family*, which includes the elements fluorine, chlorine, bromine, and iodine. In valence and in chemical properties these elements are remarkably alike. The same is true for other groups of elements.

In 1862 **de Chancourtois** proposed plotting the elements by atomic weight on a helical curve, such that corresponding points differed by 16, the atomic weight of oxygen. This brought the elements which were known to resemble each other closely into corresponding positions on the curve. The next year an Englishman named **Newlands** pointed out that if the elements are written down in order of increasing atomic weight, every eighth element is similar in properties. In those days the rare gases (helium, neon, and so on) were unknown and Newlands' scheme started out as follows:

Element:	Li	Be	B	C	N	O	F
Approximate atomic weight:	7	9	11	12	14	16	19
Element:	Na	Mg	Al	Si	P	S	Cl
Approximate atomic weight:	23	24	27	28	31	32	35
Element:	K	Ca					
Approximate atomic weight:	39	40					

(The lightest element, hydrogen, is omitted from this scheme because its properties are unique.)

So far as these elements go, the scheme does work. Every eighth element is similar in valence and in types of compounds formed. However, when carried beyond calcium, the Newlands scheme does not work so well. In trying to explain his scheme, Newlands drew an analogy between his scheme and the musical scale in which every eighth note is similar. He even gave his scheme the name **law of octaves.**

In view of what we know today, it seems strange that his colleagues in the London Chemical Society did not accept Newlands' suggestion with enthusiasm. Far from it! They greeted it with scorn and ridicule —one member, in sarcastic vein, rose to ask Newlands if he had tried arranging the elements alphabetically. The Society refused to publish his paper. Newlands was not the first prophet without honor, nor the last. Disheartened, he retired to the relative obscurity of the sugar industry. Nevertheless in 1882, after Mendeléeff had established the periodic table, the Royal Society awarded Newlands the Davy medal, one of the highest honors it could bestow, for his discovery of the periodicity of the elements.

Dmitri Ivanovich Mendeléeff, the father of the periodic table, is perhaps the greatest physical scientist Russia has so far produced. On the one hundredth anniversary of his birth a Russian stamp was issued having a background of the periodic table over which a portrait of Mendeléeff was superimposed. (*Journal of Chemical Education*)

The periodic table and Mendeléeff

In 1869 the Russian chemist **Dmitri Ivanovich Mendeléeff** published the first of a series of papers that soon led to the establishment and wide acceptance of his **periodic table.** The basis of his table was the same as that of Newlands, namely, that the properties of the elements are related to their atomic weights. Therefore, when the elements are written down in order of increasing atomic weight, there is a *periodic recurrence of elements with similar chemical properties.* Mendeléeff succeeded where Newlands had failed for several reasons: (1) because of certain differences in detail of arrangement, which you will read about in the next paragraph; (2) because his ideas were presented clearly, forcefully, and logically; and (3) because he was able to predict the existence and properties of three elements unknown at that time. Within a few years, these elements were discovered and their properties were found to be very nearly what Mendeléeff had predicted. You can see this in Table 16–1.

TABLE 16–1. Predicted and actual properties of element number 32

Property	Ekasilicon, predicted by Mendeléeff in 1871	Germanium, discovered by Winkler in 1886
Atomic weight	72	72.6
Density, g/cm^3	5.5	5.47
Formula for oxide	EsO$_2$	GeO$_2$
Formula for chloride	EsCl$_4$	GeCl$_4$
Boiling point of chloride	Below 100°C	86°C

The periodic table

Figure 16–1 shows a modern form of the periodic table, for the most part arranged as Mendeléeff proposed. He proposed that the elements be written down in order of increasing atomic weight. However, instead of forcing the elements into seven groups as Newlands had done, he said, in effect: Write the elements down in a horizontal line until there is a recurrence of elements having similar properties. We find actually that the different horizontal lines, known as **periods,** contain different numbers of elements. Mendeléeff realized that a missing (undiscovered) element might throw the rest of the series out of order unless a vacant space was allowed for it. He therefore provided vacant spaces wherever it seemed necessary to get good agreement between elements in the same vertical groups. It was in this way that he was able to predict the existence of elements unknown at that time.

The modern periodic table shown in Fig. 16–1 shows all the elements now known, not just those known to Mendeléeff. Hydrogen and helium constitute Period 1. Period 2 begins with the next element, lithium, and includes eight elements, ending with neon. The next element is sodium, which closely resembles lithium. It is placed under lithium to start Period 3. The other elements in Period 3 resemble those in Period 2, which they are directly below. Period 3 also contains eight elements.

Period 4, which starts with potassium, really contains 18 (count them) elements before it finally ends with krypton (atomic number 36). This long period of 18 elements is divided into two **subperiods.** Some of these elements in Period 4 have no counterparts in the preceding periods, although, as you can see from the table, eight of these elements correspond closely to the eight elements in Period 3.

Period 5, which starts with rubidium and ends with xenon, also contains 18 elements and is treated exactly as Period 4 above. Each of the elements in Period 5 closely resembles the corresponding element in Period 4. Also, eight of the elements in Period 5 closely resemble the corresponding elements in Periods 2 and 3.

Period 6 shows 18 elements just as do Periods 4 and 5. In addition, it has 14 more elements lying between lanthanum, atomic number 57, and hafnium, atomic number 72. These elements are a group known as the **lanthanide series** or the **rare earths,** and they are placed in a footnote at the bottom of the table. It would be awkward to place them in the table, since they are all very nearly identical in chemical properties and therefore should all occupy the same space in the table —the one space between barium and hafnium.

Period 7 is unfinished and ends abruptly (at present) with the element with atomic number 102, nobelium. It used to be thought that uranium was the heaviest element capable of existence, but 10 heavier ones are now known. These elements—neptunium, plutonium, americium, curium, berkelium, californium, einsteinium, fermium, mendelevium, and nobelium—are referred to as the **transuranium elements,** and some of them are closely related to the development of the atomic bomb and nuclear energy. We shall learn more about them later. There is no reason to assume that nobelium is the heaviest element capable of existence. Even before this book is in print a heavier element may be discovered. The elements starting with actinium, atomic number 89, and running through to nobelium are known as the **actinide series** because they resemble each other in much the same way as do the members of the lanthanide series of Period 6.

Valence and the periodic table

The valence *toward oxygen* (and other nonmetals except hydrogen) of every element in the same vertical **group** is the same. These principal valences are as follows:

Group	Valence toward oxygen	Group	Valence toward oxygen
Zero	0	IV	4
I	1	V	5
II	2	VI	6
III	3	VII	7

Therefore, the formula for an oxide of any element in Group I should be R_2O, where R is the element in question. Similarly elements of Group II have oxide formulas of the type RO, and so on. The type formulas for the oxides are shown at the tops of the respective columns in the periodic table. They are as follows:

Group	Type formula	Group	Type formula
Zero	No compounds	IV	RO_2
I	R_2O	V	R_2O_5
II	RO	VI	RO_3
III	R_2O_3	VII	R_2O_7

Note that the valence toward oxygen is the same as the number of the group in which the element is found.

THE PERIODIC TABLE

Hydride / Oxide	Ia RH R_2O	IIa RH_2 RO	IIIa R_2O_3	IVa RO_2	Va R_2O_5	VIa RO_3	VIIa R_2O_7	VIII RO_4

ATOMIC NUMBERS ABOVE SYMBOLS

PERIODS

Period	Ia	IIa	IIIa	IVa	Va	VIa	VIIa	VIII		
1	1 H 1.0080									
2	3 Li 6.940	4 Be 9.013								
3	11 Na 22.991	12 Mg 24.32								
4	19 K 39.100	20 Ca 40.08	21 Sc 44.96	22 Ti 47.90	23 V 50.95	24 Cr 52.01	25 Mn 54.94	26 Fe 55.85	27 Co 58.94	28 Ni 58.71
5	37 Rb 85.48	38 Sr 87.63	39 Y 88.92	40 Zr 91.22	41 Nb 92.91	42 Mo 95.95	43 Tc [99]	44 Ru 101.1	45 Rh 102.91	46 Pd 106.7
6	55 Cs 132.91	56 Ba 137.36	57 La 138.92	58* to 71	72 Hf 178.58	73 Ta 180.95	74 W 183.86	75 Re 186.22	76 Os 190.2	77 Ir 192.2	78 Pt 195.0
7	87 Fr [223]	88 Ra 226.05	89 Ac 227	90† to 103						

RARE EARTH

	58 Ce 140.13	59 Pr 140.92	60 Nd 144.27	61 Pm [145]
*Group IIIa Lanthanide Series				
†Group IIIa Actinide Series	90 Th 232.05	91 Pa 231	92 U 238.07	93 Np [237]

Fig. 16–1. A modern form of

OF THE ELEMENTS

GROUPS

Ib	IIb	IIIb	IVb	Vb	VIb	VIIb	0	Electronic Structure of Inert Gases
HR R_2O	H_2R RO	H_3R R_2O_3	H_4R RO_2	H_3R R_2O_5	H_2R RO_3	HR R_2O_7	Inert Gases	

ATOMIC WEIGHTS
BELOW SYMBOLS

							2 He 4.003	2
		5 B 10.82	6 C 12.011	7 N 14.008	8 O 16.0000	9 F 19.00	10 Ne 20.183	2 8
		13 Al 26.98	14 Si 28.06	15 P 30.975	16 S 32.066	17 Cl 35.457	18 A 39.944	2 8 8
29 Cu 63.54	30 Zn 65.38	31 Ga 69.72	32 Ge 72.60	33 As 74.91	34 Se 78.96	35 Br 79.916	36 Kr 83.80	2 8 18 8
47 Ag 107.880	48 Cd 112.41	49 In 114.82	50 Sn 118.70	51 Sb 121.76	52 Te 127.61	53 I 126.92	54 Xe 131.30	2 8 18 18 8
79 Au 197.0	80 Hg 200.61	81 Tl 204.39	82 Pb 207.21	83 Bi 209.00	84 Po 210	85 At [210]	86 Rn 222	2 8 18 32 18 8

ELEMENTS

62 Sm 150.35	63 Eu 152.0	64 Gd 157.26	65 Tb 158.93	66 Dy 162.51	67 Ho 164.94	68 Er 167.27	69 Tm 168.94	70 Yb 173.04	71 Lu 174.99
94 Pu [242]	95 Am [243]	96 Cm [245]	97 Bk [249]	98 Cf [249]	99 E [254]	100 Fm [252]	101 Mv [256]	102 No [257]	103

Periodic table of the elements.

ELECTRONS IN INERT GAS ATOMIC STRUCTURE

It has been found that the valence of an element toward metals and also toward hydrogen is not always the same as its valence toward oxygen. The valence toward hydrogen and metals and the type formula of the hydrogen compounds are as follows:

Group	Valence	Type formula	Group	Valence	Type formula
Zero	0	No compounds	IV	4	RH_4
I	1	RH	V	3	RH_3
II	2	RH_2	VI	2	RH_2
III	3	RH_3	VII	1	RH

These type formulas also are located at the head of the "Group" columns in the periodic table.

You will notice that the valence toward hydrogen and metals starts with zero, increases by steps to 4, and then decreases again by steps to 1.

In using these valences and type formulas, three things must be kept in mind:

1. Valence does not guarantee that a certain compound will form. If it does form, however, its formula can be predicted with the help of the chart.

2. Some elements have variable valence. In this case the periodic chart obviously gives only one of the valences.

3. The chart does not give the valences of radicals, such as nitrate $(NO_3)^-$ and sulfate $(SO_4)^=$.

Metals and nonmetals and the periodic table

Within any one group, the metallic properties (see Chap. 43, page 540) become more pronounced as the atomic weight increases. That is, as you go down in any one group, the metallic properties of the elements become more pronounced. You can see this illustrated clearly by Group IV*b*, which starts with carbon, a nonmetal, and ends with lead, a metallic element. Of course, the most nonmetallic elements are at the tops of the groups.

Some of the groups contain only metals, for example, Group I. Group II also contains only metals, but the metallic properties of these elements are somewhat less pronounced than those of Group I. In Group III*b* the metallic properties are still less pronounced, and the first member of the series, boron, is classed as a nonmetal. Thus the most metallic elements are in Group I, and as you move across the table from left to right, the elements you find become less metallic and more nonmetallic. The most typically nonmetallic elements are found in Group VII*b*, and they are the halogens. Considering both of these facts about the arrangement of the periodic table, you can see that the most typical metals are found in the lower left-hand corner of the table, and the most typical nonmetals are found in the upper right-hand corner.

The subgroups

You have seen that the periods containing 18, or more, elements are divided into two subperiods. Connecting each of these two subperiods, there are three elements which are all placed in Group VIII. These triads are known as **transition elements.** Thus in Period 4, the elements iron, cobalt, and nickel are so placed in Group VIII. Similarly the transition elements in Period 5 are ruthenium, rhodium, and palladium; and in Period 6 osmium, iridium, and platinum.

Chemically all the transition elements show variable valence. Some of them do, as you would expect from their position in the table, show a valence toward oxygen of eight. For example, OsO_4 is well known. On the whole, however, these nine elements form compounds in which their valence ranges between two and four. You will learn later the real reason, in terms of the electronic structure of the elements, why these groups of three elements fall in the same group in the periodic table. For the present, you can see that it is necessary that they all be in Group VIII, in that the elements which follow fall into their proper groups.

It is useful to keep in mind that each group is subdivided into subgroups, such as (in Group I) Subgroup I*a* and Subgroup I*b*. This division is indicated in the table. **Within a subgroup, the similarity of the elements is very close.** Generally the chief relationship between the two subgroups within a group is a common valence. This is well illustrated again by manganese (Subgroup VII*a*) and chlorine (Subgroup VII*b*). Whereas manganese is a pinkish, hard metal, chlorine is a greenish gas; but both may show a valence of 7 as in the compounds

$KClO_4$ potassium perchlorate
$KMnO_4$ potassium permanganate

Similarly, sulfur (Group VI*b*), a typical nonmetal, and chromium (Group VI*a*) a hard silvery-white metal both form compounds with oxygen in which they show a valence of 6.

SO_3 sulfur trioxide K_2SO_4 potassium sulfate
CrO_3 chromium trioxide K_2CrO_4 potassium chromate

However, here as in other such cases, the chief point of similarity between such elements is a common valence.

The prediction of new elements

You can understand the use of the periodic table in the prediction of new elements and their properties from the illustration with gallium, atomic number 31, and germanium, atomic number 32. At the time Mendeléeff established the table, these elements were unknown. The next *known* element heavier than zinc was arsenic. But arsenic clearly belonged in Group V*b* because it has a valence of 5 toward oxygen (As_2O_5) and because it clearly resembles phosphorus. Similarly the next two elements, selenium (which resembles sulfur) and bromine (a halogen) would be out of place unless two spaces were left between zinc and arsenic. Mendeléeff reasoned that the unknown element with atomic number 31 should resemble aluminum, which it would lie beneath, but that its properties should be sort of a cross between those of aluminum and those of indium. From this he predicted the existence and properties of the element with atomic number 31, calling it eka-aluminum. As expected, the Frenchman Lecoq de Boisbaudran, seeking this new element, discovered it in 1875 in an ore of zinc from the Pyrenees. He named it *gallium* after his native land. Its properties were strikingly similar to those predicted by Mendeléeff. Eleven years later, in 1886, a German named Winkler discovered element number 32 in a tin ore. Not to be outdone by de Boisbaudran, Winkler named it *germanium* after *his* native land. The accuracy with which Mendeléeff had predicted the properties of germanium is shown in Table 16–1.

At the present time the periodic table shows that all the spaces up to atomic number 102 are filled. Therefore, there are no undiscovered elements with numbers less than 102. The periodic table does not tell us what elements, if any, with atomic weights greater than that shown for nobelium, atomic number 102, may be capable of existing.

Defects of the table

Useful and important as it was, Mendeléeff's original table had one serious defect. It was that, in order to get certain elements into their proper positions, he found it necessary to reverse them according to the order of their atomic weights. You can see that the atomic weight of potassium is 39.096, which is less than that of argon, 39.944. Yet argon obviously belongs under neon, since both are inert gases; and potassium belongs under sodium. In the same way, cobalt and nickel, and also iodine and tellurium, are reversed in so far as atomic weights are concerned. The reason for these reversals is now easy to understand in terms of atomic structure and isotopes, and you will learn about it in a later chapter. Scientists no longer consider these reversals a defect.

There is another defect of the periodic table which exists even today. The table tends to emphasize one valence for each of the elements. In the cases of some of the elements, like the alkalis, this is not a problem, since these elements have only one valence. But all the elements lying near the middle of a long series show two or more valences and, of course, the table gives only one of these. You will have to learn the other valences for some of these elements as you study the elements.

The significance of the periodic table

Many useful classifications can be found in the table. You have read about only a few of the basic ones so far. The real importance of the periodic system is that it furnishes a comprehensive classification of the elements. Also, the regularities uncovered by Mendeléeff aided greatly in the development of our present knowledge of the structure of the atom.

KEY WORDS

actinide series	Mendeléeff	subgroup
de Chancourtois	Newlands	subperiod
group	period	transition elements
lanthanide series	periodic table	transuranium elements
law of octaves	rare-earth series	

HIGHLIGHTS

In 1869 **Mendeléeff,** a Russian chemist, arranged the chemical elements in the order of their atomic weights. Other chemists had made somewhat similar attempts, but Mendeléeff succeeded in attracting almost world-wide attention to the idea. The basis of his scheme is the fact that there appears to be a distinct periodicity of properties in the arrangement of the elements according to atomic weight. Mendeléeff's arrangement is in the form of a table which has become a sort of "rack" or "filing cabinet" for facts about the elements.

In the table the vertical columns are spoken of as **groups,** or *families*, whereas the horizontal rows are called **periods.** Within any group, the elements nearer the bottom are more metallic than those above. Within a period, the elements on the left are more metallic.

The **periodic table** is used in many ways. It gives a basis, for example, for writing many formulas.

Mendeléeff predicted the existence of certain elements unknown at the time. Later discoveries justified his predictions.

QUESTIONS

1. Using the periodic table, write probable formulas for the oxides of sulfur and chromium. The following acids are known: H_2SO_4 and H_2CrO_4. What are their anhydrides? Compare these with your answer to the first question.
2. Write the probable formulas for the chlorides of beryllium, magnesium, and cadmium.
3. What would you expect to be the formula for silver oxide? For gallium oxide?
4. What would you expect to be the formulas for the hydrogen compounds of silicon, phosphorus, sulfur, and chlorine?
5. From its position in the periodic table, would you expect gallium to be a metal or a nonmetal? Why?
6. What formula would be expected for a compound between hydrogen and boron? Between hydrogen and arsenic?
7. Write the formula for the chloride and oxide of silicon.
8. Write the probable formula for the compound between sulfur and zinc. Between sulfur and aluminum. Does the periodic table predict that sulfur and aluminum will unite?
9. Would you expect zirconium to resemble tin or titanium more closely? Why?
10. What is meant by the term *lanthanide* (or *rare-earth*) series?

CHAPTER 17

radioactivity

We are now ready to inquire into questions such as: What really happens when two elements combine? What forces hold the atoms together in chemical compounds? What is the reason for the regularity in chemical properties found in the periodic table? Of what is the atom made? The answers to these questions have slowly been accumulating since the start of the twentieth century and are among the most important discoveries of all times. They already have influenced, and are continuing to influence, the entire course of history, since these discoveries led in the early 1940s to the development of the atomic bomb. Important as it is, the atom bomb is only one of many significant developments that have come out of this field of research.

In some cases the evidence upon which our answers to the above questions are based is indirect and comes from many different sources. Consequently the evidence for the theories will not always be given.

Early ideas of the structure of matter

Ever since the earliest days of recorded history, man has speculated about the ultimate nature of matter. This speculation from the early days down to our present century has involved the question: What is the ultimate structure of matter? That is, if a sample of matter could be magnified without limit, would it be found to be continuous, as a slab of butter appears to be to the naked eye? Or would it be found to be made up of some tiny building blocks? If so, what are these building blocks and what are they like? Is there some one or a few parent materials of which all other materials are built up? The early Greeks believed at different times that the parent materials were fire, earth, air, and water. Doubtless this belief was influential in the rise of alchemy, for if you accept such a proposition, you will also believe that lead—or, for that matter, anything else—could be changed into gold. These concepts existed in one form or another for centuries. But you have seen that in 1805 Dalton rejected these notions and said that there were (as we know them today) 102 different parent materials or types of atoms and that the atom was the smallest possible particle since (according to Dalton's theory) it could not be divided. After it became established, Dalton's theory was widely accepted until the discovery of radioactivity in 1896. This discovery started a revolution in the thinking about the structure of the atom which is not complete even yet. Among many other things this discovery has led to the development of atomic energy and to all that we know about the real nature of reactions and the forces which hold compounds together.

The discovery of radioactivity

You may have read that the discovery of radioactivity was an accident. Perhaps it was. If so, only trained scientists could have been prepared to take advantage of the accidental observations which led to its discovery. In any case it happened in this way: In 1896 a Frenchman, Henri Becquerel, was conducting experiments with crystals of uranium compounds. One day he placed a crystal of potassium uranyl sulfate, $K_2UO_2(SO_4)_2 \cdot 2H_2O$, in a laboratory drawer on top of a photographic plate which was wrapped in the usual black paper to prevent its being damaged by light (see Fig. 17–1). After 24 hr the plate was developed in the usual way. Usually when a plate which has not been exposed to light is developed, it comes out perfectly clear and transparent. However, when Becquerel developed his plate, an image of the crystal appeared on it! The crystal had given off some mysterious rays which were able to penetrate the black paper in which the plate had been wrapped and which had the same effect on the photographic plate as visible light. This behavior soon was known as **radioactivity,** a term suggested by the fact that radiant energy is given off.

It is very easy to duplicate Becquerel's experiment. Thorium nitrate produces the same effect, but more rapidly than uranium. If you dip a square of surgical gauze into a solution of thorium nitrate and then dry it, the gauze becomes impregnated with crystals of this salt, which is radioactive. Then place such a gauze over a black envelope contain-

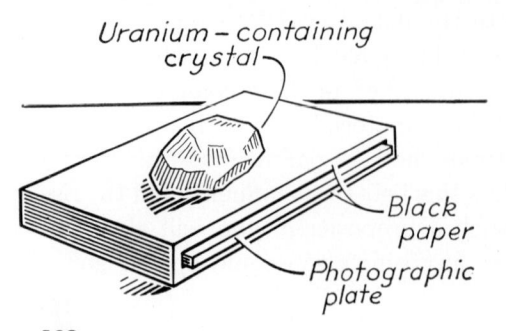

Fig. 17–1. Sketch of Becquerel's experiment. The uranium-containing crystal gives off rays that are able to penetrate the black paper surrounding the photographic plate. These rays affect the plate like visible light.

Madame Curie at work in her laboratory. Madame Curie and her husband Pierre discovered polonium and radium in 1898. These discoveries led to the establishment of the fact that atoms are made up of smaller particles. Today the results of these discoveries have been used to relieve much human suffering. (*Journal of Chemical Education*)

ing photographic film or printing paper and allow it to remain there for several days. When you develop the film you will find on it a clear image of the surgical gauze.

Becquerel quickly showed that other uranium compounds and also metallic uranium possessed this same property.

About this time a young Polish girl named Maria Sklodowska, better known to the world as **Madame Curie,** was a graduate student at the University of the Sorbonne in Paris. She was working for the advanced degree of Doctor of Science. In those days, as today, one of the requirements for earning such a degree was that the candidate must carry out some original research. At just about the time that Becquerel, who also was at the Sorbonne, discovered the peculiar properties mentioned above, Madame Curie was looking for a subject for her research work. By a happy coincidence she selected as her topic the problem of comparing the intensities of this peculiar radiation when it was produced from various uranium-containing substances.

The principle of the method by which she measured these radiation intensities is simple. It depends upon the fact that, if a radioactive material is brought near a charged gold leaf **electroscope,** the leaves will collapse. An electroscope consists of a thin metal foil suspended from a metal support inside a glass-walled box (Fig. 17–2). When a negatively charged object, such as a rubber rod which has been rubbed with fur, is brought into contact with the metal support, the negative charge spreads over the leaves of the electroscope. This causes the leaves to separate, since like charges repel each other. This is one of the ways in which an electroscope may be charged. When a sample of uranium or other radioactive material is brought near these charged

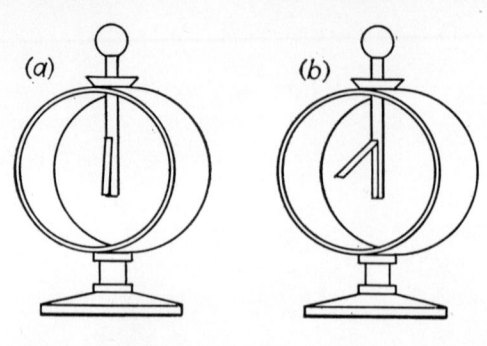

Fig. 17-2. A gold leaf electroscope uncharged (a) and charged (b).

leaves, the leaves slowly collapse. Evidently the radiations produced allow the charge to leak off. Madame Curie compared the intensity of the radiations from various uranium-containing substances by measuring the length of time required for each of the substances to discharge the electroscope. She obtained some very peculiar results.

Typical results are given in Table 17-1.

TABLE 17-1. Comparative radioactivity of various substances

Uranyl sulfate [(UO$_2$)SO$_4 \cdot$ 3H$_2$O]	1.0
Uranium metal	3.3
Carnotite (a complex uranium ore)	8.9
Pitchblende (a complex uranium ore)	10.0

The results in Table 17-1 are relative only. That is, taking the intensity of a certain weight of uranyl sulfate as 1, the intensity from the same weight sample of uranium metal is 3.3 times as great, and so on. The lesser intensity from the uranyl sulfate than from the uranium metal might be explained by the fact that the radiation was due to the uranium atoms and their concentration is less in a uranium compound than in the pure metal. **But the intensity from both uranium ores was several times greater than from pure uranium!** Since both the minerals contain only a small percentage of uranium, Madame Curie reasoned that they must contain some element which is much more active in giving off these radiations than is uranium. Moreover, since these ores had been analyzed by ordinary methods many times before and no such element had been found in them, she reasoned that this element must be present in the ores in only very small quantities.

Madame Curie and her husband Pierre started the search for this element, using a ton of pitchblende donated by the Bohemian government. The procedure employed to find the unknown element is too complicated to be given here. Essentially it involved separating the various families of elements as they exist in the periodic table from the ore and testing each group for radioactivity. In July, 1898, the Curies discovered the element with atomic number 84, which they named

polonium in honor of Madame Curie's native country. From the ton of ore, less than 2/10,000 of 1 g of polonium was obtained. It was found to be intensely radioactive. In December, 1898, the Curies announced the discovery of a second new radioactive element which closely resembled barium in chemical properties. They named it **radium** and soon found that it occupied position number 88 directly under barium in the periodic table. From the original ton of ore, they obtained about 0.2 g of radium as radium bromide ($RaBr_2$).

What are some of the properties of radioactive elements?

Today we know many radioactive elements. Some of these are found in nature, such as polonium, radium, uranium, and thorium. Those found in nature are referred to as naturally radioactive. In addition, scientists have learned how to make radioactive forms of almost all the elements which are not normally radioactive in nature. For example, radioactive forms of carbon and nitrogen can be made. These man-made radioactive elements are said to be *artificially radioactive*.

Any radioactive element has two sets of properties:

1. Its characteristic chemical properties, which are independent of the fact that it is radioactive. For example, radium is a metallic element chemically very similar to barium. It has a valence of 2, and forms compounds such as radium bromide, $RaBr_2$ and radium hydroxide, $Ra(OH)_2$. The chemical properties of an artificially radioactive element are exactly the same as those of the natural forms of that element which are not radioactive. For example, radioactive carbon, which is now made in Oak Ridge, Tenn., is identical in its chemical reactions with ordinary carbon.

2. Those properties due to the radioactivity of the element. We shall learn of these in the next paragraph. Properties due to radioactivity are all in addition to, and have no influence on, the chemical properties of the elements.

What are some of the characteristics of radioactivity?

You have already learned one characteristic of radioactivity, namely, that the radiations produced can penetrate black paper which does not transmit light. These radiations can also penetrate metals, particularly those with low atomic weights.

Another characteristic is the effect on photographic film. You have seen that the radiations have the same effect on a photographic film that ordinary light rays have, although the radiations cannot be seen directly by the eye. A photographic film is therefore useful in detecting these radiations and has been used for this purpose since the discovery of radioactivity (see Fig. 17–3).

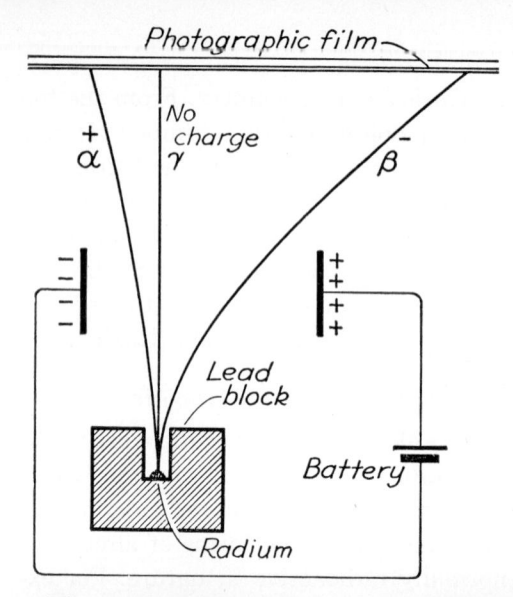

Fig. 17-3. An experiment to demonstrate the three types of rays emitted by radium. By using electrically charged plates to deflect the course of rays bearing a charge, it is possible to separate α rays, which are positively charged; β rays, which are negatively charged; and γ rays, or x rays, which bear no charge.

The rays emitted from radioactive materials are of three kinds. This was shown by one of the first experiments conducted after the discovery of radium. It is illustrated in Fig. 17-3.

A hole is drilled in the end of a lead block. Into the hole is placed a sample of radium. The radium is, of course, giving off its rays in all directions, as a burning match gives off light rays. However, since those rays that strike the lead are absorbed, only a thin beam of the rays is produced. On each side of the beam a metal plate is placed. These plates are connected to a battery so that one of them is charged positively and the other negatively. Beyond the plates is placed a photographic film which, on development, will tell where the rays strike it. The film shows three types of rays. These are called:

1. α rays. The α (pronounced alpha) rays are identical with helium atoms carrying two positive charges. That is, they are really charged helium atoms (He^{++}) shot off from the radium. Because of their charge, the α rays are deflected toward the negatively charged plate and strike the film on the side closer to the negative plate.

2. β rays. The β (pronounced beta) rays are negatively charged particles of matter having a mass of about 1/1840 the mass of a hydrogen atom. They are *electrons* identical with those which move through a copper wire when an electric current is flowing through it. It has been shown that they are present in all atoms. Being negatively charged and low in mass, the β rays are deflected toward the positive plate and strike the film closer to the side near that plate.

3. γ rays. The γ (pronounced gamma) rays are more like light rays. That is, they are not particles of matter and are not electrically charged. Hence they shoot straight through, undeflected by the charged plates. γ rays are the same as **x rays.**

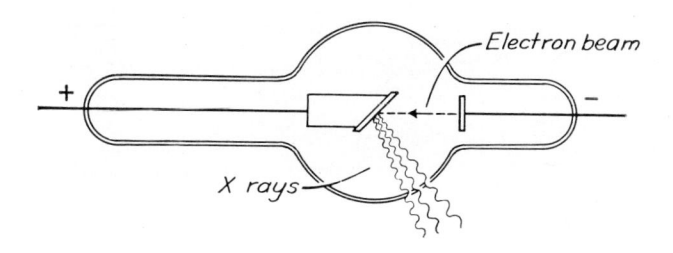

Fig. 17-4. An x-ray tube.

X rays, because of their penetrating power, are commonly used by physicians to photograph broken bones or internal organs of the body. They were discovered in 1895 by the German Roentgen. They may be produced by driving a stream of electrons at high speed across an evacuated tube and causing the electrons to strike a metal target. When the electrons strike the target, they cause it to emit x rays in much the same way as pebbles dropped into a quiet pool send off water waves. In the analogy, the pebbles correspond to electrons, the water to the target, and the waves to the x rays (Fig. 17-4).

X rays are energy waves, very much like light waves except of much shorter wave length. Their wave length is too short for the human eye to "see" them. But they can be photographed, and they can also be detected by other means. One of the methods of detection is the discharge of a gold leaf electroscope similar to Madame Curie's.

Another important characteristic of radioactivity is its physiological effect. The radiations from radioactive elements, as well as x rays, have the ability to destroy living cells because of complex chemical changes which they produce on striking a cell. Hence excessive dosages of radiation cause death in man or other organisms. Smaller doses have been shown to produce mutations[1] in seeds of plants and also in certain insects. So far as is known now, no mutations have been observed in man from this cause. All the information at present available fails to indicate any mutations in human beings exposed to either of the bombs used against Japan in 1945. However, this does not prove that such mutations may not yet appear in future generations of offspring of the individuals exposed to the atom bomb blasts in Japan.

The danger of overexposure to radiation is a real hazard in working with radioactive elements. Much of the experimental work is done by remote control to protect the life of the experimenter.

How do we explain radioactivity?

As a result of the experiment described on page 186 and others which will not be treated in this book, it is possible to make the following explanation for the radioactivity of radium.

An atom of radium is made up, among other things, of electrons and

---

[1] A mutation is a variation in the offspring from some of the characteristics of its parents, which variation is transmissible to future generations.

Monitoring badges are used to protect workers from radiation hazards. These badges contain photographic film. Periodically the film is developed. If any darkening is observed on the developed film, it indicates the wearer has been exposed to radiation. (Westcott, Oak Ridge National Laboratory)

α particles. The atom of radium is unstable and gives off an α particle. In so doing, the radium atom ceases to be a radium atom and becomes instead an atom of the inert gas, **radon** (element with atomic number 86). This atom of radon also is unstable (radioactive) and gives off another α particle, thereby becoming a radioactive atom of polonium (element with atomic number 84), which in turn gives off an α particle and is changed into a radioactive form of lead (element with atomic number 82). This radioactive lead disintegrates by giving off an electron, thereby becoming another element. The process ends only when eventually one of the steps leads to the formation of a type of lead atom which is stable.

It is as though a large office building built of gray stone blocks and brick suddenly ejected a block of stone (an α particle), the remaining blocks rearranging themselves to form an apartment house. The apartment house ejects another stone block, resulting in the formation of a theater. This in turn, by ejecting a brick (electron), becomes a store. The process continues through various stages until a railroad station (lead) is formed which is stable. That is,

Radium → He^{++} + Radon
  ↳ He^{++} + Polonium
    ↳ He^{++} + Lead
      ↳ electron + Bismuth
        ↳ and so on leading eventually to a stable form of lead

Office building → stone block + apartment house
　　　　　　　　　↳ block + theater
　　　　　　　　　　　↳ brick + store
　　　　　　　　　　　　　↳
　　　　　　　　　　　　　　↳ and so on
　　　　　　　　　　　　　　　railroad station

Now suppose we start with 1000 office buildings and suppose that during the first second 1 percent of them change themselves into apartment houses. During the second second, two processes will be occurring: 1 percent of the remaining office buildings will be changing into apartment houses and a certain percentage of the apartment houses will be changing into theaters. Eventually we will have some office buildings, some apartment houses, some theaters, some stores, and so on. And, very soon there will be a constant hail of escaping bricks and stone blocks.

This is the way it is with the disintegration of radium. One product leads to another which, in turn, leads to a third. Consequently a sample of radium will contain all the intermediate radioactive products and will be giving off both α particles and electrons. The γ rays are energy rays given off as a result of the disturbances within the atom when it ejects an α particle or electron. You will see later that actually the starting point of this radioactive series is not radium but uranium. That is, radium is itself one of the products formed by the radioactive disintegration of uranium. A complete description of this radioactive series will be given in a later chapter, after you have learned more about the structure of the atom.

Can man influence the rate of radioactive disintegration?

There are methods by which it is possible to count the α particles and electrons which are emitted from a radioactive sample. Measurement of the rate at which these particles are thrown off shows that the rate of disintegration is *completely independent* of temperature and other external conditions. Radium disintegrates at the same rate, whether it is at the temperature of liquid air, at room temperature, or in a white-hot furnace. Nor is it possible to start or stop natural radioactive disintegration. Man has absolutely no control over it. The only thing which influences the number of α particles and β particles shot off each second is the size of the sample. **The larger the sample, the greater the number of atoms disintegrating each second.** It works out this way: In any sample of radioactive material, a certain percentage of all radioactive atoms present will disintegrate each second. For simplicity, let us say that 1 percent of all the atoms present disintegrate each second. Now let us assume that we have two samples of radium, Sample 1 containing 1000 atoms and Sample 2 containing 10,000 atoms of radium.

Sample 1: 1000 atoms—1 percent disintegrate during the first second, giving 10 α particles.

Sample 2: 10,000 atoms—1 percent disintegrate during the first second, giving 100 α particles.

You can see that the larger the sample, the greater the number of α particles given off per unit time.

Now consider Samples 1 and 2 again.

Sample 1 has 990 atoms of radium left after 1 sec.
Sample 2 has 9900 atoms of radium left after 1 sec.

During the second second,

Sample 1 will emit 1 percent of 990 or 9.9 α particles.[1]
Sample 2 will emit 1 percent of 9900 or 99 α particles.

Thus we see that, as time passes, the number of atoms disintegrating per second becomes less. Consequently the sample will *never be completely* disintegrated, but rather the amount of radium in it will become smaller and smaller as time goes on.

Different radioactive elements differ in their rates of disintegration. The rate of disintegration cannot be stated by stating the length of time needed for a sample to be completely disintegrated because, as we have seen, this would take forever. That is, the sample will never be completely disintegrated. The rate of disintegration is therefore generally expressed by giving the length of time needed for a sample to become one-half disintegrated; that is, **the length of time required for one-half of all the atoms present in the sample to disintegrate.** For a given radioactive element **this is the same regardless of the size of the sample.** This time is known as the **period of half-life.** It varies greatly for different radioactive elements. For example,

Period of half-life for radium = 1630 years
Period of half-life for uranium = 4.5 billion years

When Madame Curie visited the United States, she was presented with 1 g of radium on behalf of the women of America. This sample will contain only ½ g of radium 1630 years from that time, the other

---

[1] These numbers are averages only. Of course there must be a whole number of α particles emitted.

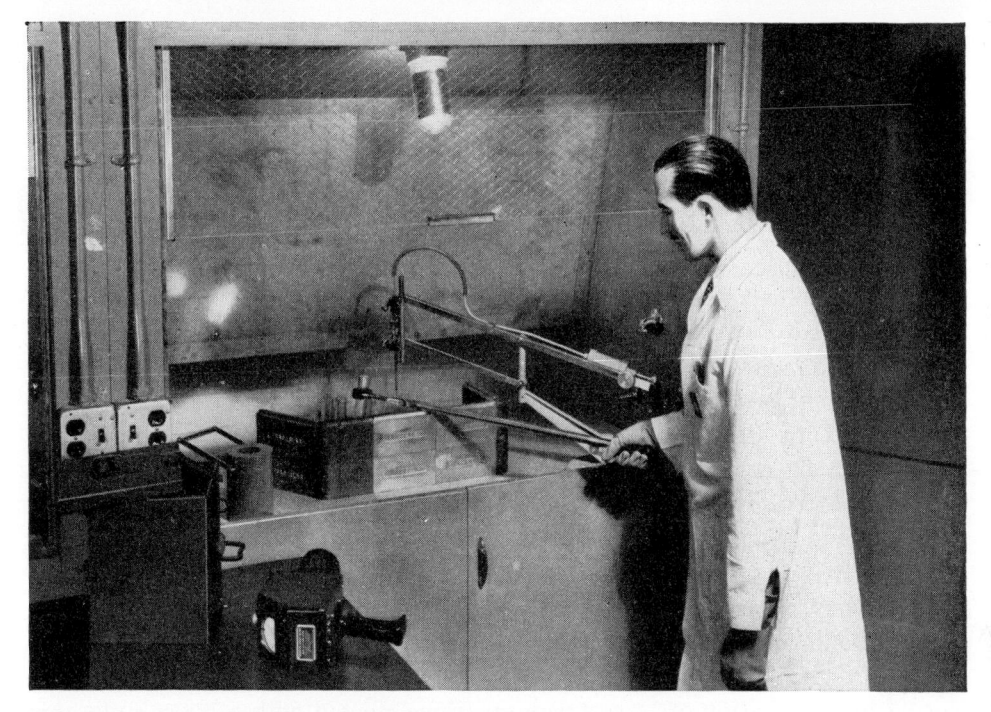

Lead bricks are used to protect workers from radioactive emanations. Note the use of extra-long tongs, also. (Tracerlab, Inc.)

half having undergone disintegration, leaving its disintegration products. At the end of another 1630-year period, this sample will contain only $\frac{1}{4}$ g of radium. You can see that, compared with radium, the radioactive disintegration of uranium is exceedingly slow, since it requires 4.5 billion years for a sample of uranium to become one-half disintegrated. Some radioactive elements disintegrate much more rapidly than those cited above; some have half-life periods as short as a few seconds or less.

The age of the earth

The problem of how old the earth is has interested many men, both scientists and nonscientists. There are several methods for estimating the earth's age. One is based on the rate of disintegration of uranium. As we have seen, uranium is the starting point of the radioactive series which leads to the production of radium and ultimately to the production of a stable form of lead. Consequently uranium ores always contain lead. By chemical analysis, the amount of lead in a given uranium ore can be determined. Since we know the rate at which lead is formed from uranium, it is possible to calculate how long ago this particular uranium-containing rock was laid down. Such a calculation indicates that these rocks were laid down about 2.8 billion years ago. This represents at least a minimum age of the earth.

The energy liberated in the disintegration of radium

The energy liberated in radioactivity is of two forms: (1) kinetic energy of the particles (α or β) ejected, and (2) radiant energy. You will remember that kinetic energy is really heat energy. Radiant energy is that illustrated by light, ultraviolet rays, x rays, and so on. Radiant energy is also transformable into heat when it is absorbed. This is well illustrated by what happens when some of the radiant energy of the sun strikes a black macadam road. Sometimes the road is heated to the softening point of the macadam. The road is heated more than the air because the black road absorbs the radiant energy better.

Thus all the energy liberated by the disintegration of radium is, or can be converted into, heat. Hence we can express the quantity in calories. It is found by measurement that a 1-g sample of radium gives off energy at the rate of 132 calories per hour (cal/hr). Now 132 cal is not very much heat in terms of the amount it takes to heat your home. It is about enough to heat a teaspoon of water to its boiling point. But remember that a radium sample will continue giving off heat, hour after hour, day after day! It is estimated that in the disintegration of $\frac{1}{2}$ g of radium (if we started with a 1-g sample, this would require 1630 years), 1,000,000,000 cal of heat are liberated. This is enough to heat 2500 gal of water from 0°C to its boiling point! And this heat is produced from less than one-fiftieth of an ounce of radium. To put it another way, the energy from 1 lb of radium is as much as that produced by burning 250,000 lb of good grade coal! **Compared with chemical reactions the energy liberated by radioactive processes is tremendous.**

Perhaps you will think: Here in radium is a good source of atomic energy. Why do we not heat our houses with it? There are two reasons: (1) Small samples of radium give off energy very slowly; that is, 1 g gives off 132 cal/hr. (2) Radium is very rare in nature so that only small samples can be obtained. If this were not the case, we could increase the rate of liberation of energy by collecting large samples of radium. For example, 100 g of radium would give off 13,200 cal/hr. By getting together sufficiently large samples, it should be possible to establish a practical source of atomic energy from radium. While such a source would not be everlasting, it would last for a long time. It would take 1630 years for the rate of energy production of the radium to decrease to one-half its original value. Unfortunately radium is so rare that ever since its discovery in 1897 the entire world's production has amounted to only a little over two pounds. For these reasons the production of atomic energy on a practical scale was delayed nearly half a century after the discovery of radioactivity. It took place only after science discovered another process, *nuclear fission,* which is somewhat similar to, but not the same as, natural radioactivity. Moreover, nuclear fission can be started and stopped by man. But this is the subject of another chapter.

Importance of discovery of radioactivity and radium

Madame Curie is considered one of the greatest scientists, man or woman, of all time. For her work she received, not once but twice, that most coveted of all scientific awards, the Nobel Prize.[1] There are three reasons why Madame Curie's discoveries were important.

1. The discovery of two new elements is important wherever and whenever it occurs. By comparison with the other aspects of her discovery, however, this is of relatively minor importance.

2. Radium and the products formed from it, particularly radon, produce radiations (x rays) which have the ability to arrest, and possibly in some cases to cure, cancer. Radium and x ray treatment are still standard methods of treating cancerous conditions. It should be emphasized that not all cancer is curable by these methods. Nevertheless, many lives have been saved by radium treatment, and, therefore, the discovery of radium is important medically.

3. The great importance of the discovery of radium, however, is that it led to establishing the fact that atoms are made up of smaller particles which are the same in all atoms. It also established the fact that atoms of one element are convertible into atoms of another element. This conversion occurs spontaneously in radioactivity. A large part of what we know now about the structure of the atom, atomic energy, and the nature of chemical reactions has come from a study of natural radioactivity and related behavior.

KEY WORDS

α (alpha) ray	Curie	Nobel	radium
Becquerel	electroscope	pitchblende	radon
β (beta) ray	γ (gamma) ray	polonium	uranium
carnotite	half-life	radioactivity	x rays

[1] Alfred Nobel (1833–1896) was a Swedish engineer and chemist who devoted his life to the study of explosives. Among his inventions are dynamite and blasting gelatin. From these inventions he made a tremendous fortune. Before his death he became alarmed at the possible consequences of his discoveries and became a very active pacifist. On his death he left his estate in a trust fund. The interest from it is to be used to award five prizes annually, without regard to nationality, to the persons who are judged to have done most to advance the welfare of mankind in chemistry, physics, medicine, promotion of world peace, and literature. Nobel's support of science is recognized in naming after him element 102.

HIGHLIGHTS

From the discovery of natural **radioactivity** by **Becquerel** in 1896 has come a large part of the new knowledge of atomic structure, atomic energy, and the nature of chemical reactions.

A careful study of the relative intensities of the radioactivity of **uranium,** and of its salts and ores, enabled the **Curies** to discover and isolate the elements **polonium** and **radium,** both of which are naturally radioactive.

Besides the elements which are radioactive as they occur in nature, radioactive forms of other elements can be made by man.

Radioactivity involves three types of rays: α **rays** (positively charged helium atoms), β **rays** (electrons), and γ **rays** (**x rays**). The first two are actual particles of matter and as such possess kinetic energy; the third is not matter but a form of radiant energy. Radioactive disintegration releases energy many thousand times more than that of ordinary chemical reactions, per unit mass of material involved.

The rate of radioactive disintegration of an element is expressed in terms of the **half-life** of the element. On the basis of the half-life of uranium it has been estimated that the earth is at least 2.8 billion years old.

Radioactivity, both natural and man-made, is being applied to the control of cancer.

QUESTIONS

1. How and by whom was radioactivity discovered?
2. What two elements did Madame Curie discover?
3. Explain what led Madame Curie to the discovery of two new elements.
4. Describe two methods by means of which radiations from radioactivity may be detected.
5. What is meant by artificial radioactivity?
6. Name four radioactive elements found in nature.
7. What are α rays, β rays, and γ rays?
8. Is it possible to control the rate of disintegration of a certain sample of radium?
9. How is the rate of disintegration of a radioactive element expressed? Explain.
10. Why is radium impractical as a source of atomic energy?
11. Give three reasons why the discovery of radioactivity was important.

CHAPTER 18

the nucleus of the atom

Radioactivity studies showed clearly that certain atoms are divisible. Moreover, these studies showed that atoms of the various elements are made up of the same types of particles since it is possible for atoms of one element to be transformed into atoms of another. What, then, are the particles of which atoms are built?

The building blocks of atoms

Although there is much yet to be learned about the particles of which atoms are made, we may consider that atoms are made up of the following:

1. Electrons. **Electrons** are the same as the beta particles produced by radioactivity (see Chap. 17, page 186). They are present in all atoms, and as already noted, have a negative charge. Their mass is very small (about $1/1840$ of the mass of the hydrogen atom). They are symbolized by e^-.

2. Protons. **Protons** are particles which have a unit positive charge and a mass about the same as that of the hydrogen atom (about 1840 times the mass of an electron). The proton is, in fact, a hydrogen atom which has lost its electron. In other words the simplest atom, which is hydrogen, consists of one proton and one electron. Protons are present in atoms of all elements. The symbol for them is p or $(+)$.

3. Neutrons. As the name suggests, **neutrons** are electrically neutral particles. Their mass is almost the same as that of a proton. It is helpful to imagine that a neutron consists of a proton and an electron in very close association (not the same kind of association as in the hydrogen atom). In fact under certain conditions, as you will see later, a neutron undergoes transformation into an electron and a proton. Neutrons are present in atoms of all elements except the simplest hydrogen atom, that is, hydrogen 1. They are symbolized n or $(\pm)$. Neutrons are particularly important in the production of

195

atomic energy and you will learn more of their characteristics later.

4. *Positrons.* **Positrons** are particles identical with ordinary electrons except that they carry a positive charge. They are observed in certain man-caused radioactive disintegrations. Whenever they appear an additional neutron is formed and a proton disappears. Hence for our purposes it is convenient to consider that a proton consists of a neutron associated with a positron. The symbol for a positron is e^+. Thus we may consider $p = ne^+$.

5. *Energy.* Atoms also contain vast amounts of energy which man is just learning to release in controlled fashion. We should consider this energy as one of the constituents of atoms.

The α particles which are released in natural radioactivity (see Chap. 17, page 186) are known to consist of two protons and two neutrons each. An α particle, therefore, has a double positive charge and a mass about four times the mass of the hydrogen atom.

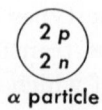

$$\begin{pmatrix} 2\,p \\ 2\,n \end{pmatrix}$$
α particle

The solar atom

How are these particles put together in the atoms of the various elements? The first part of the answer to this question was given by **Rutherford,** a New Zealander who was working at McGill University in Montreal. As a result of experiments which cannot be explained here, he was able to show that the atom consists of several parts, one of which is the small (even compared with the size of the entire atom) **nucleus.** The nucleus is now known to contain all the protons and neutrons, and to be surrounded by **electrons** which revolve around it. The nucleus, since it contains protons, is positively charged. The number of protons present determines the amount of the positive charge. The nucleus is surrounded by the same number of electrons as the number of protons it contains, thus making the atom as a whole electrically neutral. Since protons and neutrons have much greater masses than electrons, more than 99.9 percent of the mass of the entire atom is concentrated in its nucleus. The atom is thus a sort of miniature solar system in which the nucleus corresponds to the sun in our solar system and the electrons revolving around it correspond to the various planets. In fact the electrons are frequently referred to as *planetary* electrons.

Rutherford and his co-workers were able to measure the charge on the nuclei of many of the elements. They found in each case that the nuclear charge was the same as the position of that element in Mendeléeff's periodic table. For example, the nuclear charge for gold is $+79$, and gold is the seventy-ninth element in the order in which they were arranged by Mendeléeff. This number is known as the **atomic number,** and it represents the number of protons in the nucleus of an atom. Thus the atomic number of hydrogen is 1; of carbon, 6; and of sodium, 11.

The atomic number is the most important property of an element because it determines the chemical properties of the element. Just how it does so will be the subject of a later chapter.

Rutherford was able also to determine the radius of the atomic nucleus as compared with the radius of the atom as a whole. You will see that the radius of the entire atom will be determined by the distance from the center of the atom to the farthest-away planetary electron. That is, the orbit of the outermost planetary electron determines the volume in space which the atom occupies. It was found that in the case of the different elements measured, the radius of the nucleus is about one ten-thousandth of the radius of the entire atom. Thus if you imagine a hydrogen atom to be magnified until its nucleus has a radius of 1 ft, its planetary electron would be located almost 2 miles away from the nucleus, with no matter in between! This is why it is sometimes said: The atom is mostly empty space. Even so, almost all the mass is concentrated in the tiny nucleus. Since the volume of a sphere is proportional to the cube of its radius, the volume of the nucleus is only $\frac{1}{10^{12}} = \left(\frac{1}{10^4}\right)^3$ as great as the volume of the entire atom. This means that the density of the nucleus must be 10^{12} times as great as the actual observed density of the solid element. Such a density would amount to many tons per cubic inch, a density so great as to be unimaginable. However, astronomers have computed the density of certain stars to be of this order of magnitude. At first such a high density seemed incomprehensible, but now it seems likely that the high temperatures in the stars have resulted in stripping away all or most of the planetary electrons. This allows the nuclei to come closer together, producing a star of extremely high density.

Isotopes

As stated earlier, the atomic number, which represents the number of protons in the nucleus, determines the chemical properties of an atom. Thus, for example, all atoms having 17 protons in their nuclei have identical chemical properties—they are all atoms of chlorine. The weight of an atom, however, is determined by the total number of protons plus neutrons which it contains, although the neutrons do not influence the chemical properties. You may ask: Could two atoms have the same number of protons but differ in the number of neutrons which they contain? Yes, they can. Such atoms have identical chemical properties but different weights. They are said to be *isotopes*. This term comes from the Greek word for *equal place* and refers to the fact that such atoms would occupy the same position in the periodic table. **Isotopes are atoms with the same atomic number but different atomic weights.**

For example, we know today that chlorine as found in nature actually consists of atoms of two types, as diagramed below:

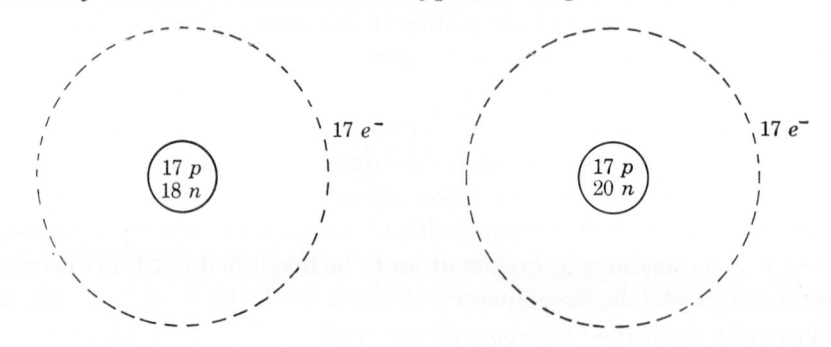

Both atoms contain 17 protons and 17 planetary electrons; hence they are chemically identical. One variety, however, contains 18 neutrons in its nucleus, whereas the other contains 20 neutrons. This results in atoms of two different weights called, respectively, chlorine 35 and chlorine 37 since their individual weights would be approximately 35 and 37 on the atomic-weight scale. They are symbolized as follows:

$$_{17}Cl^{35} \quad \text{and} \quad _{17}Cl^{37}$$

The small upper number (superscript) indicates the **mass number,** which is the total of protons plus neutrons, and is also the whole number nearest to the atomic weight of that atom. The lower number (subscript) refers to the atomic number of the atom. Of course, having written the symbol for the element, the atomic number is in a sense superfluous, since the periodic table tells us that the element with atomic number 17 is chlorine. Nevertheless, it is conventional today to refer to isotopes this way and you should become familiar with it.

The mass spectrograph

Isotopes were first discovered early in the twentieth century in connection with studies on the nature of natural radioactivity. Definite proof that isotopes of stable elements also exist was established about 1920 by the Englishman **F. W. Aston,** who invented the **mass spectrograph,** the instrument used for detecting and measuring the ratio of isotopes. The importance of this instrument to present-day

The mass spectrometer is an indispensable tool in modern scientific research. The photograph shows the control panel on a modern mass spectrometer. In general, the mass spectrometer differs from the mass spectrograph only in the method of detecting the ion beams. Most modern instruments are called *mass spectrometers* as the ion beams are detected and measured electronically. The instruments in which the ion beam is detected photographically are called *mass spectrographs*. (Fisher Scientific Co.)

atomic science can hardly be overestimated. It is probable that without its development scientists would not have realized that atomic energy was a possibility, much less made it an actuality.

Present-day atomic science depends to a great extent on the use of the mass spectrograph (or mass spectrometer, which is basically the same), and one or more of these instruments are usually found in any laboratory where research is done on isotopes. Although the present-day mass spectrograph is electronically very complicated, the principle upon which it is based is the same as that of Aston's original machine, which is very simple. Suppose that on a windy day you drop from a second-floor window three balls, a baseball, a tennis ball, and a lead ball. (For simplicity we shall imagine they are all the same size.) The lead ball, which is the heaviest, will fall most nearly straight down, the baseball next, and the tennis ball will be deflected most by the wind. This is the basis of the modern mass spectrograph. The balls are

Fig. 18–1. Illustrating the principle of the mass spectrograph. If balls of the same size but different weights (representing isotopes of the same element) are dropped in a strong wind (corresponding to an electromagnetic field), the heaviest ball will fall most nearly straight down, while the lightest ball will be deflected the most by the wind.

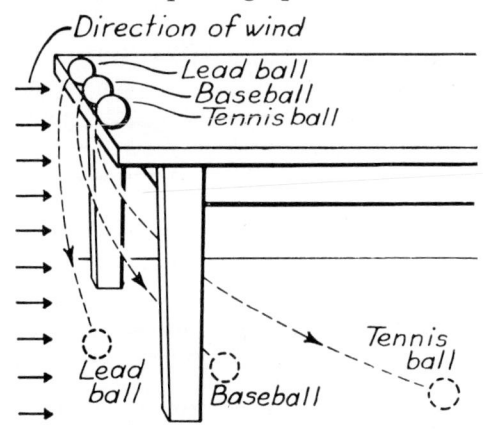

electrically charged atoms of the element to be examined. The wind is a magnetic field[1] which bends the path of the atoms. When all other factors are the same, the atoms are sorted out into as many beams as there are isotopes in the original sample.

Thus if hydrogen is introduced into the ionization chamber of the mass spectrograph, positively charged hydrogen ions are produced. These are shot out of the ionization chamber into a magnetic field. Here the single beam is separated into three beams which strike a photographic plate. On development the plate will show three lines, thus proving there are three isotopes of this element.

Isotopes and atomic weights

It has been found that almost all the elements, as they occur in nature, are made up of mixtures of two or more isotopes. Thus for the case of hydrogen there are actually three isotopes.

It has been found that in nature there are about 6400 parts of $_1H^1$ to 1 part of $_1H^2$ and that the amount of $_1H^3$ is very, very small.

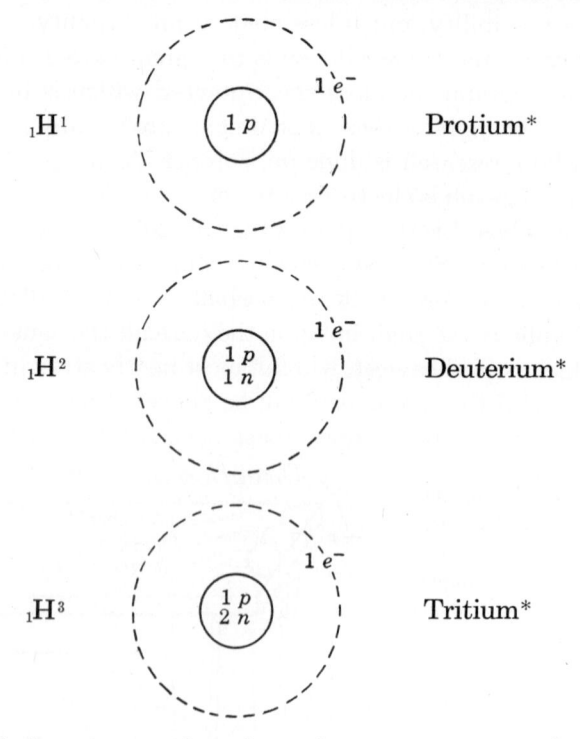

$_1H^1$ — (1 p, 1 e⁻) — Protium*

$_1H^2$ — (1 p, 1 n, 1 e⁻) — Deuterium*

$_1H^3$ — (1 p, 2 n, 1 e⁻) — Tritium*

* Although these isotopes have been given separate names for the sake of convenience, it is important to keep in mind that they are all hydrogen and chemically identical.

[1] The field that exists between two magnetic poles is a magnetic field.

Fig. 18-2. A single beam of charged hydrogen ions is separated into three beams by a magnetic field. If these beams are directed onto a photographic plate, the plate will show three lines when it is developed because hydrogen has three isotopes. If chlorine were treated in this way, the plate would show only two lines since chlorine has two isotopes.

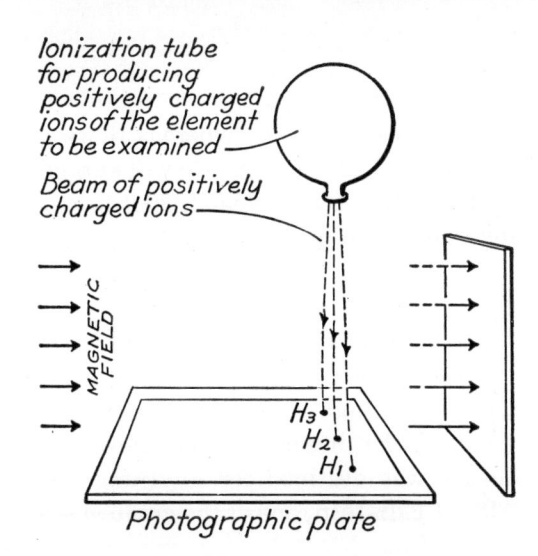

Similarly, chlorine consists of two isotopes, $_{17}Cl^{35}$ and $_{17}Cl^{37}$. The element tin consists of 10 isotopes ranging in mass from 112 to 124. Two elements that have no isotopes in nature are $_{11}Na^{23}$ and $_{53}I^{127}$.

When an element consists of a mixture of two or more isotopes, it is easy to see that one should not expect that element to have a whole number for its atomic weight. The atomic weight shown on the periodic chart must be a weighted average of the weights of all the isotopes present. Shortly after the discovery of isotopes it was thought that the fractional atomic weights of the elements were due *entirely* to isotopes. *This was found not to be the case.* The discovery that fractional atomic weights were not due entirely to isotopes was among the most important discoveries of all time, and it caused a revolution in certain branches of scientific thinking.

The mass-energy relationship

Careful measurement with the mass spectrograph shows that the weight of $_2He^4$ is 4.0028.

$$\text{Weight of one proton} = 1.0073$$
$$\text{Weight of one neutron} = 1.0087$$

Now you have seen that $_2He^4$ consists of a nucleus containing two neutrons and two protons plus two planetary electrons. (The planetary electrons have such small mass as to be negligible.)

$$\text{Two protons weigh } 2 \times 1.0073 = 2.0146$$
$$\text{Two neutrons weigh } 2 \times 1.0087 = \underline{2.0174}$$
$$\text{Total weight of particles in } _2He^4 \text{ nucleus} = \overline{4.0320}$$
$$\text{Actual weight of } _2He^4 \text{ nucleus} = 4.0028$$

A similar discrepancy was found in other cases. The $_{11}Na^{23}$ atom has a mass of 22.997, whereas if we add together the masses of 11 protons and 12 neutrons, we will obtain a number considerably greater than 23. Thus by the year 1930 it became clear that, atomically speaking, the weight of the whole did not equal the sum of the weights of its parts. Scientists began to ask themselves the question: How could this be?

They found that the answer had been given even before the question had been posed. In 1905 an obscure clerk in a Swiss patent office had published a highly mathematical scientific paper which contained the origin of what has come to be known as the **theory of relativity.** The author was destined for anything but obscurity for his name was **Albert Einstein,** one of the greatest scientists of all time. In this early paper of his, Einstein came mathematically to the conclusion that in interstellar space the mass of bodies changes as their velocities (energy contents) change. Actually he showed that the mass of a body should increase as its energy content increases according to the relation

$$E = Mc^2 \quad (1)$$

Where E = energy content of body
M = mass of body
c = velocity of light (3×10^{10} cm/sec)

Or for changes in mass accompanying changes in energy,

$$\text{Change in } E = (\text{change in } M)c^2 \quad (2)$$

Inserting proper units so that energy is given in calories instead of ergs one obtains:

$$\text{Change in energy in calories} = \text{change in mass in grams} \times 2 \times 10^{13} \quad (3)$$

Probably few physical scientists of 1905 understood the paper and perhaps none believed it would have any application to scientific processes occurring on earth. How far from the truth this was!

Later when the discrepancy in atomic weights was observed, it was seen that Einstein's equation offered a possible explanation. Could it be proved experimentally? It could be and was.

Einstein's equation says in effect that if the energy content of a body changes, its mass changes, and vice versa. Thus returning to the case of $_2He^4$, suppose one could cause two protons (p) and two neutrons (n) to unite into one helium nucleus according to the equation

$$2p + 2n = {_2He^4}$$
$$4.0320 \quad\quad 4.0028$$

Thus when one gram atom of helium is formed, there would be lost from this system a mass of

$$\frac{\begin{array}{r}4.0320\\4.0028\end{array}}{0.0292 \text{ gram units}}$$

This system would *give off* to its surroundings the corresponding amount of energy, which can be calculated by equation (3) page 202.

$$\begin{aligned}\text{Energy loss in calories} &= 0.0292 \times 2 \times 10^{13}\\&= 0.0584 \times 10^{13}\\&= 584{,}000{,}000{,}000 \text{ cal}\end{aligned}$$

This amount of energy is roughly equivalent to the energy produced in burning 100 tons of coal!

This type of process in which several small nuclei react to form a larger one is called **fusion.** It is believed that it is this process occurring on the sun which is responsible for the production of the sun's energy. Thus the sun is continually transforming its mass into energy which is radiated into space. The mass of the sun today is therefore somewhat less than its mass yesterday. The rate of loss, however, is extremely slow.

If a transformation like the above one could be accomplished on earth, it is obvious that it would have tremendous possibilities both as a weapon of destruction and as a useful source of energy if it could be controlled. A few years ago such an accomplishment seemed impossible, yet the United States government has announced that a military bomb in which this process occurs has become a reality. Such a bomb, known commonly as the hydrogen bomb (since it involves the conversion of hydrogen into helium) or **thermonuclear** bomb, is tremendously more destructive than is the fission-type bomb.

The same principle applies to all atomic nuclei; their weights are not equal to the sum of the weights of the individual particles of which they are made up. The mass of a body varies according to the amount of energy which it contains.

You may ask: What about the law of conservation of mass and the law of conservation of energy? Did they not form the cornerstone of science for over one hundred years? They did. We know today that, taken separately, they are incorrect, but for most cases where they were applied their error was so slight as to be *unobservable experimentally*. This is because of the size of the factor in the Einstein equation relating mass and energy.

According to the equation, 2×10^{13} cal has a mass of 1 g. This means that if we carried out a chemical reaction which gave off

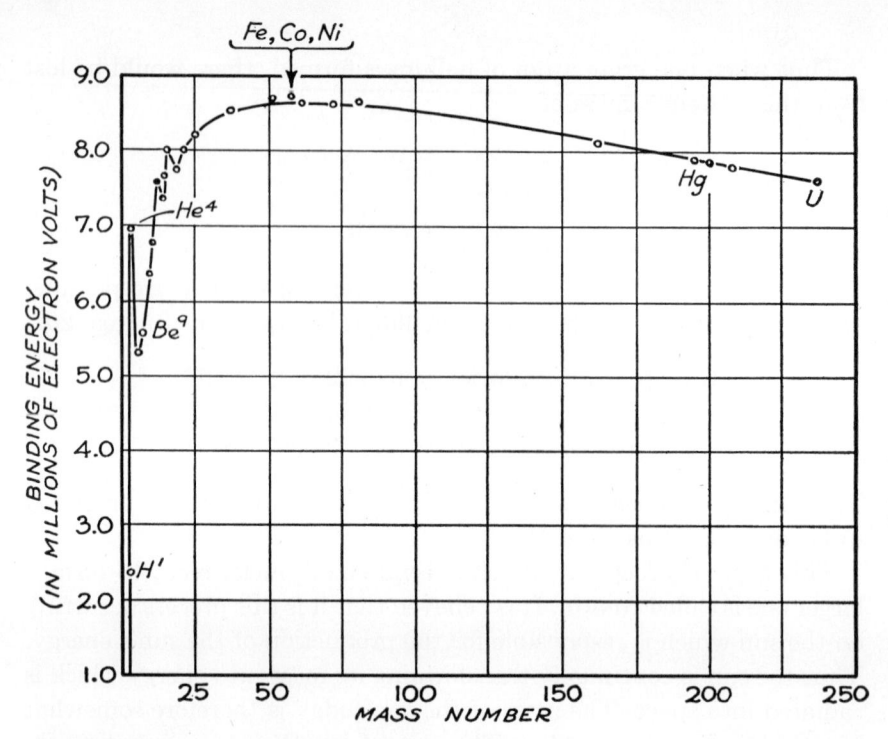

Fig. 18-3. Binding energy of the elements. Note that iron, cobalt, and nickel have the highest binding energy of any of the elements.

2×10^{13} cal (such as the burning of carbon) **the chemical products of that reaction would weigh less than the reactants by one gram.** Now 2×10^{13} cal is roughly the amount produced when 3500 tons of coal are burned. Where such a large quantity is involved it is impossible to compare the weights of products and reactants with an accuracy of anything like 1 g. In the laboratory we are more apt to deal with quantities of reactants which produce about 10,000 cal. But 10,000 cal has a weight of only

$$\frac{10{,}000}{2 \times 10{,}000{,}000{,}000{,}000} = 0.0000000005 \text{ g}$$

Such a small mass cannot be detected on any balance known.

Thus the law of conservation of mass was established and considered to be correct for 150 years because *within the limit of experimental error* it was correct for the systems on which it was tested and applied. It is only in the case of the tremendous energy changes encountered in nuclear processes that the deviations from this law can be detected experimentally and become important. Thus while neither the law of conservation of mass nor the law of conservation of energy is correct when taken separately, we now know that the total mass plus energy of a system cannot be changed although one may be changed into the other.

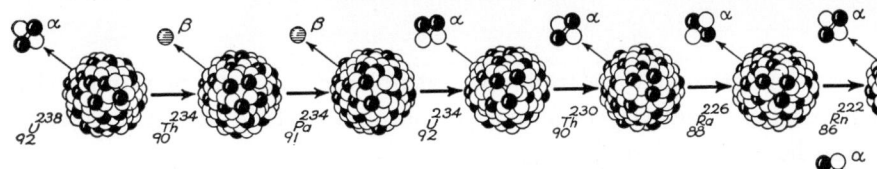

Fig. 18–4. The uranium-238 disintegration series.

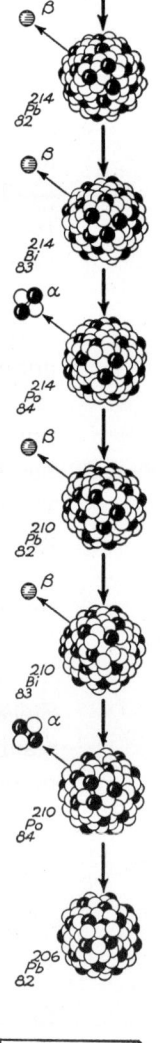

Binding energies

Looking at the proton + neutron → helium reaction in the opposite way, it is apparent that if the helium nucleus were broken up into two protons and two neutrons, a mass increase would occur. Per gram atom of helium this would be 0.0292 g. Now obviously an amount of energy corresponding to this mass increase would have to be supplied to the helium atom in order to disrupt it.

This energy is referred to as the **binding energy** of the nucleus because it represents the minimum amount of energy necessary to break up the nucleus (by bombardment with nuclear projectiles or otherwise). The binding energy is a measure of the stability of the nucleus. It is found that the binding energy varies in a regular way with the atomic number of the element. The binding energy is low for the lighter elements, increases regularly with atomic number until iron, cobalt, and nickel are reached, then decreases regularly thereafter. Thus the binding energies of both the light and heavy elements are less than of iron, cobalt, and nickel. Hence the very heavy elements are unstable and break down into lighter ones, thereby liberating energy. This is natural radioactivity and nuclear fission. The light elements under the right conditions (probably very high temperatures) can unite to form heavier nuclei, thereby liberating energy. This process, called fusion, is illustrated by the hydrogen to helium reaction on the sun. Only the elements in the vicinity of iron, cobalt, and nickel have really stable nuclei. This is particularly interesting in view of the fact that the best guess (and it is little more than that) about the composition of the interior of the earth is that it is made up of iron and nickel (see Chap. 49, page 634).

Nuclear transformations

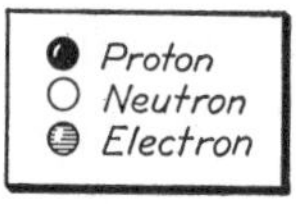

In this mid-twentieth-century period we have indeed come a long way from Dalton's concept of atoms as indivisible spheres. Although his original ideas are still applicable to ordinary chemical reactions, hundreds of cases of nuclear transmutations have by now been studied. You will learn about a few such cases.

Historically, the earliest cases of nuclear transmutation which were understood were from the natural radioactivity of radium. In natural radioactivity radium gives off an α particle (helium nucleus) and becomes radon. That is,

$$_{88}Ra^{226} \rightarrow {}_2He^{4++} + {}_{86}Rn^{222} \tag{1}$$

The radon in turn disintegrates

$$_{86}Rn^{222} \rightarrow {}_2He^{4++} + {}_{84}Po^{218} \tag{2}$$

In writing these nuclear reactions, note that the total atomic number of the reactants must equal the total atomic number of the products. Also, the total mass number (not the exact atomic weight) of the reactants must equal the total mass number of the products.

Thus in equation (1) above, if a helium nucleus which contains two protons is split out of the nucleus of a radium atom which contains 88 protons, then the remainder will be an atom with atomic number 86, which is radon. The same reasoning applies to equation (2).

In the natural radioactivity of the uranium series, of which radium and radon are members, it has been seen that only two types of particles are emitted. In the case of beta particle (e^-) emission, the atomic number of the nucleus increases by one unit since a negative particle has been removed from the nucleus. This is easy to understand by visualizing the electron as coming from a neutron which is thereby converted into a proton. Thus one step in the natural radioactivity of the uranium series is the disintegration of an isotope of lead by beta particle emission:

$$_{82}Pb^{214} \rightarrow {}_{-1}e^0 + {}_{83}Bi^{214}$$

Since the beta particle has no appreciable mass, the mass of the resulting atom is the same as that of the mother atom. It is to be noted that an electron is a particle of zero mass number and -1 atomic number.

The entire uranium-238 radioactive series is shown in Fig. 18–4.

KEY WORDS

Aston	isotope	positron
atomic number	mass-energy relationship	proton
binding energy	mass number	Rutherford
Einstein	mass spectrograph	theory of relativity
electron	neutron	thermonuclear
fusion	nucleus	

HIGHLIGHTS

The atom is not the simplest form of matter. Atoms may be considered as made of **protons, electrons,** and **neutrons.**

The atom is like a miniature solar system. The **nucleus** corresponds to the sun and contains all the protons and neutrons. Like the sun it accounts for nearly all the mass of the system. The electrons revolve around the nucleus somewhat like planets.

Isotopes are atoms of the same element which contain different numbers of neutrons and therefore differ in weight.

The **mass spectrograph** invented by **Aston** is an instrument for detecting and measuring the ratio of the isotopes of an element.

The sum of the weights of the particles composing an atom is not the same as the weight of the atom. This difference represents the **binding energy.** This value calculated by the **Einstein** equation ($E = Mc^2$) is tremendous and is the basis of the **thermonuclear** or hydrogen bomb.

QUESTIONS

1. Draw schematic diagrams for atoms of the following: $_{17}Cl^{35}$, $_1H^2$, $_{20}Ca^{40}$.
2. What is a positron?
3. What is meant by the term *solar atom?* By *planetary electron?*
4. What is meant by the term *atomic number?*
5. Why is the atomic number an important property of an atom?
6. Why is the statement sometimes made: The atom is mostly empty space?
7. How did Rutherford's work offer a possible explanation for the extremely high density of some stars?
8. What are isotopes? Illustrate.
9. What is meant by the term *mass number?*
10. For what purpose is a mass spectrograph used?
11. Explain the principle upon which the mass spectrograph is based.
12. What is deuterium?
13. Give two reasons why the elements do not have whole numbers as atomic weights.
14. What is the reason for thinking that the reaction of protons and neutrons to form helium would liberate large amounts of energy?
15. What is the basis of the hydrogen bomb?

CHAPTER 19

the uranium bomb

It has already been pointed out that, in a sense, we had nuclear energy before 1940. Radium and other naturally radioactive elements give off energy as a result of nuclear processes. Nuclear **transmutations** brought about by man (see below) sometimes release very large amounts of energy per atom changed. These are sources of nuclear energy. It was realized, however, that neither type was a practical source of nuclear energy because (1) in the case of natural radioactivity the rate of liberation of energy is too slow, and this rate of radioactivity cannot be varied by any known means, and (2) transmutations brought about by man were too inefficient. Consider, for example, the reaction:

$$_3\text{Li}^7 + {_1\text{H}^1} \rightarrow {_2\text{He}^4} + {_2\text{He}^4}$$

This process liberates considerable energy. It can be brought about by producing a stream of very fast-moving hydrogen ions (protons) in a cyclotron and directing this stream onto a lithium target. However, in order for the above process to occur, the proton must enter the lithium nucleus. Now you have already learned that Rutherford showed that the atom is mostly empty space. Hence most of the protons fail to strike a lithium nucleus and thus are wasted. Perhaps only one in a million actually succeeds in bringing about the reaction. As a result, more energy is wasted than the reaction produces.

Trying to get energy from such a reaction is like having to ignite separately and individually every carbon atom that enters a furnace as coal. We all realize that this is unnecessary. Instead we ignite paper; the heat of the burning paper ignites wood, which in turn starts coal burning; the heat of the burning coal causes the ignition of additional lumps of coal. This is a sort of **chain reaction** in which the energy released by the burning of one atom causes the ignition of succeeding atoms. It was realized early that if nuclear energy was to be a reality, a similar chain reaction system was necessary. But no such nuclear processes were known.

The discovery

In 1939 a new type of nuclear transmutation was discovered in Germany by **Hahn** and **Strassmann**. They discovered that when **uranium-235,** that is, the isotope of uranium with mass number 235, is struck by slow-moving neutrons, the uranium nucleus splits approximately in half *and additional neutrons are produced* plus a lot of energy. Schematically

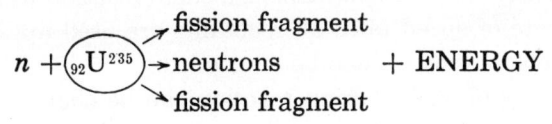

$$n + {}_{92}U^{235} \rightarrow \text{fission fragment} + \text{neutrons} + \text{fission fragment} + \text{ENERGY}$$

The process is different from any previously known, in that one of the products of the reaction (neutrons) is the same as that required to bring it about. Since the uranium-235 nucleus is split approximately in half, the process is known as **fission.** The exact products formed by a uranium-235 fission appear to depend on the conditions but seem to be elements ranging in atomic number from about 30 to 65.

Chain reactions

Here then was a nuclear process which might be the basis of a chain reaction. Suppose one had a sample of uranium-235, and suppose one of the atoms was caused to undergo fission. Such a fission might produce, on the average, two new neutrons. Now these two neutrons might in turn cause the fission of two more uranium-235 atoms, which together would release four neutrons. These four in turn might cause the reaction to continue.

Such was the thinking of scientists when Hahn and Strassmann announced their discovery. Six years and $2 billion later the first nuclear-fission bomb was detonated at **Alamogordo,** N.M.

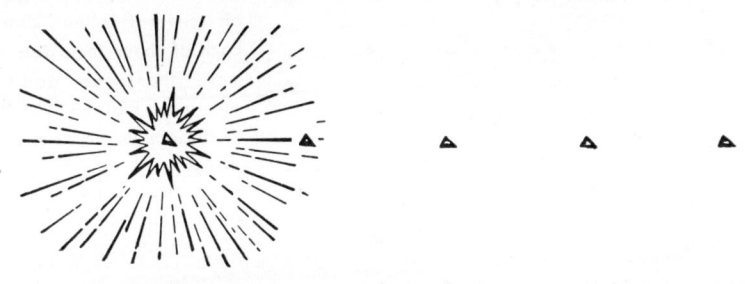

Fig. 19–1. A row of dynamite charges placed to give a chain efficiency of 1.

It is important that you clearly understand the requirements for a continuing chain reaction. In this connection an analogy may be helpful to you.

In some sections of the country drainage ditches are dug with dynamite. The operator carefully places charges of dynamite in the earth at regular distances along the line where the ditch is to be (see Fig. 19-1). The first charge is set off; the shock of this explosion detonates the second, which in turn detonates the third, and so on. Under ideal conditions we have here a self-sustaining chain reaction in which each individual reaction brings about one additional reaction. Where such a situation exists, we shall say that the efficiency of the chain is 1. Where this efficiency exists, a chain reaction will continue at a constant rate of speed until all reactants are used up. You can see that such a chain reaction can be controlled.

The efficiency of such a chain reaction can be changed by varying the arrangement of the charges. Suppose the charges are placed in concentric circles as shown in Fig. 19-2. If the center charge is detonated, it will cause detonation of all those in the first circle, which in turn detonate all those in the second circle, and so on. In this case the number of charges exploded by each charge is greater than 1, and the reaction proceeds with ever-increasing speed until all are consumed.

Thus a chain efficiency greater than 1 leads to a reaction of ever-increasing rate, that is, to an explosion, whereas a chain efficiency of exactly 1 leads to a reaction proceeding at a constant rate. It can further be seen that if, on the average, the chain efficiency is less than 1, the reaction will not continue even if it is started.

Fig. 19-2. If dynamite charges are placed as shown, detonation of the first charge sets off several other charges. Each of these then detonates more than one additional charge, so that the rate of the explosions increases progressively.

A *Nuclear* Power Plant

...like most other types of power plant, uses heat to change water into steam. In both kinds of plant, the steam jets against turbine blades to turn them and to turn an electric generator. For both conventional and nuclear power plants, the steam and electricity are the same — only the heat source is different. Conventional power plants burn coal; nuclear power plants produce heat by splitting uranium nuclei. This splitting is known as "fission." One pound of uranium 235 contains as much heat as about three million pounds of coal; such concentrated energy is what makes nuclear fuel attractive as a useful power source.

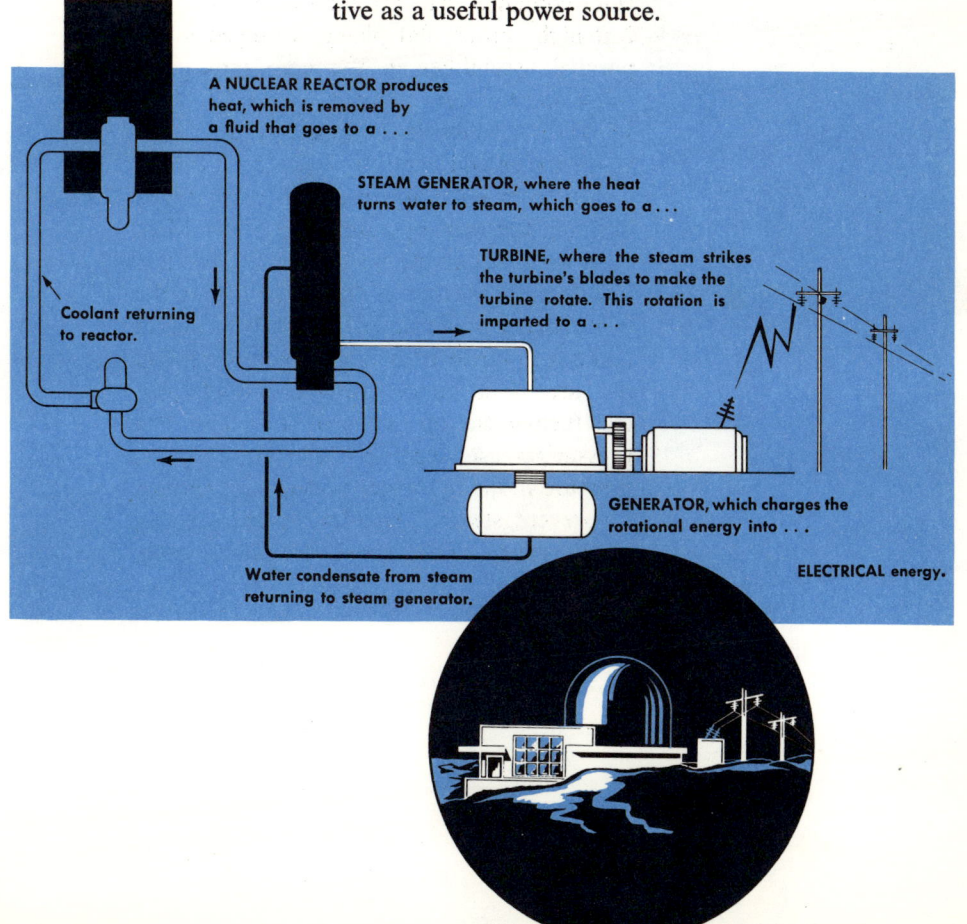

A NUCLEAR REACTOR produces heat, which is removed by a fluid that goes to a...

STEAM GENERATOR, where the heat turns water to steam, which goes to a...

TURBINE, where the steam strikes the turbine's blades to make the turbine rotate. This rotation is imparted to a...

Coolant returning to reactor.

GENERATOR, which charges the rotational energy into...

Water condensate from steam returning to steam generator.

ELECTRICAL energy.

In a sense, no reactor system being built today can be said to be "typical" for the nuclear power plants of the future. Although nuclear power is now a technical fact, the search is still on for a reactor system that will make best use of the advantages of nuclear fuel in producing cheaper electricity. In this search, many types of reactors and various systems are being planned, built, and studied; and reactors built for military uses differ somewhat from those built for civilian power.

The plant described here uses a reactor that is typical of those most fully developed today; for example, pressurized water-cooled reactors are used for propelling the U.S.S. *Nautilus* and for generating electricity in the power station at Shippingport, Pennsylvania. The particular reactor described here, known as the Army Package Power Reactor (APPR), was built for the Army by Alco Products, Inc., Schenectady, New York.

A TYPICAL *Nuclear* POWER PLANT

At right is shown a partial cutaway of the reactor container. The uranium is in a series of 2 ft high vertical flat plates, arranged in 45 parallel assemblies in the core tank. The water and the steel cylinders in the 4 ft thick shield serve as insulation to keep radiations — gamma rays and neutrons — given off during fission from escaping from the reactor and harming the men operating the plant. Most reactors use concrete for this shield, but this one does not because of the desire to ship the components by airplane. The APPR has an additional shield of 5 ft of concrete around the sides of the vapor container so as to protect further the operators of the plant. The pressurizer uses electric heaters to keep the pressure in the hot-water system high enough to prevent steam formation in the reactor, where steam would cause difficulties in its control.

The core tank is 4 ft in diameter and 13½ ft high. When the fuel is to be changed (once every one or two years), the reactor is shut down and the operators enter the vapor container and, with long-handled tools, reach down through the water-filled shaft above the reactor and unbolt the reactor cover plate. After removing the cover plate and the upper grid over the fuel elements, they lift the radioactive fuel assemblies several feet and pass them through a transfer tube leading to a storage pit outside the vapor container. At least 9 ft of water shielding is always between the fuel and the operators. The new fuel assemblies are not radioactive and can be lowered from above. In order that the control rods may not be disconnected during this refueling operation, they are driven by mechanisms entering the core from be-

continued on next page

neath. In the event of power failure, a magnetic clutch disengages the rods from their drive motors, and the rods fall by gravity into the reactor to shut it down (the neutron-absorbing material is in the upper portions of the control rods shown protruding above the fuel assemblies).

The APPR develops 10,000 kilowatts of heat, which is used to generate about 2,000 kilowatts of electricity.

OTHER TYPES of
Nuclear Power Reactors

There are many possible types of nuclear power plants. All use a fissionable fuel (uranium 235, which is found in nature; uranium 233, which is made from thorium 232 exposed in a reactor; or plutonium 239, which is made by exposing uranium 238 in a reactor — thorium 232 and uranium 238 are much more abundant than uranium 235) and a turbine-generator to convert the heat of fission into electricity.

They vary as to the form and shape of the fuel, the heat-removing fluid used, and the systems used to make the heat energy drive the turbine. Here are the features of some of these types of reactor system:

Pressurized-water reactors. The APPR described here is a typical example. The heat from the fuel plates is removed by water pressurized to prevent boiling in the reactor. Steam is formed in a steam generator outside the reactor.

Boiling-water reactors. Steam is allowed to form inside the reactor, thus eliminating the need for a separate steam generator. Control innovations are needed to stabilize the power output.

Fluid-fuel reactors. Instead of the fissionable fuel being in solid form as it is in other reactors, it is dissolved in the coolant in the form of a water-acid solution or in a liquid metal. The fuel solution is circulated from the reactor to an external steam generator.

Sodium-cooled reactors. Liquid sodium, a good heat-transfer fluid that does not need to be pressurized to prevent boiling, is used to transmit the heat to an external steam generator. Special provisions must be made to prevent any steam-generator leak that would let the radioactive sodium react chemically with the water in the steam system.

Gas-cooled reactors. Pressurized gas passes through the reactor to remove its heat to an external steam generator. For relatively low-output plants (below 20,000 to 60,000 kilowatts), the gas from the reactor can be used directly to turn a gas turbine (high-output gas turbines have not as yet been perfected).

Nuclear engineers are hard at work improving these and other reactor systems and their components and materials in order to make more adaptable plants that produce cheaper power. Solutions to the problems involve nearly every phase of science and engineering. A nuclear engineer has a firm background in the fundamentals of some form of conventional science plus a keenly comprehensive knowledge and awareness of the interrelated aspects of the nuclear factors. His ingenuity and perseverance are likely to extend the frontiers of the application of atomic energy for many years to come.

The gaseous diffusion plant for concentration of $_{92}U^{235}$. (Oak Ridge National Laboratory)

The uranium-235 bomb

If, then, an explosion based on uranium-235 fission is to occur, a chain reaction must be set up in which, *on the average*, every uranium-235 fission shall bring about more than one additional fission. You may think: This seems simple enough. Only one neutron is required for fission of one uranium-235 atom. This one fission produces, we are told, on the average, two additional neutrons. All that is necessary is to make sure that the two neutrons produced (or even, on the average, more than one of the neutrons produced) are used for the same process. And that is all quite true. The difficulty comes in making sure that nothing else happens to the neutrons.

Imagine that one has a sample of uranium and that, by the introduction of a neutron, one uranium atom undergoes fission, thereby releasing two more neutrons. Any one of four things may happen to these neutrons:

1. They may be captured by (that is, enter the nucleus of) an impurity present in the uranium sample.

2. They may be captured by an atom of uranium-238. (As found in nature uranium consists mostly of two isotopes, uranium-235 and uranium-238. Of these, only uranium-235 is fissionable.)

3. They may escape from the sample to the surroundings.

4. They may be captured by an atom of uranium-235, thereby causing another fission.

In order to bring about the chain reaction, the occurrences described in items 1, 2, and 3 must be reduced to such a point that, on the average, they account for less than one neutron per fission reaction.

1. To minimize capture by impurities, it is necessary to remove all other elements from the uranium sample. Although this would have been easy in 1940 for some elements, the chemical properties of uranium and its preparation from its ore were very poorly understood at that time. This was mainly because up to that time uranium had very few practical uses. (Its principal use had been as the oxide, in producing yellow glass such as is used for auto reflectors!)

Uranium occurs in nature mainly as pitchblende and carnotite. Both these minerals contain a wide variety of other metals.

The presence in the final purified uranium of almost any other element is objectionable since almost all other elements absorb neutrons. Boron is a particularly good absorber of neutrons. We are told that the presence of ½ part of boron per million parts of uranium is enough to prevent the chain reaction.

2. Only a small proportion of the uranium in nature consists of the fissionable isotope $_{92}U^{235}$. The proportions are $_{92}U^{238}$ 99.3% and $_{92}U^{235}$ 0.7%.

Uranium-238 also absorbs neutrons and hence most of it must be removed if a chain reaction is to occur. The separation of these two isotopes must be based on slight differences in their physical properties since their chemical properties are identical. This separation was, and still is, one of the most difficult steps in making a uranium-235 bomb. One of the principal parts of the **Oak Ridge,** Tenn., plant was devoted to this separator.

3. Assuming then a sample of pure uranium-235, there can be only one other diversion of the fission-produced neutrons. This is that they can escape from the sample.

Imagine a small sphere of uranium-235. A neutron released within this sphere might move between the nuclei of the atoms present and escape through the surface. The chances of such an escape before fission capture of the neutron by uranium-235 *decrease* as the size of the sample increases. Thus there is *one certain size* of sample below which the proportion of neutrons escaping is too great to allow a chain reaction. But above this size the chain reaction proceeds with ever-increasing rate, that is, an explosion occurs. This size is known as the **critical size.** Below it, no chain reaction occurs—above it, the introduction of a single neutron (and there are always some neutrons in the atmosphere, since they are produced by cosmic rays) causes the explosion. Thus the detonation of the bomb consists in bringing together quantities of purified fissionable material which add up to a total size

Nuclear-bomb explosion. The small dark objects are navy ships. (U.S. Navy)

greater than the critical size. When this has been accomplished, a single neutron can start the explosion. The exact way in which this is accomplished has not been made public for reasons of security.

This critical size condition is remarkable because it means that no small-scale explosions are possible. Up to the present time the critical size of the nuclear-fission bomb has been a guarded secret.

The rest is recorded history. The first bomb was exploded in a test at Alamogordo, N.M., July 16, 1945, which date marks mankind's transition into the nuclear age. On Aug. 6, 1945, the first nuclear-fission bomb was employed in warfare against **Hiroshima,** Japan; on Aug. 9, 1945, the second one was dropped over **Nagasaki:**[1] and 5 days later the Japanese government opened negotiations for surrender.

Effects of the bomb

We are told that the first bombs released energy equivalent to 20,000 tons of TNT. The bomb dropped on Hiroshima killed 100,000 people. Persons who inspected the Japanese cities after their destruction report that most buildings within a mile of the explosion collapsed. A few of stone or brick stood. Where bricks were exposed to the direct flash, their surfaces were melted. The explosion is mainly ordinary heat at work in tremendous amounts. Bomb metal becomes incandescent vapor with a temperature of several million degrees. This as well as the surrounding glowing air radiates a blinding flash which will char human flesh at half a mile. Following the flash, there is an onrushing destructive shock wave which is caused by the expansion of the heated

---

[1] The Nagasaki bomb was plutonium rather than uranium (see Chap. 20, pages 218 and 219).

air. Deadly γ rays and neutrons speed out from the point of explosion as do radioactive fission products.

Thus the principal injuries from atom-bomb attack appear to come under three headings:

1. Flash burns. Flash burns result from a direct exposure to the flash accompanying the explosion. Fires will be started and persons exposed to the direct flash will be killed. The flash is many times brighter than the sun.

2. Air blast damage. As already noted, the heating effect of the blast causes tremendous expansion of the air. This causes an air blast of great violence to move outward from the explosion point.

3. Radiation damage. **Radiation damage** is caused when the explosion liberates large numbers of neutrons. These neutrons are absorbed by elements in the vicinity, thereby making them radioactive. In addition the fission products themselves are highly radioactive. The radiations produced by the radioactive decay of these elements may be very injurious to living tissue. Fortunately those radioactive elements which are the most injurious are the ones which have the shortest half-life period (see Chap. 17, pages 190 and 191); hence after the proper length of time, the vicinity again becomes habitable.

It seems fitting to close this chapter with an eye-witness description of the New Mexico test explosion, which is reproduced here from the famous Smyth report,[1] page 254.

The effects could well be called unprecedented, magnificent, beautiful, stupendous and terrifying. No man-made phenomenon of such tremendous power had ever occurred before. The lighting effects beggared description. The whole country was lighted by a searing light with the intensity many times that of the midday sun. It was golden, purple, violet, gray and blue. It lighted every peak, crevasse and ridge of the nearby mountain range with a clarity and beauty that cannot be described but must be seen to be imagined. It was that beauty the great poets dream about but describe most poorly and inadequately. Thirty seconds after, the explosion came first, the air blast pressing hard against the people and things, to be followed almost immediately by the strong, sustained, awesome roar which warned of doomsday and made us feel that we puny things were blasphemous to dare tamper with the forces heretofore reserved to the Almighty. Words are inadequate tools for the job of acquainting those not present with the physical, mental and psychological effects. It had to be witnessed to be realized.

[1] Henry DeWolf Smyth, *Atomic Energy for Military Purposes:* The Official Report on the Development of the Atomic Bomb under the Auspices of the United States Government, 1940–1945, Princeton University Press, Princeton, N.J., 1945.

KEY WORDS

Alamogordo	fission	Nagasaki	Strassmann
chain reaction	Hahn	Oak Ridge	transmutation
critical size	Hiroshima	radiation damage	uranium-235

HIGHLIGHTS

In 1939 **Hahn** and **Strassmann** in Germany discovered that a neutron on striking the **uranium-235** nucleus broke it into two smaller particles of approximately equal size, with the release of additional neutrons. This discovery is the basis for a self-sustaining nuclear **chain reaction,** and because of the tremendous amount of energy released, it is the basis of the nuclear bomb.

The reaction is self-sustaining only if the mass of uranium-235 is of a certain minimum or **critical size.**

QUESTIONS

1. What two sources of nuclear energy were known before 1940?
2. Why was neither important as a practical source of energy?
3. What discovery of Hahn and Strassmann made possible the development of the nuclear bomb?
4. Why is the process involved in the bomb called fission?
5. What is meant by a chain reaction?
6. Explain the term *critical size* as applied to the bomb.
7. Why is it necessary, in making the bomb, to use highly purified fissionable material?
8. Explain the three principal sources of injury from nuclear-bomb attack.
9. It is said that white clothing is better protection than dark-colored clothing in a nuclear-bomb attack. Explain.
10. Why are civilians taught to face away from a possible point of a nuclear-bomb explosion and to turn up the collars of their coats?

CHAPTER **20**

the uranium reactor:

constructive applications

of nuclear energy

Nuclear energy is not confined to military and destructive uses. Less familiar to the public, but perhaps of greater long-range significance, are applications of nuclear energy to the needs of the civilian world.

A controlled chain reaction

Return once again to the conditions necessary for a chain reaction (see Chap. 19, pages 209 and 210). Suppose you have a sample of uranium, free of other elements, but containing both isotopes uranium-235 and uranium-238. You can see that neutrons released in the sample could (1) escape, (2) cause additional uranium-235 fission, or (3) be absorbed by uranium-238.

Now suppose the sample of purified uranium is made larger. The probability of a certain neutron escaping from it is thereby decreased so that as the sample is made larger, a greater proportion of released neutrons are accounted for by factors 2 and 3.

Scientists find that the relative tendencies of uranium-235 and uranium-238 to absorb neutrons is such that a chain reaction is possible with purified uranium metal, if the proper conditions of size and shape of the uranium sample are met.

You may recall from Chap. 19, pages 209 and 210, that, if the efficiency of a chain reaction is just 1, the reaction will occur at a constant

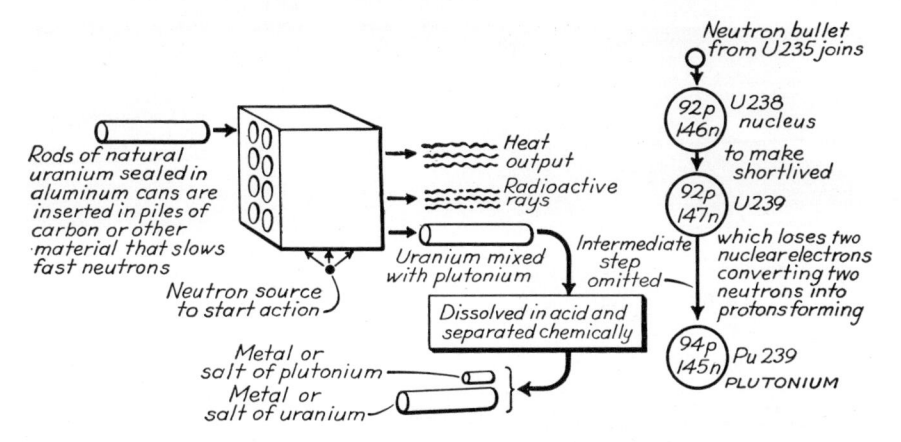

Fig. 20-1. How plutonium is made from uranium.

rate. A chain reaction of ever-increasing rate leading to an explosion requires a chain efficiency of more than 1. It is therefore possible to control the rate of the fission reaction by inserting, into the mass of uranium, rods containing boron which strongly absorbs neutrons. Insertion of such rods slows the fission reaction and keeps it from getting out of hand.

The uranium reactor

A controlled chain reaction can be carried out on the basis described in the preceding paragraph. Such a system is known as a uranium **pile** or **reactor.** One type of reactor consists of rods of uranium metal containing uranium-235 and uranium-238 (in the same ratio as they occur in nature), inserted into a large cubic structure made up of graphite[1] bricks.

The graphite bricks are necessary because a neutron, as it is released by a fission reaction, is moving with very high velocity. Such a neutron, on entering a uranium-235 nucleus, might plow right through it without causing fission, because of its high velocity. The neutron is much more likely to produce a fission if it first has been slowed down. Graphite does not absorb neutrons, but a neutron's velocity is reduced when it passes through a layer of graphite. When used in this way, graphite is known as a **moderator.** Heavy water (D_2O) also is used as a moderator (in place of graphite) in at least one uranium reactor.

Figure 20-1 is a schematic diagram of a uranium reactor. Neutrons released in one uranium rod wander through the graphite and are thereby slowed down until they enter another rod. There some of the neutrons enter a uranium-235 nucleus, producing another fission, which keeps the reaction going. Other neutrons enter the nucleus of a uranium-238 atom.

[1] A form of pure carbon.

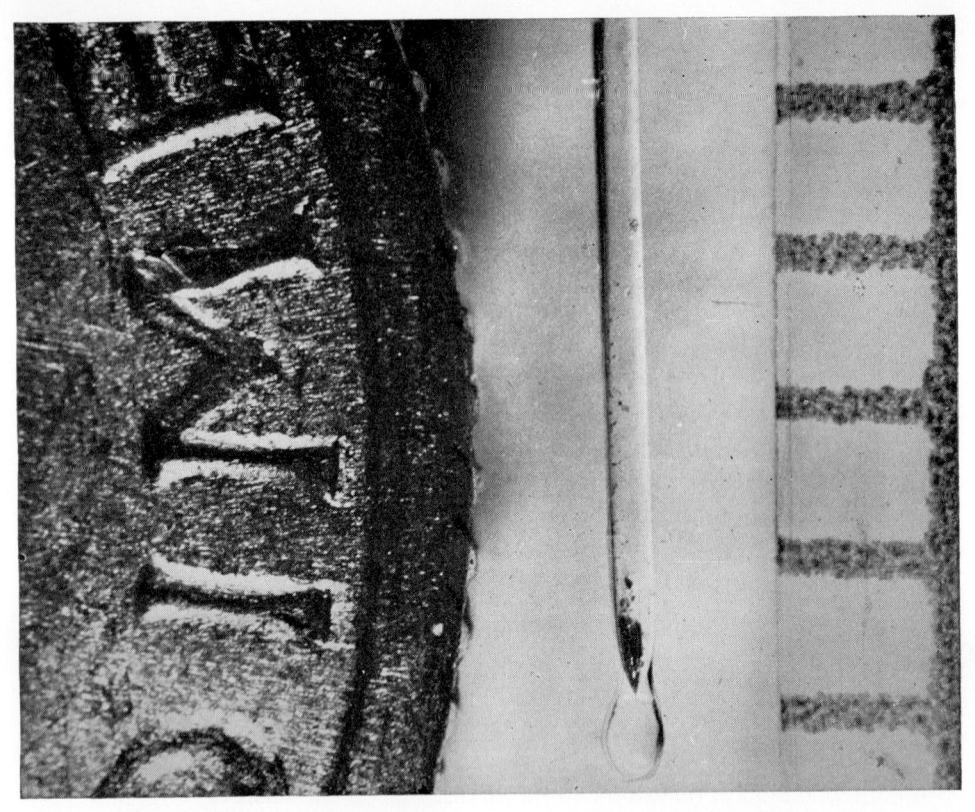

A very small amount of neptunium oxide in a capillary tube. (Compared with dime and millimeter scale.) Neptunium is formed by the disintegration of uranium-238.

Those neutrons which enter the uranium-238 nucleus set up the following series of reactions:

$$_{92}U^{238} + {_0}n^1 \rightarrow {_{92}}U^{239}$$
(radioactive)

$$_{92}U^{239} \rightarrow {_{93}}Np^{239} + {_{-1}}e^0$$

(Np is the element with atomic number 93, named neptunium. The half-life period for this *reaction* is only 23 min.)

$$_{93}Np^{239} \rightarrow {_{94}}Pu^{239} + {_{-1}}e^0$$

(Pu is the element with atomic number 94, named plutonium. This reaction also is rapid; its half-life period is 2.3 days.)

Plutonium-239, while it is somewhat radioactive (it emits α particles), emits particles slowly. *It is fissionable in essentially the same way as uranium-235.*

Applications of the uranium reactor

There are three principal uses for the uranium reactor: (1) the production of plutonium for use in a nuclear bomb, (2) the production of energy, and (3) the production of radioactive isotopes.

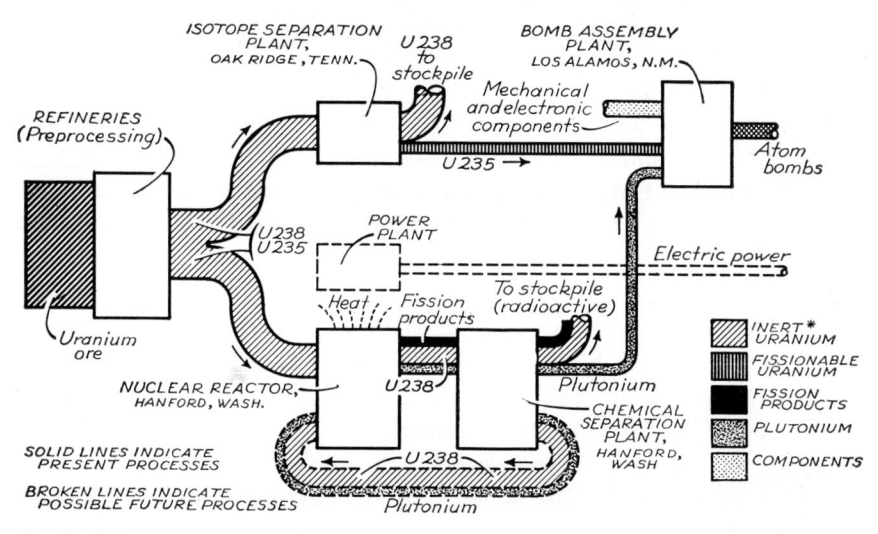

Fig. 20-2. The atomic process. The development from uranium ore to bombs, isotopes, and power.

The production of plutonium

Plutonium can be made into a nuclear bomb, as can uranium-235. The bomb dropped on Nagasaki was a plutonium bomb.

In the production of plutonium, the reactor is shut down after operation for the proper length of time. The uranium rods are removed, and the plutonium which has been formed is separated by chemical means.

In this country plutonium is at present produced principally at the **Hanford,** Ore., plant of the U.S. Atomic Energy Commission.

The production of energy

The fission going on in the reactor liberates energy. This energy appears as heat. The amount of heat depends, of course, on the size of the pile and the rate at which the reaction is allowed to run. However, in terms of the amount of uranium used, the energy released is enormous. One pound of uranium-235 on fission releases 8,600,000,000,000 cal, which is equivalent to the energy from 3,000,000 lb of coal or 200,000 gal of gasoline.[1]

This energy may be used to heat water or air, generate steam for electric power, drive battleships, submarines, even perhaps drive rocket ships through interstellar space.

This application of nuclear energy is one which gives promise of being of great benefit to mankind; and, if enough uranium is found on the earth, may one day furnish most of the energy which man needs.

[1] This is equivalent to approximately three percent of all the electrical energy generated in the United States per day during 1939.

The design of a reactor to be employed for the production of useful energy differs in detail from that of a reactor employed for the production of plutonium. The reactor at Hanford, Ore., run by the U.S. Atomic Energy Commission, was built to produce plutonium, not useful amounts of energy. Yet such a reactor does produce heat when it operates and this heat must be removed to keep the reactor from overheating. At Hanford, the heat is removed by the water of the Columbia River. We are told that the temperature of the Columbia River is measurably higher below the reactor than above it.

Experimental reactors for the production of useful energy are now in operation in many different countries.

From the limited information made available to the public on reactors, it was generally believed that they were necessarily very massive affairs containing thousands of pounds of uranium metal and graphite and shielded by walls of concrete many feet thick. It now appears that this is the case for a reactor operating on uranium metal of the same ratio of uranium-235 to uranium-238 as found in nature. More recently, however, a reactor has been developed which is entirely contained within a hollow metal ball 1 ft in diameter! It operates on uranium which has been enriched in the uranium-235 isotope.

The production of radioactive isotopes

Many elements, when placed in a reactor, absorb neutrons and become radioactive. Thus cobalt, when inserted into the reactor, becomes radioactive as follows:

$$_{27}Co^{59} + {}_{0}n^{1} \longrightarrow {}_{27}Co^{60}$$
$$\text{(from pile)} \qquad \text{(radioactive cobalt)}$$

Its radioactivity is as follows:

$$_{27}Co^{60} \rightarrow {}_{28}Ni^{60} + {}_{-1}e^{0} + \gamma \text{ rays}$$

The γ rays so produced have been found equivalent to those from radium in the treatment of cancer. **Radiocobalt** is largely replacing radium for this purpose. Unlike radium, which costs many thousands of dollars per gram, radiocobalt can be produced very cheaply. It is formed by placing a sample of ordinary cobalt metal in the reactor for the proper length of time. Radiocobalt can, therefore, be made available to almost anyone who has need of it. The U.S. Atomic Energy Commission has made it available to qualified physicians in this country without charge other than the cost of transporting it from Oak Ridge, Tenn., where it is produced.

A radioisotope of iodine can be produced in the reactor in the same fashion. This **radioiodine** gives great promise as a cure for cancer of the thyroid. It will be recalled that all isotopes of an element, whether

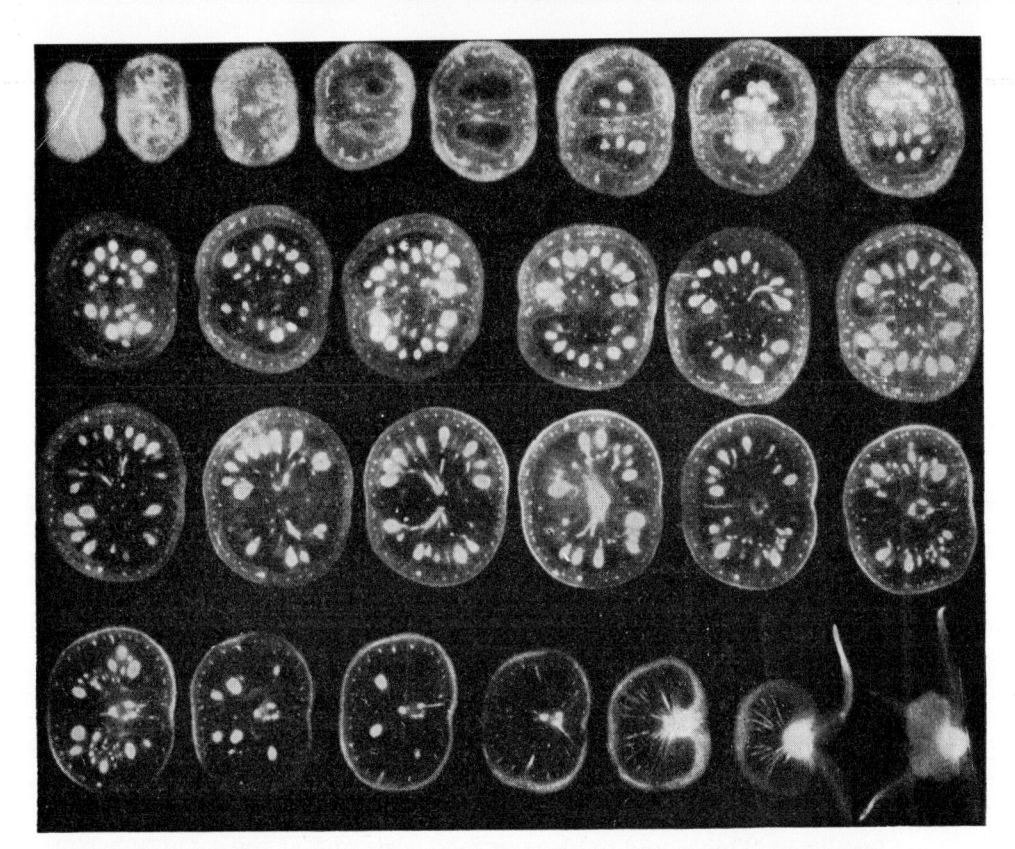

Photograph of tomatoes grown in soil containing radiozinc. The radiozinc causes the light areas. (University of California)

radioactive or not, have the same chemical properties (see Chap. 18, pages 197 to 201). When radioiodine is taken by mouth into the human body, most of it goes, as does ordinary iodine, into the thyroid gland. In this way a radioactive substance can be sent to the actual seat of the malignancy. Many cases of thyroid cancer have been arrested in this way, although no one can say for certain that they have been cured, since sufficient time has not yet passed.

It has been found that a compound containing **radiophosphorus** ($_{15}P^{32}$) prepared in the reactor, when administered to human beings, concentrates in the bone cells. This promises to be a method of arresting cancer of the bone. Cancer of the bone is a particularly difficult condition to treat by radium or external x rays because it is almost impossible to get radiations from external sources to the seat of the malignancy without serious damage to the body as a whole.

One other illustration will serve to show another type of use for radioisotopes. The photograph on this page shows tomatoes grown in soil containing radiozinc compounds. This element takes its own picture because of its ability to affect a photographic plate. It is apparent at first glance just what part of the fruit contains the zinc.

The west face of a uranium reactor at the Brookhaven National Laboratories. It is in reactors such as these that plutonium is made. Radioactive isotopes can also be prepared in this type of reactor. (Brookhaven National Laboratories)

The technique used with radiozinc may also be applied to radiophosphorus. Phosphorus is an element of great importance in plant growth. Every year millions of dollars' worth of phosphorus fertilizers are used in this country. Yet up to now science has found out very little about the way in which phosphorus becomes available and is absorbed from the soil into the plant. Nor do we know just what role it serves in the growth of the plant. If these things were understood more fully, we could expect to develop methods for more efficient use of phosphorus fertilizers. This would reduce our food costs and at the same time conserve our natural resources of this highly essential element. Studies with radiophosphorus will in time supply the answers to these questions.

A radioactive form of any element can be employed to study the role of that element in a certain process. This is true because the radioelement behaves chemically in the same way as stable forms of that element. However, because of its radiations, a radioelement is easily traced through a process. This method of study is usually known as **tracer** technique.

A large number of different elements in radioactive form are now available through the Atomic Energy Commission, to any qualified scientist in this country, for such tracer studies.

It has been said that the discovery of controlled nuclear energy is the greatest discovery since man discovered the use and control of fire. In the words of one scientist, "Radioactivity gives us the best tool since the invention of the microscope for the study of living organisms."

KEY WORDS

| Hanford | pile | radioiodine | reactor |
| moderator | radiocobalt | radiophosphorus | tracer |

HIGHLIGHTS

The uranium **reactor** is a device for producing nuclear energy under controllable conditions in contrast to the explosive release of energy in the nuclear bomb. Uranium metal (containing 0.7 percent uranium-235) and bricks of graphite are built into a **pile** in such a manner as to leave cavities into which control rods may be inserted. The neutrons emitted by fission of uranium-235 nuclei are slowed down by the graphite which is therefore called a **moderator.** If the action becomes too rapid, rods of cadmium or boron steel are inserted into the cavities of the pile to absorb the neutrons.

The reactor is used to produce the element plutonium which in turn may be used to make a nuclear-fission bomb such as was used at Nagasaki.

The reactor is the most practical device now known to generate the tremendous quantities of energy that can be used for peaceful purposes. The reactor is also being used to prepare the radioactive isotopes of such elements as cobalt, iodine, and phosphorus, which are used in medicine, industry, and for research purposes.

QUESTIONS

1. What is a uranium reactor?
2. What important products may be produced in a uranium reactor?
3. What means can be employed in a uranium reactor to keep the reaction from becoming too rapid?
4. What is plutonium? Of what importance is it?
5. How are radioactive isotopes prepared in a uranium reactor?
6. What are the uses for radiocobalt?
7. What are the uses for radioiodine?
8. Explain how radioactive isotopes are used as tracers.

CHAPTER 21

the planetary electrons: chemical properties and atomic number

In an earlier chapter you read that the chemical properties of an atom are determined by its atomic number. Now you will see why this is true and learn to relate the properties of an element to its atomic number.

Briefly the relation is as follows: Chemical combination between two elements comes about as a result of the tendency of the reacting atoms to either lose or gain planetary electrons. The number of planetary electrons which an atom in the uncombined state possesses is equal to its atomic number. This number determines whether the atom tends to lose or gain electrons; hence it determines the elements with which it will combine. The nucleus of an atom is never changed in any way in chemical reactions.

Electron orbits

You have probably learned that the planets revolve about the sun. Further you probably know that the force of gravitation between a planet and the sun tends to draw the two bodies together. This force, however, is just balanced by the centrifugal force of the planet, which tends to make it travel out into space in a straight line, like water flying off a rotating automobile wheel. This situation is somewhat like that of a ball on the end of a rubber string being rotated, at constant speed, about a boy's finger. The tendency of the rubber band to contract just balances the centrifugal force of the ball.

These cases are roughly analogous to the structure of the atom. A positively charged nucleus is surrounded by negatively charged electrons equal in number to the nuclear charge if the atom is in the uncombined state. These planetary electrons are prevented from falling into the nucleus by the fact that they are moving (in circles or ellipses[1]) about the nucleus. The centrifugal force which each electron possesses as a result of its orbital motion just balances the electrical force tending to pull the electron into the nucleus. Thus in the normal unexcited atom each planetary electron moves in a definite orbit around the nucleus.

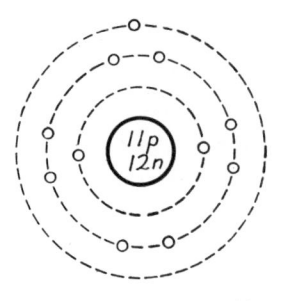

Fig. 21–1. Sodium atom. Note planetary electrons.

This situation is described schematically in Fig. 21–1, which shows the sodium atom ($_{11}Na^{23}$). For simplicity, the orbits are all shown as circles, although actually some of them are ellipses. Since the atomic number of sodium is 11 and since all atoms in the uncombined state are electrically neutral, there are eleven planetary electrons. You will see that two of these are shown in the orbit closest to the nucleus, eight in the next orbit, and one in the third orbit from the nucleus.

The arrangement of the electrons in the various orbits

It has been found that only certain numbers of electrons can be in a given orbit at the same time. The maximum number of electrons which can be in a given orbit at the same time is given by the expression $2(N^2)$, where N is the number of the orbit starting from the nucleus. Thus,

Orbit Number	Maximum Electron Capacity
1	2
2	8
3	18
4	32

There are two limitations to this rule:

1. The outermost orbit which contains electrons can never contain more than 8 for the free element, regardless of which orbit it is. Thus the preceding table says that orbit number 3 can contain 18 electrons. But if orbit number 3 is the outermost orbit to contain electrons, it cannot hold more than 8. If, however, there are electrons present in orbit number 4, then orbit number 3 can contain up to 18.

2. The next to the outermost orbit can never contain more than

[1] An ellipse can be considered as a flattened circle.

18 electrons whatever its number happens to be. This rule limits only the capacity of orbits greater than 3. If, for example, there are electrons in orbit numbers 1, 2, 3, 4, and 5, then orbit number 4 is limited to a capacity of 18. Only when there are electrons in all orbits up to and including orbit number 6 can orbit number 4 reach its maximum capacity of 32 electrons.

The electronic structure of some of the elements

Figure 21-2 shows the electronic structure of some of the elements. The structure of each can be predicted by use of the rules just given.

The element with atomic number 1, hydrogen, has but one electron. It is in orbit number 1. The element with atomic number 2, helium, has two electrons, both in orbit number 1. The element with atomic number 3, lithium, has three electrons, two of which are in orbit number 1, leaving one for orbit number 2. As the atomic number increases, each additional electron is found in orbit number 2 until the element with atomic number 10, neon, is reached. Orbit number 2 is now filled. The additional electron of the sodium atom, then, is found in orbit number 3, and so on, through the other elements shown.

The electron structure of the **inert gases** (Group Zero) are particularly important since they furnish the key to the structures of the other elements. They are given in Table 21-1. You should study the

TABLE 21-1. The electron structures of the inert gases

Element	Atomic number	Orbit number 1	Orbit number 2	Orbit number 3	Orbit number 4	Orbit number 5	Orbit number 6
Helium	2	2					
Neon	10	2	8				
Argon	18	2	8	8			
Krypton	36	2	8	18	8		
Xenon	54	2	8	18	18	8	
Radon	86	2	8	18	32	18	8

table in connection with the rules given on page 225 and should learn to reproduce the table by application of these rules.

The electron structures of all the elements are given in the Appendix, page 688. You will note that in the case of each element its electronic structure is closely related to the electronic structures of the two inert gases nearest it in the periodic table. Thus the structure of potassium is that of argon plus one electron. Carbon has an electron structure intermediate between that of helium and that of neon.

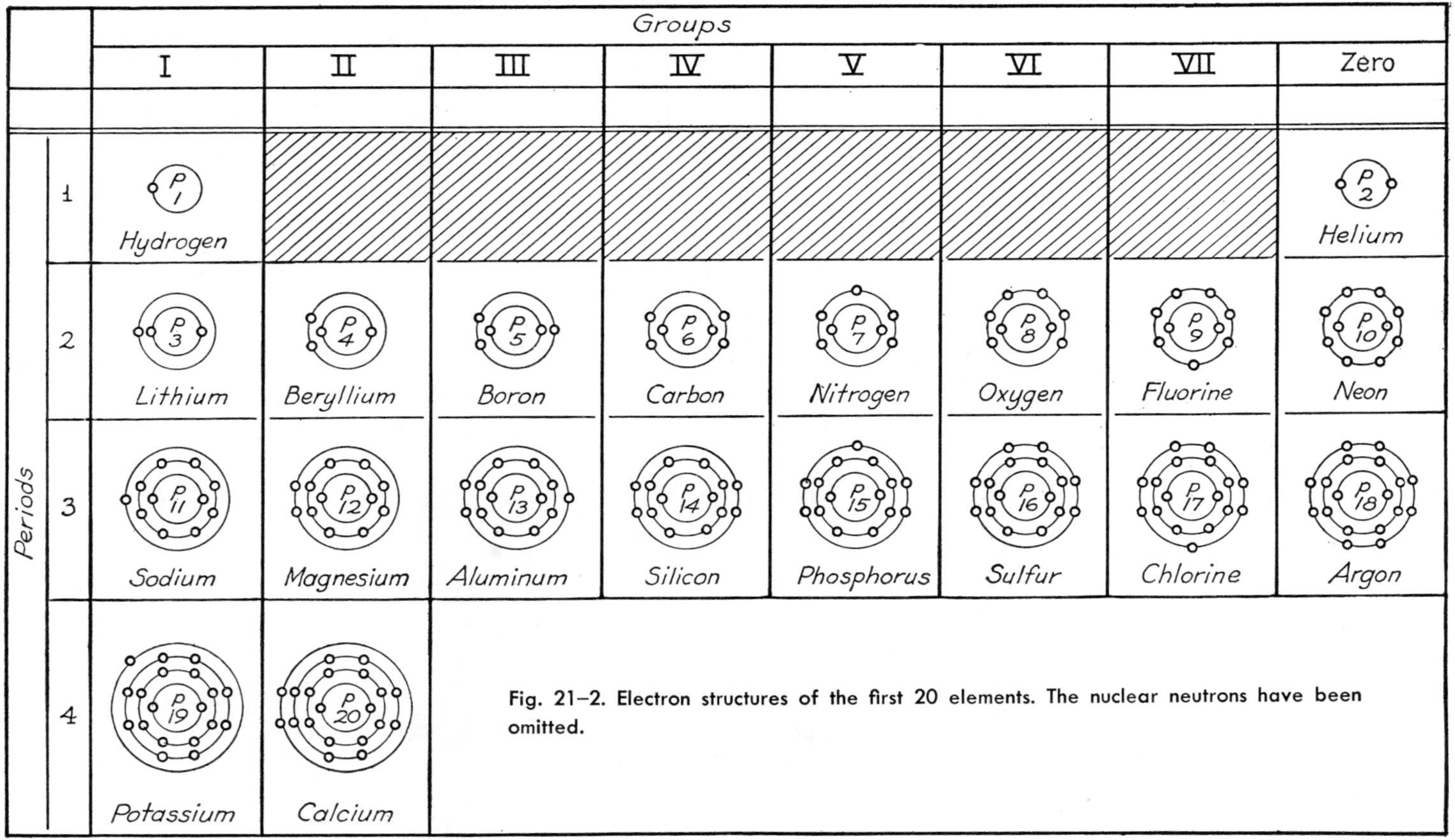

Fig. 21-2. Electron structures of the first 20 elements. The nuclear neutrons have been omitted.

Electrovalence

"Atoms of one element unite with atoms of another and are held together by forces of chemical affinity." It is known now that Dalton's "forces of chemical affinity" are electrical in nature. When an atom enters into chemical combination, it does so by losing or gaining or sharing electrons. Each atom tends to acquire, as nearly as possible, the electronic structure of the inert gas nearest it in the periodic table. Generally only the electrons in the outermost orbit are involved in chemical reactions. For this reason this orbit is known as the **valence orbit**.

Consider sodium and chlorine:

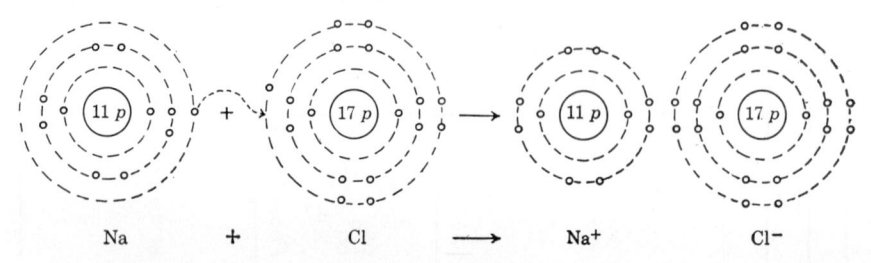

Na + Cl → Na⁺ Cl⁻

By losing one electron, sodium could acquire the electronic structure of the inert gas neon. By gaining one electron, chlorine could acquire the electronic structure of argon. Therefore, when sodium atoms and chlorine atoms come into contact, one electron is transferred from sodium to chlorine, forming sodium chloride:

$$2Na + Cl_2 \rightarrow 2Na^+Cl^-$$

The sodium atom thereby becomes positively charged, the chlorine negatively charged.

Consider magnesium and fluorine:

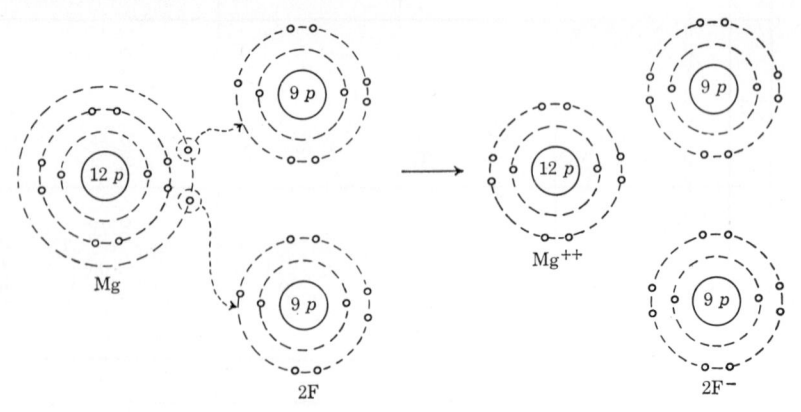

Mg   2F   Mg⁺⁺   2F⁻

The magnesium atom tends to lose two electrons. The fluorine atom tends to gain only one. Therefore one magnesium atom will combine

228

with two fluorine atoms to form magnesium fluoride. The formula of this compound will be MgF_2.

$$Mg + F_2 \rightarrow Mg^{++}(F^-)_2$$

Valence is determined by the number of electrons which an atom tends to lose or gain.

In the formation of compounds of this type, the atoms become charged electrically as the result of loss or gain of electrons. The force which holds the atoms together is the electrical attraction between the oppositely charged atoms. For this reason this type of valence is called **electrovalence** and the resulting compounds are said to be **electrovalent compounds.**

Electrovalent compounds will be formed when a metal, which tends to lose electrons, reacts with a nonmetal, which tends to gain electrons. Examples of electrovalent compounds are:

$$KCl \quad BeO$$
$$CaS \quad K_2S$$
$$Li_2O \quad MgBr_2$$

The student should work out for himself the electron shift involved in each case.

Electrovalent compounds are always solids at room temperature and generally have high melting points. This is because these solids are made up of positive and negative ions which strongly attract each other. The numerical value of the electrovalence is equal to the number of electrons a neutral atom gains or loses in entering into a compound.

Covalence

Not all compound formation involves electrovalence. Many compounds are formed in another way. Imagine two chlorine atoms:

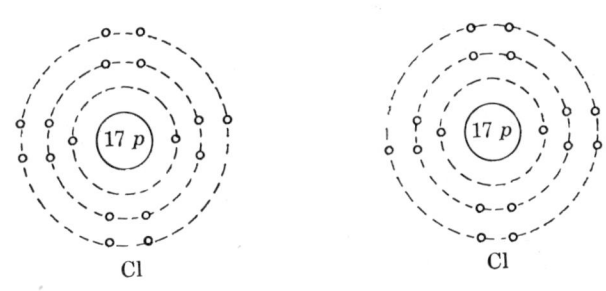

Now each of these chlorine atoms tends to acquire another electron (and thereby have the same electronic structure as argon). But neither atom wishes to give up an electron. The only way both atoms can satisfy their tendencies to have eight electrons in the outermost orbit is for the two to share two electrons together. In this way both have

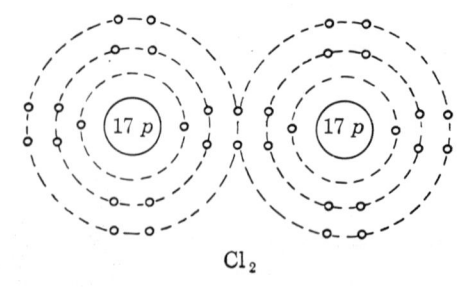

Cl$_2$

the use of eight electrons in the valence orbit although there are only 14 electrons involved. Since this is a cooperative affair, this type of valence is called covalence. The numerical value of the covalence is equal to the number of pairs of electrons which an atom shares with other atoms when it enters into **covalent compound** formation.

In this particular case the result of sharing electrons is not a compound, since both atoms are the same element. However, this illustration does explain why elementary chlorine has a formula Cl$_2$.

The compound between hydrogen and chlorine is of the same valence type. The hydrogen atom, having one electron, needs to acquire another (and thereby resemble helium); so a pair of electrons is shared between the hydrogen and the chlorine.

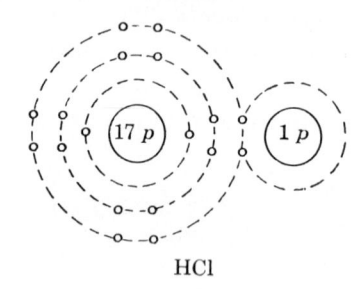

HCl

Water also is a covalent compound.

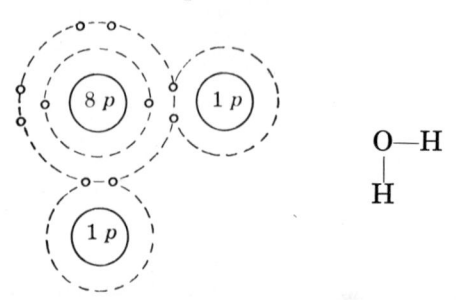

O—H
|
H

Here both oxygen and hydrogen tend to gain electrons. But since oxygen needs to gain two electrons, it shares electrons with two separate hydrogen atoms. In the additional schematic diagrams below only the electrons in the outer orbits are shown.

Nitrogen and hydrogen give ammonia, NH$_3$.

(H) : (N) : (H)   Note that the covalence of nitrogen here is 3.

(H)

Methane, or marsh gas, is CH$_4$.

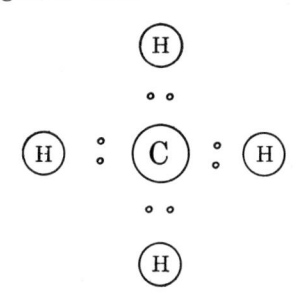

(H)

(H) : (C) : (H)

(H)

It is important to understand the difference between the forces holding the atoms together in electrovalence and those holding the atoms together in covalence. In covalence charged atoms are not formed—electron transfer does not occur. The atoms are held together by the pair of electrons which both must use. For this reason the bond is sometimes called an **electron pair** bond. Covalent bonds result from two electrons spinning in opposite directions.

The covalent compounds

Covalent compounds can be formed only between two elements which are both electron gainers. These are the nonmetals.

Covalent compounds are generally gases or liquids at room temperature or solids with low melting points. Examples are water (H$_2$O), ammonia (NH$_3$), carbon dioxide (CO$_2$), hydrogen chloride (HCl), and hydrogen sulfide (H$_2$S).

Electronic structure and activity of the metals

It has been found that the most active metals are those in Group Ia. These are the elements which follow the inert gases in the periodic table. Their high activity is due to the fact that, on losing their valence electron, they acquire the electronic structure of an inert gas. The activity of a metal represents its tendency to lose electrons.

The next most active group of metals is Group IIa. In the periodic table these elements all follow an inert gas by two places. Hence the elements which make up Group IIa acquire an inert gas structure by losing two electrons.

Within Group Ia the order of activity is found to be

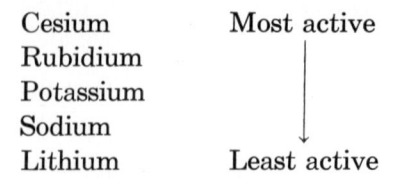

        Cesium   Most active
        Rubidium
        Potassium
        Sodium
        Lithium   Least active

This variation in activity is due to the variation in size of the atoms involved. All have comparable structures. Taking the two extremes

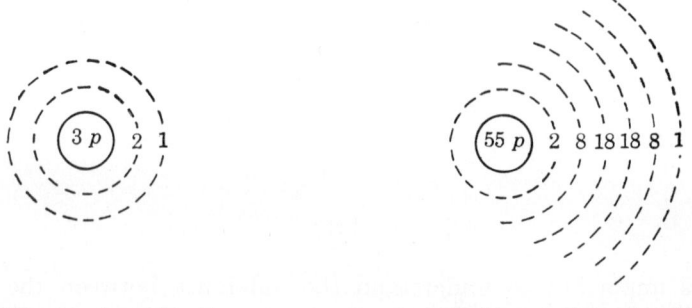

Lithium, atomic number 3   Cesium, atomic number 55

(The figures represent the total numbers of electrons in the various orbits.) The valence electron in the case of cesium is farthest from the nucleus. The positive nucleus attracts the electron least in the case of cesium and most in the case of lithium. Therefore, the electron on cesium is removed more easily than the electron on lithium, and cesium is more active than lithium.

It should be noted that not all the elements of Group I are high in activity. Copper, silver, and gold all are notably low in activity. The low activity of these metals is due to their electronic structures, all of which are similar. Taking copper as an example, its structure is

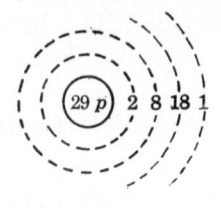

Although copper does have one electron in its outermost orbit, it **does not have an inert gas structure underneath.** Thus even by losing one or two electrons, copper cannot acquire an inert gas structure. As a result it shows only a slight tendency to lose any electrons.

Activity of the nonmetals

The most active nonmetals are the halogen group consisting of the elements fluorine, chlorine, bromine, and iodine. Activity of a nonmetal indicates the tendency to acquire electrons. It is therefore to be expected that the halogens would be the most active since each of them needs only one electron to assume an inert gas structure.

The variation of activity within the group is

Fluorine	Most active
Chlorine	↑
Bromine	↓
Iodine	Least active

In understanding why the activity is in the given order, remember that the valence electrons are farthest from the nucleus in iodine. Remember also that by the activity of a halogen we mean a tendency to gain an electron. Therefore, the electron will be gained most readily by fluorine and least readily by iodine.

The modern periodic system

Valence and other chemical properties are thus determined by *atomic number*. Mendeléeff's periodic table, which was based on *atomic weights*, succeeded only because of the coincidence that the atomic weights of the elements are approximately twice their atomic numbers. The reversals which he found in three cases were due to the relative abundance of different isotopes of these elements, which gave them average atomic weights in reverse order of their atomic numbers.

The modern periodic table, such as that given in Chap. 16, page 174, is thus actually based on atomic number.

KEY WORDS

covalence	electron pair	inert gases
covalent compounds	electrovalence	valence orbit
electron orbit	electrovalent compounds	

HIGHLIGHTS

The number of planetary electrons of a neutral atom always equals the number of protons in the nucleus (that is, the atomic number). The planetary electrons are arranged in **orbits** about the nucleus. The maximum number of electrons in each orbit is determined by the relative position of the orbit and the total number of orbits.

The **inert gases** (helium, neon, argon, krypton, xenon, and radon) are the elements containing the maximum number of electrons in each orbit, the total number of orbits being one, two, three, four, five, and six, respectively.

When atoms of other elements unite, they tend to do so in such a way that the number of electrons in the outermost (or **valence**) orbit becomes in effect that of the most closely related inert gas. When a metal loses electrons to a nonmetal, the resulting compound is said to be **electrovalent**. When two or more nonmetals combine by sharing electrons which are in their outermost orbit, the resulting compound is said to be **covalent**.

The relative activity of elements depends largely on how many valence electrons must be gained or lost to attain an inert gas electronic structure and on how strong the attraction of the nucleus is for valence electrons, that is, how close the **valence orbit** is to the nucleus.

QUESTIONS

1. Which property, the atomic number or the atomic weight, determines the chemical properties of an atom? Explain.
2. Draw a schematic diagram of the electron structure of calcium and of fluorine.
3. From the diagrams of question 2, show what happens when calcium and fluorine combine.
4. Explain in terms of electron structures why the formula for chlorine gas is Cl_2.
5. Explain in terms of electron structures why the valence of beryllium is 2, whereas that of sodium is 1.
6. Draw electron-structure diagrams illustrating the formation of an electrovalent compound.
7. What types of elements form electrovalent compounds? Why?
8. Would you expect an electrovalent compound to be a solid, a liquid, or a gas at room temperature?
9. What is a covalent compound? Give an electron-structure diagram to illustrate such a compound.
10. What type of elements form covalent compounds?
11. What can you say about the physical properties of covalent compounds?
12. Explain why potassium is more active than sodium.
13. Would you expect magnesium to be more active than calcium? Explain.
14. Fluorine is the most active nonmetal known. Can you explain this fact in terms of electron structures?

CHAPTER **22**

the halogen family

The group known as the **halogens** and made up of the elements fluorine, chlorine, bromine, iodine, and astatine (At) is an excellent illustration of the classifications given by the periodic table.

Astatine was unknown before 1940 and, so far as is known, does not occur in appreciable quantities in nature. This element was prepared artificially by bombarding bismuth with high-speed α particles in a cyclotron.

$$_{83}Bi^{209} + {}_2He^4 \rightarrow {}_{85}At^{211} + 2\,{}_0n^1$$

The element is radioactive. It is from this fact that the name astatine (from the Greek word meaning *unstable*) is derived. At present astatine is of no practical importance and we shall not consider it further.

The halogens are typical nonmetals, all of which react with the active metals to form compounds similar to sodium chloride. Their name, halogen (from the Greek word meaning *salt former*), is due to this fact. All show a valence of 1. All are poisonous in the free state. When inhaled in low concentrations, they destroy the tissue of the nose and throat.

Chlorine

Chlorine has the dubious distinction of being the first poison gas used in modern warfare. In 1915 the Germans made a surprise attack on the Allies in which gaseous chlorine was released from steel cylinders containing the element. In this way the gas warfare for which World War I is noted was started.

The element chlorine was first prepared in 1774 by the Swedish chemist Scheele, who obtained it by heating manganese dioxide and hydrochloric acid (HCl). The English chemist **Humphry Davy** (1778–1829) proved that it was an element and gave it the name chlorine (from the Greek word meaning *light green*).

Crystals of halite. Halite is the mineral name for rock salt, or sodium chloride. This mineral is one of our most important industrial materials. (The American Museum of Natural History)

Occurrence of Chlorine

It is estimated that 0.2 percent of the earth's crust is chlorine. It is much too reactive to occur uncombined in nature, but it is found in nature combined with various metals as chlorides. By far the most important compound containing chlorine is sodium chloride, or rock salt. The mineral name for this compound is **halite.** Sea water contains about 2.8 percent sodium chloride. Including the smaller amounts of other metal chlorides, sea water contains 1.9 percent of chloride. This is equivalent to nearly 90 million tons of the element per cubic mile of sea water. Here indeed is a natural resource which is inexhaustible.

In past geologic periods, parts of oceans were cut off by shifting land surfaces and the water made to evaporate slowly. In this way great mineral deposits of rock salt have been formed in the United States, Germany, Russia, and other places. There are large deposits in New York State, Michigan, and Louisiana. In America, rock salt is one of

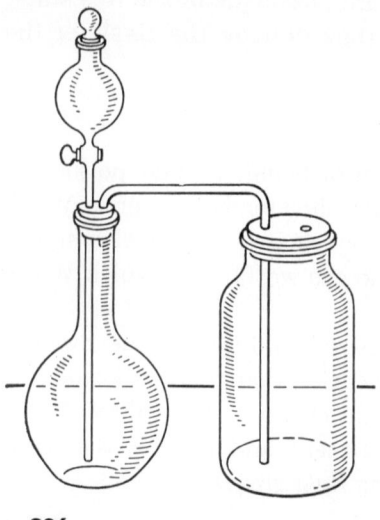

Fig. 22–1. A setup for the laboratory preparation of chlorine. The gas is collected by the upward displacement of air.

our cheapest and our most important industrial raw materials. In some other parts of the world less generously supplied with the mineral, sodium chloride is obtained directly from sea water. Sometimes it is obtained by evaporation of the water by heat from the sun after the water has been pumped into shallow basins. In very cold climates the salt in sea water may be concentrated by freezing. Only water freezes out when sea water is cooled. The salt remains in the solution. The resulting concentrated brine is then evaporated by artificial heat.

Preparation of Chlorine

In the laboratory, chlorine may be obtained by heating hydrochloric acid with manganese dioxide. This is the method that Scheele used.

$$4HCl + MnO_2 \rightarrow MnCl_2 + 2H_2O + Cl_2 \uparrow$$

The reaction is somewhat awkward to carry out since the mixture must be kept heated and it is apt to "bump."

A more expensive but also easier method of laboratory preparation is to use potassium permanganate in place of manganese dioxide. In this case the reaction takes place as soon as the reactants are mixed, and no heating is required. The reaction is best carried out by dropwise addition of hydrochloric acid, made up of equal volumes of concentrated acid and water, to crystals of the potassium permanganate in a flask as shown in Fig. 22–1.

$$2KMnO_4 + 16HCl \rightarrow 2KCl + 2MnCl_2 + 8H_2O + 5Cl_2 \uparrow *$$

*This reaction, which is more complicated to balance than most of those in this book, is of the type known as an oxidation-reduction reaction. A general method for balancing this type of reaction is given in Chap. 51, which at the discretion of the teacher, may be omitted or taken up at any time after Chap. 27.

Since chlorine is rather soluble in water and is more dense than air, it should be collected by the upward displacement of air (Fig. 22–1).

Chlorine is prepared industrially by the electrolysis of water solutions of sodium chloride.

$$2NaCl + 2H_2O \xrightarrow{electrolysis} Cl_2 \uparrow + H_2 \uparrow + 2NaOH$$

This reaction is of great economic importance because it produces not only chlorine but two other substances which are widely used industrially. When the reaction is carried out, chlorine is liberated at the positive electrode, hydrogen is liberated at the negative electrode, and sodium hydroxide accumulates in the solution surrounding the negative electrode. The sodium hydroxide is obtained as a white solid by evaporating the solution removed from around the negative electrode. An explanation of this and other electrolysis reactions will be given in Chap. 27, pages 297 to 299 and 302 to 303.

Electrolysis cells for the production of chlorine on an industrial scale. (Pennsylvania Salt Manufacturing Co.)

Physical properties of chlorine

Chlorine is a greenish-yellow gas with a boiling point of $-34.6°C$. Its critical temperature (Chap. 11, pages 97 and 98) is $144°C$. It can therefore exist as a liquid at room temperature and higher temperatures. Commercially chlorine is stored and shipped as a liquid under pressure in stout steel cylinders.

You have read that the element is too soluble in water to be collected over water. One volume of water dissolves 4.6 volumes of chlorine at room temperature.

Chlorine has a sharp, suffocating odor and is very poisonous if inhaled for any length of time, even in concentrations as low as 100 parts per million of air.

Chemical properties of chlorine

The element chlorine is very active chemically. The relation between this fact and the electronic structure of the element has been discussed in the preceding chapter.

1. Reaction with metals. Under proper conditions chlorine combines directly with all the metals, including the noble[1] metals. With many the reaction is so vigorous that light is produced. This occurs when powdered antimony is dusted into a cylinder containing chlorine.

$$2Sb + 3Cl_2 \rightarrow 2SbCl_3$$

[1] Silver, gold, and platinum are often called the noble metals.

Chlorine is shipped as a liquid in strong steel tanks. The tanks are filled with chlorine gas at a pressure that liquefies the chlorine. (Pennsylvania Salt Manufacturing Co.)

Sodium burns brilliantly in chlorine, forming crystalline sodium chloride.

$$2Na + Cl_2 \rightarrow 2NaCl$$

Since chlorine combines so vigorously with the metals you may wonder how it is possible to store the chlorine in steel cylinders. The reason is that for this reaction to occur, a trace of water is generally required as catalyst. Dry chlorine does not attack a steel cylinder.

2. Reaction with nonmetals. Chlorine unites vigorously with hydrogen. A jet of hydrogen lighted in air will continue to burn with a greenish flame when placed in a cylinder of chlorine. The reaction is

$$H_2 + Cl_2 \rightarrow 2HCl$$

The reaction is much like the combination of hydrogen and oxygen and almost as vigorous. The product is a gas known as hydrogen chloride. A water solution of this gas is known as hydrochloric acid.

A mixture of hydrogen and chlorine when cold and in the dark shows no tendency to react. But sunlight or a burning magnesium ribbon starts the reaction, which then takes place with explosive violence.

$$H_2 + Cl_2 \xrightarrow{\text{radiant energy}} 2HCl$$

Chlorine does not combine *directly* with carbon, oxygen, or nitrogen.

Chlorine water

When added to water, chlorine forms two acids

$$H_2O + Cl_2 \rightarrow \underset{\substack{\text{hydro-}\\\text{chloric}\\\text{acid}}}{HCl} + \underset{\substack{\text{hypo-}\\\text{chlorous}\\\text{acid}}}{HClO}$$

Dry chlorine is not a bleaching agent. This photograph shows that a colored piece of cotton may be placed in a bottle filled with chlorine without being bleached so long as no water is present.

The disinfecting action of chlorine water, which was mentioned in Chap. 13, pages 135 and 136, is due to the presence of **hypochlorous** acid formed by this reaction.

Chlorine water is also a good bleaching agent. Litmus paper, calico, and most natural pigments are bleached by it. The bleaching action of chlorine water is due to the hypochlorous acid formed by the above reaction. For this reason *dry* chlorine is not a bleaching agent.

Tests for chlorine

A water solution of chlorine when added to a solution of an iodide liberates free iodine.

$$Cl_2 + 2KI \rightarrow I_2 + 2KCl$$

The resulting solution is intensely brown in color. *Bromine will also give this same reaction* but since bromine is reddish and chlorine is light greenish-yellow, these two gases may readily be distinguished from one another by their color.

Chlorides will not give this test, but may be identified by another reaction. A water solution of any metal chloride gives a white precipitate of silver chloride (AgCl) when silver nitrate ($AgNO_3$) solution is added. This white precipitate is insoluble in dilute nitric acid (HNO_3).

$$NaCl + AgNO_3 \rightarrow AgCl \downarrow + NaNO_3$$

When you apply this test, the unknown should first be made acid with nitric acid, after which the silver nitrate reagent is added. A white precipitate under these conditions indicates the presence of a chloride in the unknown. If the solution is not acid with nitric acid, other silver

When large amounts of chlorine are needed for industrial purposes, the element is frequently shipped in tank-car lots as a liquid. (Pennsylvania Salt Manufacturing Co.)

salts may precipitate, such as carbonate ($CO_3^=$), phosphate ($PO_4^=$), or thiocyanate (SCN^-).

Uses of chlorine

About 1.5 million tons of chlorine are produced annually in the United States. The greater part of the chlorine produced is employed in bleaching paper and cotton. Most white paper and also most cotton textiles have been bleached with chlorine or chlorine derivatives. Chlorine may also be used to bleach linen. Chlorine is not used to bleach silk and wool because it causes disintegration of these fibers.

The use of chlorine for treating municipal water supplies has already been discussed.

Chlorine is also employed in the manufacture of many compounds important in our daily lives. Among these are carbon tetrachloride (CCl_4), chloroform ($CHCl_3$), hydrochloric acid, and certain synthetic rubbers (neoprene) and plastics (Koroseal, Pliofilm).

Chlorine, as chloride, is essential for the functioning of the human body. Normal human gastric juice contains about 0.2 percent hydrochloric acid. This is formed in the body from the sodium chloride of the diet.

Occurrence of bromine

It is estimated that the earth's crust is 0.001 percent **bromine**. Like chlorine, bromine never occurs free in nature but only as metal bromides. Sea water contains about 70 parts per million of bromine. The Strassfurt, Germany, salt beds formerly supplied most of the world's bromine. Today, the entire United States' production comes either from brine wells, particularly in Michigan, or directly from sea water.

Fig. 22-2. A setup for the laboratory preparation of bromine. Note that the receiver must be cooled to condense the bromine gas formed.

Preparation of bromine

1. Laboratory. Any method used for the liberation of chlorine from a chloride may be used to liberate bromine from a bromide. The reactions are similar to those given before under chlorine.

$$4HBr + MnO_2 \xrightarrow{heat} MnBr_2 + 2H_2O + Br_2$$

$$2KMnO_4 + 16HBr \rightarrow 2KBr + 2MnBr_2 + 8H_2O + 5Br_2$$

$$2NaBr + 2H_2O \xrightarrow{electrolysis} Br_2 + 2NaOH + H_2$$

In addition there is one other method. Chlorine will liberate bromine from bromides.

$$2NaBr + Cl_2 \rightarrow 2NaCl + Br_2$$

In the laboratory a convenient method of preparation consists of heating a mixture of sodium bromide (NaBr), sulfuric acid (H_2SO_4), and manganese dioxide (MnO_2), since hydrogen bromide (HBr) may not be readily available in some laboratories. (Sodium bromide and sulfuric acid react to form hydrogen bromide.)

$$2NaBr + 3H_2SO_4 + MnO_2 \xrightarrow{heat} 2NaHSO_4 + MnSO_4 + 2H_2O + Br_2$$

The bromine is a liquid at room temperature but is easily vaporized by heating (since it boils at 59°C). In this way bromine may be separated from the other products by distillation. A convenient setup is shown in Fig. 22-2.

2. Industrial. Most industrial bromine is obtained directly from sea water. Although sea water contains only 70 parts per million of bromine, it has been an industrial source of the element since 1934. On the coasts of North Carolina and Texas, plants now "mine bromine from the sea." Actually, the process consists of pumping the sea water into vats, where it is chlorinated. The chlorine liberates the bromine (see reaction above). Air blown through the water then removes the bromine by carrying the bromine vapor along with it. The bromine is separated from the air by suitable absorbing agents. Chemical and engineering ingenuity make it possible to extract the element profitably even at the very low concentration at which it is found.

Physical properties of bromine

Bromine is a liquid of deep red color, which boils at 59°C. It is quite volatile even at room temperature and evaporates to a red-brown vapor with a suffocating odor similar to chlorine. The name of the element comes from a Greek word meaning *bad smell*.

Bromine liquid should be handled with great care since it produces serious burns if spilled on the flesh.

Bromine is moderately soluble in water. It produces a brown solution that has properties similar to chlorine water.

The density of bromine is about 5.5 times that of air.

Bromine dissolves in carbon tetrachloride, producing a yellow-to-brown solution. The color of the solution depends on the concentration of the bromine.

Chemical properties of bromine

The chemical properties of bromine are very similar to those of chlorine. In general it enters into the same reactions that chlorine does but somewhat less vigorously. Compounds of the same type formulas are formed. You should be able to explain in terms of electron structures why bromine is a less active element than chlorine (see Chap. 21, page 233).

Test for bromine

Bromine is recognized by its color and odor and by the further fact that it will liberate iodine from an iodide.

$$2NaI + Br_2 \rightarrow 2NaBr + I_2$$

This is a test for free bromine.

Bromides give a silver nitrate reaction similar to that of chlorides.

$$NaBr + AgNO_3 \rightarrow AgBr \downarrow + NaNO_3$$

The precipitate of silver bromide is cream-colored. The solution to be tested should be acid with nitric acid, as in the case of testing for a chloride.

Petroleum distillation columns in Baywater, N.J., for the production of gasoline. One of the major industrial uses for bromine is in the preparation of ethylene dibromide. This compound prevents the deposit of lead on the engines of automobiles from the tetraethyllead in antiknock gasolines. (Standard Oil Co.)

Uses of bromine

The principal commercial use of bromine is in the making of so-called *ethyl gasoline*. The active ingredient of these gasolines is the compound tetraethyllead [$Pb(C_2H_5)_4$]. The tetraethyllead volatilizes and enters the engine along with the gasoline vapor where its presence produces the well-known antiknock qualities of such ethyl gasolines (for further details see Chap. 36, pages 425 and 426). Without proper precautions, however, lead from this compound will deposit on the inside of the engine where the fuel combustion occurs. This lead deposit will foul the spark plugs and other parts. It has been found that *ethylene dibromide* ($C_2H_4Br_2$), when added to the fuel, prevents the accumulation of lead inside the engine by forming compounds with lead which are volatile at the temperature of the exhaust. Most commercial bromine is used for making ethylene dibromide for this purpose. Bromine thus plays an important, if unsuspected, part in present-day transportation.

Bromine is important in our lives in another way, also. The silver halides are sensitive to light. This fact is the basis of the photographic process. Silver bromide is used extensively in making photographic papers and films (see Chap. 46, page 601).

The bromides of sodium and potassium are used as sedatives.

Bromine is used in the manufacture of certain tear gases (for example, benzyl bromide, C_7H_7Br) and in the synthesis of certain dyes.

Occurrence of iodine

Iodine (as iodides) occurs in small amounts throughout the plant, animal, and mineral kingdoms. Most, if not all, higher forms of life require it in small quantities. In low concentrations iodine is found in all sea water. The Atlantic Ocean contains 0.0035 parts per million of iodine. Seaweed and sponges concentrate the iodine from sea water in growth. One source of the element is the ash formed from the burning of seaweed. Some iodine is produced from the brine pumped from certain oil wells in California, but the principal source is Chile, where iodine occurs as sodium iodate ($NaIO_3$) which makes up 0.2 percent of the crude Chilean nitrate of soda (*caliche*).

Preparation of iodine

1. Laboratory. Iodine can be obtained from an iodide by any method used to obtain chlorine from a chloride or bromine from a bromide. You should be able to work out the equations for yourself (pages 237 and 242). In addition bromine will liberate iodine from an iodide as will chlorine.

$$2NaI + Br_2 \rightarrow I_2 + 2NaBr$$

2. Industrial. From sodium iodate, iodine is produced by reaction with sodium hydrogen sulfite.

$$2NaIO_3 + 5NaHSO_3 \rightarrow 3NaHSO_4 + 2Na_2SO_4 + H_2O + I_2$$

Physical properties of iodine

Iodine is a steel gray solid. Its vapor is violet. Although a solid at room temperature, iodine is sufficiently volatile (by sublimation) to give a characteristic halogen smell. Its vapor is *very* dangerous to inhale. You should use extreme caution in working with iodine, particularly at elevated temperatures. The melting point of iodine is 113.7°C; its boiling point, 184.35°C.

Iodine is only very slightly soluble in water (solubility 0.02 g per 100 g water). Its solubility in water is very greatly increased by the presence of potassium iodide. If a few crystals of iodine are added to water and stirred, the iodine dissolves scarcely enough to color the water brownish. If, then, potassium iodide is added, the color of the solution immediately becomes more intense. This is due to the following reaction:

$$KI + I_2 \rightleftarrows KI_3$$

A small amount of iodine is needed to supplement the diet of people in certain regions to prevent simple goiter. Iodized salt is prepared for this purpose. (Caterpillar Tractor Co.)

The resulting compound (KI_3) easily breaks down by reversal of the above reaction; hence the solution has all the properties of free iodine. This reaction is an unusual one but important in the preparation of concentrated solutions of iodine (see tincture of iodine, page 247).

Iodine is soluble in carbon tetrachloride or carbon disulfide, in which solutions it is violet, the same color as its vapor.

Tests for iodine

Free iodine produces an intensely blue color in the presence of starch. This is an exceedingly delicate test for either of these substances. The reason for the color is not clearly known, but it is nevertheless a useful property. The production of the blue color can also be used to increase the sensitivity of tests for the other haolgens when these tests depend on the liberation of iodine from an iodide. Iodide ion will not produce the blue color with starch—free iodine is necessary. Chlorine and bromine do not react with starch.

A convenient way of testing for the halogens other than iodine is by the use of *starch-iodide paper*. This paper is easily made in the laboratory by dissolving a small amount of sodium iodide in a solution of starch in water. Pieces of filter paper are dipped into this solution, dried, and cut into strips the size of litmus paper. No color is found on the paper as long as the iodine is not liberated from the sodium iodide. If, however, a strip of starch-iodide paper is moistened and exposed to either chlorine or bromine, it immediately turns deep blue.

Solutions of iodides (acid with dilute nitric acid) react with silver nitrate forming yellow silver iodide precipitate.

$$NaI + AgNO_3 \rightarrow AgI \downarrow + NaNO_3$$

You will recall that bromides and chlorides also give a precipitate with silver nitrate. Therefore, this reaction in itself, although conclusive evidence for a halide, does not satisfactorily distinguish between the halides. The distinction between a chloride, a bromide, and an iodide can be made by treating the unknown with chlorine water. If no reaction is observed, the halide is a chloride. If a reaction occurs, you can tell either by the color of the solution or by the starch test whether it is bromine or iodine that is liberated.

Uses of iodine

Iodine must be present in the diet of man for the proper functioning of the human body. The principal function of the iodine is in the formation of thyroxine ($C_{15}H_{11}O_4NI_4$) by the thyroid gland. This thyroxine is one of the hormones which regulates the rate of metabolism.[1] Obviously if there is insufficient iodine in the diet, the compound cannot be made by the thyroid gland. *Simple goiter* is caused by insufficient iodine in the diet and is preventable by daily intake of small amounts of sodium iodide. The amount of iodine required by the normal adult is about 0.00015 to 0.0003 g per day. People living close to the sea generally get at least this much from sea food and indirectly from sea spray which is carried inland many miles. Thus it is found that the iodine content of soils and water is definitely higher along the eastern coastal regions of the United States than in the central part of the country. It is believed that this is due to the evaporation of sea spray, producing very fine particles of sea salts which are carried many miles inland by the wind. The use of iodized table salt (sodium chloride containing a small amount of sodium or potassium iodide) will generally supply the normal iodine requirement for an individual. This is the purpose in making iodized salt.

Silver iodide is used in the photographic industry. It is more sensitive to light than the other silver halides and is mostly used for making photographic film.

Tincture of iodine, used as an antiseptic, is a solution of iodine dissolved in an alcohol-water solution containing potassium or sodium iodide. Although tincture of iodine is a good antiseptic, it is somewhat destructive of the tissue and its use is declining in favor of other substances such as the sulfa drugs.

---

[1] The sum of all the chemical processes occurring in a living plant or animal, including building up and breaking down of protoplasm, is called *metabolism*.

Occurrence of fluorine

Fluorine is the most active nonmetal known. Because of its extreme activity, fluorine does not resemble the other halogens as closely as they resemble each other. For this reason the discussion of fluorine has been postponed until the other members of the halogen series have been described.

Fluorine makes up 0.1 percent of the earth's crust and is the most plentiful halogen, except chlorine, on the earth. It occurs in nature mainly as CaF_2, known as **fluorite. Cryolite** is Na_3AlF_6 and is found in Greenland. Cryolite is important in aluminum metallurgy. **Apatite** is $CaF_2 \cdot 3Ca_3(PO_4)_2$, a common mineral, important as a source of phosphorus as well as of fluorine.

Preparation of fluorine

The element fluorine is so active that it was not prepared in the free state until 1886. The difficulty in the preparation of the element lies in the fact that fluorine has the greatest affinity for electrons of any substance known. This is to be expected from the electronic structure of the element. Hence there is no substance which will remove the electron from the fluoride ion (as in Na^+F^-). This electron must be removed to prepare the free element. It was thought that electrolysis would liberate fluorine. However, in the early experiments the fluorine always reacted with the vessel or the electrodes used for carrying out the electrolysis. Finally in 1886 Henri Moissan prepared fluorine by electrolyzing solutions of sodium fluoride (NaF) and liquid hydrogen fluoride (H_2F_2), using a vessel and electrodes made of an alloy of platinum and iridium. Fluorine is still made by the same process today. It has been found that the vessel and electrodes can be made of copper or even of steel. The metal of the cell reacts with the fluorine released, but a coating of fluoride is formed that protects the metal underneath from further attack by the fluorine freed. The reaction for the electrolysis of liquid hydrogen fluoride is

$$H_2F_2 \xrightarrow{\text{electrolysis}} H_2 \uparrow + F_2 \uparrow$$

The sodium fluoride is not decomposed in the process. Its role is the same here as that of sulfuric acid in the electrolysis of water (see Chap. 6, pages 48 and 49).

Fluorine may also be made by the electrolysis of fused (that is, melted) sodium fluoride.

$$2NaF \xrightarrow{\text{electrolysis}} 2Na + F_2 \uparrow$$

Properties of fluorine

Fluorine is a light yellow gas which boils at $-188°C$ and freezes at $-223°C$. It combines directly with every element except the inert gases, in most cases with violent results.

With hydrogen, fluorine explodes:

$$H_2 + F_2 \rightarrow H_2F_2$$

Carbon ignites spontaneously in fluorine.

Alcohol, ether, and turpentine spontaneously take fire on contact with fluorine gas.

Oxygen is displaced from water.

$$2F_2 + 2H_2O \rightarrow 2H_2F_2 \uparrow + O_2 \uparrow$$

The *test* for fluorine depends on the formation of hydrogen fluoride (see page 250).

Uses of fluorine

The free element fluorine is now being manufactured commercially and has certain uses in industrial syntheses.

Fluorine forms many different compounds with carbon. These are known as **fluorocarbons.** Some of these compounds are gases; others are liquids and solids. All fluorocarbons are exceedingly stable; they do not burn, decay, corrode, or mold. Neither rodents nor insects find nourishment in them. In the future they may be used to make lubricants, paints, cloth, oils, solvents, and plastics which resist fire and decay. Through the use of a fluorocarbon lubricant, for example, one can foresee an automobile with a sealed engine which will never need additional lubrication. The chemistry of the fluorocarbons is just in its infancy.

Freon 12(CCl_2F_2) is an important refrigerant (see Chap. 12, page 127). Other fluorine compounds are used for the same purpose.

Hydrogen fluoride is an important catalyst in the manufacture of certain types of aviation gasoline.

Sodium fluoride is employed as an ant and roach poison. All soluble fluorides are exceedingly poisonous.

Fluorine and the teeth

Some years ago it was observed that inhabitants of certain localities commonly had teeth with mottled (discolored) enamel. It was noted that the mottled teeth were unusually resistant to decay. This mottled enamel was shown, in 1931, to be caused by drinking water containing small amounts of fluoride. This discovery raised the following questions: Could the addition of fluoride to city water supplies help prevent tooth decay among the inhabitants of those cities? Was it possible to prevent tooth decay without using enough fluoride to cause discoloration of the teeth or produce other harmful effects on the body?

In 1945 the New York State Department of Health started a 10-year, large-scale experiment which was designed to answer these questions. Two cities, Newburgh and Kingston, were selected for the experiment. The two communities are about the same size and have a common water supply which normally is fluoride-free. Since 1945 fluoride (to the extent of 1.0 to 1.2 parts per million) has been added to the Newburgh water supply, and that of Kingston has remained fluoride-free. Periodic examination of the school children five to twelve years old is being made. At the beginning of the experiment in 1945 children in both cities showed the same percentage of decayed, missing, or filled teeth. In the first 6 years of the experiment the number of decayed, filled, or missing teeth was reduced 47 percent in Newburgh, whereas the number remained unchanged in Kingston! No undesirable effects of the fluoride have yet been noted. Such results have led to a great deal of interest in fluoride treatment of water supplies by public health authorities. The treatment is already being carried out in some cities. Doubtless the practice will spread if no harmful side effects are discovered.

Hydrofluoric acid

Hydrogen fluoride is a colorless gas which is very soluble in water. It is prepared by treatment of a fluoride, such as calcium fluoride, with concentrated sulfuric acid.

$$CaF_2 + H_2SO_4 \rightarrow H_2F_2 \uparrow + CaSO_4$$

Hydrogen fluoride boils at 19°C and hence comes off as a vapor when the mixture is warmed. The water solution of hydrogen fluoride is known as *hydrofluoric acid*.

The most remarkable property of the acid is that it dissolves sand (SiO_2) and glass.

$$SiO_2 + 2H_2F_2 \rightarrow 2H_2O + SiF_4 \uparrow$$

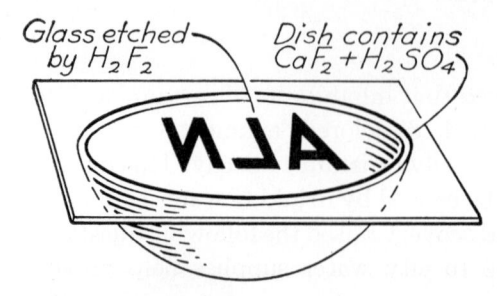

Fig 22–3. Etching glass with hydrogen fluoride. The glass plate is first coated with paraffin. The paraffin is then scratched away wherever marks on the glass are desired.

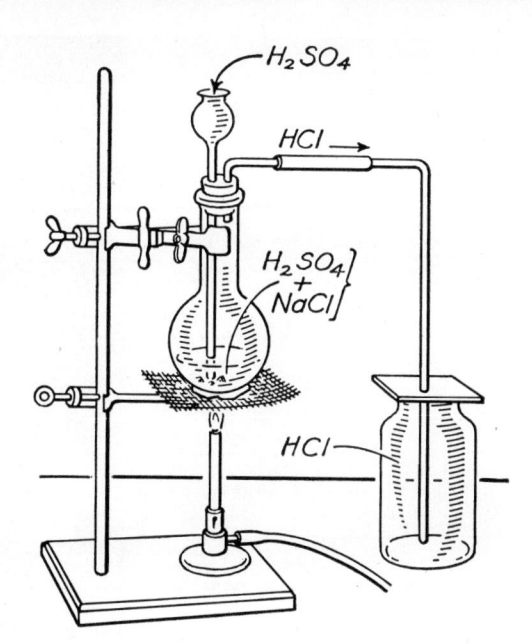

Fig. 22–4. A convenient laboratory setup for the production of hydrogen chloride. If the gas were collected in a vessel containing water, it would dissolve and be known as hydrochloric acid.

With glass the reaction is much the same since glass contains silicon dioxide and silicates. This reaction is used in etching glass. In making laboratory glassware, the object to be marked is given a coat of paraffin. The paraffin is scratched away where lines or letters are desired on the glass (Fig. 22–3). The object is exposed to hydrofluoric acid vapors and the glass is etched where the paraffin has been removed. Frosted electric-light bulbs are etched on the inside with hydrofluoric acid.

Obviously the acid cannot be kept in a glass container. It is usually kept in a bottle of wax, polyethylene plastic, or hard rubber.

Hydrofluoric acid burns of the flesh are very dangerous and slow healing. You should always wash your hands carefully after using hydrofluoric acid and should avoid inhaling the vapors.

Test for a fluoride may be made by treating the unknown with concentrated sulfuric acid and noting if the vapor will etch glass.

Hydrochloric acid

Hydrogen chloride is prepared by a method analogous to that used for hydrogen fluoride. Thus by the action of concentrated sulfuric acid on sodium chloride

$$H_2SO_4 + NaCl \rightarrow HCl \uparrow + NaHSO_4$$

Also, by the combination of hydrogen and chlorine

$$H_2 + Cl_2 \rightarrow 2HCl$$

The first method is a suitable laboratory preparation, and both are commercial methods.

Some of the rock salt mined in huge mines such as the one shown in this photograph is used to make chlorine. Chlorine is combined directly with hydrogen to make hydrogen chloride which, dissolved in water, gives hydrochloric acid, an important industrial chemical. (International Salt Co., Inc.)

Hydrogen chloride is a colorless gas. It has a sharp, choking odor and forms a dense fog when the moisture of the breath is blown into it. Hydrogen chloride is extremely soluble in water; the solution is known as *hydrochloric acid* or **muriatic acid.** Commercial concentrated hydrochloric acid contains 35.5 percent hydrogen chloride (HCl) in water or about twelve moles per liter (moles/liter).

Hydrochloric acid is a typical acid. With zinc or other active metal it gives hydrogen and the metal chloride:

$$Zn + 2HCl \rightarrow ZnCl_2 + H_2 \uparrow$$
$$Fe + 2HCl \rightarrow FeCl_2 + H_2 \uparrow$$

Hydrochloric acid gives the same reaction with silver nitrate as other chlorides.

Hydrochloric acid is one of the cheapest commercial acids. It is used to clean metals preparatory to plating or soldering them, in the manufacture of dextrose from starch, in making glue, dyes, and metal chlorides, and for many other purposes. The presence of hydrochloric acid in gastric juice has already been mentioned.

Hydrobromic acid

Hydrogen bromide cannot be made by the methods used for hydrogen chloride. When concentrated sulfuric acid is added to a bromide, *bromine* is formed.

$$2NaBr + 3H_2SO_4 \rightarrow Br_2 + SO_2 \uparrow + 2NaHSO_4 + 2H_2O$$

In fact the bromine formed is so easily recognized that this constitutes a rough test for a bromide.

Hydrogen bromide may be prepared by dropwise addition of water to phosphorus tribromide. The phosphorus tribromide is prepared by mixing red phosphorus and bromine:

$$2P + 3Br_2 \rightarrow 2PBr_3$$
$$PBr_3 + 3H_2O \rightarrow 3HBr \uparrow + H_3PO_3$$

Like hydrogen chloride, hydrogen bromide is a colorless gas that is very soluble in water. Its water solution is known as *hydrobromic acid*. Hydrobromic acid has all the properties of a typical acid and in addition gives the silver nitrate reaction characteristic of all bromides.

Hydrobromic acid has no important industrial uses.

Hydriodic acid

Like hydrogen bromide, hydrogen iodide cannot be prepared by adding concentrated sulfuric acid to an iodide. This reaction produces iodine.

$$9H_2SO_4 + 8NaI \rightarrow 4I_2 + H_2S \uparrow + 8NaHSO_4 + 4H_2O$$

It may be prepared by the reaction of water, red phosphorus, and iodine.

$$2P + 3I_2 \rightarrow 2PI_3$$
$$PI_3 + 3H_2O \rightarrow 3HI + H_3PO_3$$

The water solution of hydrogen iodide, known as *hydriodic acid*, has all the properties of a typical acid as well as giving the reactions characteristic of the iodides. It has no important industrial uses.

Comparison of the halogens

Table 22–1 summarizes the important properties of the halogen family. You should remember that the activities of the halogens decrease as the atomic weight increases. This is due to increasing atomic size. The stability of the hydrogen compound decreases as the activity of the element decreases.

TABLE 22–1. Properties of the halogens

	Fluorine, F	Chlorine, Cl	Bromine, Br	Iodine, I
Atomic weight	19.0	35.5	79.9	126.9
Boiling point, °C	−188	−34.6	59	184.35
State at room temperature	gas	gas	liquid	solid
Color	light yellow	greenish yellow	red	steel gray solid or violet vapor
Radius of atom, angstroms	...	1.07	1.19	1.36
Tendency to gain electrons	decreases $\longrightarrow$			

KEY WORDS

apatite	cryolite	halite	hydrofluoric
astatine	Davy	halogen	hydrogen halide
bromine	fluorine	hydriodic	hypochlorous
chlorine	fluorite	hydrobromic	iodine
chlorine water	fluorocarbon	hydrochloric	muriatic

HIGHLIGHTS

The **halogens** include **fluorine, chlorine, bromine, iodine,** and **astatine.** Fluorine is the most active of all the nonmetals. Chlorine, bromine, and iodine resemble each other to a remarkable degree. Little is known about astatine.

Fluorine occurs in such minerals as **fluorite** and **apatite,** chlorine in common salt, bromine in sea water, iodine in brine and seaweeds.

Fluorine is obtained by the electrolysis of liquid hydrogen fluoride containing sodium fluoride. The three other important halogens are made in the laboratory by the oxidation of their binary acids by such compounds as manganese dioxide and potassium permanganate.

The test for fluoride depends upon the ability of hydrogen fluoride to etch glass. The chloride, bromide, and iodide ions react with silver nitrate to form white or near-white precipitates.

Hydrochloric and **hydrofluoric** acids are prepared by treating their corresponding salts with sulfuric acid. **Hydrobromic** and **hydriodic** acids are prepared by the reaction of water on phosphorus tribromide and phosphorus triiodide, respectively.

Fluorine is used for etching glass; chlorine for bleaching, disinfecting, and the manufacture of chlorides; bromine in making dyes and antiknock gasoline and in photography; and iodine is used in medicine.

QUESTIONS

1. Which of the halogens is most plentiful in nature?
2. Which of the halogens is radioactive?
3. What three products are obtained by the electrolysis of a water solution of rock salt? Write the equation for the reaction.
4. Give one laboratory method for the preparation of chlorine from hydrochloric acid. How is the chlorine collected? Why?
5. With what metals does chlorine unite directly?
6. Explain why dry chlorine is not a bleaching agent.
7. Give a test for chlorine. Write the reaction.

8. List as many ways as you can in which sodium chloride and products derived from it enter into your life.
9. What are the principal uses for bromine?
10. Explain in terms of the electron structures and the atomic radii given in Table 22-1 why fluorine is the most active halogen.
11. An unknown solution, when acidified with nitric acid, gave a precipitate on the addition of silver nitrate solution. Explain how you would proceed to identify the halide present.
12. Why is simple goiter apt to be more common in the Middle West than along the eastern seaboard?
13. What steps have been taken to prevent iodine dietary deficiency in this country?
14. What is tincture of iodine?
15. With what elements does fluorine combine directly?
16. What has fluorine to do with mechanical refrigeration?
17. Describe a large-scale experiment which is being carried out to test the effect of fluorides in drinking water on tooth decay.
18. Explain how glass is etched.
19. Write two equations showing commercial methods for manufacturing hydrochloric acid.

Suggested Projects for Unit Five

1. Repeat the Becquerel experiment. Try different grades of photographic paper and different periods of exposure. What is your conclusion of the best way to do this experiment?
2. See how many examples of static electricity you can list. Can you think of any original examples?
3. Find out how the solar energy received by 1 square mile (mile^2) of surface on the earth in one day compares with the energy of one Hiroshima bomb.
4. Start a file on matters relating to atomic energy. See how much information you can collect while studying this unit.
5. Make a list of all the atomic explosions so far. Keep your list up to date as we go along in this atomic age.
6. Find out what precautions should be taken in the use of iodine in the home.
7. Learn the arguments for and against the wholesale fluoridation of drinking water.
8. Devise some original models for such atoms as hydrogen, oxygen, and carbon.

UNIT SIX: Some Theoretical Chemistry

CHAPTER 23

some quantitative chemistry: Avogadro's law and chemical calculations

Chemistry is a science which, at least in part, is *quantitative* as well as *qualitative*. That is, chemistry is concerned with *what* products are formed by a reaction (qualitative chemistry) and also with *how much* (the **yield**) of these products will be formed from a certain amount of starting materials (quantitative chemistry). This kind of information is important in the laboratory and also in chemical manufacturing, where the yield of product partly determines the cost of manufacturing it.

Yields are only one part of the quantitative side of chemistry. The *theoretical chemist* is constantly striving to learn how to calculate such things as the physical properties of substances without having to determine them in the laboratory. Such ability would have the great practical importance of enabling the chemist to predict that a certain compound would be useful for a certain purpose, even before that compound had been prepared.[1] This goal has as yet been only partly

[1] Thomas Midgley, of the General Motors Research Laboratories, who discovered the use of Freon 12(CCl_2F_2) for refrigeration (Chap. 12, page 127), *predicted* that this compound would be an efficient and valuable refrigerant before its properties had been measured.

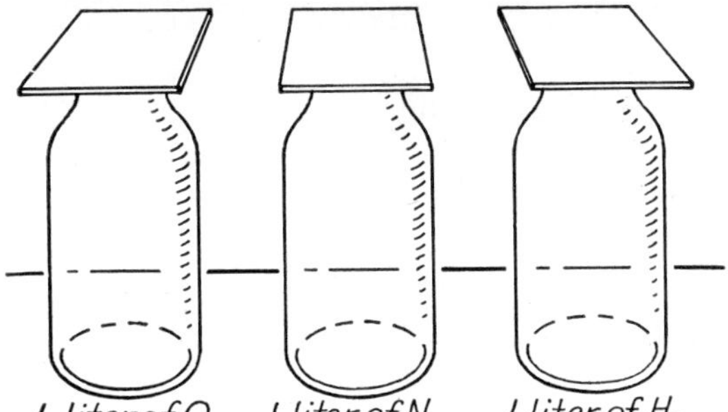

Fig. 23–1. Each bottle contains the same number of molecules at the same temperature and pressure.

1 liter of O_2 1 liter of N_2 1 liter of H_2

reached. You will see in this chapter one important case in which properties can be predicted by calculation. The densities of gases can be calculated from a knowledge of their molecular weights.

Avogadro's law

A relationship, first suggested by the Italian physicist Avogadro in 1811, has proved exceedingly useful in predicting some physical properties of gases. According to Avogadro's law, **equal volumes of all gases, at the same temperature and pressure, contain the same number of molecules.** This means that if you have 1 liter each of three different gases, for example, hydrogen, oxygen, and nitrogen (Fig. 23–1), and each of the gases is at the same temperature and pressure, then the number of molecules of hydrogen is the same as the number of molecules of oxygen, which is the same as the number of molecules of nitrogen.

You may think this is impossible since hydrogen, oxygen, and nitrogen molecules are different sizes. Even though these molecules are different in size, Avogadro's law is nevertheless possible. This is true because the size of a gas molecule is very, very small compared with the distance between the molecules. What is more important, Avogadro's law has been subjected to many tests by laboratory experiments and is known to be correct. Let us now consider some applications of this law.

Applications of Avogadro's law

1. *The molar volume of gases.* We have seen in Chap. 5, pages 30 and 31, that a mole of any substance contains the same number of molecules. Since Avogadro's law says this same number of molecules of *any gas* will occupy the same volume (at the same temperature and pressure) then it can be seen that the volume of one mole of all gaseous substances will always be the same at the same temperature and pressure.

Measurement shows that the volume of one mole of oxygen (= 32 g of O_2) at standard temperature and pressure (STP—see page 86) is 22.4 liters. This, therefore, is also the **molar volume** of any other gas at STP. That is, one mole of any gas at STP occupies a volume of 22.4 liters. It may help you to know that 22.4 liters is approximately 5.9 gal or a little more than 23 qt (Fig. 23–2).

WARNING: Avogadro's law applies only to gases—not to solids and liquids.

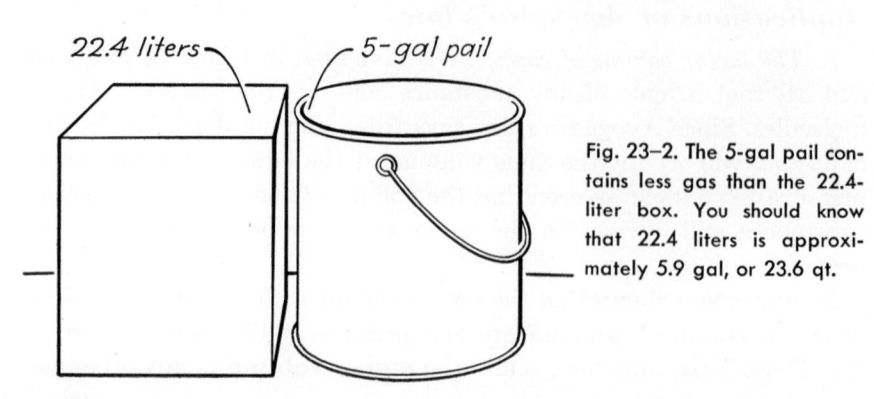

TABLE 23–1. Molar volumes of some gases at STP

Gas	Formula	Molecular weight	Weight of one mole, g	Volume of one mole at STP, liters
Oxygen	O_2	32	32	22.4
Hydrogen	H_2	2	2	22.4
Nitrogen	N_2	28	28	22.4
Carbon dioxide	CO_2	44	44	22.4
Methane	CH_4	16	16	22.4
Helium	He	4	4	22.4
Ammonia	NH_3	17	17	22.4

2. *The density of gases.* If we wish to know the density of a solid or liquid, we must either measure it or look it up in a table which has been prepared from the measurements someone else has made. For gases, the density can be calculated if the formula of the gas is known.

What is the density in grams per liter of hydrogen gas at STP?

From Table 23–1 we see that 2 g of hydrogen occupies a volume of 22.4 liters; hence its density at STP is

$$\text{Density} = \frac{\text{mass}}{\text{volume}} = \frac{2 \text{ g}}{22.4 \text{ liters}} = 0.0893 \text{ g/liter}$$

The density of any other gaseous substance can be calculated in a similar manner.

Thus we see that one *quantitative* goal of chemistry has been reached.

Fig. 23–2. The 5-gal pail contains less gas than the 22.4-liter box. You should know that 22.4 liters is approximately 5.9 gal, or 23.6 qt.

TABLE 23-2. Densities of some gases

Gas	Formula	Density at STP, g/liter	
Oxygen	O_2	$\frac{32}{22.4} =$	1.43
Hydrogen	H_2	$\frac{2}{22.4} =$	0.0893
Nitrogen	N_2	$\frac{28}{22.4} =$	1.25
Carbon dioxide	CO_2	$\frac{44}{22.4} =$	1.97
Methane	CH_4	$\frac{16}{22.4} =$	0.714
Helium	He	$\frac{4}{22.4} =$	0.179
Ammonia	NH_3	$\frac{17}{22.4} =$	0.758

3. Buoyancy of gases. It can be seen from Table 23-2 that hydrogen is the least dense substance in existence (since it has the lowest possible molecular weight) and that helium is the next least dense. In other words, these two gases are the most buoyant substances known today. Because of their **buoyancy,** these substances have been used for filling balloons and dirigibles (see Chap. 8, pages 69 and 73, and Chap. 30, pages 339 and 340). Although air is not a pure compound, measurement shows that 22.4 liters of air at STP weighs 28.95 g. Hence any gas having a molecular weight lower than 28.95 will be less dense than air and, therefore, will be buoyed up by air.

Two grams of hydrogen in air could thus lift $28.95 - 2 = 26.95$ g.
Four grams of helium in air could thus lift $28.95 - 4 = 24.95$ g.

The very low densities of hydrogen and helium, compared to air, explain why these gases *are not* found in any appreciable amounts in the atmosphere. Even if they had originally been present in the atmosphere (and the hydrogen had remained unreacted), their low density would have caused them to float to the top of the atmosphere. That is, any hydrogen and helium added to the atmosphere would tend to collect at the very top of the atmosphere rather than remain close to the earth.

In the same way, gases more dense than air tend to remain in old wells and cisterns if formed there. Thus carbon dioxide, with a molecular weight of 44, is frequently found in large quantities in such places.

4. *Determining the molecular weight of gases.* From Avogadro's law, the molecular weight of an unknown gas can be determined. This involves determining the weight in grams of the unknown gas which would occupy 22.4 liters at STP. This weight is the molecular weight of the unknown gas. Suppose, for example, an unknown gas is found to have a density of 2.61 g/liter at STP.

Molecular weight of gas = weight in grams of 22.4 liters at STP
$$= 2.61 \times 22.4 = 58.5$$

To find molecular weight you need only the gas density at STP.

Calculation of percentage composition from formula

It frequently is desirable for the chemist to know the percentage of an element contained in a certain compound. This information is very easily obtained from the formula for the compound. Thus you have seen in Chap. 5, pages 29 and 30, that the formula of a compound implies the proportions by weight of the elements contained in it. It is only necessary to convert this proportion to a percentage basis. For example, consider the compound hydrogen chloride. From its formula and the atomic weights of hydrogen and chlorine you can see that the weight ratio of hydrogen to chlorine is 1:35.5.

	H : Cl
Weight ratio	1 : 35.5

Thus in one mole of hydrogen chloride (=36.5 g) there are 35.5 g of chlorine and 1 g of hydrogen. Hence

$$\text{Percentage of hydrogen in HCl} = \frac{1}{36.5} \times 100 = 2.74\%$$

$$\text{Percentage of chlorine in HCl} = \frac{35.5}{36.5} \times 100 = 97.26\%$$

PROBLEM 1: Calculate the percentage of iron in hematite (Fe_2O_3). First obtain the molecular weight of Fe_2O_3.

$$2Fe = 2 \times 55.8 = 111.6$$
$$3O = 3 \times 16.0 = 48.0$$
$$\text{Molecular weight hematite} = 159.6$$

Thus in 159.6 g of hematite there are 111.6 g of iron and hence

$$\text{Percentage of iron} = \frac{111.6}{159.6} \times 100 = 69.9\%$$

$$\text{Percentage of oxygen} = \frac{48}{159.6} \times 100 = 30.1\%$$

A laboratory technician weighing a small sample of a metal on a laboratory balance. The sample will then be analyzed to determine its composition. From this information the percentage composition of the material from which the sample was taken can be calculated. Accurate weighing is necessary if a chemist wishes to make precise calculations. (E. I. du Pont de Nemours & Co.)

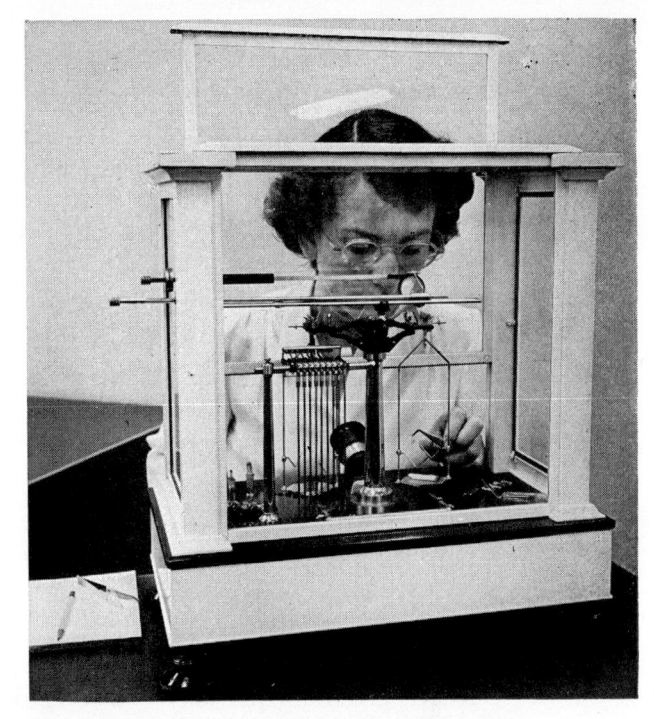

PROBLEM 2: Calculate the percentage composition of sugar ($C_{12}H_{22}O_{11}$).

$$12C = 12 \times 12 = 144$$
$$22H = 22 \times 1 = 22$$
$$11O = 11 \times 16 = 176$$
$$\text{Molecular weight sugar} = 342$$

$$\text{Percentage of carbon} = \frac{144}{342} \times 100 = 42.1\%$$

$$\text{Percentage of hydrogen} = \frac{22}{342} \times 100 = 6.4\%$$

$$\text{Percentage of oxygen} = \frac{176}{342} \times 100 = 51.5\%$$

The amount of water in a hydrate is calculated by the same method.

PROBLEM 3: Calculate the percentage of water in washing soda ($Na_2CO_3 \cdot 10H_2O$). First calculate the molecular weight.

$$2Na = 2 \times 23 = 46$$
$$1C = 1 \times 12 = 12$$
$$3O = 3 \times 16 = 48$$
$$10H_2O = 10 \times 18 = 180$$
$$\text{Molecular weight washing soda} = 286$$

$$\text{Percentage of water} = \frac{180}{286} \times 100 = 63.0\%$$

Weight–weight calculations

Starting with 10 g of potassium chlorate, calculate the weight of oxygen produced when the potassium chlorate reacts

$$2KClO_3 \rightarrow 2KCl + 3O_2$$

The solution of problems of this kind involves only an understanding of what the equation says and the use of elementary arithmetic.

Two molecules of $KClO_3$ yield two molecules of KCl plus three molecules of O_2

Since two molecules of $KClO_3$ weigh 2×122.6 units (122.6 is the molecular weight of $KClO_3$) and three molecules of O_2 weigh 3×32 units, the equation also says (by implication)

$$2 \times 122.6 \text{ parts by weight } KClO_3 \xrightarrow{\text{yield}} 3 \times 32 \text{ parts by weight } O_2$$

Therefore, 10 g of $KClO_3$ will yield a similar proportion of O_2. Or

$$\underset{2 \times 122.6}{\overset{10 \text{ g}}{2KClO_3}} \rightarrow 2KCl + \underset{3 \times 32}{\overset{x \text{ g}}{3O_2}}$$

$$\frac{(KClO_3 \text{ given in equation})}{(O_2 \text{ given by equation})} = \frac{2 \times 122.6}{3 \times 32}$$

$$= \frac{10 \text{ g } (KClO_3 \text{ given in problem})}{x \text{ g } (O_2 \text{ sought})}$$

$$x = 3.91 \text{ g of } O_2 \text{ from 10 g of } KClO_3$$

Problems of this type are best solved as follows:
1. Write a *balanced* equation for the reaction involved.
2. Place the reaction weights of the substances below their formulas. (Reaction weight = molecular weight multiplied by the number of molecules of that substance appearing in the equation.)
3. Place the given weight above the appropriate formula.
4. Place an x above the quantity sought.
5. Set up and solve the resulting proportion.

PROBLEM 1: What weight of zinc is formed by the reduction of 100 g of zinc oxide ore, using carbon as the reducing agent? The reaction is

Steps 3 and 4: $\quad \overset{100 \text{ g}}{ZnO} + C \rightarrow \overset{x \text{ g}}{Zn} + CO$
Step 1:
Step 2: $\qquad\qquad\quad\; 81.4 \qquad\qquad 65.4$

Step 5: $\qquad\qquad \dfrac{81.4}{65.4} = \dfrac{100 \text{ g}}{x \text{ g}}$

$$81.4x = 65.4 \times 100$$
$$x = 80.3 \text{ g}$$

PROBLEM 2: How much oxygen is required to burn 5 lb of gasoline (assume the gasoline to have the formula C_8H_{18})? The reaction is

Steps 3 and 4: 5 lb x lb
Step 1: $2C_8H_{18} + 25O_2 \rightarrow 16CO_2 + 18H_2O$
Step 2: 2×114 25×32

Step 5: $\dfrac{2 \times 114}{25 \times 32} = \dfrac{5 \text{ lb}}{x \text{ lb}}$

$$228x = 5 \times 800$$
$$x = 17.5 \text{ lb}$$

Note that the answer comes out in pounds. Since the equation gives only a reaction ratio, any desired unit of weight may be used in the problem as long as the *same* units are used in Steps 3 and 4.

PROBLEM 3: What weight of carbon dioxide is formed by burning the 5 lb of gasoline in Problem 2?

Steps 3 and 4: 5 lb x lb
Step 1: $2C_8H_{18} + 25O_2 \rightarrow 16CO_2 + 18H_2O$
Step 2: 2×114 16×44

Step 5: $\dfrac{2 \times 114}{16 \times 44} = \dfrac{5 \text{ lb}}{x \text{ lb}}$

$$228x = 3520$$
$$x = 15.4 \text{ lb}$$

Volume changes in chemical reactions

Where a reaction involves only gases, the volume change which accompanies the reaction can be predicted from Avogadro's law.

$$\underset{\text{(gas)}}{H_2} + \underset{\text{(gas)}}{Cl_2} \rightarrow \underset{\text{(gas)}}{2HCl}$$

The reaction uses one mole of each of the reactants and forms two moles of the product. From Avogadro's law the relative volumes of these gases can be predicted. Thus the volume of hydrogen and the volume of chlorine which react will be the same and each will be equal to one-half the volume of hydrogen chloride formed.

$$\underset{\text{(gas)}}{H_2} + \underset{\text{(gas)}}{Cl_2} \rightarrow \underset{\text{(gas)}}{2HCl}$$
1 vol   1 vol   2 vol
    2 vol $\rightarrow$ 2 vol

Hence when this reaction occurs (at a constant temperature), *no change in volume results.*

PROBLEM 1: What volume change occurs in the reaction:

$$N_2 \text{ (gas)} + 3H_2 \text{ (gas)} \rightarrow 2NH_3 \text{ (gas)}$$

1 vol   3 vol   2 vol
     4 vol $\rightarrow$ 2 vol

Volume change: there is a decrease in volume from 4 volumes to 2 volumes, or a 50 percent reduction in volume as the reaction occurs.

Solids and liquids have such small volumes relative to gases that their volume can be ignored in computing the volume change for a reaction which involves both gases and solids (or liquids).

PROBLEM 2: What is the volume change in the reaction:

$$H_2O \text{ (steam)} + C \text{ (solid)} \xrightarrow{\text{high temp}} CO \text{ (gas)} + H_2 \text{ (gas)}$$

1 vol   (neglect)   1 vol   1 vol
   1 vol $\longrightarrow$ 2 vol

Hence there is a doubling, or 100 percent increase, in volume accompanying this reaction at a given temperature.

Many years ago (1805) Joseph Louis Gay-Lussac formulated a law based on his own and other scientists' experiments. This law came to be known as *Gay-Lussac's law of combining volumes*. It is stated as follows: **The volumes of gases used and produced in chemical reactions always stand to each other in the ratio of small whole numbers.** Problems 1 and 2 which precede this paragraph furnish illustrations of this law. However, from Avogadro's law we are able to predict not only that the volume changes will be in the ratio of small whole numbers, but also just exactly what the volume changes will be. Hence, Gay-Lussac's law becomes unnecessary and unimportant if you know Avogadro's law, since Avogadro's law tells you all that Gay-Lussac's would and much more besides.

KEY WORDS

Avogadro's law   buoyancy   molar volume   yield

HIGHLIGHTS

One of the main goals of scientists is to be able to make predictions. Applied to chemistry, one of the best illustrations of this idea is the use of **Avogadro's law** in determining such values as the molecular weight and density of gases.

From the formula the percentage composition of a compound can be calculated. By using the equation as a basis, it is possible to determine the exact proportions in which substances react with each other.

QUESTIONS

1. State and illustrate Avogadro's law.
2. Explain why gram molecular weights of all gases occupy a volume of 22.4 liters at STP.
3. If a certain gas has a density of 1.97 g/liter at STP, what is its molecular weight?
4. What is the density of argon (molecular formula A) at STP?
5. Which of the following gases are less dense than air: (a) CH_4, (b) NH_3, (c) He, (d) CO_2, (e) HBr, (f) C_2H_4?
6. With the exception of helium, would any of the gases listed in question 5 be suitable for filling airships? Explain your answer.
7. Calculate the percentage of copper in cuprite ore (Cu_2O).
8. What is the percentage of water in $CuSO_4 \cdot 5H_2O$?
9. What is the percentage of hydrogen and oxygen in water?
10. Calculate the percentage of nitrogen in the following compounds which are used as fertilizers: (a) $NaNO_3$, (b) $(NH_4)_2SO_4$, (c) NH_4NO_3, and (d) $CO(NH_2)_2$ (urea).
11. How many pounds of each of the compounds listed in question 10 would be necessary to supply 40 lb of nitrogen?
12. Calculate the percentage of potassium in the following compounds which are used as fertilizers: (a) KCl and (b) K_2SO_4.
13. What weight of oxygen is required to burn a ton of coke, assuming coke to be pure carbon?

$$C + O_2 \rightarrow CO_2$$

14. Some rockets use alcohol as fuel. They must also carry oxygen to burn the alcohol. What weight of oxygen is required to burn 100 lb of alcohol according to the equation

$$C_2H_5OH + 3O_2 \rightarrow 2CO_2 + 3H_2O$$

15. What weight of hydrogen is produced from 100 g of water?

$$4H_2O + 3Fe \rightarrow Fe_3O_4 + 4H_2$$

16. What is the volume change occurring in the following reaction?

$$2SO_2 + O_2 \rightarrow 2SO_3$$
$$(gas) \quad (gas) \quad (gas)$$

17. What volume change occurs when hydrogen combines with oxygen to form water vapor?

CHAPTER 24

energy and chemical change

Chemical reactions are carried out for one of two reasons: either to obtain some material produced by the reaction or to obtain the energy liberated by the reaction. An example of the use of a reaction to obtain some material is the reduction of iron ore with coke to make steel. An example of carrying out a chemical reaction to obtain energy is the burning of coal or fuel oil to heat our homes. In the latter case the oxides formed are a nuisance which must be disposed of, the valuable product of the reaction being energy.

Thermochemical equations

Every known chemical change involves an energy change as well as a material change. But not all reactions liberate energy while taking place—some consume energy from the surroundings as they occur.

An equation which shows the energy change as well as the material change is called a **thermochemical equation.** For example, when one gram atom (=12 g) of carbon burns to carbon dioxide, 94,400 cal of heat are liberated. A thermochemical equation to state this fact is written as follows:

$$C + O_2 \rightarrow CO_2 + 94{,}400 \text{ cal}$$

The reaction may be interpreted in words as follows: One gram atom of carbon plus one mole of oxygen yields one mole of carbon dioxide plus 94,400 cal of energy. A reaction, such as this one, which liberates energy is called an *exothermic reaction*.

$$N_2 + O_2 \rightarrow 2NO - 43{,}000 \text{ cal}$$

This reaction says: One mole of nitrogen plus one mole of oxygen yields two moles of nitric oxide *minus* 43,000 cal of energy. This means that when nitrogen and oxygen combine to form nitric oxide, energy is *consumed* from the surroundings. Another way of saying the same thing is: One mole of nitrogen plus one mole of oxygen *plus* 43,000 cal yields two moles of nitric oxide. This type of reaction which consumes heat is called an *endothermic reaction*.

Unless otherwise noted, the quantity of energy given in a thermochemical equation always applies to the reaction of the number of moles shown in the equation. Quantities of reactants different from that shown in the equation produce a proportionate amount of energy. For example, the first equation above says that the burning of 1 gramatomic weight ($=12$ g) of carbon liberates 94,400 cal. Two gramatomic weights ($=24$ g) of carbon would therefore liberate $2 \times 94,400 = 188,800$ cal; 6 g of carbon, $94,400/2 = 47,200$ cal, and so on.

Another point to be noted is that when the reaction occurs in the opposite direction from that given, the magnitude of the energy change is the same but its sign is opposite to that given. For example, the decomposition of carbon dioxide is an endothermic reaction *consuming* 94,400 cal from the surroundings.

$$94{,}400 \text{ cal} + CO_2 \rightarrow C + O_2$$

The decomposition of nitric oxide (NO) is exothermic:

$$2NO \rightarrow N_2 + O_2 + 43{,}000 \text{ cal}$$

Also, to make a certain reaction occur, it may be necessary to heat the reactants for either of two reasons: (1) to supply the energy which the reaction requires if it is endothermic or (2) to speed the reaction. The fact that heat is necessary to speed the reaction has no bearing on whether the reaction is exothermic or endothermic. Thus to burn carbon it is necessary to heat the reactants in order to make the reaction rapid enough to be observable. None of the heat supplied is used in the reaction. To cause nitrogen and oxygen to combine, it is also necessary to heat the reactants. But in this case, some of this heat actually disappears and is stored as chemical energy in the resulting compound, nitric oxide.

Heat of formation

The energy change accompanying the formation of one mole of a compound by reaction of the necessary elements is called its **heat of formation**. Thus from the preceding paragraphs the heat of formation of carbon dioxide is 94,400 cal and of nitric oxide is $-43{,}000 \div 2 = -21{,}500$ cal.

Heats of formation of some common substances are given in Table 24–1.

TABLE 24–1. Heats of formation per mole at 25°C*

Name	Formula	Heat of formation, calories
Aluminum oxide	Al_2O_3	399,000
Calcium oxide	CaO	151,700
Zinc oxide	ZnO	84,300
Mercuric oxide	HgO	21,700
Silver oxide	Ag_2O	6,900
Carbon dioxide	CO_2	94,400
Water (liquid)	H_2O	68,400
Nitric oxide	NO	−21,500[a]
Nitric acid	HNO_3	42,400
Sodium chloride	NaCl	98,400
Potassium chloride	KCl	104,300
Ferric chloride	$FeCl_3$	96,300
Lead chloride	$PbCl_2$	85,700
Carbon disulfide	CS_2	−22,000[a]

* Data from the *Handbook of Chemistry and Physics*, 34th ed., Chemical Rubber Publishing Co., Cleveland, Ohio, 1953.

[a] This negative sign means an endothermic reaction.

Heat of formation and stability

From Table 24–1 you may notice that the most stable compounds have large positive heats of formation, whereas the less stable compounds, such as mercuric and silver oxides, have low heats of formation. This may make you wonder whether the amount of heat liberated when a compound is formed is a measure of the stability of that compound. About a hundred years ago, scientists believed that the heat of formation was a true measure of stability—that is, that the most stable compounds had the largest heats of formation, and the least stable ones had the smallest (sometimes negative) heats of formation. However, careful experiments and theoretical considerations have shown that this is *not* true in every case, and science has known for at least seventy-five years that heat of formation is not an infallible measure of stability. It is true, however, that the order of stability is the same as the order of the heats of formation in many cases. Hence if no other information is available, chemists sometimes use heats of formation to estimate relative stabilities of compounds. But it must be borne in mind that this may give incorrect conclusions about stabilities in some cases.

Photosynthesis is the most important reaction occurring on the earth because it is a means of storing radiant energy from the sun in chemical compounds. These compounds can be used later to keep our bodies warm and to do useful work. (Standard Oil Co.)

The source of energy involved in a chemical reaction

A question sometimes asked is this: Where does the energy come from which is released in a chemical reaction, such as the burning of carbon? This question cannot be fully answered. It is helpful, however, to think of elements and compounds as being reservoirs of energy. These elements and compounds, by undergoing chemical change, may give off energy to the surroundings or, in other cases, absorb and store energy from the surroundings. The energy stored in elements and compounds is spoken of as **chemical energy** because it may be released by a chemical change.[1] Thus carbon and oxygen release some of their chemical energy on combining to form carbon dioxide. The chemical energy stored in carbon dioxide is thus less than that stored in elementary carbon and oxygen. The energy stored in nitric oxide is greater than the energy contained in a corresponding amount of elementary nitrogen and oxygen.

The most important reservoirs of chemical energy on all the earth are compounds of hydrogen, oxygen, and carbon, which are involved in photosynthesis.

[1] Of course, it is also potential energy.

Photosynthesis

In growing, plants take in carbon dioxide and water and convert these into carbohydrates (starch, sugars, cellulose) and oxygen. This reaction is endothermic. The energy used in the reaction is sunlight. Chlorophyll, the green coloring matter in plants, is the catalyst. Thus, the over-all reaction for glucose formation may be written:

$$\underset{\substack{\text{(as radiant energy} \\ \text{from sunlight)}}}{673{,}000 \text{ cal}} + 6CO_2 + 6H_2O \xrightarrow{\text{chlorophyll}} \underset{\substack{\text{glucose or} \\ \text{grape sugar}}}{C_6H_{12}O_6} + 6O_2 \uparrow$$

Starches and cellulose (the woody part of trees, cotton fibers, and so on) are formed by a similar reaction. The carbohydrates are therefore reservoirs of chemical energy which contain energy supplied from the sun. When glucose is burned as food in the body, the reaction just described is reversed and this same amount of energy, 673,000 cal, is released in the body, in this case as heat or as heat plus work.

Since all our common fuels, including coal, natural gas, petroleum, and wood, are believed to have been derived from plants, each of them on being burned releases energy, the ultimate source of which was the sun. Waterpower also comes indirectly from the sun. Since the sun's energy is surely the result of atomic transmutations (that is, nuclear energy—see Chap. 18, page 203) all the energy we have here on the earth comes indirectly from nuclear energy.

Forms of energy involved in a chemical reaction

Although the energy change accompanying a chemical reaction is given in calories, this does not mean that the energy involved is always in the form of heat. We shall see that various forms of energy may be used or produced in chemical reactions. But since all other forms of energy are transformable into heat, it is convenient to express the energy change in calories.

Certain reactions use, or produce, radiant energy. Examples are the burning of magnesium or aluminum—reactions employed as sources of light in signal flares and photoflash bulbs. An excellent example of a reaction which liberates almost all its energy as radiant energy is found in phosphorescence—the slow oxidation of white phosphorus (see Chap. 33, pages 372 and 373). The most important example of a reaction which uses radiant energy is photosynthesis. Other reactions that use radiant energy are made use of in photography (see Chap. 46, pages 600 to 602) and in making blueprints.

Mechanical energy is released in the explosion of dynamite, or in the burning of gasoline in an internal combustion engine. In each case some of the energy is also released as heat.

Dynamite can easily be made to release large amounts of mechanical energy very rapidly. Because of this valuable property, dynamite is used for blasting purposes. In the photograph shown here, a row of dynamite charges has just been set off to blast out a ditch. (E. I. du Pont de Nemours & Co.)

Electrical energy is released by the chemical reaction occurring in a flashlight battery or an automobile storage battery. This will be more fully discussed in Chap. 52. You have seen already that the electrolysis of water uses electrical energy to bring about the decomposition of the water into hydrogen and oxygen.

Chemists, physicists, and engineers are frequently interested in the energy aspects of chemical reactions, and some of them are particularly interested in the form in which the energy is liberated.

One gram of gasoline, on being burned in air to carbon dioxide and water, releases approximately 10,000 cal of heat energy. The automobile engine is a device for transforming the energy of gasoline and oxygen into mechanical energy. The principal objective of the automotive engineer is to design an engine which will convert as large a percentage as possible of this energy into mechanical energy. Notwithstanding the many marvelous features of the modern automobile, the automotive engineer still has not been very successful in his primary objective. Of the energy obtained by burning gasoline, the modern automobile engine converts less than a quarter into useful mechanical energy—the rest is wasted as heat. Steam engines are even less efficient.

KEY WORDS

chemical energy
heat of formation
photosynthesis
thermochemical equation

HIGHLIGHTS

All chemical changes involve energy changes. A reaction which liberates energy is said to be an *exothermic* reaction. A reaction which absorbs energy is said to be *endothermic*. The energy change of the reaction is usually expressed in calories and is included as a part of the **thermochemical equation.**

The **heat of formation** of a compound represents the energy change accompanying the formation of one mole of the compound from its elements. In general, high stability in compounds is correlated with high heat of formation. However, there are exceptions.

Photosynthesis is the all-important process by which the green leaf uses solar energy to change carbon dioxide and water into sugar.

Certain chemical changes release energy in forms other than heat. Examples are radiant energy, electrical energy, and mechanical energy.

QUESTIONS

1. For what two reasons are chemical reactions carried out?
2. What is meant by a thermochemical equation?
3. What is an endothermic reaction? Give an example.
4. What is an exothermic reaction? Give an example.
5. Using Table 24–1 (page 268), would you expect calcium oxide or zinc oxide to be more stable? Can one answer this question with certainty from the table of heats of formation? Explain.
6. If 200 g of glucose are burned to carbon dioxide and water, how much energy is liberated?
7. In order to make hydrogen and oxygen combine, they must be heated. What does the heating accomplish?
8. What is meant by the heat of formation of a compound?
9. Trace to its ultimate source the energy released when a log of wood burns in a fire.
10. Trace to its ultimate source the energy released in your body by the burning of foodstuffs.
11. Is there any energy on the earth which did not come from the sun as radiant energy? Explain.
12. Why is photosynthesis considered the most important chemical reaction occurring on the earth?

CHAPTER **25**

the factors which affect the speed of chemical reactions

In previous chapters you have seen illustrations of reactions which occur with explosive violence. You have also seen examples of other reactions which occur fairly rapidly, and of others which occur only very slowly under the conditions described. The question to consider in this chapter is this: Can the rate of a chemical reaction be changed? If so, by what means? Before proceeding with the answers to these questions, let us consider two cases of reactions which proceed with characteristically different rates.

When silver nitrate solution is added to sodium chloride solution, the reaction is almost instantaneous. You can see this easily by noting the rate of appearance of the precipitate.

$$AgNO_3 + NaCl \rightarrow AgCl\downarrow + NaNO_3$$

When hydrochloric acid is added to a solution of sodium thiosulfate ($Na_2S_2O_3$, photographer's hypo), a precipitate of free sulfur is obtained.

$$Na_2S_2O_3 + 2HCl \rightarrow SO_2\uparrow + 2NaCl + H_2O + S\downarrow$$

You may note the rate of this reaction by observing the time required for the appearance of the precipitate of sulfur. In contrast to the first reaction mentioned in this chapter, it may require a minute or more for the sulfur to appear.

The chemist is concerned with reactions varying in speed all the way from those which occur almost instantly to those which require

months or years to occur appreciably. Frequently he wishes to change the rate of a certain reaction—sometimes to decrease it, sometimes to increase it. There are four factors which he employs for this purpose.
1. Temperature
2. Concentration of reactants
3. Surface area, if a solid or liquid is involved
4. The presence or absence of a catalyst

Temperature

Food spoils more rapidly at high temperatures than at low temperatures. Coal piled in the yard slowly disappears by oxidation but in a red-hot furnace oxidizes rapidly. These are common illustrations of the universal effect of temperature on reaction rate. An increase in temperature always increases the speed of a reaction. Moreover, a given temperature increase always has about the same effect on the rate of all chemical reactions. A rough rule which it is useful to remember is this: **A ten-degree centigrade increase in the temperature of a reaction approximately doubles the speed of the reaction.** This is an enormous effect as the following illustration will show. Suppose a certain reaction to be occurring at 0°C at a certain rate. If the temperature is raised to 10°C, its rate is doubled. If raised to 20°C, its rate is doubled again or becomes four times the rate at 0°C. In raising the temperature from 0 to 100°C, a reaction would be

$2 \times 2 \times 2 \times 2 \times 2 \times 2 \times 2 \times 2 \times 2 \times 2$ (or 2^{10}) = *1024 times* the rate at 0°C

When you realize that temperatures as low as −200°C and as high as 2000°C are conveniently available in the laboratory, you can see that the scientist has here a tool of great power in controlling reaction rate.

If a chemist wishes to carry out a certain reaction and he finds on mixing the **reagents**[1] at room temperature that no apparent reaction occurs, it may be that the reaction is just very slow. Therefore he heats the reagents to see if this will bring about the reaction.

Refrigeration and quick-freezing

You can find in everyday life many illustrations of this temperature effect. Perhaps the most striking is the use of refrigeration. The entire refrigeration industry exists in order to apply this relationship. Although food spoilage is a complicated process and different for different foodstuffs, in each case it is the loss in quality due to chemical changes. We use refrigeration to *slow down* these chemical reactions. Thus if food is stored at 0°C (32°F), its rate of loss in quality should

---

[1] A reagent is a substance or a mixture of substances used to bring about or influence a chemical reaction.

The commercial freezing of peas. If food is stored at low temperatures, such as −20°C, its deterioration is delayed. Therefore, these peas can be kept frozen for a long time and still retain the appearance and taste of the fresh vegetable. (Birds Eye–Snider Division, General Foods Corp.)

be roughly one-eighth the rate at 30°C (86°F). Furthermore, if the food is stored at −20°C (−4°F), the rate of deterioration should be considerably less than when stored at 0°C. This is the principle behind quick-freezing. Many people have a mistaken impression of the principle involved in quick-freezing. Freezing in itself is not the point at all. The object is to get a temperature low enough to slow down greatly the chemical changes which cause spoilage. The freezing is an unavoidable, and sometimes undesirable, consequence of reaching the necessary low temperature. (It is undesirable because freezing may rupture the cells and cause a change in the consistency of the food.) Moreover, it is not true that food which has been quick-frozen will keep forever, as some people seem to think. Chemical changes still go on in the freezer but at a much slower rate, so that it requires months for the same amount of deterioration that would take place in a few hours at room temperature.

Spontaneous combustion

Insurance companies tell us that millions of dollars' worth of property are destroyed each year by fires caused by spontaneous combustion. Some people seem to think that such fires are of unknown cause and are therefore unavoidable. This is not true. The conditions which cause spontaneous combustion are well understood and almost every such case could have been avoided by proper knowledge on the part of the people concerned.

One common cause of this type of fire is the accumulation of linseed-oil-soaked or paint-soaked rags. Linseed oil and other vegetable oils used in paint have the ability to combine with oxygen of the air at room temperature. (In combining with oxygen, these oils produce a tough film which holds the pigment onto the painted surface, and that is why they are used in paints.) This oxidation reaction liberates heat. When the paint is spread over a surface, no rise in temperature occurs because the heat is given off to the surroundings as rapidly as it is formed. But if paint-soaked rags or papers are piled in a loose heap in contact with air, the heat is not conducted to the surroundings as rapidly as it is formed. This raises the temperature of the rags and causes the oxidation reaction to go even faster, which in turn raises the temperature even higher, and so on until the mass bursts into flame. Such rags should either be burned immediately after use, stored in an airtight container, or spread out flat on a good heat conductor to eliminate the danger of spontaneous combustion.

A laboratory demonstration of spontaneous combustion is easily made: Dissolve a piece of white phosphorus the size of a pea in a few milliliters of carbon disulfide. (Handle white phosphorus only with forceps and do not expose it to air.) Pour a few drops of the solution onto a filter paper supported on an iron ring. The carbon disulfide evaporates rapidly, depositing crystals of white phosphorus which oxidize at room temperature. Within a few seconds the paper begins to smoke and then bursts into flame. If the filter paper is placed on a flat stone or metal surface, it generally will not catch fire.

Coal stored in bunkers sometimes ignites by spontaneous combustion. Here the cause is much the same as explained in the preceding paragraph. Large and small lumps of coal stored together allow enough air to enter the pile to cause oxidation of the coal but not enough air to remove the heat of this oxidation by air circulation. The temperature of the pile rises until eventually it begins to burn. If the coal in the pile is all about the same size, this condition is avoided. Large lumps allow enough air circulation to carry off the heat of oxidation and hence a temperature rise is avoided. Fine coal leaves only very small air spaces between the pieces and not enough air can enter the pile to do any damage.

Incompletely cured hay, when loose in large piles, will "heat" and is very apt to lead to fire unless steps are taken to prevent it. Many barns are burned every year because of this. Formerly the only known way of preventing a fire if the hay started to heat was to remove the hay from the barn. If much hay was involved, its removal was a great deal of work, which took several men many hours. Sometimes it was impossible to move the hay fast enough to prevent the fire. Now such fires can be prevented by the use of dry ice, which is widely available. Cakes of dry ice (solid carbon dioxide), distributed over the top of the pile, sublimate. The cold carbon dioxide gas formed is more dense than air and percolates down into the hay, thereby "floating" out the air and at the same time cooling the mass of hay.

Fig. 25–1. Schematic diagram of carbon burning in air (a) and in oxygen (b).

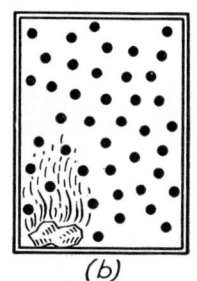

● = Oxygen molecules
○ = Nitrogen molecules

Why does temperature influence the speed of a reaction?

The kinetic molecular theory gives us the explanation. It is obvious that before two molecules can react, they must collide with each other. Temperature is a measure of the kinetic energy of substances. Therefore, increased temperature means faster-moving molecules and hence *more* collisons per second and *harder* collisions between reacting molecules. This causes the increase in the speed of the reaction with temperature, which occurs for all reactions.

Concentration of reactants

The test for oxygen illustrates the effect of the concentration of reactants. Substances which burn in air burn more rapidly in oxygen. Another illustration is encountered in the preparation of hydrogen by reaction of zinc with an acid. As the concentration of the acid is increased, the rate of formation of hydrogen is increased. Without exception, **an increase in the concentration of a reactant increases the rate of the reaction.** The reason for this is easy to see if it is remembered that concentration refers to amount per unit volume and not to total amount. Figure 25–1 shows a lump of carbon burning in air (*a*) and in pure oxygen at 1 atmosphere (*b*). In order for the reaction to occur, oxygen molecules must collide with the carbon lump. Since the concentration of oxygen molecules is much greater in *b* than in *a*, there will be a greater number of the necessary collisions per second, and hence the rate in *b* will be greater than in *a*. This is precisely the reason for using pure oxygen in the oxyacetylene torch for welding (Chap. 6, pages 60 and 61).

In the hands of the chemist, changing concentration of reactants is a very useful tool for controlling reaction rates without changing temperature. You will see many illustrations of it throughout the book.

One application of changing the concentration of reactants is a new development in apple storage. Even when kept in cold storage, certain

Dust explosions are the result of the increase in the reaction rate which accompanies the increase in the surface area of reactants. These explosions are a serious hazard in industries such as flour milling and coal mining. (New York Fire Dept.)

oxidative reactions go on within the apple. These reactions use oxygen from the surrounding air. It has been found that by replacing part of the air in a cold storage warehouse by carbon dioxide (thereby reducing the concentration of oxygen) the length of time an apple will retain its quality in storage is increased one or more months.

Surface area of solids and liquids

The effect of surface area of solids and liquids is really an extension of the principle of concentration of reactants. Where a solid or a liquid is involved in a reaction with a gas, the reaction can occur only on the surface of the solid or liquid. This is because the surface of the solid or liquid is the only place where the two reactants can come in contact. Suppose in *b* (Fig. 25–1, page 277) the solid is divided into four pieces. The resulting increase in area of contact between solid and gas will result in increased speed of reaction.

It is a well-known fact that wood shavings burn more rapidly than a solid stick of wood of the same weight. Massive iron will not burn in air but steel wool will. These are illustrations of an increased surface area increasing the speed of a reaction.

By very fine grinding the surface area of solids can be increased greatly. For example, a cube 1 cm on edge has a surface area of 6 square centimeters (cm^2). If this cube is ground so that the average particle size is 0.000001 cm on each edge, the total area of the solid becomes equivalent to about 6200 square feet (ft^2) or one-seventh of an acre. Many substances which are not normally considered dangerous become serious explosion hazards when finely ground and suspended in air. Coal dust and starch or flour are examples. In one explosion in a flour mill in Illinois 30 people were killed. The coal dust accompanying mining is an ever-present hazard to the miners. Persons have been seriously burned by dumping the contents of a floor-sanding machine (wood flour) into an open flame. All these effects are due to increased reaction rate which accompanies increased surface area of the reactants.

The same kind of effect is found to an even greater degree where volatile liquids are involved. Gasoline or ether contained in a dish will burn quietly if lighted before any evaporation occurs. But if either liquid is allowed to evaporate into the air and then ignited, a dangerous explosion will occur. Here, in evaporation of a liquid, the ultimate subdivision of the substance down to single molecules has taken place.

Catalysts

You have already met one example of a catalyst in the preparation of oxygen. You learned that the presence of manganese dioxide increased the rate of liberation of oxygen from potassium chlorate, although the manganese dioxide itself was not permanently changed. **A catalyst is something which influences the speed of a chemical reaction without itself being permanently changed.**

Another illustration of a catalyst is found in the decomposition of hydrogen peroxide (H_2O_2) which is catalyzed by manganese dioxide. The ordinary drugstore variety of hydrogen peroxide is a 3 percent solution in water. It decomposes slowly, liberating oxygen.

$$2H_2O_2 \rightarrow 2H_2O + O_2 \uparrow$$

At room temperature under normal conditions the reaction requires several months to be complete. If a small amount of manganese dioxide is added to some hydrogen peroxide in a test tube, copious evolution of oxygen is observed immediately. Within a few minutes the reaction is completed.

The following experiment will illustrate strikingly the ability of catalysts to increase reaction rates. A milk bottle is filled two-thirds full of hydrogen and then filled with oxygen, by displacement of water. The stoppered bottle could be kept at room temperature many months without any evidence of a reaction. (The reaction probably is going on but so slowly as to be undetectable.) **Platinized asbestos,**[1] warmed in a flame and *allowed to cool* to room temperature, when

---

[1] Platinized asbestos is prepared by soaking asbestos fibers in a dilute solution of chloroplatinic acid, then heating in a bunsen flame to deposit platinum on the asbestos fibers.

$$H_2PtCl_6 \xrightarrow{heat} 2HCl \uparrow + 2Cl_2 \uparrow + Pt$$

Platinized asbestos loses its catalytic activity on standing in air but can be regenerated by heating in a flame.

placed in the milk bottle, immediately causes a loud bang. It catalyzes the reaction of hydrogen and oxygen.

$$2H_2 + O_2 \xrightarrow{Pt} 2H_2O$$

WARNING: The milk bottle should be enclosed in a wire shield, since it sometimes breaks.

The functions of catalysts are not well understood and chemists still have a great deal to learn about them. It is not possible to predict in advance what agent will catalyze a certain reaction. There is no necessary relationship between catalysts for two different reactions. It is a coincidence that the catalyst was the same in two illustrations mentioned on page 279. A more complete knowledge of the function of catalysts is highly desirable because sometimes in industry the discovery of a catalyst makes the difference between a practical, profitable process and a worthless one. For example, the manufacture of all synthetic ammonia, so essential in food production, and the nitric acid from ammonia for explosives, would be impossible without certain catalysts for the reactions involved.

In living organisms the most important and also the most complex cases of catalysts are found. In biochemistry the catalysts involved in living processes are called **enzymes.** There is, for example, the enzyme known as **ptyalin** found in saliva, which catalyzes the breakdown of starches. In the stomach there is **pepsin,** which catalyzes the breakdown of the protein of food. Yeast is a low form of plant life, which in its growth process produces an enzyme that promotes the conversion of sugar (glucose) to alcohol and carbon dioxide.

$$C_6H_{12}O_6 \xrightarrow{\text{yeast enzyme, zymase}} 2C_2H_5OH + 2CO_2$$

It formerly was believed that enzymes were themselves living organisms because of the mysterious way in which their presence brought about certain chemical reactions. This belief has been completely disproved. Some enzymes have been isolated, crystallized, and shown to be merely chemical compounds, although very complicated ones.

KEY WORDS

enzyme	platinized asbestos	spontaneous combustion
particle size	ptyalin	surface area
pepsin	reagent	

HIGHLIGHTS

The factors which affect the speed of chemical reactions are temperature, concentration of reactants, surface area of particles, and the presence of a catalyst.

An increase of 10°C generally doubles the speed of a reaction.

The rate of a reaction increases with an increase in the concentration of the reactants.

The rate of a reaction increases with an increase in the surface area of the reacting particles.

Certain reactions are speeded up by the presence of a catalyst. **Enzymes** are complex catalysts formed by living things and controlling many of the reactions upon which life depends.

QUESTIONS

1. Cite one illustration of a chemical reaction which is almost instantaneous and one of a reaction which occurs over a period of months.
2. How may each of the reactions you cited in your answer to question 1 be slowed down?
3. Do you think it would improve the quality of frozen foods if it were practical to store them at −50°C rather than at −20°C? Why?
4. In commercial packing of frozen fruits and vegetables, it is considered very important to freeze them as soon as possible after picking. Sometimes freezing units are moved right into the field to accomplish this. Explain the relation of these facts to the known effect of temperature on reaction rates.
5. List as many illustrations as you can which you might find in your own home showing the effect of temperature on reaction rate.
6. Tents are sometimes waterproofed by brushing on linseed oil. Why is it dangerous to treat a tent with linseed oil and then roll it up and put it away in the attic?
7. Why is coal dust considered a hazard in coal mining?
8. Why is it unwise to throw wood flour into an open fire?
9. Define a catalyst. Cite three illustrations of catalysts.
10. What is an enzyme?
11. In the experiment showing spontaneous combustion of white phosphorus (page 276), why is the phosphorus less apt to catch fire if the paper is placed on a stone topped desk?

CHAPTER **26**

chemical equilibrium

In previous chapters you have read statements which appear to be contradictory. In one place you read that on heating, mercuric oxide breaks down into mercury and oxygen.

$$2HgO \xrightarrow{heat} 2Hg + O_2 \uparrow$$

In another place you read that, on heating, mercury and oxygen combine to form mercuric oxide.

$$2Hg + O_2 \xrightarrow{heat} 2HgO$$

You may well ask whether both these statements can be true. To understand how both can be true, you must understand **chemical equilibrium**.

No single principle in the whole field of chemistry is of more use to you or the professional chemist than the principle of chemical equilibrium. Industrial chemistry makes wide use of it. Many industrial processes would be impossible without application of this principle.

In the past, before chemical equilibrium was so well understood, many thousands of dollars were spent by industry to carry out certain chemical processes at higher temperatures or higher pressures in the hope of increasing the yield of product only to find after the new equipment had been built and tried out that the yield was no greater than before—or perhaps was even less. One illustration of such a mistake, which is recorded in history, involves the reduction of iron oxide in the making of pig iron. The reaction is

$$\underset{\text{iron ore}}{Fe_2O_3} + 3CO \rightarrow 2Fe + 3CO_2 \uparrow$$

This reaction is carried out in the blast furnace. It was known that the gases leaving the furnace contained considerable quantities of carbon monoxide. It was thought originally that this incomplete reaction was due to the fact that the carbon monoxide was not in contact with the iron ore long enough. In England, a steel company built blast furnaces much taller than normal, hoping thereby to cause all the carbon monoxide to react and in this way cheapen the process. They found, after spending thousands of dollars to build these extra high furnaces, that the gases escaping from them contained the same proportion of carbon monoxide as in ordinary blast furnaces!

Such mistakes as this are no longer made, however, because now all well-trained chemists have an understanding of chemical equilibrium and related factors.

What is chemical equilibrium?

There is an old and obsolete process for making chlorine known as Deacon's process. It consists of mixing oxygen and hydrogen chloride at about 350°C. The following reaction occurs:

$$4HCl \text{ (gas)} + O_2 \text{ (gas)} \rightleftarrows 2Cl_2 \text{ (gas)} + 2H_2O \text{ (gas)}$$

But if one mixes together four moles of hydrogen chloride (HCl) and one mole of oxygen (O_2) and allows them to react, one does not obtain two moles of chlorine (Cl_2) and two moles of water (H_2O). The actual yield is only about 20 percent of this amount of chlorine and water. (This low yield is one reason why the process is obsolete.) What has happened to the other 80 percent? After the reaction has *apparently* stopped, it is found that this 80 percent is still in the form of hydrogen chloride and oxygen.

The reaction given in the preceding paragraph is actually *reversible*. By this we mean that it can occur, as written from left to right and also from right to left. When a reaction is reversible, this fact is indicated by a double arrow ($\rightleftarrows$), as in the equation referred to. Now, since this reaction is reversible, as soon as chlorine and water are formed by the forward reaction, these begin to react with each other to produce hydrochloric acid and oxygen. When the reaction has *apparently* stopped, the rates of these two opposing reactions have become equal. Although neither reaction has actually stopped, the effect of one is just exactly overcome by the reverse reaction. This condition is *chemical equilibrium*. Chemical equilibrium will always result whenever a *reversible reaction* is carried out in such a way that the products cannot escape from the system. Thus a reversible reaction carried out in a closed system never goes to completion but always reaches a state of equilibrium. Since most reactions in inorganic chemistry are reversible, you can see that this condition of equilibrium will be encountered frequently.

The concept of chemical equilibrium, once you grasp it, is very simple. It is important, however, to realize that the apparent stoppage of a reaction when less than complete is not actually due to the reaction's having stopped, but rather to two opposing reactions occurring with equal rates. The situation can be compared to the coming and going of shoppers to and from a large store. Suppose for a moment that every time a person entered the store, one also left the store. Then, although there might be a steady stream of shoppers into and out of the store, the number in the store at any one time (corresponding to the concentration of products in a reversible reaction) would be the same.

The reduction of iron oxide by carbon monoxide in the blast furnace is also a reversible reaction. This explains why the stack gases always contain some unreacted carbon monoxide.

How reversible reactions go to completion

Chemists generally want to obtain the maximum yield of products from a reaction. To obtain the maximum yield, they must make the reaction go to completion. There is only one way this can be accomplished. **The reverse reaction must be prevented.** This can be done by separating the products so that they have no opportunity to react. Sometimes it is practical to do this and sometimes it is not. For example, consider making hydrogen chloride by the reaction

$$H_2SO_4 + NaCl \rightleftarrows NaHSO_4 + HCl \uparrow$$

This reaction is a reversible one. This fact can be proved by adding concentrated hydrochloric acid to a saturated solution of sodium hydrogen sulfate. A precipitate of sodium chloride will be formed. Yet as the above reaction is carried out for the manufacture of hydrogen chloride, it goes to completion because the hydrogen chloride is insoluble in sulfuric acid and escapes from the reaction container. If water is present, the reaction will not go to completion because the hydrogen chloride is soluble in water and therefore it will not escape.

The reaction

$$3Fe + 4H_2O \rightleftarrows \underset{\text{(solid)}}{Fe_3O_4} + \underset{\text{(gas)}}{4H_2}$$

is reversible. Yet in the industrial manufacture of hydrogen by this method, all the iron is made to react because the hydrogen is separated from the solid iron oxide and the reverse reaction is thereby prevented. The reaction is carried out by passing steam over the iron, the excess steam carrying the hydrogen out with it. If the hydrogen is not removed as fast as it is formed, the reaction will not go to completion.

Fig. 26–1. A sealed container of iron and steam (a) gives only a small amount of hydrogen. However, if steam is passed over iron (b), all the iron can be made to react. On the other hand, by passing hydrogen over iron oxide, all the iron oxide can be reduced to iron (c).

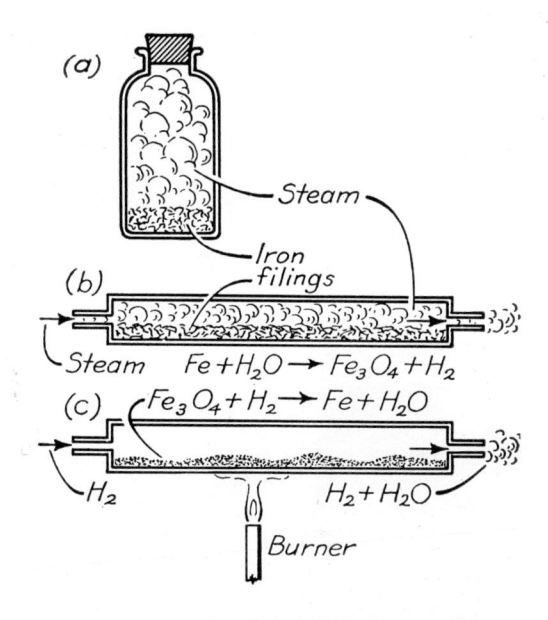

On the other hand, if hydrogen is passed over heated iron oxide, the water formed will be carried off, and under these conditions iron oxide can be completely reduced to iron.

In some cases, particularly where the reactants are all gases or are all in solution, it is not possible to separate the products. Although the reaction cannot be made to go to completion when all the products are gases or are in solution, the actual yield can be influenced by selecting the proper conditions for carrying out the reaction. You will read more about this later.

How concentration of reactants influences yield

You will recall that in the preceding chapter you learned that the rate of a reaction is proportional to the concentration of the reacting substances. This statement is generally known as the law of mass action.

Returning to the illustration originally used on page 283,

$$4HCl + O_2 \rightleftarrows 2Cl_2 + 2H_2O$$

suppose the concentration of oxygen is increased by adding more oxygen to the system when it is at equilibrium. This will have the direct effect of increasing the rate of the forward reaction without directly influencing the rate of the reverse reaction. Consequently chlorine and water will begin to be formed at a rate greater than the rate at which they are reacting. Hence the concentration of the chlorine and the water will begin to increase, and the concentration of hydrogen chloride will begin to decrease. This will then result in an increase in the rate of the reverse reaction and a decrease in the forward reaction,

The equilibrium point of any reversible reaction is affected by the concentration of the reactants. By the addition of one of the reactants, a precipitate like that in the bottom of the test tube can be caused to dissolve. Solution of the precipitate is brought about by shifting the equilibrium point. (Corning Glass Works)

and eventually a new equilibrium point will be established. You can see from the preceding discussion that at the new equilibrium point, the concentration of chlorine and water is greater and that of hydrogen chloride is less than at the original equilibrium point. That is, increasing the concentration of oxygen causes the formation of more chlorine and water, leaving less hydrogen chloride unreacted. This effect is described by the chemist as *shifting the equilibrium point to the right.* In general, **an increase in the concentration of any component will shift the equilibrium in the direction which uses up that component.** This statement can be illustrated by the following:

Prepare a solution containing approximately 45 g of ammonium thiocyanate (NH$_4$SCN) per liter and another containing approximately 16 g of ferric chloride (FeCl$_3$) per liter. Add 1 ml of each of these solutions to 200 ml of water in a beaker and stir well. These substances react as follows:

$$FeCl_3 + NH_4(SCN) \rightleftarrows \underset{\text{(red)}}{FeSCNCl_2} + NH_4Cl*$$

* Actually all the compounds shown are ionized. For the sake of simplicity they are written here in the un-ionized form (see Chap. 27, page 297).

All the substances involved in this reversible reaction are colorless except ferric thiocyanyl chloride (FeSCNCl$_2$), which is an intense red. The equilibrium point can then be judged by noting the color of the solution. Now divide the solution prepared into four equal parts. To part one add a few drops of the original ferric chloride solution, thereby increasing the concentration of ferric chloride. An immediate deepening of the red color is produced, showing that the equilibrium point has been displaced to the right. The addition of ammonium thiocyanate to part two produces the same effect. You may want to determine the effect of adding solid ammonium chloride (NH₄Cl) to part three. Part four is kept as a control for comparison.

This experiment illustrates the very important fact that the yield of products in a reversible reaction can be controlled, within limits, by varying the concentration of one of the reactants. This is known by chemists as the **mass action effect,** and it is one of their most important tools.

For example, returning to the illustration in this chapter on page 283, the yield of chlorine from hydrogen chloride can be increased by using a high concentration of oxygen (which is free when supplied in the form of air). You will find many other illustrations of the mass action effect throughout this book.

How does temperature affect the yield of products?

The effect of temperature can be predicted from the following statement: **An increase in temperature shifts the equilibrium in the direction which uses up heat.** This statement is known as **van't Hoff's law.** Consider the oxidation of sulfur dioxide to sulfur trioxide in the contact process for sulfuric acid.

$$2SO_2 + O_2 \rightleftarrows 2SO_3 + \text{heat}$$

The forward reaction is exothermic. The reverse reaction is endothermic. Van't Hoff's law says that an increase in temperature favors the endothermic reaction, that is, the equilibrium will be shifted toward the left. Consider the actual experimental data obtained.

Temperature, °C	Yield of SO_3, %
400	98
600	60
900	Very small

Thus for an exothermic reaction, the higher the temperature the lower the yield. Why not, then, use very low temperatures, such as 0°C, and thereby obtain an almost 100 percent yield? The lower the temperature the longer the time required to reach equilibrium because both reactions are slower. If it takes too long to reach equilibrium, it does not matter what the equilibrium yield would be. That is, at 0°C the above reaction will give 99+ percent yield but it would probably take several years to reach equilibrium! In actual practice 400°C is found to be the lowest temperature at which this reaction is rapid enough to be practical and then a catalyst is still necessary.

Van't Hoff's law applies to physical processes which involve equilibrium as well as to chemical equilibrium. Consider the vaporization of water (see Chap. 12, pages 116, 118, and 122 to 124).

$$\text{heat} + \underset{\text{(liquid)}}{H_2O} \rightleftarrows \underset{\text{(vapor)}}{H_2O}$$

The process is endothermic from left to right. And as is well known, higher temperatures cause water to have higher vapor pressures.

Van't Hoff's law is applicable also to predicting the effect of a temperature change on solubility (see Chap. 14, pages 149 and 150).

How does pressure influence equilibrium point?

The effect of pressure is given by **Le Châtelier's**[1] **law: When some stress is applied to a system in equilibrium, the equilibrium point is displaced in the direction which tends to offset the effect of the stress.** Consider the combination of nitrogen and hydrogen to form ammonia:

$$\underset{\text{(gas)}}{N_2} + \underset{\text{(gas)}}{3H_2} \rightleftarrows \underset{\text{(gas)}}{2NH_3}$$

$$1 \text{ vol} + 3 \text{ vol} \rightarrow 2 \text{ vol}$$

$$4 \text{ vol} \rightarrow 2 \text{ vol}$$

All the substances are gases and their relative volumes can be predicted from Avogadro's law. As the reaction proceeds, there will be a shrinkage in volume (4 volumes → 2 volumes). Le Châtelier's law says that if an increased pressure is applied to this system, more ammonia will form, since this has a smaller volume and its formation will thereby *tend* to decrease the pressure. Increased pressure always forms more of those substances which have the smaller volumes, and decreased pressure always forms more of those substances which have the larger volumes. The actual data for this reaction are as follows:

Pressure in Atmospheres	Yield of NH_3 at 600°C, %
40	2
80	3.5
120	4.5
240	9.5

[1] Henri Le Châtelier was born in Paris in 1850. He received the degree of Doctor of Physical and Chemical Science from the University of the Sorbonne, where later he was professor. In 1907 he became Professor of General Chemistry at the University of Paris. Some of his students are among our most prominent chemists in America today. He worked on metallurgy and explosives, but his most lasting work is the law of equilibrium bearing his name. He died in 1936.

Fig. 26-2. An application of Le Châtelier's law to physical equilibrium. The pressure of the wire on the ice causes the ice to melt and the wire moves downward. When the pressure is released, the ice refreezes.

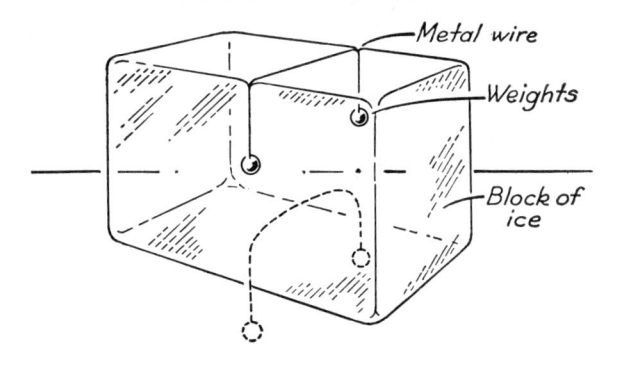

Reactions involving only solids and liquids have small volume changes, and pressure has a correspondingly slight effect on the equilibrium point.

Le Châtelier's law applies to physical equilibrium, also. Thus in the melting of ice,

$$H_2O \rightleftarrows H_2O$$
$$\text{(ice)} \quad \text{(liquid)}$$

This reversible change involves a decrease in volume from left to right. If pressure on the ice is increased, its melting point is reduced in accordance with the prediction of Le Châtelier's law. In the laboratory this can be demonstrated by placing across an ice cube a piece of fine wire, to the ends of which weights are tied. The wire will cut its way through the ice cube, the water will refreeze as the wire passes through, and after the wire has moved all the way through, there will still be only one solid cube of ice! The explanation is that, because of the pressure, the ice immediately under the wire has a melting point slightly below 0°C. Now the cube has a temperature of 0°C (if it is in a room warmer than 0°C); hence the ice under the wire melts. As the wire moves downward, the pressure is released and the water refreezes (Fig. 26-2).

That pressure makes ice easier to melt is no news to anyone who has squeezed a handful of snow into a snowball or has observed the change of snow into ice on a highway, even when the temperature does not rise above 0°C. Skiers and other residents of the colder sections of this country know that snow just below 0°C (32°F) packs readily merely from the pressure[1] of their feet. If, however, the temperature is well below 0°C, the snow has a gritty feel and crunches and cries as they walk on it. This is because the pressure of their shoes is insufficient to cause any melting if the temperature is too low.

Le Châtelier's law is one of the greatest principles of science—one

[1] The actual pressure under your foot is of course very small, but when you realize that snowflakes are mostly points and edges, you can see that your foot might create a really considerable pressure on the areas of actual contact between snowflakes.

of the really grand classifications. It is applicable to a wide variety of systems. If you take further training in science, you will find many such applications. For example, Le Châtelier's law covers both van't Hoff's law and the effect of concentration on equilibrium point.

If the temperature of a system in equilibrium is raised, Le Châtelier's law says the system will react in the direction which uses up heat, thereby tending to reduce the temperature. But this is exactly van't Hoff's law, which is really a special case of Le Châtelier's law.

Suppose the concentration of nitrogen is increased in the ammonia reaction on page 288. Le Châtelier's law says the system will react in the direction which tends to use up this extra nitrogen; that is, it will displace the equilibrium to the right. But this is exactly what was predicted on page 288; it is a special case of the more general law.

KEY WORDS

chemical equilibrium   Le Châtelier   van't Hoff
mass action effect

HIGHLIGHTS

The term **chemical equilibrium** refers to the balanced state arrived at when two opposing reactions occur at the same speed. Equilibrium is reached whenever a reversible reaction occurs in a closed system. Double arrows ($\rightleftarrows$) are used to represent a reversible reaction.

The most comprehensive statement yet made concerning chemical and physical equilibria is that made by **Le Châtelier** in 1888. This is known as Le Châtelier's law or principle and states that: **If a stress is imposed upon a system in equilibrium the change will be in the direction which tends to relieve the stress.** This applies to changes in concentration, temperature, and pressure. Note the following applications:

In order to make a desired reaction go to completion, the reverse reaction must be prevented by removing the products of the desired reaction as rapidly as they are produced.

Increasing the temperature favors the endothermic reaction (the one which absorbs heat)—**van't Hoff's law.**

An increase in pressure will shift the equilibrium point in the direction of the reaction which produces the lesser volume of products.

By applying the law of Le Châtelier in its various phases, engineers are able to design chemical manufacturing plants which will operate at the highest possible degree of efficiency.

QUESTIONS

1. What is meant by chemical equilibrium?
2. In general, how can a reaction which is reversible be made to go to completion?
3. Explain how it is possible to make the reaction of iron oxide and hydrogen occur in either direction.
4. In the manufacture of hydrogen chloride by the reaction of sulfuric acid and salt, why does the reaction go to completion?
5. State the effect on the equilibrium point produced by increasing the concentration of any reactant.
6. State the law of mass action. What is the relation between this law and the answer to question 5.
7. State the van't Hoff law relating to the effect of temperature on the equilibrium point. Apply it to the following reaction:

$$H_2 + S \rightleftarrows H_2S + \text{heat}$$

8. What conclusion do you reach in question 7 about the effect of temperature on the stability of H_2S?
9. Apply van't Hoff's law to the following:

$$\text{Heat} + N_2 + O_2 \rightleftarrows 2NO$$

   What can you say about the effect of temperature on the stability of nitric oxide (NO)?
10. Are all compounds more stable at low temperature than at high temperature? Explain.
11. State Le Châtelier's law. Show how it predicts the effect of pressure on the reaction:

$$2SO_2 + O_2 \rightleftarrows 2SO_3$$
$$\text{(gas)} \quad \text{(gas)} \quad \text{(gas)}$$

12. What effect does pressure have on the reaction given in question 9?
13. Would you say that all compounds are more stable at high pressure than at low? Explain.
14. Cast iron expands on solidifying. What effect would you expect high pressure to have on its melting point?

CHAPTER 27

solutions of acids, bases, and salts

The terms acid, base, and salt are already familiar to you. In this chapter you will learn more of the properties of each and the reasons for these properties.

What is an acid?

The term acid refers to a group of compounds all of which have certain properties:

1. All acids contain hydrogen (but not all hydrogen compounds are acids).
2. In water solution all acids have a sour taste. The sour taste of vinegar is due to acetic acid; that of lemon juice, to citric acid.
3. Water solutions of acids liberate hydrogen when they come in contact with an active metal such as zinc (see Chap. 8, page 68).
4. Acids neutralize bases. The product of this reaction is a salt (see page 293) and water.
5. Water solutions of acids are conductors of electricity (see page 294).
6. Water solutions of all acids have the same effect on what are known as acid-base indicators. A common indicator is litmus, which in the presence of acids is changed from blue to pink. Pink phenolphthalein becomes colorless in the presence of an acid. **Indicators** are organic dyes, some of which are found in nature. Cherry juice and beet juice are acid-base indicators.

Familiar examples of acids are sulfuric acid (H_2SO_4), hydrochloric acid (HCl), lactic acid in sour milk, and citric acid found in citrus fruits and most soda pop.

What is a base?

The term **base** refers to a group of compounds all of which have certain properties:

1. Water solutions of bases have a characteristic bitter taste. The bitter taste of baking soda or soap is due to the fact that both of these substances form basic solutions.
2. Bases neutralize acids to form salts (see below).
3. Water solutions of bases are conductors of electricity (page 294).
4. Water solutions of all bases have the same effect on acid-base indicators. For example, litmus turns blue in the presence of a basic solution; colorless phenolphthalein turns pink.

Common bases are sodium hydroxide (or lye, NaOH) and calcium hydroxide [also known as hydrated lime, $Ca(OH)_2$]. It may be noted that most, but not all, bases are metallic hydroxides.

Salts and neutralization

A **salt** is the product (other than water) formed by neutralizing an acid with a base. Thus if hydrochloric acid and sodium hydroxide are put together in just the correct ratio, the properties of both acid and base are destroyed and the result is a solution of common table salt.

$$HCl + NaOH \rightarrow H_2O + NaCl$$
$$(acid) + (base) \rightarrow (water) + (salt)$$

$$2HCl + Ca(OH)_2 \rightarrow 2H_2O + CaCl_2$$
calcium chloride (a salt)

$$H_2SO_4 + 2KOH \rightarrow 2H_2O + K_2SO_4$$
potassium hydroxide   potassium sulfate (a salt)

$$2HCl + Cu(OH)_2 \rightarrow 2H_2O + CuCl_2$$
copper hydroxide   copper chloride (a salt)

Note that in **neutralization** the hydrogen of the acid combines with the hydroxyl of the base to form water. The remaining parts of the acid and base unite to form a salt.

Compounds which contain two acid hydrogen atoms per molecule are known as *dibasic* acids; those with only one acid hydrogen per molecule are known as *monobasic* acids. A common dibasic acid is sulfuric acid. If sulfuric acid and sodium hydroxide are mixed in the ratio of one mole of each, the acid is only half neutralized:

$$H_2SO_4 + NaOH \rightarrow NaHSO_4 + H_2O$$

The product is both a monobasic acid and a salt. It is called *sodium acid sulfate* or *sodium hydrogen sulfate*. Dibasic acids, therefore, form

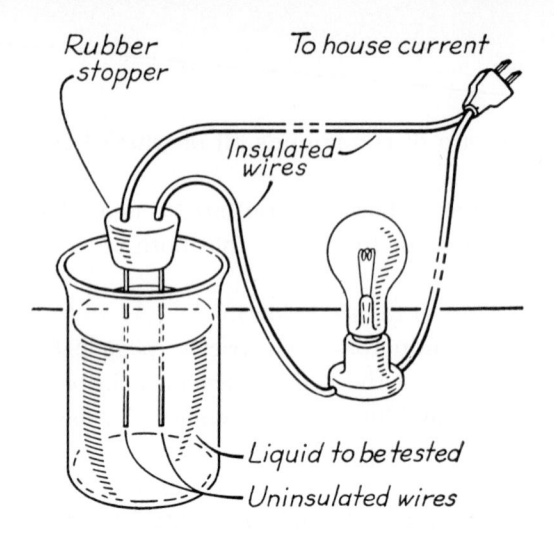

Fig. 27–1. A convenient setup for testing conductivity. Water solutions of all acids, bases, and salts conduct electricity. If a solution of an electrolyte is in the beaker when the apparatus is plugged in, the bulb will light up.

two types of salts: the *acid salts* and the normal salts. The *normal salts* are the completely neutralized ones, such as sodium sulfate (Na_2SO_4).

A tribasic acid, such as phosphoric, forms three types of salts.

$$NaOH + H_3PO_4 \rightarrow \underset{\text{sodium dihydrogen phosphate}}{NaH_2PO_4} + H_2O$$

Sodium dihydrogen phosphate is used in some baking powders.

$$2NaOH + H_3PO_4 \rightarrow \underset{\text{disodium monohydrogen phosphate}}{Na_2HPO_4} + 2H_2O$$

$$3NaOH + H_3PO_4 \rightarrow \underset{\text{trisodium phosphate or normal sodium phosphate}}{Na_3PO_4} + 3H_2O$$

Trisodium phosphate is used in some water softeners and soap powders.

Electrical conductivity

A convenient apparatus for testing the electrical conductivity of solutions is shown in Fig. 27–1. Two pieces of copper wire are inserted through a rubber stopper so that the wires are about 1 in. apart. An incandescent lamp is connected in series with one of the wires. A cap is connected to the ends of the wires so that the wires can be plugged into an outlet of house current. All the wires except those below the stopper should be insulated. You can see that when connected to the house current, electricity can flow in the circuit and the lamp will glow only if there is an electrical conductor between the two bare wires below the rubber stopper. These wires are known as the *electrodes*. Consequently the glow of the lamp is an indicator of the electrical conductivity of the medium into which the wires are dipping. When dipped into distilled water, the lamp does not glow. However, if a little sodium chloride is dissolved in the water, the lamp glows brightly, showing that sodium chloride solution is a good electrical conductor. **Water solutions of all acids, bases, and salts are electrical conductors.** For this reason they are known as **electrolytes.** Nothing except an acid, a base, or a salt, is an electrolyte. For example, sugar or alcohol or glycerin when dissolved in water will not cause the water to become a conductor. Such substances are called *non-electrolytes.*

Whenever a solution conducts an electric current, a chemical change occurs at each electrode. This is known as *electrolysis.* This process is the basis of all electroplating, which is the method used in many metal-plating operations, such as the production of silver plate or the chrome plate used on the modern automobile. For example, if the electrolyte is the salt copper chloride, when the current passes through the solution this is decomposed as follows:

$$CuCl_2 \xrightarrow{\text{electric current}} Cu + Cl_2 \uparrow$$

(at negative electrode) (at positive electrode)

The copper will plate out at the negative electrode. The chlorine is formed at the positive electrode. For satisfactory electroplating, direct, rather than alternating, current is necessary, since with alternating current a mixture of products is obtained at both electrodes.

How do we explain the properties of acids?

When dissolved in water, hydrogen chloride reacts with the water

$$HCl + H_2O \rightleftarrows \underset{\text{hydronium ion}}{OH_3{}^+} + \underset{\text{chloride ion}}{Cl^-}$$

Or electronically:

$$H:\overset{..}{\underset{..}{Cl}}: + H:\overset{..}{\underset{..}{O}}:H \rightarrow H:\overset{..}{\underset{H}{O}}:H^+ + :\overset{..}{\underset{..}{Cl}}:^-$$

hydronium ion   chloride ion

This reaction is known as the **ionization** of hydrochloric acid. The hydrogen nucleus from the hydrochloric acid shares a pair of electrons with the oxygen atom of the water. The chloride **ion** is not to be confused with free, uncombined chlorine. It is a chlorine atom which has gained an electron and is the same as the combined chlorine in a solution of sodium chloride or any other metal chloride.

The acid properties of hydrochloric acid are due to the **hydronium ion (OH_3^+)**. That is, the sour taste, the reaction with metals, the action on indicators, and so on, are properties of this ion. **Hydronium ion is formed whenever an acid dissolves in water.**

With sulfuric acid, the ionization reaction is:

$$H_2SO_4 + 2H_2O \rightleftarrows 2OH_3^+ + SO_4^=$$
$$\text{sulfate ion}$$

which differs from the case of hydrochloric acid only in that the sulfuric acid molecule has two acid hydrogens instead of one.

In general, where HA is *any* acid, an acid ionizes

$$HA + H_2O \rightleftarrows OH_3^+ + A^-$$

The properties common to all acid solutions are the properties of the hydronium ion. In other words the exact properties of any given acid are the sum of two sets of properties: (1) the properties of the hydronium ion and (2) the properties of the negative ion.

How do we explain the properties of bases?

Sodium hydroxide, when dissolved in water ionizes as follows:

$$Na^+OH^- \rightarrow Na^+ + OH^-$$
$$\text{sodium ion} \quad \text{hydroxyl ion}$$

Most bases are electrovalent type compounds. When they dissolve in water, the water causes a separation of the positive and negative parts of the compound. This separation sets free in solution the positive ion and the **hydroxyl ion. The properties common to all bases are the properties of the hydroxyl ion.**

$$Ca^{++}(OH^-)_2 \rightarrow Ca^{++} + 2OH^-$$

A few bases do not contain the hydroxyl radical. These bases react with water to form the hydroxyl ion. The only common example is ammonia. This substance is a gas having the formula NH_3. When ammonia dissolves in water, it forms a basic solution known as *ammonium hydroxide*. Household ammonia is dilute ammonium hydroxide.

$$NH_3 + H_2O \rightleftarrows NH_4^+ + OH^-$$
$$\text{ammonium ion}$$

Electronically it is

$$H:\underset{\cdot\cdot}{\overset{\cdot\cdot}{N}}:\; +\; H:\underset{\cdot\cdot}{\overset{\cdot\cdot}{O}}:H \rightarrow \left[H:\underset{H}{\overset{H}{N}}:H\right]^+ + \left[:\underset{\cdot\cdot}{\overset{\cdot\cdot}{O}}:H\right]^-$$

(with H below each N)

Fig. 27–2. A schematic diagram of a sodium chloride crystal. Ions are the structure units in the crystals of a salt like sodium chloride. The dark dots may be considered sodium ions and the light dots chloride ions.

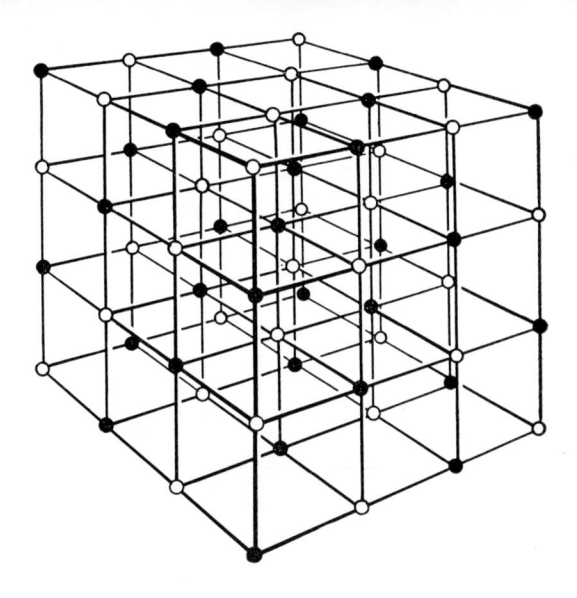

Salts

Salts are all electrovalent compounds. The ions exist in the crystal, but because of the rigidity of the crystal, they are not free to move. Therefore, solid salts are not electrical conductors.[1] When dissolved in water, the ions become separated and free to move under the influence of an electric current. The ionization of a salt is represented like the ionization of a metallic hydroxide.

$$Na^+Cl^- \rightarrow Na^+ + Cl^-$$
$$Ca^{++}(NO_3^-)_2 \rightarrow Ca^{++} + 2NO_3^-$$
$$Cu^{++}(Cl^-)_2 \rightarrow Cu^{++} + 2Cl^-$$

Salts exist in solution entirely in the form of ions. The properties of a solution of a certain salt, therefore, are the sum of two sets of properties: (1) those of its positive ion and (2) those of its negative ion.

Electrolysis

The ability of electrolytes to conduct the electric current is due to the fact that they furnish *ions* (or charged atoms) in solution and these ions can move through the solution.[2] This movement, and the electrolysis which always accompanies it, can be understood by reference to Fig. 27–3. When the electrodes are connected to a battery or other source of current, one electrode is made positive and the other negative. (You should remember that a battery or dynamo is only an electron pump which causes electrons to circulate through the metallic circuit connected to it. Batteries and dynamos do not make electrons.) As a result of the charges on the electrodes, the copper ions (Cu^{++})

---

[1] Dry salts are conductors when in the molten condition.
[2] The word *ion*, from the Greek word meaning *wanderer*, comes from this fact.

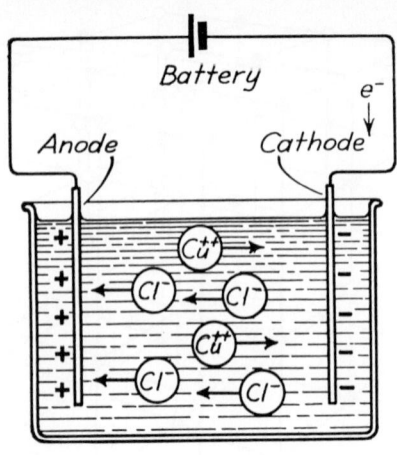

Fig. 27–3. The electrolysis of a solution of copper chloride.

begin to move toward the cathode, which is the negative electrode, and the chloride ions (Cl⁻) start toward the anode, which is the positive electrode. These ions travel through the solution slowly—normally only a few centimeters an hour. Since the different ions are at various distances from the electrodes, they reach the electrodes at varying times. On reaching the electrode, a copper ion gains two electrons from the electrode and becomes an atom of metallic copper.

At the negative electrode: $Cu^{++} + 2e^- \rightarrow Cu^0$

These electrons are immediately replaced by the battery because at the same time two chloride ions released two electrons at the anode.

At the positive electrode: $2Cl^- \rightarrow Cl_2^0 \uparrow + 2e^-$

Consequently electricity flows in the circuit and the solute is decomposed at the electrodes. The over-all electrolysis reaction is obtained by adding the two preceding equations.

$$Cu^{++} + 2Cl^- \xrightarrow{\text{electrolysis}} Cu^0 + Cl_2^0 \uparrow$$

If hydrochloric acid is electrolyzed, the electrode reactions are

$$2OH_3^+ + 2e^- \rightarrow H_2 \uparrow + 2H_2O$$
$$2Cl^- \rightarrow Cl_2 \uparrow + 2e^-$$
$$\overline{2OH_3^+ + 2Cl^- \rightarrow H_2 \uparrow + Cl_2 \uparrow + 2H_2O}$$

Thus all acids yield hydrogen on electrolysis. All chlorides yield chlorine.

The case of a base is a bit more complex. Consider the electrolysis of copper hydroxide [Cu(OH)₂]. The product at the negative electrode would, as usual, be copper:

$$2e^- + Cu^{++} \rightarrow Cu^0$$

Negative hydroxyl ion loses an electron at the positive electrode:

$$OH^- \rightarrow OH^0 + 1e^-$$

But the free OH⁰ is unstable and reacts with other free hydroxyls to form water and oxygen:

$$4OH^0 \rightarrow 2H_2O + O_2 \uparrow$$

The over-all reaction at the negative electrode is, therefore,

$$4OH^- \rightarrow 2H_2O + O_2 \uparrow + 4e^-$$

Consequently all bases yield oxygen (and water) on electrolysis.

Weak and strong acids

If you compare the conductivity of a solution of $1M$ acetic acid and that of $1M$ hydrochloric acid in an apparatus like that shown in Fig. 27–1, page 294, you will find that the lamp glows brightly with the hydrochloric, and dimly with the acetic, acid. Furthermore, if you drop some pieces of zinc into each of these solutions, you will find that hydrogen is liberated much more rapidly from the hydrochloric acid than from the acetic acid. Because of differences such as these, chemists speak of hydrochloric acid as being a *strong* acid and acetic acid as being a *weak* acid.

Hydrochloric acid and all other strong acids are ionized in solution almost completely.

$$H_2O + HCl \rightleftharpoons OH_3^+ + Cl^-$$

The ionization of all acids is a reversible process and, therefore, can never be complete. However, in the case of a strong acid, the equilibrium point is so far to the right that for all practical purposes the acid is completely ionized. This is indicated by the relative lengths of the arrows in the ionization equation. A weak acid is one in which the ionization equilibrium is further to the left. Hence weak acids exist in solution less than completely ionized. That is, for acetic acid

$$HC_2H_3O_2 + H_2O \rightleftharpoons OH_3^+ + C_2H_3O_2^-$$

(Acetic acid has four hydrogen atoms in its formula but only one of them is an acid hydrogen. The others, like the hydrogens in sugar or alcohol, do not ionize.)

This means that in a solution of this acid only part of the acetic acid molecules exist in the ionized form at any one time. (The actual amount which is ionized depends on the concentration.) Since acetic acid furnishes fewer ions than hydrochloric acid, its conductivity, rate of reaction with metals, and taste, at the same total concentration, will be different because these properties depend upon the presence of ions.

Almost all organic acids are weak and we are fortunate that they are. Many natural products, such as vinegar, lemon juice, and grapefruit juice, consist of a 0.5M or greater concentration of an organic acid. Because the acid is weak, vinegar and fruit juices have only a slightly sour taste and you can drink them without harm to your teeth. If you were to drink 0.5M hydrochloric or another strong acid, it would literally dissolve your teeth.

Of course, not all weak acids ionize to the same extent. They vary from those which are just less than completely ionized, all the way to some which are almost totally un-ionized at the same concentration. An example is boric acid, which is so weak that it is used as an eyewash.

To make the difference a little clearer, let us assume two solutions:

Acid	Degree of Ionization, %
1M hydrochloric acid	Greater than 99.9
1M acetic acid	Approximately 1

The acetic acid, therefore, furnishes only $\frac{1}{100}$ as many ions at any one time as the hydrochloric acid. In taste, electrical conductivity, and *rate* of reaction with zinc, the 1M acetic acid would be equivalent to $\frac{1}{100}$M hydrochloric acid.

Both weak and strong acids have the same base-neutralizing ability at equivalent concentrations, however. This is because base-neutralizing ability, unlike the other properties mentioned earlier, depends on the total amount of acid present rather than the actual concentration of hydronium ions at any one time. Writing ionically the neutralization of hydrochloric acid by sodium hydroxide,

$$\underbrace{Na^+ + OH^-}_{\text{from NaOH}} + \underbrace{OH_3^+ + Cl^-}_{\text{from HCl}} \rightarrow 2H_2O + Na^+ + Cl^-$$

Or since Na^+ and Cl^- are unchanged, the only change which takes place is

$$OH^- + OH_3^+ \rightarrow 2H_2O$$

TABLE 27–1. Common strong and weak acids

Strong		Weak	
Hydrochloric	HCl	Sulfurous	H_2SO_3
Nitric	HNO_3	Carbonic	H_2CO_3
Sulfuric	H_2SO_4	Acetic	$HC_2H_3O_2$
Hydrobromic	HBr	Hydrosulfuric	H_2S
Hydriodic	HI	Phosphoric	H_3PO_4
		Citric	$H_3C_6H_5O_7$
		Hydrofluoric	H_2F_2
		Nitrous	HNO_2
		Boric	H_3BO_3

Two chemists at work in an analytical laboratory. Such laboratories are common in large industrial concerns where the products must be continually tested for uniformity and purity. Cities often maintain analytical laboratories also to test the purity of food products and medicinals. (New York City Department of Health)

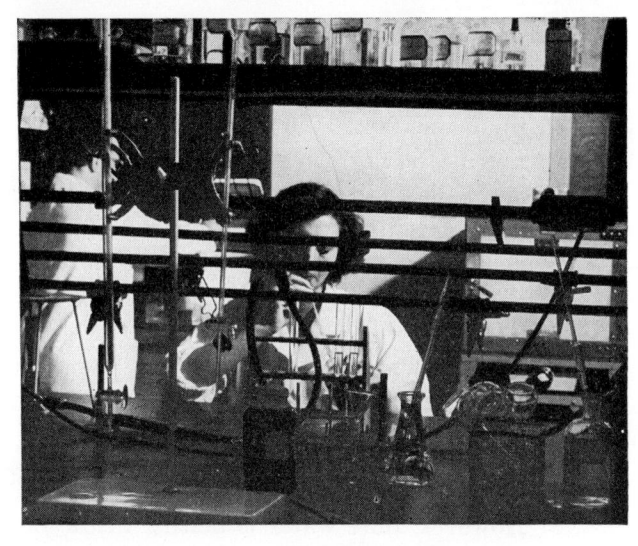

In neutralizing a weak acid, such as acetic, the only difference is that, as the hydronium ions present react with the hydroxyl ions to form water, the ionization equilibrium is displaced to the right. This causes some of the un-ionized acetic acid to ionize. The newly ionized material in turn is neutralized, and the process continues until eventually all the acetic acid has ionized and been neutralized.

$$HC_2H_3O_2 + H_2O \rightleftarrows OH_3^+ + C_2H_3O_2^-$$
$$+$$
$$Na^+OH^- \rightarrow OH^- + Na^+$$
$$\rightarrow 2H_2O + Na^+ + C_2H_3O_2^-$$

Thus 1 liter of $1M$ hydrochloric acid and 1 liter of $1M$ acetic acid will each require one mole of sodium hydroxide for complete neutralization.

Strong and weak bases

The hydroxides of Group Ia as well as those of calcium, strontium, and barium are all *strong bases* which are completely ionized in solution. The hydroxides of all other metals behave in solution as weak bases.

The strength of an acid or base must not be confused with its solubility. Thus calcium hydroxide is not very soluble in water (solubility = 1.7 g/liter at 18°C), but its solution is nevertheless completely ionized.

Ammonia is an important example of a weak base. In solution only a small part of the ammonia is actually in the form of ammonium and hydroxyl ions. The remainder is dissolved ammonia (NH_3) which is in equilibrium with these ions:

$$NH_3 + H_2O \rightleftarrows NH_4^+ + OH^-$$

In fact the suitability of ammonia as a household cleaner depends upon this fact. If ammonia were a strong base, the housewife would find it too corrosive to use. It would be like lye (NaOH). Instead, ammonia ionizes slightly, but as the hydroxyl ions present are used up in cleaning, more are formed to take their place because of the chemical equilibrium which must exist.

The ionization of water

From what you have already read, you have probably concluded that water is not ionized. This idea is not quite correct. Water is very, very slightly ionized into hydronium ions and hydroxyl ions.

$$2H_2O \rightleftarrows OH_3^+ + OH^-$$

However, pure water is neither acidic nor basic because it produces equal quantities of hydronium ions and hydroxyl ions. Pure water is actually ionized in this way to the extent of about 0.0000002 percent. No wonder this ionization could not be detected by the electric-light-bulb conducting apparatus! Yet even this very slight degree of ionization of water is important in understanding some of the properties of solutions.

Even in a strongly acid solution there will always be some hydroxyl ions from the ionization of water. Also, in a strongly basic solution there will always be some hydronium ions from the ionization of the water. That is, since the ionization reaction of water is reversible, neither the concentration of hydronium ions nor of hydroxyl ions can ever be zero in a water solution. An acid solution is one which contains an excess of hydronium ions over hydroxyl ions, whereas a basic solution contains an excess of hydroxyl ions over hydronium ions.

You have seen that the electrolysis of dilute sulfuric acid yields hydrogen and oxygen (Chap. 6, pages 48 and 49). The liberation of hydrogen has already been explained. In this case two kinds of negative ions move toward the positive electrode. These are

Sulfate ion, $SO_4^=$, from the sulfuric acid
Hydroxyl ion, OH^-, from the ionization of water

The hydroxyl ion loses its electron more readily than the sulfate ion; hence the reaction at the positive electrode is the same as that involving a base (see page 298).

$$4OH^- \rightarrow 2H_2O + O_2 \uparrow + 4e^-$$

In general, any sulfate or nitrate will yield oxygen at the positive electrode when electrolyzed.

If an electrolyte containing an ion from an active metal like sodium is electrolyzed, hydrogen is evolved at the negative electrode and the active metal ion and hydroxyl ion accumulate around the electrode. This is because the sodium ion, Na^+, and the hydronium ion, OH_3^+, from the ionization of the water both move toward the electrode. But the hydronium ion (also written $H_2O \cdot H^+$) has a greater tendency to *gain* an electron than sodium because sodium is more active than hydrogen (see Chap. 8, pages 73 to 75). Hence the reaction at the negative electrode is

$$2OH_3^+ + 2e^- \rightarrow 2H_2O + H_2 \uparrow$$

Remember that the hydronium ion came from the ionization of water

$$2H_2O \rightleftharpoons OH_3^+ + OH^-$$

Therefore, around the negative electrode sodium ions and hydroxyl ions accumulate as the hydrogen is liberated. Thus the complete reaction in the electrolysis of sodium chloride is:

$$2Na^+ + 2Cl^- + 2H_2O \xrightarrow{\text{electrolysis}} \underbrace{2Na^+ + 2OH^-}_{\substack{\text{(accumulate in} \\ \text{the solution} \\ \text{around negative} \\ \text{electrode)}}} + \underset{\substack{\text{(liberated} \\ \text{at nega-} \\ \text{tive elec-} \\ \text{trode)}}}{H_2 \uparrow} + \underset{\substack{\text{(liberated} \\ \text{at posi-} \\ \text{tive elec-} \\ \text{trode)}}}{Cl_2 \uparrow}$$

You can easily see that this is true from the following experiment: Dip two wires from a battery or other source of direct current into a salt solution. Place a drop of phenolphthalein in the solution around each of the wires. When the current is turned on, the solution around the negative electrode turns pink instantly, showing the formation of base around that electrode.

The pH scale

The *p*H scale is a system for expressing the degree of acidity or alkalinity of a solution. The scale was originated by the Danish chemist Sörensen. To explain the basis of the *p*H scale is beyond the scope of this book. Its use is nevertheless quite simple.

Pure water or any perfectly **neutral** solution has a *p*H of 7. Any solution having a *p*H of less than 7 is acid, the smaller the *p*H numerically the more acid the solution. Solutions having *p*H values numerically greater than 7 are alkaline, the greater the *p*H value the greater the concentration of hydroxyl ions (that is, the greater the alkalinity).

The pH Scale

0	1	2	3	4	5	6	Water 7	8	9	10	11	12	13	14
		Increasing acidity					Neutral				Increasing alkalinity			

←——————————————————   ——————————————————→

TABLE 27-2. Some pH values

	pH		pH
1M hydrochloric acid	Approximately 0	Cows' milk	6.4–6.8
0.1M hydrochloric acid	1	Vinegar	2.4–3.0
1M acetic acid	2.4	Human blood	7.3–7.5
A cola beverage	2.0–3.0	Soil	4.0–8.5[a]
Lemon juice	2.0–2.5	Distilled water	5.2–5.5[b]
Orange juice	3.0–4.0	Household ammonia	11.0–12.0
Tomatoes	4.1–4.4	Washing soda solution	11.5
Beer	3.0–4.0	Baking soda solution	8.5–9.0

[a] See below.

[b] Due to dissolved carbon dioxide from the air. If perfectly pure, pH would be 7.0.

A change of one *p*H unit means a *tenfold* change in acid or base concentration. Thus a solution with a *p*H of 5 is ten times as concentrated in hydronium ions as a solution with a *p*H of 6.

The actual degree of acidity or alkalinity of a solution is frequently a matter of very great importance both in biological and in man-made processes. For example, the optimum *p*H for yeast fermentation is 5.5. The *p*H of the blood is very closely controlled in spite of the fact that quantities of acids or bases may frequently enter the body. The widest variation in the *p*H of the blood which has ever been observed without death is from a *p*H of 7.0 to a *p*H of 7.8. The way in which the body is able to hold nearly constant the *p*H of the blood is a most interesting chemical phenomenon but it cannot be discussed here. (The interested reader is referred to books on biochemistry.)

The *p*H of soil is a matter of critical importance in determining the ability of soil to support plant growth. Most plants require a soil having a *p*H close to 7. This is particularly important in the case of most legumes (beans, peas, clover, alfalfa). Many of these plants fail to grow at all or grow only very poorly if the soil is more acid than a *p*H of 6. The same is true but to a lesser extent for the grasses. Lime is used to neutralize soil acidity. Every year millions of tons of "lime"[1] are used on the farms of America to correct soil acidity. In many cases the yield of a crop can be *doubled* by applying 2 tons of lime to the acre. Interestingly enough, there are certain plants which require an acid soil for best growth. Among these are rhododendron, azalea, and the boxwood so famous in the gardens of Virginia. All these grow best at a *p*H of about 5.0. The blueberry also requires an acid soil. In fact the discovery that blueberries require an acid soil made possible their

[1] In agriculture both hydrated lime [$Ca(OH)_2$] and limestone ($CaCO_3$) are used to correct soil acidity. The former works faster in neutralizing the soil but limestone is cheaper.

A modern pH meter. The sample to be tested is placed in the little cup shown and the electrodes are inserted into it. The pH is read on the white dial on the top of the meter.

commercial cultivation. Before this was known, all attempts to grow blueberries under cultivation ended in failure. The cheapest way to acidify soil is to add sulfur. The sulfur is slowly oxidized to form sulfuric acid in the soil.

The measurement of pH

In industry, agriculture, and the laboratory, pH measurement is a matter of great importance. There are two practical methods for measuring pH. The best, simplest, and most accurate method is based upon the fact that an electrode, made of a special glass, assumes an electrical potential which depends upon the medium in which it is immersed. Small, portable glass-electrode pH meters employing this principle are now available. Some of these are almost as simple to operate as a portable radio. With these devices you can measure, in a matter of a minute or so, the pH of almost any solution or moist, pasty solid (such as soil or cheese).

In case a pH meter is not available, you may use a method of measurement involving acid-base indicators. This method is based on the fact that each indicator changes from its acid to its basic color over an interval of about two pH units. Also, within this interval of color change the exact color of the indicator depends upon the exact pH of the solution. For example, phenolphthalein is colorless at any pH less than 8.0. At any pH greater than 9.6 it has the same cerise-red color. At any pH between 8.0 and 9.6 the color of phenolphthalein depends upon the exact pH of the solution. Each indicator has a similar characteristic interval of color change. For example, for litmus the interval of color change is from a pH of 6.0 to 8.0; for methyl orange, it is from a pH of 3.0 to 4.4. You will note that most indicators do not change color at exact neutrality, that is, at a pH of 7.0. By preparing a series of solutions of known pH and adding the indicator to each of them, you can obtain colored solutions of known pH. If you then add the same concentration of the same indicator to the unknown, the pH of the unknown can be determined by comparing its color with that of the knowns. The method is only approximately accurate, and it will not work for opaque or colored unknowns. You must also first determine the approximate pH of the unknown in order to know which indicator to use. However, the method is simple and cheap, and it does not require expensive equipment. Various commercial kits of this kind for measuring pH of soil, water, and so on, are available. These commercial kits contain permanent color standards, indicator solutions, and instructions for testing the unknown. Although useful, they are not as reliable as a good pH meter.

The pH of salts: hydrolysis

Of all the various salts formed by reactions of acids and bases, only a few form solutions which are actually neutral. For example, sodium acetate solutions have a pH of about 9.0, ammonium chloride solutions have a pH of about 5.0, and sodium chloride solutions are truly neutral. These differences in pH are related to the strengths of the acids and bases from which these salts are formed. For example, when sodium acetate is placed in water, a reaction occurs between the acetate ion and the water:

$$Na^+ + C_2H_3O_2^- + H_2O \rightleftarrows HC_2H_3O_2 + Na^+ + OH^-$$

This change consists of the removal of a proton (H^+) from the water by the acetate ion. This results in the formation of a hydroxyl ion. The resulting solution, which contains a small amount of sodium hydroxide ($Na^+ + OH^-$), is basic. This type of process is called **hydrolysis,** which means a double decomposition reaction involving water. The reaction is reversible and equilibrium is reached when only a small proportion of the acetate ion has reacted with the water. This reaction occurs because acetic acid is a weak acid (has a great tendency to hold its proton). The same type of reaction will occur for any salt derived from a strong base and a weak acid. **Salts of strong bases and weak acids will form solutions which are alkaline.** This is the same as saying that if a strong base and a weak acid are mixed in chemically equivalent quantities, the result will be a basic rather than a neutral solution.

Other examples are

$$2H_2O + 2Na^+ + CO_3^= \rightleftarrows H_2CO_3 + 2Na^+ + 2OH^-$$
$$H_2O + 2K^+ + S^= \rightleftarrows H_2S + 2K^+ + 2OH^-$$

TABLE 27-3. Hydrolysis of some salts

Form acid solutions	Form basic solutions	Form neutral solutions
NH_4Cl	Na_2CO_3	$NaCl$
$(NH_4)_2SO_4$	$NaHCO_3$	$NaNO_3$
$Al_2(SO_4)_3$	$NaC_2H_3O_2$	K_2SO_4
$FeCl_3$	KNO_2	KBr
$Cu(NO_3)_2$	K_2S	KI
	Na_2SO_3	
	Na_3PO_4	

In the same way, **salts derived from a weak base and a strong acid give solutions which are acid.** For this reason almost all the heavy metal chlorides and sulfates form acid solutions. Thus cupric chloride solution is acid:

$$Cu^{++} + 2Cl^- + 4H_2O \rightleftarrows Cu(OH)_2 + 2OH_3^+ + 2Cl^-$$

Aluminum sulfate solution is also acid:

$$2Al^{+++} + 3SO_4^= + 12H_2O \rightleftarrows 2Al(OH)_3 + 6OH_3^+ + 3SO_4^=$$

as is ammonium chloride solution:

$$NH_4^+ + Cl^- + H_2O \rightleftarrows NH_3 + OH_3^+ + Cl^-$$

Salts of strong bases and strong acids form solutions that are really neutral. These are such salts as sodium chloride, potassium chloride, and calcium nitrate.

Sometimes the hydrolysis of salts is of great practical importance. The use of sodium carbonate (Na_2CO_3) and sodium phosphate (Na_3PO_4) in laundry soaps depends partly upon the alkalinity which such substances produce in solution. The use of limestone ($CaCO_3$) to neutralize soil also depends upon its hydrolysis. Papermaker's alum [$Al_2(SO_4)_3 \cdot 16H_2O$] is extensively used in the papermaking industry. Its use depends upon the fact that solutions of papermaker's alum are acid by hydrolysis. The same compound, again because of its hydrolysis, is sometimes used to acidify soil to grow blueberries or broadleaf evergreens.

Titration

Titration refers to a procedure for determining the amount of acid or base in an unknown. It consists of careful addition of a solution of acid (or base) of known concentration to a sample of the unknown base (or acid). This addition is carried out in the presence of an indicator until the unknown is just neutralized. An illustration will make

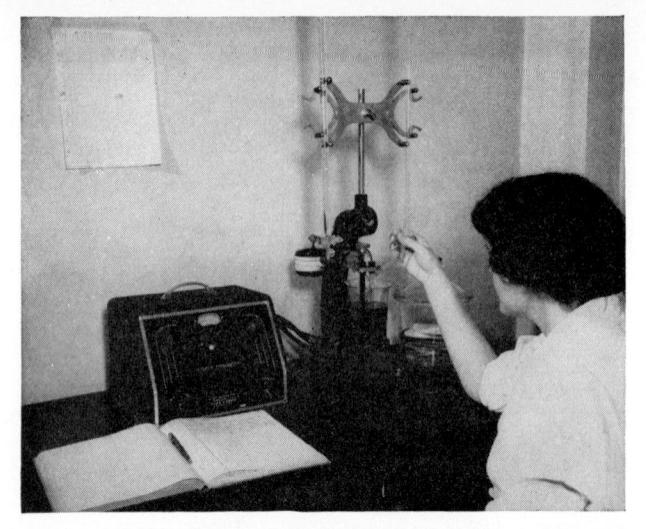

This chemist is analyzing the chlorine content of DDT samples by titration. She is using a modern titration instrument called a *titrimeter*. This instrument is very useful for deeply colored solutions in which the color change of an indicator cannot be seen.

the procedure clear. Suppose you want to find the percentage of sodium hydroxide in household lye. Prepare a solution of hydrochloric acid of known concentration. A solution of known concentration is called a **standard solution.** Suppose this standard solution is 0.50M hydrochloric acid. (Such a solution contains 0.50 × 36.5 = 18.25 g/liter of hydrogen chloride.)

Weigh a sample of the lye accurately on a balance. Transfer it to a beaker or erlenmeyer flask. Dissolve it in distilled water and add a few drops of litmus solution. Fill a burette with the standard hydrochloric acid. Add the acid solution from the burette carefully to the lye until *one* drop of the reagent causes the indicator to change color. This is the **end point.** Stop the titration and record the volume of standard acid solution used.

The data obtained:

Weight of lye sample = 0.517 g
Volume of 0.50M hydrochloric acid to neutralize = 22.5 ml

Calculations:

Weight of hydrochloric acid used is

$$\frac{0.50 \times 36.5}{1000} \times 22.5 = 0.411 \text{ g}$$

The reaction is

$$\underset{36.5}{\overset{0.411}{\text{HCl}}} + \underset{40}{\overset{x}{\text{NaOH}}} \rightarrow \text{NaCl} + \text{H}_2\text{O}$$

$$\frac{36.5}{40} = \frac{0.411}{x}$$

$$x = 0.450 \text{ g}$$

Therefore, there are 0.450 g of sodium hydroxide in the sample.

Percentage of sodium hydroxide is

$$\frac{0.450}{0.517} \times 100 = 87.0\%$$

Titration is a very common laboratory procedure.

Normality

You can easily see that sulfuric, hydrochloric, and phosphoric acids have different base-neutralizing abilities because these substances have different numbers of replaceable hydrogen atoms per molecule.

$$HCl + NaOH \rightarrow H_2O + NaCl$$
$$H_2SO_4 + 2NaOH \rightarrow 2H_2O + Na_2SO_4$$
$$H_3PO_4 + 3NaOH \rightarrow 3H_2O + Na_3PO_4$$

A $1M$ solution of sulfuric acid has twice the base-neutralizing ability of a $1M$ hydrochloric acid solution, volume for volume. A similar situation exists for the bases calcium hydroxide [$Ca(OH)_2$] and sodium hydroxide (NaOH).

In order that solutions of all acids and bases shall be comparable in neutralizing ability, chemists sometimes express their concentration in **normality**. **A normal solution of an acid (or base) contains one gram of acid hydrogen (or seventeen grams of hydroxyl) per liter.** Thus to make 1 liter of 1 normal (N) solution of some common acids and bases, use the amounts shown below in Table 27-4. That is, one mole of hydrogen chloride furnishes 1 g of acid hydrogen, but one mole of sulfuric acid furnishes 2 g of acid hydrogen. Hence to make 1 liter of a $1N$ solution of sulfuric acid, one-half mole of the acid is used. **Normal solutions of all acids and bases have the same neutralizing ability per milliliter.**

TABLE 27-4. Weights of common substances for 1N solutions

Compound	Molecular weight	Weight to make 1 liter of 1N solution, g
HCl	36.5	36.5
H_2SO_4	98	$\frac{98}{2} = 49$
H_3PO_4	98	$\frac{98}{3} = 32.66$
NaOH	40	40
$Ca(OH)_2$	74	$\frac{74}{2} = 37$

Reactions between electrolytes

When solutions of two electrolytes are mixed, a reaction occurs only if certain conditions are met. Failure to realize this fact is a mistake frequently made by beginning students. Suppose a solution of sodium chloride is mixed with a solution of potassium nitrate. No precipitate forms and no observable reaction occurs. The equation

$$NaCl + KNO_3 \rightarrow NaNO_3 + KCl$$

is meaningless. Actually no reaction should be expected, as you will see. All the substances shown in the preceding equation are soluble and ionized; hence they should be written in ionic form.

$$Na^+ + Cl^- + K^+ + NO_3^- \rightarrow Na^+ + NO_3^- + K^+ + Cl^-$$

Thus a mixing of ions is all that happens.

In general, where a substance is soluble and ionized, it should be written in ionic form. If, however, silver nitrate is substituted for potassium nitrate in the equation given, then a reaction really occurs. A white precipitate of silver chloride is formed.

$$Na^+ + Cl^- + Ag^+ + NO_3^- \rightarrow AgCl \downarrow + Na^+ + NO_3^-$$

Since sodium ion and nitrate ion are unchanged, we may omit them:

$$Ag^+ + Cl^- \rightarrow AgCl \downarrow$$

Either of the above equations is a correct way to describe the change.

In general, a reaction between two electrolytes will occur on mixing if one of the following conditions is met:

1. If one of the possible pairs of ions from the mixture represents an insoluble solid. Thus the reaction previously described occurs because silver chloride is insoluble. Two more examples follow:

$$Ca^{++} + 2Cl^- + 2Na^+ + CO_3^= \rightarrow CaCO_3 \downarrow + 2Na^+ + 2Cl^-$$
or
$$Ca^{++} + CO_3^= \rightarrow CaCO_3 \downarrow$$
$$Cu^{++} + 2NO_3^- + 2Na^+ + 2OH^- \rightarrow Cu(OH)_2 \downarrow + 2Na^+ + 2NO_3^-$$
or
$$Cu^{++} + 2OH^- \rightarrow Cu(OH)_2 \downarrow$$

If you remember the rules of solubility given in Chap. 14, page 157, you can predict most such reactions.

2. If one of the possible pairs of ions represents an insoluble gas as in the following examples:

$$2Na^+ + S^= + 2OH_3^+ + 2Cl^- \rightarrow H_2S \uparrow + 2H_2O + 2Na^+ + 2Cl^-$$
or
$$S^= + 2OH_3^+ \rightarrow H_2S \uparrow + 2H_2O$$
$$2Na^+ + CO_3^= + 2OH_3^+ + 2Cl^- \rightarrow CO_2 \uparrow + 2H_2O + 2Na^+ + 2Cl^-$$
or
$$CO_3^= + 2OH_3^+ \rightarrow CO_2 \uparrow + 2H_2O$$

3. If one of the possible pairs of ions represents a soluble but weakly ionized substance as in the following examples:

$$Na^+ + OH^- + OH_3^+ + Cl^- \rightarrow 2H_2O + Na^+ + Cl^-$$
or
$$OH_3^+ + OH^- \rightarrow 2H_2O$$
$$Na^+ + C_2H_3O_2^- + OH_3^+ + Cl^- \rightarrow HC_2H_3O_2 + H_2O + Na^+ + Cl^-$$
or
$$C_2H_3O_2^- + OH_3^+ \rightarrow HC_2H_3O_2 + H_2O$$

The reaction in the last example given can be detected by the odor of the solution. Sodium acetate has no odor, but acetic acid molecules have the odor characteristic of vinegar.

Freezing point, boiling point, and osmotic pressure

In Chap. 15, which dealt with the quantitative properties of solutions, all the solutions considered were solutions of non-electrolytes, such as sugar, glycerin, and alcohol. The elevation of boiling point is always greater for a solution of an electrolyte than for a solution of a non-electrolyte of the same molal concentration. The same is true for the freezing-point depression and osmotic pressure.

This is true because the boiling-point elevation, freezing-point depression, and osmotic pressure depend upon the *number of solute particles* per 1000 g of water. Since electrolytes, because of their ionization, give more particles per mole than non-electrolytes, they also have a greater effect on the freezing point, boiling point, and osmotic pressure. For example,

Solute	Concentration	Freezing point, °C	Boiling point, °C
Sugar	0.1m	−0.186	100.051
NaCl	0.1m	−0.347	100.095

Thus the effect of sodium chloride is nearly *twice* that of sugar. This is because sodium chloride, by ionization, gives *two* ions in solution.

$$NaCl \rightarrow Na^+ + Cl^-$$

Actually the effect of sodium chloride should be exactly twice that of sugar. The value is actually slightly lower because of certain complicating effects involving interaction between ions.

A salt like calcium chloride, which ionizes to give three ions

$$CaCl_2 \rightarrow Ca^{++} + 2Cl^-$$

has an effect on the freezing point, boiling point, and osmotic pressure which is nearly three times that of a non-electrolyte of the same molal concentration.

KEY WORDS

base	hydronium ion	ionization	*p*H scale
electrolyte	hydroxyl ion	neutral	salt
end point	indicator	neutralization	standard solution
hydrolysis	ion	normality (*N*)	titration

HIGHLIGHTS

Water solutions of all acids, **bases,** and **salts** always contain both **hydronium** (OH_3^+) **ions** and **hydroxyl** (OH^-) **ions**. A **neutral** solution contains equal numbers of hydronium and hydroxyl ions.

The **normality** (*N*) of an acid is determined by neutralizing it with a **standard** basic solution of known normality. The procedure is called **titration.**

Water solutions of acids, bases, and salts always conduct an electric current and are, therefore, called **electrolytes.**

The degree of acidity or alkalinity is expressed by the *p*H **scale.**

The reaction of a salt and water is known as **hydrolysis.**

Reactions between electrolytes go to completion if any one of three conditions is met: (1) the formation of an insoluble solid or precipitate, (2) the formation of an insoluble or volatile gas, and (3) the formation of a weakly ionized substance.

Electrolytes as compared with the same number of moles of nonelectrolytes have a much greater effect in elevating the boiling point, depressing the freezing point, and in exerting osmotic pressure.

QUESTIONS

1. List six properties common to all acids.
2. Name and give the formulas for five acids.
3. List four properties common to all bases.
4. Name and give the formulas for three bases.
5. Define the term salt.
6. Write the ionic equation for the neutralizing of an acid with a base.
7. What is meant by a dibasic acid? Give one example.
8. What is meant by an acid salt? Give one example.
9. What classes of compounds are electrolytes?
10. The properties of acids are due to the presence of what ion? Do you think it would be possible to have these properties without water being present?
11. What is the difference between chlorine and chloride ion?

12. Write the equation for the reaction of ammonia and water.
13. Explain the difference between a strong and a weak acid. Give three examples of each.
14. Give three examples of weak bases. Which of the metal hydroxides are strong bases?
15. State whether solutions having the following pH values are acid, basic, or neutral: (a) 6.5, (b) 7.0, (c) 5.1, (d) 9.2, and (e) 3.0.
16. Cite some examples of the importance of proper pH in nature.
17. How may the pH of soils be changed?
18. What types of salts give alkaline solutions? Give two examples.
19. What types of salts give acid solutions? Give two examples.
20. What types of salts give neutral solutions? Give two examples.
21. Under what conditions can one expect to obtain a reaction when solutions of two different electrolytes are mixed?
22. Explain why solutions of electrolytes have abnormal freezing points, boiling points, and osmotic pressures when compared with non-electrolytes.

Suggested Projects for Unit Six

1. If your school does not have a mole model (22.4 liter box) you might construct one and present it to the chemistry department.
2. Design your own dust explosion apparatus and demonstrate to the class.
3. Make a list of the common substances which may cause dust explosions.
4. Visit an industrial plant to see how theoretical chemistry is applied to industrial processes. Look out for applications of Le Châtelier's law.
5. See if you can find a case in which two electrolytes react to form two insoluble products. Demonstrate it to the class.
6. See if you can find any original catalysts for the decomposition of hydrogen peroxide. (*Hint:* Try cigarette ashes but try other substances, too.)
7. Work out your own original method for determining the weight of 1 liter of air.
8. Make separate lists of gases which are more dense and less dense than air.
9. Make a list of all catalysts you can identify and indicate the processes to which they apply.
10. List as many applications of pH as you can.

UNIT SEVEN: Sulfur, Nitrogen, and Phosphorus

CHAPTER **28**

sulfur and hydrogen sulfide

Salt, limestone, and sulfur are the chief raw materials of the chemical industry. Of these perhaps the most important is sulfur. Here in the United States we consume close to fifty pounds of sulfur each year for every man, woman, and child in the country. This is four times as much as the copper we use and at least three times as much as the rubber. Like iron, petroleum, and coal, sulfur is one of the essentials of our modern civilization. In America, where we produce 80 percent of all the sulfur consumed in the world, we should be thankful that it is a cheap and readily available commodity. Yet many Americans, who think of sulfur as something for killing the fleas on a dog, know little about how it is produced and the various ways in which it influences their lives.

Occurrence of sulfur

Sulfur occurs free in nature, frequently mixed with volcanic rock. It has been known since prehistoric times and may have been the first pure chemical element found and used by man. The use of brimstone (that is, sulfur) for fumigation was mentioned by Homer (900 BC).

The oldest-known deposits of any size are those on the island of Sicily. Until after 1900 these were the chief sources of the world's sulfur. In Sicily the sulfur occurs mixed through volcanic rock. The separation is expensive and it is doubtful whether our great American chemical industry could have developed without the discovery and development of the vast sulfur deposits in Louisiana and Texas. These

A series of photographs showing the processing of sulfur. Top, drilling a sulfur well. Middle, sump, or gathering station, where sulfur is collected from wells and then pumped to storage vats. Bottom, storage bins of sulfur ready for shipping. (Texas Gulf Sulfur Co., Inc.)

deposits were discovered in 1867 when geologists, hoping to strike oil, drilled a well in Louisiana. Instead they struck sulfur at 500 ft, thereby discovering the world's largest-known sulfur beds.

Sulfur is also found in nature combined as **gypsum** ($CaSO_4 \cdot 2H_2O$), and as various metal sulfides, such as **sphalerite** (ZnS), **galena** (PbS), and **pyrite** (FeS_2). Many of these sulfides are important as metal ores, their sulfur content being of only secondary importance. It is also found in nature as hydrogen sulfide (see page 322).

Sulfur is found also in all living tissue. Here it is an essential constituent of the proteins which make up the living part of the cell. Therefore, sulfur is necessary for all life.

Sulfur mining: the Frasch process

Although discovered in 1867, the great Louisiana and Texas deposits did not produce commercial sulfur until about 1900. This delay occurred because the peculiar location of the deposits made mining by normal methods impossible. The problem of mining this sulfur was solved by **Herman Frasch**.[1]

The Frasch method is illustrated in Fig. 28–1 and in principle is very simple. A hole 6 in. in diameter is drilled through the earth into the sulfur. Three pipes having diameters 6 in., 3 in., and 1 in. respectively, are inserted, one inside the other, into the well. Water, heated under pressure to 170°C, is forced through the outermost pipe into the sulfur, thus melting it (melting point of sulfur is 119°C). Compressed air blown into the smallest pipe forces the molten sulfur-water mixture up through the intermediate pipe. This mixture is pumped into vats where the sulfur solidifies and the water is drained off. The sulfur is 99.5 percent or better in purity and is pure enough for almost any use without further treatment. If necessary, the sulfur can be purified further by distillation (bp 444.6°C).

As with most of our other mineral resources, the great deposits of sulfur along the coast of the Gulf of Mexico will not last indefinitely. Furthermore, the United States consumption of sulfur is increasing— it has doubled since 1939.

It is known that there are millions of tons of sulfur, mixed with volcanic rock, in California and northwest Wyoming. A similar vein

[1] Herman Frasch was born in Württemburg, Germany, on Christmas Day, 1851. When nineteen years old, he came to America, settling in Philadelphia, where he became a laboratory assistant to Professor Maisch in the Philadelphia College of Pharmacy. A good chemist and skilled engineer, he made some of the greatest contributions to the early technology of petroleum refining. He discovered a way for making white lead directly from the lead ore, galena (PbS); a way for making electric light carbons; and numerous other things of commercial importance. His discoveries literally added millions of dollars to the national wealth.

Fig. 28–1. The Frasch process for mining sulfur. After the well is drilled, superheated water is forced down the outermost pipe and compressed air is forced down the innermost pipe. This causes a mixture of molten sulfur and water to come up the middle pipe. The mixture is pumped into vats where it is allowed to cool. Upon cooling, the sulfur solidifies and the water may be drained off.

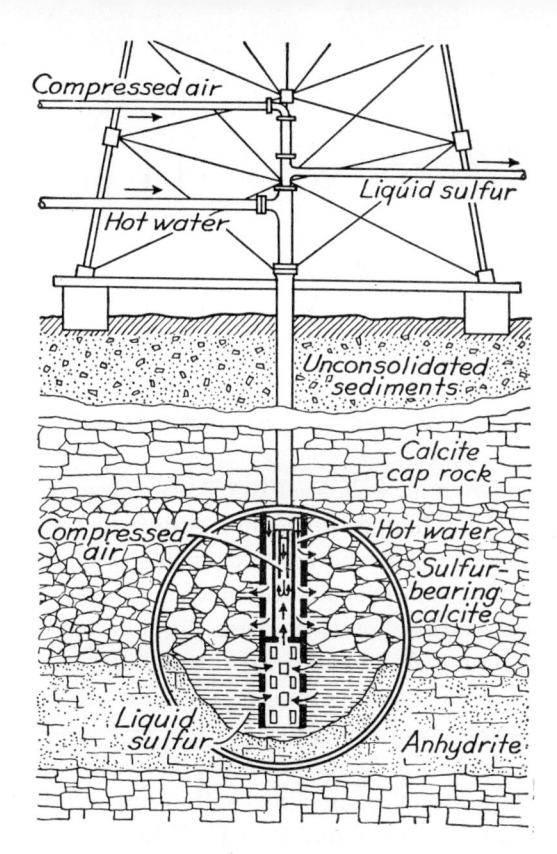

running through the South American Andes is estimated to contain one hundred million tons. Up to fairly recently there has been no need to extract sulfur from these sources, but eventually we shall have to use them. A process for extracting sulfur cheaply from these rocks was reported in 1951. It consists of crushing the rock finely, heating it to above the melting point of sulfur, and pouring it into water. The molten sulfur forms solid nodules larger in size than the rock particles so that it can be separated by screening.

Physical properties of sulfur

Sulfur, like the first member of its group, oxygen, exists in more than one physical form. Sulfur exists in two solid forms, two liquid forms, and one vapor form.

Ordinary crystalline sulfur is called **rhombic sulfur** and consists of crystals of the type shown in Fig. 28–2(a). The crystals are yellow and opaque, with a density of 2.06. They are soluble in carbon disulfide (CS_2). Well-formed crystals are obtained by dissolving sulfur in carbon disulfide and allowing the liquid to evaporate *slowly*. Rhombic sulfur is completely stable at temperatures below 95.5°C and is the only form of sulfur that is stable below that temperature. This is analogous to ice being the only form of water stable below 0°C. Just

(a) Rhombic   (b) Monoclinic

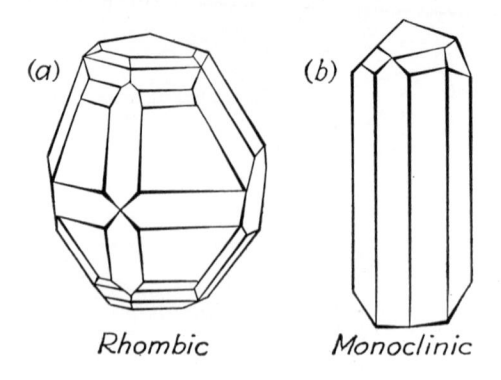

Fig. 28-2. Two allotropic forms of sulfur. Rhombic sulfur (a) is stable below 95.5°C. Monoclinic sulfur (b) is stable above 95.5°C and below its melting point.

as when ice is heated to 0°C it changes into liquid water, so sulfur at 95.5°C changes form. For sulfur, however, the new variety is also a solid and the change takes place very slowly.

You can prepare this new form of sulfur best by heating sulfur to its melting point, pouring the liquid into a paper cone made from a filter paper, and allowing it to solidify. As soon as crystallization starts, pour off the remaining liquid. You will obtain long, needlelike crystals as shown in Fig. 28-2(b). The crystals are light yellow, transparent, and have a density of 1.96. They are known as **monoclinic sulfur.** Crystals of monoclinic sulfur are stable below their melting point (119°C) and above 95.5°C. When cooled below 95.5°C, they slowly (in a matter of minutes or hours) change into rhombic sulfur. That is, the crystals become opaque, although they retain the same outward needlelike form.

When either variety of sulfur is heated to its melting point, it produces a straw yellow, transparent, fluid liquid. As this liquid is heated higher, it *becomes less fluid, darker, and less transparent.* It eventually boils at 444.6°C. This peculiar behavior occurs because there are *two liquid forms* of sulfur, which, for want of better names, are called **sulfur lambda** (Sλ) and **sulfur mu** (Sμ).

Sλ is the light-colored, fluid liquid formed at the lower temperature. Sμ is the dark, viscous liquid formed by heating Sλ.

If Sμ is poured into cold water, a rubbery material known as *plastic sulfur* is formed. This is not stable and at room temperature it hardens and becomes brittle because it changes into rhombic sulfur. Plastic sulfur is simply supercooled Sμ, that is, Sμ which although cooled below its crystallization temperature, has failed to crystallize.

Such names as *roll sulfur* and *flowers of sulfur* do not refer to distinct varieties of sulfur. Roll sulfur consists of rodlike masses made by pouring molten sulfur into cylindrical molds. Flowers of sulfur is very fine particles made by cooling sulfur vapor. Both are rhombic sulfur.

Fig. 28-3. The ring of eight sulfur atoms (a) is Sλ. The open chain (b) is Sμ. The sulfur atoms can rotate about the electron-pair bonds which connect them to each other.

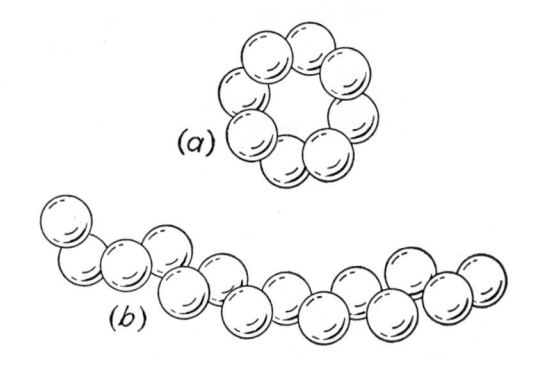

Why are there so many forms of sulfur?

Part of the explanation of why there are so many forms of sulfur is to be found in the electron structure of sulfur. Sulfur has *six valence electrons*.

Needing to gain two more, it shares a pair from another sulfur atom (coordinate valence):

$$\underset{B}{S} : \underset{A}{S}$$

Now the sulfur atom labeled A is electronically satisfied but B is not; hence another atom is added.

But the atom on the end is always unsatisfied electronically.

Actually the sulfur atoms are not in a straight line but are staggered in such a way that when eight atoms are present the chain ends may meet. Thus every atom is electronically satisfied.

Both rhombic and monoclinic sulfur are made up of S_8 molecules having the ring structure. The differences in the two forms are due to slightly different arrangements of the S_8 molecules making up the crystals. The Sλ produced on melting either rhombic or monoclinic sulfur also consists of S_8 molecules. The conversion of Sλ into Sμ consists of the breaking open of the ring to form threadlike molecules [Fig. 28-3(b)]. The long threadlike molecules of Sμ easily get tangled

An extremely important use for sulfur is in the vulcanization of rubber. If rubber were not vulcanized, it would be soft and sticky and could not be used to make rubber tires such as the ones shown in this photograph. (Firestone Tire and Rubber Co.)

around each other. This tangling causes the increase in viscosity observed when $S\lambda$ is converted into $S\mu$ by heating.

The reverse process (conversion of $S\mu$ to $S\lambda$) occurs if $S\mu$ is cooled, but the process is slow because the long threadlike $S\mu$ molecule has to bend around so that its ends can join. Hence if $S\mu$ is cooled rapidly, it does not have time to form $S\lambda$ rings and the result is simply supercooled $S\mu$ or plastic sulfur.

Chemical properties of sulfur

As would be expected from its position in the periodic table, sulfur closely resembles oxygen in chemical properties. Both have the same number of valence electrons.

Thus sulfur reacts with all the metals except gold and the platinum group, forming sulfides in which the sulfur has a valence of -2.

$$Cu + S \xrightarrow{heat} CuS$$
$$Ni + S \xrightarrow{heat} NiS$$

For the moderately active metals, the reaction with sulfur is violent once it has started. A mixture of powdered sulfur and zinc placed on an asbestos board reacts with almost explosive violence when heated gently with a bunsen burner.

Sulfur combines with many nonmetals. The carbon disulfide of commerce is made by heating carbon and sulfur.

$$C + 2S \xrightarrow{heat} CS_2$$

Sulfur and chlorine combine to form a product known as *sulfur monochloride*, an important solvent in the rubber industry.

$$Cl_2 + 2S \xrightarrow{heat} S_2Cl_2$$

Sulfur combines with hydrogen to form hydrogen sulfide.

$$H_2 + S \xrightarrow{heat} H_2S$$

When heated in air, sulfur forms sulfur dioxide. The so-called odor of burning sulfur is really the odor of sulfur dioxide.

$$S + O_2 \xrightarrow{heat} SO_2$$

Uses of sulfur

The modern automobile would be impossible without sulfur. This is true because, without this substance, we would have no rubber tires. Sulfur is used to **vulcanize** rubber. This process changes rubber from a soft, sticky, useless material into a material having the properties which are commonly associated with the word rubber.

Vulcanization was discovered in 1844 by Charles Goodyear, and from this discovery, more than any other single one, has grown the great rubber industry of our times. Vulcanization consists of heating the rubber with sulfur; the greater the proportion of sulfur, the harder the product. Materials ranging all the way from soft rubber laboratory tubing to hard rubber combs can thus be obtained.

Free sulfur is a good fungicide. It is widely used as an ingredient of both sprays and dusts to control fungus on fruits, flowers (roses and delphinium), and vegetables. As a dust, very finely divided sulfur powder is used. As a spray, sulfur is generally used as lime-sulfur, which is a solution of calcium sulfide containing excess free sulfur.

Sulfur compounds are essential in paper manufacture. Sulfur is an essential ingredient of black gunpowder. Sulfur makes a satisfactory cement for fastening steel bolts into holes in concrete or stone. (The sulfur is melted and poured into the hole around the bolt.)

By far the most important use for sulfur is in the manufacture of sulfuric acid.

Biologically sulfur is important not only as an ingredient of proteins but as a constituent of two essential vitamins, *thiamine* (vitamin B_1) and *biotin*. Plants require sulfur and assimilate it from the sulfur compounds in the soil during their growth process. The pungent odors of onions, garlic, horseradish, and mustard are due to organic compounds containing sulfur. Sulfur is rarely deficient in soils.

The sulfa drugs are also compounds which contain this element.

Hydrogen sulfide

Hydrogen sulfide, a gaseous compound, is found dissolved in some mineral waters. Such waters are known as *sulfur waters.* Hydrogen sulfide is also produced by bacterial decomposition of animal protein—especially eggs. The odor of rotten eggs is largely due to the presence of this substance.

Preparation of hydrogen sulfide

Hydrogen sulfide is best prepared by the reaction of an acid on a metal sulfide. Iron sulfide is the compound generally used:

$$FeS + 2HCl \rightarrow H_2S \uparrow + FeCl_2$$

The gas is collected by the upward displacement of air.

A convenient laboratory source of hydrogen sulfide is the Kipp generator shown in Fig. 28–4. In this apparatus the gas is produced as long as the stopcock is open and it can escape. If the stopcock is closed, the pressure of the hydrogen sulfide formed forces the liquid (acid) away from the solid (FeS), thus stopping the reaction.

As noted on page 321, hydrogen sulfide can also be formed by passing hydrogen gas over molten sulfur.

$$H_2 + S \xrightarrow{heat} H_2S \uparrow$$

Physical properties

Hydrogen sulfide is a colorless gas with a boiling point of $-61.8°C$. It has the nauseating odor of rotten eggs. The gas is extremely poisonous when inhaled—a fact which is not always properly recognized in laboratories. A concentration of 2 parts of hydrogen sulfide per 1000 parts of air, if inhaled, is almost instantly fatal. It is rather soluble in water; 2.9 volumes of the gas dissolves in 1 volume of water at 20°C. A water solution of hydrogen sulfide is commonly used to carry out reactions of the substance.

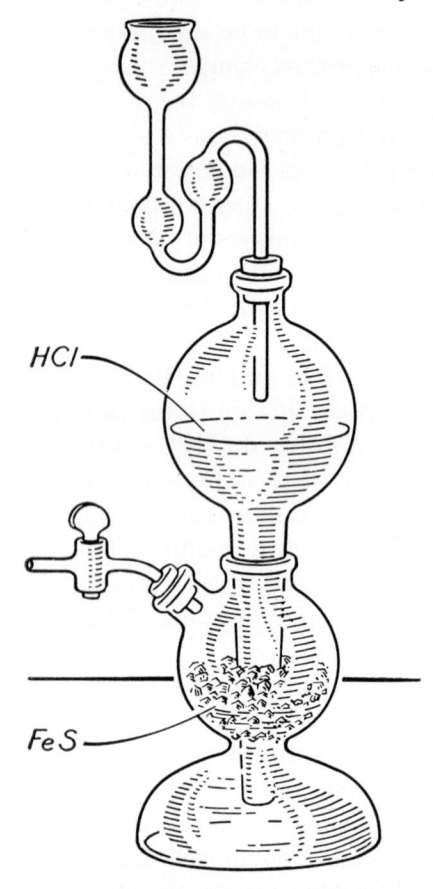

Fig. 28–4. A Kipp generator for preparing hydrogen sulfide.

Fig. 28–5. A cold dish held in a hydrogen sulfide flame becomes coated with a deposit of sulfur.

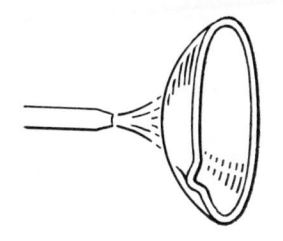

Chemical properties of hydrogen sulfide

Hydrogen sulfide gas burns in air, giving water and sulfur dioxide.

$$2H_2S + 3O_2 \rightarrow 2H_2O + 2SO_2$$

Thus a jet of hydrogen sulfide from the generator, when lighted with a match, burns with a blue flame. Hydrogen sulfide is unstable and, when heated, breaks down into sulfur and hydrogen.

$$H_2S \xrightleftharpoons{\text{heat}} H_2 + S$$

This can be shown by holding a cold porcelain dish in a hydrogen sulfide flame. In a few seconds the dish receives a deposit of yellow sulfur. This is because the heat of the flame has caused the decomposition of some hydrogen sulfide, but in the center of the flame there is no oxygen with which the sulfur and hydrogen can combine.

Hydrogen sulfide reacts with solutions of many salts to precipitate the metal sulfide. The colors of the precipitates frequently are characteristic of the metal present, and for this reason the reaction is used in analytical chemistry. Thus

$$ZnCl_2 + H_2S \rightarrow ZnS \downarrow + 2HCl$$
(white)

$$CdCl_2 + H_2S \rightarrow CdS \downarrow + 2HCl$$
(canary yellow)

$$2SbCl_3 + 3H_2S \rightarrow Sb_2S_3 \downarrow + 6HCl$$
(orange)

$$FeCl_2 + H_2S \rightarrow FeS \downarrow + 2HCl$$
(black)

$$Pb(NO_3)_2 + H_2S \rightarrow PbS \downarrow + 2HNO_3$$
(black)

Hydrogen sulfide tarnishes silver (see Chap. 46, page 597).

$$H_2S + 2Ag^0 \rightarrow H_2 \uparrow + Ag_2S \downarrow$$
(black)

The effect of eggs in blackening silver is due to the hydrogen sulfide which they produce. There is always a minute amount of hydrogen sulfide in the atmosphere, sufficient to cause the reaction with silver just described unless the silver is protected in some way from the atmosphere. The silver may be protected by a thin coating of lacquer.

Selenium and tellurium

As you would expect from their position in the periodic table, selenium and tellurium resemble sulfur.

Selenium is found free in nature and also as copper, lead, and iron selenides (CuSe, PbSe, FeSe), mixed with the sulfides. In the oxidation of these sulfides, the selenium is oxidized to selenium dioxide (SeO_2) which collects as a white powder in the flues. The element exists in two allotropic forms, a red variety soluble in carbon disulfide and a gray metal-like variety insoluble in carbon disulfide. The chief use for selenium is in glassmaking, where small amounts are used to overcome the green tint caused by the presence of iron compounds. The iron may get into the glass as an impurity in the sand used. Larger amounts of selenium give the ruby red glass used for signals and for ornamental glassware.

Selenium is an electrical conductor and its ability to conduct varies with the intensity of light. This property is used in the construction of apparatus for measuring light intensity, such as photographic light meters.

Selenium forms a gaseous, vile-smelling compound, hydrogen selenide (H_2Se), comparable to hydrogen sulfide. All selenium compounds are highly poisonous to animals, including man. Some plants, however, seem to be able to absorb selenium compounds from the soil and utilize them almost interchangeably with sulfur. Where there are appreciable amounts of selenium in the soil, as in parts of South Dakota, this gives rise to a serious problem. Plants growing in this soil absorb and assimilate the selenium. Livestock, including cattle, sheep, horses, pigs, and chickens, eating such plants are affected by selenium poisoning, sometimes with fatal results. The conditions referred to as *blind staggers* and *alkali disease* are not really diseases at all but are actually cases of selenium poisoning.

Tellurium occurs in nature as metal tellurides (analogous to sulfides), particularly of copper, lead, iron, and bismuth. It is produced commercially as a by-product in copper refining and could be produced from other metallurgical operations.

Tellurium is silvery white and semimetallic in appearance. It forms a compound with hydrogen, hydrogen telluride (H_2Te), as well as the oxides, tellurium dioxide (TeO_2) and tellurium trioxide (TeO_3).

Tellurium has little commercial application at present. Small amounts (0.05 percent) are added to lead to increase its resistance to corrosion. Additional uses for the element are desirable as fairly large amounts could be produced from a number of metallurgical operations.

KEY WORDS

Frasch	pyrite	sulfur lambda (Sλ)
galena	rhombic sulfur	sulfur mu (Sμ)
gypsum	selenium	tellurium
monoclinic sulfur	sphalerite	vulcanize

HIGHLIGHTS

Sulfur occurs in the native state and combined in such minerals as **galena, pyrite, sphalerite,** and **gypsum.** There are abundant sources in Texas, Louisiana, Wyoming, and Sicily. The American or **Frasch** method of extracting it from great depths is one of the most important achievements of chemical engineering.

There are two allotropic crystalline forms of sulfur: **rhombic** and **monoclinic.** At temperatures above the melting point there are two liquid forms: **sulfur lambda** (Sλ) and **sulfur mu** (Sμ), the former being a straw-colored, free-flowing liquid and the latter very viscous and dark red in color.

Selenium and **tellurium** are elements that belong to the same periodic-table group as sulfur. Selenium is used in glassmaking and in the photoelectric cell. Tellurium has as yet very limited uses.

QUESTIONS

1. List as many ways as you can in which you use either sulfur or products made by the use of sulfur.
2. Draw a diagram and explain the Frasch process for mining sulfur.
3. Why were the Gulf sulfur deposits not mined before the invention of the Frasch process?
4. Describe a process for separating sulfur from volcanic rock.
5. What is the molecular formula for rhombic sulfur?
6. With which metals does sulfur combine? What valence does sulfur have when it combines with metals?
7. Write two equations showing the reaction of sulfur with nonmetals.
8. What form of sulfur is present in sulfur mineral waters?
9. What precaution should be observed in working with hydrogen sulfide in the laboratory?
10. What problem is presented by soils with a high selenium content?
11. What is selenium used for industrially?
12. Give one use for tellurium.

CHAPTER **29**

the oxygen compounds of sulfur

Sulfur forms two important oxides, sulfur dioxide (SO_2) and sulfur trioxide (SO_3). Both these react with water to form acids. This chapter will deal with these oxides, their acids, and their salts.

Oxide		Acid		Sodium salt	
Name	Formula	Name	Formula	Name	Formula
Sulfur dioxide	SO_2	Sulfurous acid	H_2SO_3	Sodium hydrogen sulfite (sodium bisulfite)	$NaHSO_3$
				Sodium sulfite	Na_2SO_3
Sulfur trioxide	SO_3	Sulfuric acid	H_2SO_4	Sodium hydrogen sulfate (sodium bisulfate)	$NaHSO_4$
				Sodium sulfate	Na_2SO_4

Preparation of sulfur dioxide

Sulfur dioxide is made by burning sulfur or a metal sulfide in air.

$$S + O_2 \rightarrow SO_2$$
$$2CuS + 3O_2 \rightarrow 2CuO + 2SO_2$$
$$2ZnS + 3O_2 \rightarrow 2ZnO + 2SO_2$$
$$4FeS_2 + 11O_2 \rightarrow 2Fe_2O_3 + 8SO_2$$

Industrially most sulfur dioxide is formed by burning free sulfur. Some is produced by burning iron pyrite (FeS_2); and some is produced

Fig. 29–1. Sulfur dioxide may be prepared by burning sulfur in air in a gas-collecting bottle. Since the sulfur dioxide is more dense than air, it may be kept in the bottle simply by covering the bottle with a piece of glass or cardboard.

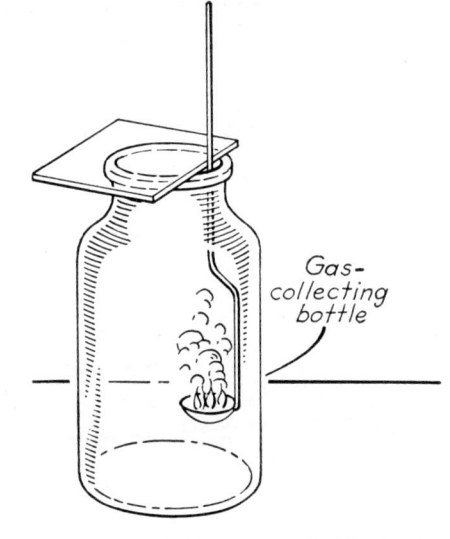

as a by-product of oxidizing zinc or copper sulfide ores, which is the first step in treating these ores to obtain the metals.

In the laboratory sulfur dioxide can be produced by burning a bit of sulfur in a gas-collecting bottle covered with a piece of glass (Fig. 29-1). A better method is to drop hydrochloric acid on sodium sulfite or sodium hydrogen sulfite.

$$Na_2SO_3 + 2HCl \rightarrow H_2O + SO_2 \uparrow + 2NaCl$$
$$NaHSO_3 + HCl \rightarrow H_2O + SO_2 \uparrow + NaCl$$

A setup similar to that used in generating chlorine can be used (Chap. 22, page 236). The gas is collected by upward displacement of air.

Properties and uses of sulfur dioxide

Sulfur dioxide is a colorless gas, more than twice as dense as air, with a choking odor. Its boiling point is $-10°C$, and hence the gas can be liquefied by passing it through a U tube surrounded by ice and salt or, on a really cold day, by simply placing the U tube outside the window. The critical temperature of sulfur dioxide is $157°C$, and the substance is commonly shipped in steel cylinders as a liquid. If any considerable quantity of sulfur dioxide is to be used, it is advisable to procure a small cylinder of it rather than to make it in the laboratory.

Sulfur dioxide bleaches many naturally colored materials, and it is used commercially to bleach feathers, straw, wool, and paper. The bleaching occurs as a result of combination of sulfur dioxide with the colored material to form a colorless compound. These colorless compounds tend to decompose with age, particularly in the presence of sunlight. Hence as a bleach, sulfur dioxide is not as permanent as could be desired. It is, however, the oldest-known bleach. Pliny (AD 23–79) mentions its use to bleach cloth.

Anhydrous sulfur dioxide was formerly much used as a refrigerating liquid in small household electric refrigerators. Its use in this respect has now largely been replaced by halogen compounds of carbon, particularly Freon 12 and methyl chloride (CH_3Cl), which are superior to sulfur dioxide for this.

Sulfur dioxide is very soluble in water (80 volumes of the gas in 1 volume of water at 0°C). With water sulfur dioxide forms sulfurous acid.

$$SO_2 + H_2O \rightarrow \underset{\text{sulfurous acid}}{H_2SO_3}$$

The most important use of sulfur dioxide is in the manufacture of sulfuric acid.

Another use of sulfur dioxide is in the commercial preparation of dried fruits. When dried apricots, peaches, and apples are prepared, one problem is that of keeping these fruits from darkening. You have probably noticed that darkening normally occurs whenever these fruits are cut open and exposed to air. Sulfur dioxide prevents the darkening of these fruits. In the preparation of these dried fruits the freshly sliced fruit is first exposed to sulfur dioxide before drying. The fruit absorbs considerable amounts of the gas. Normally this sulfur dioxide is given off again during the cooking of the fruit.

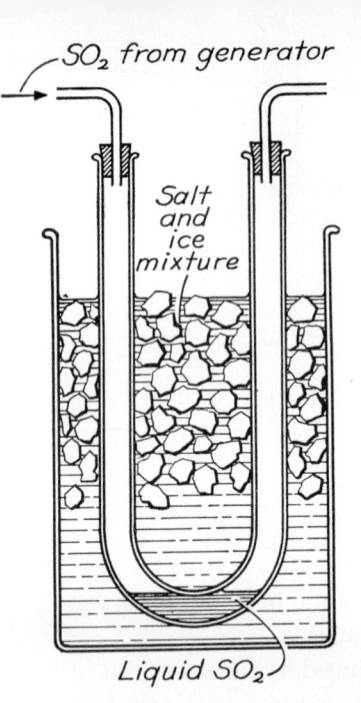

Fig. 29-2. Preparation of liquid sulfur dioxide.

Sulfurous acid and sulfites

Sulfurous acid cannot be obtained in the free state. It exists only in solution. It is prepared by passing sulfur dioxide into water.

$$SO_2 + H_2O \rightarrow \underset{\text{(in solution)}}{H_2SO_3}$$

If attempts are made to obtain the pure acid by evaporation of the excess water from the solution, the sulfurous acid decomposes by reversal of the above reaction.

$$H_2SO_3 \rightarrow SO_2 \uparrow + H_2O \uparrow$$

Both products escape as gases and nothing remains.

In contact with oxygen of the air, sulfurous acid is slowly oxidized to sulfuric acid.

$$2H_2SO_3 + O_2 \rightarrow 2H_2SO_4$$

For this reason it does not keep (unless sealed from the atmosphere), and it is generally freshly prepared just before use. The distilled water used for the preparation of sulfurous acid should be freshly boiled to remove the dissolved oxygen which it normally contains.

Because of its tendency to be oxidized to sulfuric acid, sulfurous acid is said to be a *reducing* agent. Bromine also will oxidize sulfurous acid to sulfuric acid.

$$Br_2 + H_2O + H_2SO_3 \rightarrow H_2SO_4 + 2HBr$$

Salts formed by neutralizing sulfurous acid are known as **sulfites.** There are two classes of sulfites:

1. The normal sulfites, formed by completely neutralizing the acid,

$$2NaOH + H_2SO_3 \rightarrow \underset{\text{sodium sulfite}}{Na_2SO_3} + 2H_2O$$

2. The acid sulfites

$$NaOH + H_2SO_3 \rightarrow \underset{\text{sodium hydrogen sulfite}}{NaHSO_3} + H_2O$$

Both normal and acid salts are white solids which on treatment with a stronger acid yield sulfur dioxide (see equations under preparation of sulfur dioxide, page 327).

Like sulfurous acid, the sulfites are easily oxidized (to sulfates) and hence are good reducing agents. They are used in photography and in bleaching.

Sulfur trioxide

Sulfur trioxide is of relatively little importance as such. Its chief interest for you is the fact that it is easily converted into sulfuric acid by reaction with water. Sulfur dioxide combines slowly with oxygen. The equation is

$$2SO_2 + O_2 \rightarrow 2SO_3$$

This reaction is a difficult one to bring about rapidly and requires very special conditions (see page 330).

Pure sulfur trioxide is normally a white, fibrous solid somewhat resembling asbestos fibers in appearance. It has an extreme affinity for water, with which it forms sulfuric acid.

$$H_2O + SO_3 \rightarrow H_2SO_4$$

When exposed to the atmosphere, sulfur trioxide forms droplets of sulfuric acid by combination with the moisture in the air. Therefore, when sulfur trioxide is exposed to the air, it fumes voluminously.

Sulfur trioxide also combines with sulfuric acid, forming *fuming sulfuric acid* or **oleum** (also known as **pyrosulfuric** acid).

$$H_2SO_4 + SO_3 \rightarrow \underset{\text{oleum}}{H_2S_2O_7}$$

The electronic structure of sulfur trioxide and its combination with water may be represented as follows:

$$\begin{array}{ccc}
 & :\!\ddot{O}\!: & :\!\ddot{O}\!: \\
 & \cdot\cdot\;\cdot\cdot & \cdot\cdot\;\cdot\cdot\;\cdot\cdot \\
H\!:\!\ddot{O}\!:\!H\; + & S\!:\!O\!: & \rightarrow\; H\!:\!O\!:\!S\!:\!\ddot{O}\!: \\
 & \cdot\cdot\;\cdot\cdot & \cdot\cdot\;\cdot\cdot\;\cdot\cdot \\
 & :\!\ddot{O}\!: & :\!\ddot{O}\!: \\
 & & H
\end{array}$$

$$H_2O \;+\; SO_3 \;\rightarrow\; H_2SO_4$$

Sulfuric acid

Sulfuric acid enters, directly or indirectly, into the manufacture of so many commodities which we use in our daily lives that it has been aptly named the "King of Chemicals." A high degree of industrial activity always requires a large amount of sulfuric acid. Its production rate is, therefore, a good barometer of industrial activity. Thanks to our large supplies of sulfur and to the ingenuity of our chemists and engineers, sulfuric acid is readily available at a low cost. In order to reduce transportation charges, it is generally produced near the place where it is to be used. This means that plants for the manufacture of sulfuric acid are scattered throughout the United States.

Manufacture of sulfuric acid

Since sulfuric acid is so cheap and so readily available, it is practically never prepared in the laboratory except as an exercise to illustrate its commercial manufacture.

Industrially there are two methods for the manufacture of sulfuric acid. These differ principally in the method used to convert the sulfur, which has a valence of 4 in sulfur dioxide, to the higher valence of 6, which it shows in sulfur trioxide and sulfuric acid. The more modern of these two processes is the **contact process.** In this method sulfur dioxide formed by burning sulfur is mixed with air and heated to 400 or 450°C; then it is passed over a catalyst of finely divided platinum or vanadium pentoxide, which hastens the reaction of the sulfur dioxide and the oxygen of the air to form sulfur trioxide. The sulfur

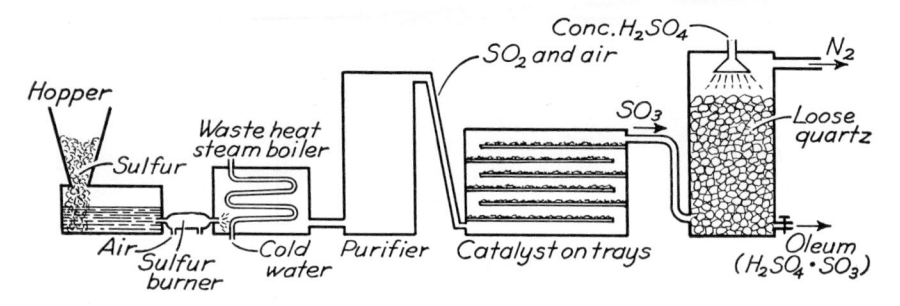

Fig. 29–3. A simplified diagram showing the contact process for making sulfuric acid.

trioxide obtained is passed into sulfuric acid, forming oleum. To the oleum, water is added to form pure sulfuric acid. The reactions are

$$S + O_2 \rightarrow \underset{\text{(air)}}{SO_2}$$

$$2SO_2 + O_2 \xrightarrow[400-450°C]{\text{catalyst}} 2SO_3$$

$$SO_3 + H_2SO_4 \rightarrow H_2S_2O_7$$
$$H_2S_2O_7 + H_2O \rightarrow 2H_2SO_4$$

A diagram of a contact plant is shown in Fig. 29–3. It is necessary that the sulfur dioxide and air be free of dust particles of any kind, since these would coat the surface of the catalyst and make it inactive.

The other method of sulfuric acid manufacture is the **chamber process.** In this method sulfur dioxide formed by burning sulfur or iron sulfide is mixed with air and steam and then passed into large lead-lined chambers containing a catalyst of nitrogen oxides (NO and NO_2). There sulfuric acid is formed and collects on the floor of the chambers.

The reactions are

$$S + O_2 \rightarrow SO_2$$

$$2SO_2 + 2H_2O + O_2 \xrightarrow[\text{catalyst}]{NO + NO_2} 2H_2SO_4$$

The chambers are lined with lead to withstand the action of the sulfuric acid. Lead is above hydrogen in activity. Therefore,

$$Pb + H_2SO_4 \rightarrow PbSO_4 \downarrow + H_2 \uparrow$$

But since lead sulfate is insoluble, the reaction occurs only on the surface, provided the acid is not more concentrated than 65 percent. If the sulfuric acid is more concentrated than 65 percent, the lead sulfate dissolves in it, the lead underneath is exposed, and the entire piece of lead is consumed by the acid. **Because sulfuric acid more concentrated than 65 percent dissolves lead sulfate, the chamber process cannot directly produce acid more concentrated than**

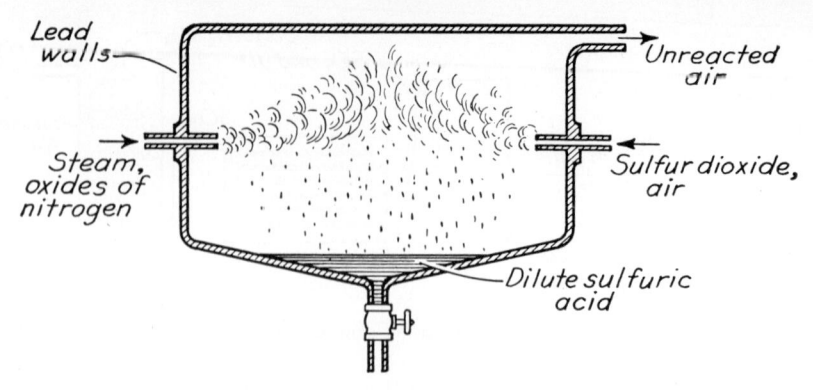

Fig. 29-4. A simplified diagram of the lead chamber process for making sulfuric acid.

65 percent, and the amount of steam blown into the chambers has to be so regulated. For the production of the commercial 96 percent concentrated sulfuric acid, the water in the chamber acid may be removed by evaporation. But removing the water adds considerably to the cost.

The greatest advantages of the contact process over the chamber process are (1) production of concentrated sulfuric acid, and (2) greater purity of the product. The chamber process has the advantage of being cheaper when used to produce the 65 percent acid. Sometimes oleum from the contact process is added to the 65 percent chamber product to produce commercial concentrated acid, thereby eliminating the expensive evaporation.

The greatest single use for sulfuric acid is in the making of **phosphate fertilizers.** For this purpose the 65 percent acid obtained from the chamber process is suitable and most of it is used in this way.

Properties of sulfuric acid

Pure sulfuric acid is a colorless liquid freezing at 10.5°C, boiling (with decomposition) at 270°C, and having a density of 1.84 g/ml. Its high boiling point makes it useful in preparing the other common mineral acids, hydrochloric and nitric, from their salts (Chap. 22, page 251, and Chap. 32, pages 357 and 358).

The most remarkable property of sulfuric acid is its great affinity for water. This property is due to the formation of several hydrates of sulfuric acid which are very stable. Because of its affinity for water, sulfuric acid is useful as a **dehydrating agent** for drying air, chlorine, and other substances which do not react with the acid. It is sometimes used in desiccators, although the fact that it is a liquid is a disadvantage when used in a desiccator.

The tendency of sulfuric acid to form hydrates is so great that it will remove combined hydrogen and oxygen from some carbon compounds, especially those compounds known as carbohydrates. All carbohydrates contain two atoms of hydrogen to one of oxygen. Thus when concentrated sulfuric acid is mixed with sugar, the hydrogen and oxygen are removed to form water, leaving carbon. The unbalanced equation is as follows:

$$H_2SO_4 + C_{12}H_{22}O_{11} \rightarrow H_2SO_4 \cdot xH_2O + C$$

When hot, concentrated sulfuric acid will oxidize:

Carbon

$$C + 2H_2SO_4 \xrightarrow{heat} CO_2 \uparrow + 2H_2O + 2SO_2 \uparrow$$

Sulfur

$$S + 2H_2SO_4 \xrightarrow{heat} 3SO_2 \uparrow + 2H_2O$$

Copper

$$Cu + 2H_2SO_4 \xrightarrow{heat} CuSO_4 + SO_2 \uparrow + 2H_2O$$

Or zinc

$$4Zn + 5H_2SO_4 \xrightarrow{heat} 4ZnSO_4 + H_2S \uparrow + 4H_2O$$

The reactions between sulfuric acid and copper and zinc are not to be confused with the reaction of these metals (or lack of it, in the case of copper) with any typical acid. The reactions just described depend on the properties of *hot, concentrated sulfuric acid* as an *oxidizing agent*.

Sulfuric acid forms two series of salts, the normal salts (for example, sodium sulfate, Na_2SO_4) and the acid salts (for example, sodium hydrogen sulfate, $NaHSO_4$).

Dilute sulfuric acid

Dilute sulfuric acid does not have the same properties as concentrated sulfuric acid (discussed in the preceding paragraphs). Since it already contains a large excess of water it has no affinity for water and is not a dehydrating agent, nor does it undergo the type of oxidation reactions described for concentrated sulfuric acid.

Fig. 29–5. Gases may be dried by bubbling them through concentrated sulfuric acid in an apparatus like the one shown here. Chemists call this a *gas-washing bottle*.

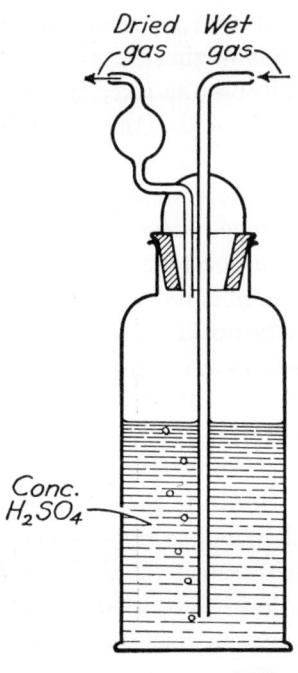

Dilute sulfuric acid should always be prepared by pouring concentrated sulfuric acid slowly and with constant stirring into water, rather than the reverse. As explained in an earlier chapter, this is because the reaction of water and sulfuric acid liberates a large amount of heat which should not be allowed to concentrate in one area.

Dilute sulfuric acid is a strong acid which has all the properties of a typical strong acid plus the properties of the sulfate ion. The sulfates of calcium, strontium, barium, and lead are insoluble. Dilute sulfuric acid, or a soluble sulfate, will precipitate any of these ions as sulfates when appropriate solutions are mixed. Thus

$$BaCl_2 + H_2SO_4 \rightarrow BaSO_4 \downarrow + 2HCl$$

The appearance of a white precipitate, insoluble in hydrochloric acid, when barium chloride solution is added to an unknown, is proof that the unknown contains sulfate ion.

Dilute sulfuric acid forms the same types of salts as the concentrated acid.

Uses of sulfuric acid

As you have already read, the largest single use of sulfuric acid is in the manufacture of phosphate fertilizers (see Chap. 33, pages 376 and 377). Since phosphorus is one of the most important elements in soil fertility, sulfuric acid is indirectly one of our most important agricultural chemicals. The next largest use of the acid is in metallurgy, where it is used for removing oxide films on steel prior to plating with zinc (galvanizing) or tin. The high boiling point of sulfuric acid makes it suitable (as already noted) for the manufacture of hydrochloric and nitric acids. As a dehydrating agent, sulfuric acid plays an essential role in the manufacture of plastics, explosives, rayon, and various organic chemicals. Sulfuric acid is an essential ingredient of the lead storage battery. Certain operations in petroleum refining require over a million tons of sulfuric acid yearly. Other uses depend on the formation of sulfates, as in the manufacture of the important white pigment **lithopone** (barium sulfate, $BaSO_4$, and zinc sulfide, ZnS), which is widely used in paints. The annual production of sulfuric acid in the United States is over fifteen million tons.

Thiosulfates

Sodium thiosulfate ($Na_2S_2O_3$) is the photographer's hypo. It is also used to remove excess chlorine in bleaching. The compound contains both divalent (valence of 2) and hexavalent (valence of 6) sulfur atoms. Sodium thiosulfate is sodium sulfate in which one of the oxygens has been replaced by divalent sulfur (hence its name).

The thiosulfate ion may be represented schematically as follows:

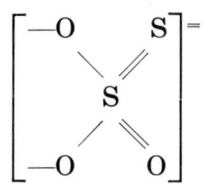

$$\begin{bmatrix} -O & & S \\ & \diagdown \diagup\!\!\!\!\diagup & \\ & S & \\ & \diagup \diagdown\!\!\!\!\diagdown & \\ -O & & O \end{bmatrix}^=$$

Sodium thiosulfate is formed by boiling sodium sulfite solution with sulfur:

$$Na_2SO_3 + S \rightarrow Na_2S_2O_3$$

The product, a white, water-soluble solid, is obtained by evaporating the water from the solution. This reaction is exactly analogous to the addition of oxygen to sodium sulfite or sulfurous acid (see page 328).

The free acid, thiosulfuric acid, is unstable and cannot be prepared even in solution. Attempts to prepare it always lead to the formation of sulfur and sulfur dioxide.

$$Na_2S_2O_3 + 2HCl \rightarrow 2NaCl + \underset{\text{(unstable)}}{(H_2S_2O_3)} \rightarrow H_2O + SO_2 \uparrow + S \downarrow$$

This reaction constitutes a test for a thiosulfate. The test is carried out by adding hydrochloric acid to the unknown. The evolution of sulfur dioxide (recognized by its odor) and the formation of a precipitate of sulfur prove the presence of thiosulfate.

If the unknown were sulfite, only sulfur dioxide would be produced. The reaction would be

$$Na_2SO_3 + 2HCl \rightarrow 2NaCl + (H_2SO_3) \rightarrow SO_2 \uparrow + H_2O$$

This gives a convenient method of distinguishing between sulfite and thiosulfate.

Sodium thiosulfate reacts with chlorine as follows:

$$Na_2S_2O_3 + 4Cl_2 + 5H_2O \rightarrow Na_2SO_4 + H_2SO_4 + 8HCl$$

For this reason, it is used to remove the excess chlorine from textiles after bleaching them.

KEY WORDS

chamber process
contact process
dehydrating agent
lithopone

oleum
phosphate fertilizer
pyrosulfuric acid
sodium thiosulfate

sulfites
sulfur dioxide
sulfuric acid
sulfur trioxide

HIGHLIGHTS

Sulfur dioxide is a gas with a sharp odor, about twice as heavy as air, very soluble in water, and easily liquefied. It does not burn but in the presence of a catalyst is converted into **sulfur trioxide,** the anhydride of **sulfuric acid.**

Concentrated sulfuric acid is made by the **contact process.** The older lead **chamber process** is used to produce 65 percent acid. Fuming sulfuric acid or **oleum** is formed by adding sulfur trioxide to concentrated sulfuric acid.

Dilute sulfuric acid has typical acid properties. Concentrated sulfuric acid, especially when hot, acts as an oxidizing agent.

Barium chloride is used to test for sulfate. A white precipitate, insoluble in hydrochloric acid, is a positive test.

QUESTIONS

1. Give the names and formulas for the acid and salts derived from sulfur dioxide.
2. Give the names and formulas for the acids and salts derived from sulfur trioxide.
3. Write equations which show three different commercial methods of manufacturing sulfur dioxide.
4. Explain how sulfur dioxide can be liquefied.
5. Explain how sulfur dioxide can be prepared in the laboratory. How is the gas collected? Why is this method used?
6. Give three uses for sulfur dioxide.
7. How is sulfurous acid prepared? Can this acid be obtained in the pure state? Explain.
8. Explain how you would prepare sodium hydrogen sulfite from water, sulfur dioxide, and sodium hydroxide. Write the equations.
9. Describe briefly the contact process for making sulfuric acid.
10. Describe briefly the chamber process for making sulfuric acid.
11. Explain why the chamber process does not produce 100 percent acid.
12. For what purpose is most of the chamber acid used?
13. Write equations for the action of hot concentrated sulfuric acid on copper and on carbon.
14. Describe a test for sulfuric acid.
15. Explain a test by means of which one can distinguish between a sulfite and a thiosulfate.
16. List five uses for sulfuric acid.

CHAPTER 30

the atmosphere and the inert gases

The atmosphere that surrounds the earth is a mixture of gases and suspended solid particles. Approximately half of the atmosphere is below a height of 3.6 miles. If you were to travel up from the earth's surface, you would find that the concentration of the air becomes lower and lower. Thus the pressure of the atmosphere decreases regularly with increasing altitude.

Composition of the atmosphere

The principal substances found in clean, dry air are listed in Table 30–1.

TABLE 30–1. Composition of dry air at sea level

Gas	Percent by volume
Nitrogen	78.04
Oxygen	20.99
Inert gases (Group Zero elements)	0.94
Carbon dioxide	0.03

In addition the atmosphere contains variable amounts of water vapor and of other substances as a result of its local contamination. Dust, ammonia, carbon monoxide, oxides of sulfur, and oxides of nitrogen are common contaminants.

The role of oxygen in the atmosphere has been discussed (see Chaps. 6 and 7). Oxygen is necessary for respiration, and man uses it in the combustion of fuels.

The role of nitrogen in the atmosphere will be discussed more fully in the chapter which follows, but essentially its role is to supply nitrogen for plant growth and thus indirectly for animal growth.

The role of carbon dioxide is in supplying the carbon for the formation of carbohydrates (sugars and starches) and other organic compounds in plant growth. This is accomplished through photosynthesis, which is illustrated by the following equation:

$$6CO_2 + 6H_2O \xrightarrow[\text{chlorophyll}]{\text{sunlight}} 6O_2 \uparrow + C_6H_{12}O_6$$

Reactions of this kind occur in the growing leaves of plants.

The water vapor in the air is necessary to provide the climates that make the world habitable (see Chap. 12, pages 109 and 115).

Even the dust in the atmosphere is believed to serve an essential purpose. Scientists believe that dust particles, along with gas ions formed by cosmic rays, serve as condensation nuclei for the formation of raindrops and snowflakes and that without them perhaps no raindrops would form. Thus without the dust particles and gas ions the atmosphere at times would become supersaturated with moisture. This moisture would condense on the walls of buildings and other solid surfaces much as a pitcher of ice water collects "dew" on a hot, muggy day.

The inert gases

It is a strange fact that, as far as is known at present, the inert gases do not have any essential role in the atmosphere. Science has found that, in general, as a result of evolution, an organism develops which can make full use of its environment. In the preceding paragraphs it has been pointed out how the forms of life on this planet make use of the other constituents of the atmosphere.

These elements are the members of Group Zero in the periodic table,

TABLE 30–2. Properties of the inert gases

	Percent of atmosphere	Density compared with air = 1	Molecular weight	Freezing point, °C	Boiling point, °C	Atomic no.	Electron arrangement
Helium	0.0004	0.14	4.00	−272.2	−268.9	2	2
Neon	0.0012	0.70	20.18	−248.7	−245.9	10	2, 8
Argon	0.94	1.4	39.94	−189.2	−185.7	18	2, 8, 8
Krypton	0.00005	2.9	83.7	−156.6	−152.9	36	2, 8, 18, 8
Xenon	0.000006	4.5	131.3	−112	−107.1	54	2, 8, 18, 18, 8
Radon	...	7.6	222.	−110	−61.8	86	2, 8, 18, 32, 18, 8

The cooling equipment of a U.S. Bureau of Mines helium plant in Kansas. Compression of the gas causes its temperature to rise. It is then cooled by passage through the pipes, or coils, shown here. (U.S. Bureau of Mines)

and all except the radioactive radon are present in the atmosphere. The properties of the inert gases are shown in Table 30–2.

The chemistry of these elements is easily remembered. They do not form any compounds. This is the reason for the name *inert gases* or, as they are sometimes called, *noble gases*. The reason for their chemical inertness is that they possess the most stable electron arrangements that it is possible to obtain.

The inert gases do not even combine with themselves. The molecules are monatomic and the molecular formula is the same as the symbol.

These elements, except helium and radon, are separated from the atmosphere by the fractional distillation of liquid air.

Helium

Helium is obtained from certain natural gases in Texas which contain from 1 to 7 percent of this element. The natural gas from these wells is processed to extract its helium and the supply is controlled by the U.S. Bureau of Mines, which makes it available for research and industrial use. At present there is an abundant supply of helium, and scientists are seeking new uses for the gas. However, these natural-gas wells are the only known source of importance. The United States is the only country that has a supply of helium.

Helium is used to fill balloons and dirigibles because of its low density and chemical inertness. Copies of the Declaration of Independence and of our Constitution have been sealed in helium to ensure their preservation. During World War II Germany had no lighter-than-air ships because she had no helium with which to fill them. In the late 1930s the United States government had refused to supply Germany with the helium which she requested.

Helium is used to inflate the tires on large bomber planes. This use also depends on its low density. By using helium instead of air, the weight of a plane can be reduced as much as several hundred pounds. Helium is used to supply the "atmosphere" in which to weld metals such as aluminum and magnesium, which readily combine with both oxygen and nitrogen when hot. It is used also to replace nitrogen in diving bells and caissons (see Chap. 14, pages 155 and 156). Because of its very low boiling point, which is the lowest of any known substance, helium is useful for conducting research at the very low temperatures in the neighborhood of absolute zero.

Helium is produced in the radioactive decay of uranium (see Chap. 18, pages 205 and 206). It is believed by some that all the helium found on the earth came from this source. There is, as yet, no way of proving or disproving this hypothesis.

Neon

Neon is used in making the familiar luminous neon tube signs. Its use in these signs depends upon the fact that when an electric current is sent through a tube containing neon at low pressures, an orange-red glow is produced. This red glow is particularly effective in penetrating fog—hence its use as airport markers. Other gases behave similarly when an electric discharge passes through them except that each element produces a characteristic color. The varicolored tube signs of commerce are generally mixtures of different gases.

Argon

Argon is widely used in filling **incandescent** electric-light bulbs. The reason for its use is as follows: The tungsten (wolfram) **filament** in an incandescent bulb must be completely protected from oxygen because otherwise, when the filament heats up, it combines with the oxygen and the lamp burns out. This is why a cracked bulb always means a burned-out bulb. In past years the oxygen was excluded from the bulb by evacuating and sealing the bulb. But because of the high temperature of the filament (about 3000°C), the tungsten atoms in these evacuated bulbs slowly vaporize while the lamp is in use and condense on the cooler glass bulb. This shortens the life of the filament and causes the glass bulb to blacken on the inside. Many years ago **Dr. Irving Langmuir** of the Research Laboratories of the General Electric Co. found that this evaporation of the tungsten could be reduced by filling the bulb with an inert gas such as argon or nitrogen. Today incandescent lamp bulbs are filled with argon or a mixture of argon and nitrogen at a pressure of about two-thirds atmosphere. The result is a lamp which is more efficient because it can operate at a high temperature, and which lasts longer. This comparatively simple dis-

Dr. Irving Langmuir during his 40-year career at General Electric has saved the American public nearly one billion dollars per year in electric-light bills. He has also helped make possible modern radio broadcasting, has helped safeguard the lives of soldiers in battle, and, more recently, has provided man with a key to the possible control of the weather. (General Electric Co.)

covery saves every man, woman, and child in this country on the average about one dollar every year!

Krypton and xenon

Krypton and xenon are exceedingly rare (Table 30–2). Their commercial production from the atmosphere has been started just recently. At the present time pure samples of these gases are quite expensive and no commercial uses exist for them as yet. On the other hand chemical industry has a habit of finding a use for almost any commodity that becomes available to it. It is entirely probable that there will soon be industrial uses for these gases. One possible use is to replace argon in electric-light bulbs. The result would be a still more efficient and longer-lasting bulb. However, the economic side of this use has not yet been worked out.

Radon

The important property of radon is its radioactivity (see Chap. 18, pages 205 and 206). As you read earlier, radon is produced by the radioactive disintegration of radium. It does not exist in the atmosphere.

KEY WORDS

argon	helium	krypton	neon
filament	incandescent	Langmuir	xenon

HIGHLIGHTS

Ninety-nine percent of clean, dry air is nitrogen and oxygen (in the proportion of about 4:1). The remaining 1 percent consists largely of carbon dioxide, **argon, helium, neon, krypton,** and **xenon.** Nitrogen and oxygen are discussed elsewhere in the book.

Carbon dioxide is one of the raw materials in the all-important natural process of photosynthesis, upon which all higher forms of life depend. Oxygen is a by-product of this process.

Argon is used widely in filling **incandescent** light bulbs. Helium is used for inflating balloons and dirigibles. Neon is the basis of the neon signs and the elaborate electrical displays so widely used today. The other gases of the atmosphere are not of much practical use at present.

QUESTIONS

1. Name the substances generally present in the atmosphere.
2. What is the biological role of the oxygen in the atmosphere?
3. What is the biological role of the carbon dioxide in the atmosphere?
4. What is the biological role of the nitrogen in the atmosphere?
5. What has the lowest boiling point of any substance known?
6. Which of the inert gases is found in the atmosphere in the largest quantities?
7. What are the uses for helium?
8. From what source is commercial helium obtained?
9. For what is argon used?
10. What is the principal use of neon?

CHAPTER 31

nitrogen and ammonia

Nitrogen is the first member of Group V. All members of this group form oxygen compounds in which they show valences of 3 and 5. All of them also form hydrides with a formula analogous to ammonia, NH_3.

Nitrogen

Nitrogen was first recognized as a distinct substance by **Daniel Rutherford** (1772) who was Professor of Botany in the University of Edinburgh, Scotland, and an uncle of Sir Walter Scott. Lavoisier in his important experiments on oxygen and combustion (see Chap. 7, pages 54 and 55) named nitrogen *azote* (from the Greek word meaning *without life*, or *lazy*). The English name of the element is due to its occurrence in niter, KNO_3.

Nitrogen is of great biological and economic importance, since all living things contain the element in the form of complex organic compounds, particularly those known as *proteins*. Animals obtain their nitrogen for building body proteins from plants. Plants obtain their nitrogen from nitrogen compounds of the soil. Hence nitrogen compounds are essential as fertilizers. All military explosives, except nuclear bombs, are nitrogen compounds.

Occurrence of nitrogen

All nitrate and ammonium compounds are soluble in water, and with one exception, mineral depositions of nitrogen compounds are not found in nature. This one exception, however, is important. It is the immense deposit of sodium nitrate, $NaNO_3$ **(Chile saltpeter),** which is found in Chile. These deposits are found in a desert region where there is practically no rainfall.

The occurrence of nitrogen in all living matter has been mentioned above.

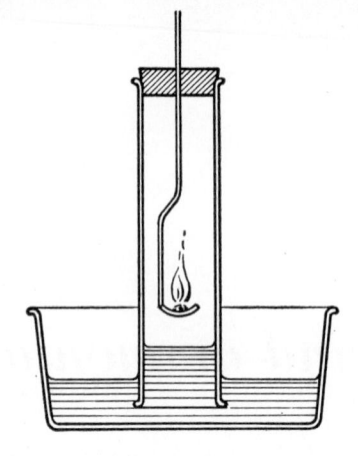

Fig. 31-1. An impure sample of nitrogen may be prepared in the laboratory by burning phosphorus in a closed tube. This procedure removes the oxygen from the air, leaving mainly nitrogen.

Except for the Chilean nitrate, the only important source of nitrogen is the atmosphere, which is approximately four-fifths by volume of uncombined nitrogen, N_2. Calculation indicates there are approximately twenty million tons of the element over each square mile of the earth's surface! This is one natural resource which we shall never exhaust.

Preparation of nitrogen

All the elementary nitrogen used in industry is obtained from the atmosphere. The separation of pure nitrogen is done by fractional distillation of liquid air (see Chap. 11, pages 101 and 102).

In the laboratory nitrogen is sometimes obtained by removing oxygen from a sample of air. This is done by burning red phosphorus in a cylinder of air contained over water (Fig. 31-1). Although the phosphorus removes all the oxygen by forming oxides of phosphorus which dissolve in the water, it does not remove argon or carbon dioxide. Hence the nitrogen obtained in this way is not pure. This experiment is a simple and easy one, however, for measuring the percentage of oxygen in the atmosphere. The shrinkage in volume of the confined gas is a measure of its oxygen content. For accurate results the levels of water inside and outside the tube should be equalized before measuring the volumes.

Pure nitrogen is formed by passing ammonia over hot copper oxide.

$$3CuO + 2NH_3 \rightarrow 3Cu + 3H_2O + N_2 \uparrow$$

It may also be prepared by carefully heating a solution of ammonium chloride and sodium nitrite.

$$Na^+ + NO_2^- + NH_4^+ + Cl^- \rightarrow Na^+ + Cl^- + N_2 \uparrow + 2H_2O$$
or
$$NO_2^- + NH_4^+ \rightarrow 2H_2O + N_2 \uparrow$$

The gas is collected over water.

Physical properties of nitrogen

Nitrogen is a colorless, odorless, and tasteless gas. It is very slightly soluble in water (2.33 volumes of nitrogen in 100 volumes of water at 0°C). Its freezing point is −210°C and its boiling point −196°C.

Chemical properties of nitrogen

The electronic structure of the nitrogen molecule may be represented

$$:N\!::\!N:$$

There are three pairs of electrons binding the atoms together. Thus the molecule is a very stable one. Since any reaction of the element would involve breaking this bond, nitrogen is quite inactive. Moreover, almost all nitrogen compounds are relatively unstable. The fact that some of them are explosive has already been mentioned.

With the more active metals, nitrogen forms **nitrides.**

$$3Mg + N_2 \xrightarrow{\text{heat}} \underset{\text{magnesium nitride}}{Mg_3N_2}$$

The same reaction is given by the other alkaline earth metals as well as by the alkalis and by boron, aluminum, and titanium.

This reaction occurs when magnesium burns in air. The white ash is really a mixture of magnesium oxide (MgO) and magnesium nitride (Mg_3N_2). The presence of the magnesium nitride can be shown by moistening the ash with water. Ammonia is given off. This can be detected by the odor of ammonia or by holding a piece of wet red litmus paper above the beaker.

$$Mg_3N_2 + 6H_2O \rightarrow 3Mg(OH)_2 + 2NH_3 \uparrow$$

This property of magnesium is made use of in evacuating radio tubes. For efficient operation the tube must have a very good vacuum. After evacuating the tube in the usual way, it is sealed. Then magnesium

Fig. 31–2. A pure sample of nitrogen can be prepared in the laboratory by warming a mixture of solutions of ammonium chloride and sodium nitrite. The nitrogen produced is collected by displacement of water.

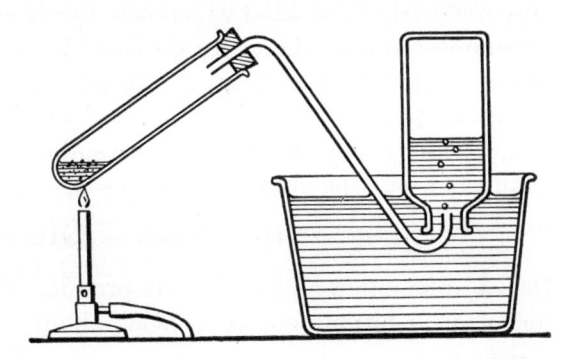

metal is vaporized electrically from within the tube. This hot magnesium reacts with both the oxygen and the nitrogen in the tube, forming solids. This produces a more nearly perfect vacuum.

The compounds of nitrogen with hydrogen and oxygen are of such importance that they will be considered separately.

Uses of nitrogen

The principal commercial use of nitrogen is in the manufacture of nitrogen compounds for **fertilizers** and **explosives.** Some is used for filling electric-light bulbs (Chap. 30, page 340).

Ammonia

Ammonia takes its name from *sal ammoniac*, NH_4Cl, so called because it is supposed to have been first isolated from camel dung near the temple of Ammon. Ammonia is a natural product of decay of animals and plants.

Ammonia is of great economic importance. Its chief uses are as a nitrogen fertilizer, a refrigerant, and in the manufacture of nitric acid. The average person thinks of ammonia only in connection with smelling salts or as a household cleanser. Yet our standard of living in America would be quite different, in so far as cost and availability of food are concerned, were it not for the fact that ammonia can be made in large quantities and very cheaply. Its low-cost, large-scale production by the direct union of nitrogen from the atmosphere with hydrogen is one of the triumphs of our chemical industry.

Manufacture of ammonia

The old name for ammonia water was *spirits of hartshorn*. This comes from the fact that it was obtained by heating horns and hoofs of deer and other animals. When these or other protein-containing materials are heated, part of the nitrogen is liberated as ammonia. Thus the heating of gelatin, leather, feathers, or fur also produces ammonia, as does wood or any other nitrogenous organic material. Coal is the only material of this kind which now furnishes quantities of ammonia of commercial importance. In the making of coke and coal gas, coal is heated in the absence of air. Along with many other substances (see Chap. 34, page 392) ammonia is produced. It is separated from the other gases by passing them through sulfuric acid. The other gases are unaffected, but the ammonia forms solid ammonium sulfate.

$$2NH_3 + H_2SO_4 \rightarrow (NH_4)_2SO_4 \downarrow$$

Hence ammonium sulfate is a by-product of the coke industry. One ton of good bituminous coal yields about five pounds of ammonia;

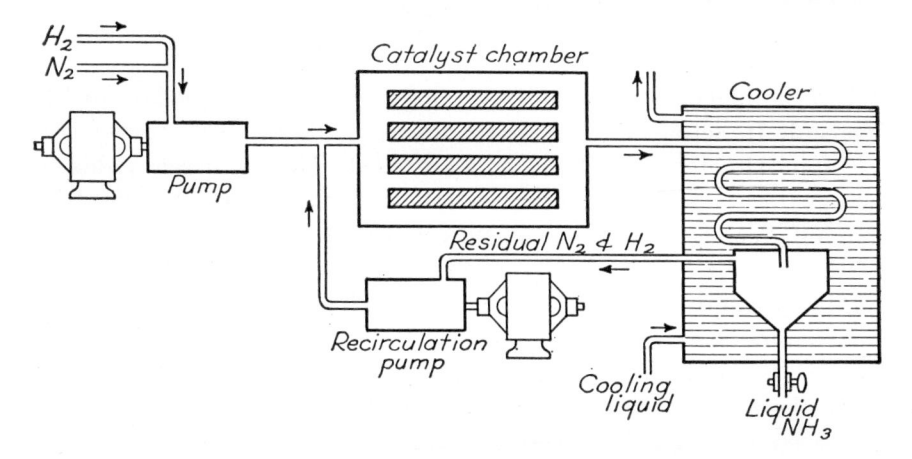

Fig. 31-3. A simplified diagram showing the essential steps in the production of ammonia by the Haber process.

consequently it is obvious that coal can never supply really large quantities of the compound. Most ammonia is now made by direct combination of nitrogen and hydrogen by the Haber process.

The Haber process

The reaction is

$$N_2 + 3H_2 \rightleftarrows 2NH_3 + 24{,}000 \text{ cal.}$$

However, when nitrogen and hydrogen are put together at room temperature, they show no tendency to react. This is true because the reaction is very slow. At higher temperatures the reaction is more rapid, but since the reaction is reversible and exothermic, the higher the temperature the lower the yield. In other words ammonia is less stable at higher temperatures. How then can this reaction be used to produce ammonia? The answer, first worked out by the German chemist Fritz Haber about 1905, was this: Use a catalyst to speed up the reaction. In America the catalyst used is generally a mixture of iron with aluminum and potassium oxides. But even in the presence of this catalyst the lowest temperature at which the reaction is fast enough to be practical is 550°C. At this temperature and 1 atmosphere pressure, the yield is less than one percent, which, of course, is too low to be practical. How can the yield be increased? According to Le Châtelier's principle, by increased pressure, since the formation of ammonia involves a reduction in volume (see Chap. 26, page 288). Thus at 550°C the yields of ammonia are

Pressure	Yield of NH_3 at 550°C
1 atmosphere	Very small
100 atmospheres	6.8%
1000 atmospheres	41%

Thus the higher the pressure, the closer the yield approaches to 100 percent. In actual practice, pressures from 200 to 1000 atmospheres (=approximately 15,000 lb/in.^{2}) are used. The increased yields of ammonia at the higher pressures are somewhat counterbalanced by having greater engineering difficulties at very high pressures.

Figure 31-3 shows a diagram of the actual process. The gases at proper pressure pass through the catalyst chamber, where equilibrium with ammonia is established, and then to a cooler, where the ammonia condenses and is drawn off as a liquid.

In the process the nitrogen is obtained from the atmosphere. The hydrogen is obtained by passing steam over iron or by the purification of water gas (see Chap. 8, pages 66 and 67).

The cyanamide process

Calcium oxide and carbon, when heated together in an electric furnace to a high temperature (3000°C), form **calcium carbide**.

$$CaO + 3C \xrightarrow{heat} \underset{\text{calcium carbide}}{CaC_2} + CO \uparrow$$

Nitrogen reacts with calcium carbide at about 1100°C to form **calcium cyanamide**.

$$CaC_2 + N_2 \xrightarrow{1100°C} \underset{\text{calcium cyanamide}}{CaCN_2} + C$$

Calcium cyanamide reacts with water to form ammonia.

$$CaCN_2 + 3H_2O \rightarrow CaCO_3 + 2NH_3 \uparrow$$

Most of the calcium cyanamide manufactured is used directly as a fertilizer. When spread on the soil, it slowly liberates ammonia by reaction with soil moisture which supplies nitrogen for plant growth.

Fixation of nitrogen

This term means conversion of free nitrogen (of the atmosphere) into nitrogen compounds. The Haber and cyanamide processes given above are processes for the fixation of nitrogen. Any practical process for **nitrogen fixation** is important because of the importance of nitrogen compounds.

Without the Haber and cyanamide processes, Germany would not have been able to fight for more than a year in World War I because she would not have had a supply of explosives. Actually she did fight for 4 years in spite of the British blockade. The Allied countries, on

Fig. 31–4. A convenient laboratory setup for the preparation of ammonia by heating an ammonium salt with calcium hydroxide [Ca(OH)$_2$]. Note that the ammonium salt and calcium hydroxide are heated in the dry state and that the ammonia produced is dried by passing it through a column containing calcium oxide (CaO).

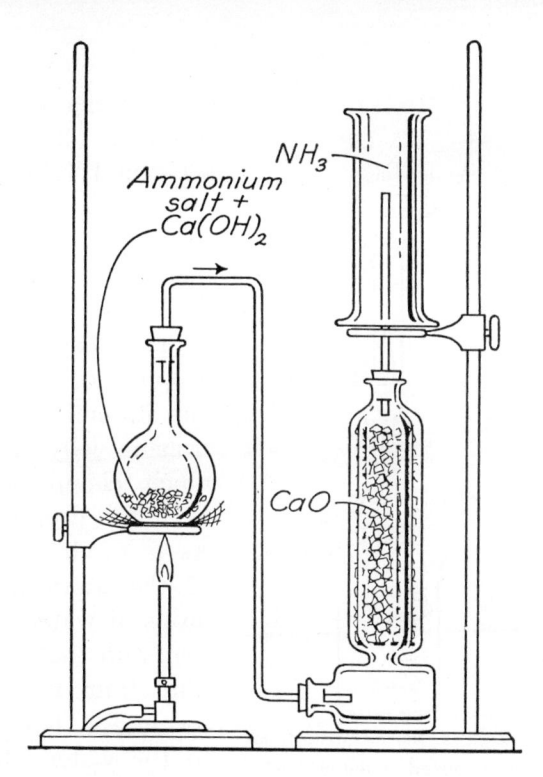

the other hand, did not employ nitrogen fixation processes very much during that war. Having control of the seas, they had access to the Chilean nitrate deposits, which they used to make their explosives.

Some people believe that a country could be kept in complete subjugation militarily and economically merely by prohibiting nitrogen fixation within the country and by preventing importation of nitrogen compounds.

Laboratory preparation of ammonia

Any ammonium salt reacts with any strong base to form ammonia. A convenient laboratory method is to heat a mixture of calcium hydroxide and ammonium chloride in the solid state (Fig. 31–4).

Liquefied ammonia is available in small steel cylinders at very low cost. These are the most convenient laboratory source of the gas.

Physical properties of ammonia

Ammonia is a colorless gas of very pungent odor. It is highly poisonous if inhaled in quantity. Its critical temperature is 133°C and its normal boiling point −33°C. Its cheapness, together with these properties, makes ammonia very useful as the refrigerant for large refrigeration plants, such as in cold-storage warehouses and ice-cream factories. However, as a refrigerant it is not as efficient as the Freons (CCl_2F_2 and others).

Ammonia is extremely soluble in water. At 0°C, 1305 volumes of ammonia dissolve in 1 volume of water. The ammonia fountain is based on this high solubility (Fig. 31-5). A large flask filled with ammonia gas is set up as shown in Fig. 31-5. The long tube is closed by means of a rubber tube and pinch clamp. The dropper contains a few drops of water and its end is closed with a smear of petroleum jelly. To start the fountain, the pinch clamp is opened and the water from the dropper squirted into the flask. As a result of the high solubility most of the ammonia dissolves in these few drops of water. This causes a partial vacuum and the water rushes in, like a fountain, from the lower tube. If an indicator and a few drops of acid are added to the water, the fountain can be made more spectacular in its effect.

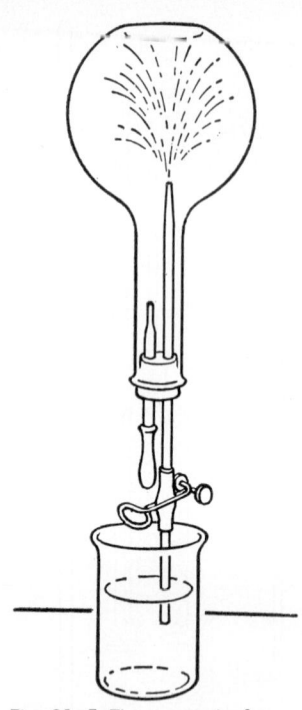

Fig. 31-5. The ammonia fountain is based on the high solubility of ammonia in water.

Chemical properties of ammonia

You have seen that ammonia is unstable when heated (see page 347). At 900 to 1000°C it is practically entirely dissociated into nitrogen and hydrogen. Because of the hydrogen present, a mixture of ammonia and oxygen explodes when heated.

$$2NH_3 \xrightarrow{heat} N_2 \uparrow + 3H_2 \uparrow$$

$$2N_2 + 6H_2 + 3O_2 \xrightarrow{heat} 6H_2O \uparrow + 2N_2 \uparrow$$

Hence $\quad 4NH_3 + 3O_2 \xrightarrow{heat} 6H_2O \uparrow + 2N_2 \uparrow$

Ammonia is a good reducing agent for metal oxides.

$$3CuO + 2NH_3 \xrightarrow{heat} 3Cu + 3H_2O + N_2 \uparrow$$

Also, because ammonia is unstable when heated, it reacts with active metals such as magnesium to form metal nitrides and hydrogen.

$$2NH_3 + 3Mg \xrightarrow{heat} Mg_3N_2 + 3H_2 \uparrow$$

The most important reaction of ammonia is with water, as discussed in the following paragraphs.

Ammonia water

The extreme solubility of ammonia has been mentioned. When it dissolves in water, ammonia reacts with the water to form a basic solution.

$$NH_3 + H_2O \rightleftarrows NH_4^+ + OH^-$$

The electronic mechanism of this reaction has been given in Chap. 27, page 296. These solutions are commonly referred to as **ammonium hydroxide.** You should note carefully that molecular ammonium hydroxide (NH_4OH) *does not form*, but rather its ions exist in solution.

That the reaction of ammonia with water is not complete is evident from cautiously smelling dilute ammonium hydroxide. One cannot smell the ions, but only the volatile gas ammonia. The strong odor of ammonia is evidence of its presence in the solution. Ammonium hydroxide is the chemist's most important *weak base*. Its degree of ionization is about the same as that of acetic acid at the same concentration.

Commercial concentrated ammonium hydroxide is about $15M$.

Household ammonia is ammonium hydroxide. The household product may also contain some soap. The use of ammonia for cleaning is based upon the fact that any alkali converts most fats and greases into water-soluble compounds.

Because of its complete volatility, ammonium hydroxide is sometimes referred to as volatile alkali.

Ammonium salts

When ammonium hydroxide solutions are neutralized by acids, ammonium salts are obtained. Almost all these can be obtained as pure solids by evaporating the solution. Thus hydrochloric acid gives ammonium chloride (or sal ammoniac), which is sometimes used in soldering.

$$NH_3 + HCl \rightarrow NH_4Cl$$

Ammonium nitrate, NH_4NO_3, is obtained from nitric acid and ammonia. The compound is unstable and should be handled carefully. It is used as a constituent of some military explosives. Since it contains a large percentage of nitrogen (46.7 percent), it is a concentrated nitrogen fertilizer and is used commercially for this purpose. The great explosion at Texas City, Tex., in 1947 involved a French ship being loaded with ammonium nitrate to be taken to France as fertilizer under the Marshall Plan.

An aerial view of the dock area of Texas City, Tex., as the fires that resulted from the explosion of a nitrate-laden ship were raging through the area for the second consecutive day. The Monsanto Chemical Co. plant in the left foreground was heavily damaged. (American Red Cross)

Many ammonium salts dissociate into ammonia and the acid on heating. If the acid is volatile, the salt can be completely vaporized by heating. Thus ammonium chloride yields hydrogen chloride and ammonia on heating.

$$\underset{\text{(solid)}}{NH_4Cl} \xrightarrow{\text{heat}} \underset{\text{(gas)}}{NH_3} + \underset{\text{(gas)}}{HCl}$$

Hence ammonium salts of volatile acids are themselves volatile.

Test for ammonia

The gas can be recognized by its odor or its basic effect on moist red litmus paper. (Ammonia changes the color of red litmus to blue.)

Ammonium salts are recognized by treating them with a solution of a strong base and noting the evolution of ammonia.

$$NH_4^+ + Cl^- + Na^+ + OH^- \rightarrow NH_3 \uparrow + Na^+ + Cl^- + H_2O$$

Test the *vapors* with red litmus paper. The sensitivity of the test is increased by warming the solution, but spattering of the solution onto the litmus paper must be avoided. This test depends upon the fact that ammonia is the only common volatile base.

Uses of ammonia

The end uses of ammonia have already been indicated. About twenty percent of it is used in the manufacture of nitric acid, which is necessary for explosives, plastics, and dyestuffs. Most of the remainder is used in fertilizers and in refrigeration.

Until recently because of the volatility of ammonia, it was considered necessary to convert the ammonia into salt form [NH_4NO_3 or $(NH_4)_2SO_4$] before it could be used for fertilizer. Recently it was found

Fig. 31–6. The test for ammonium ion depends upon the fact that strong bases liberate ammonia from ammonium salts. The liberated ammonia turns wet red litmus to blue.

Wet red litmus paper underneath watch glass

Unknown solution + sodium hydroxide

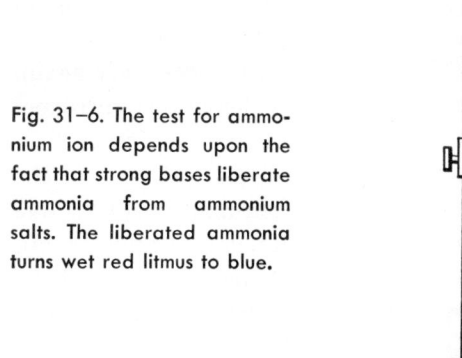

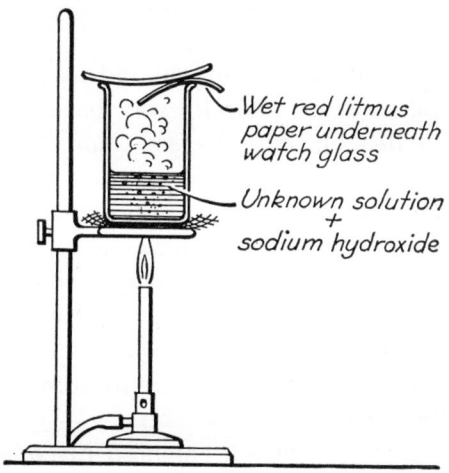

in the West that ammonia can be added directly to irrigation waters, from which plants under irrigation will absorb it. It has also been found that ammonia can effectively be added directly to the soil. Special machines release the gas an inch or two below the surface. Under conditions where soil moisture is high and the soil has a high clay content, very little of the ammonia escapes into the air. The importance of these facts is that, per pound of nitrogen, ammonia, which is $14/17$ nitrogen, is much cheaper than the salts made from it which have formerly been used. Actually a pound of combined nitrogen costs only about one-fourth as much when purchased as ammonia. As this practice becomes more widespread among farmers, it will tend to reduce the cost of food production.

The nitrogen cycle in nature

It is a strange fact that although we live at the bottom of an "air ocean" which is four-fifths nitrogen, all higher forms of life are incapable of existence without a steady and continuous supply of combined nitrogen. This is true because the living parts of both plant and animal cells are made up of proteins—complex organic compounds containing nitrogen. But plants are better adapted to life here than are animals in this respect. Plants can use a wide variety of nitrogen compounds as a source of nitrogen for forming their proteins. Animals, with a few exceptions, are entirely unable to synthesize their proteins unless they have protein in their diet. Thus man needs beans, eggs, meat, and milk in his diet partly because these are good sources of necessary protein. The source of the nitrogen in each of these substances is—directly or indirectly—the nitrogen compounds in soil. To illustrate with the case of milk:

soil nitrogen → protein in grass $\xrightarrow{\text{cow}}$ protein in milk $\xrightarrow{\text{man}}$ protein in man's body

Thus all animal life is dependent upon plants for protein.

Eventually all animal and plant protein decays. In decay, most of the nitrogen finds its way back into the soil (as ammonium salts, nitrites, and nitrates, see Chap. 13, page 134) to be used over again. But a small amount is lost to the atmosphere as elementary nitrogen. This loss is made up for in two ways: (1) Certain nitrogen-fixing bacteria exist. These bacteria have the ability to convert nitrogen of the atmosphere into nitrogen compounds. The nitrogen-fixing bacteria live on the roots of legumes (soybeans, peanuts, alfalfa, clover, and others). (2) Lightning causes the combination of some of the nitrogen and the oxygen of the atmosphere to form compounds which eventually reach the earth.

In these ways a balanced **nitrogen cycle** is established in which the essential nitrogen needs of all forms of life can be satisfied. That is, it was balanced before man started to change the nature of the earth's surface. Man burns thousands of square miles of forests and grassland—and the nitrogen in these plants is lost into the atmosphere. Burning leaves raked from the lawn has the same effect. Man burns vegetative material to warm his home. He causes soil erosion, which washes untold tons of nitrogen compounds into the ocean where they are lost. Man has changed the ratio of legumes to grasses. The result of this unbalanced cycle would be a rapid depletion of the nitrogen compounds in the soil. Fortunately as you have already seen, scientists have learned how to carry out nitrogen fixation on such a scale as to make it possible to bring the cycle back into balance. The increased emphasis on cultivation of legumes is also helpful. But considering the entire surface of the earth, it is doubtful whether there is even yet a fully balanced nitrogen cycle.

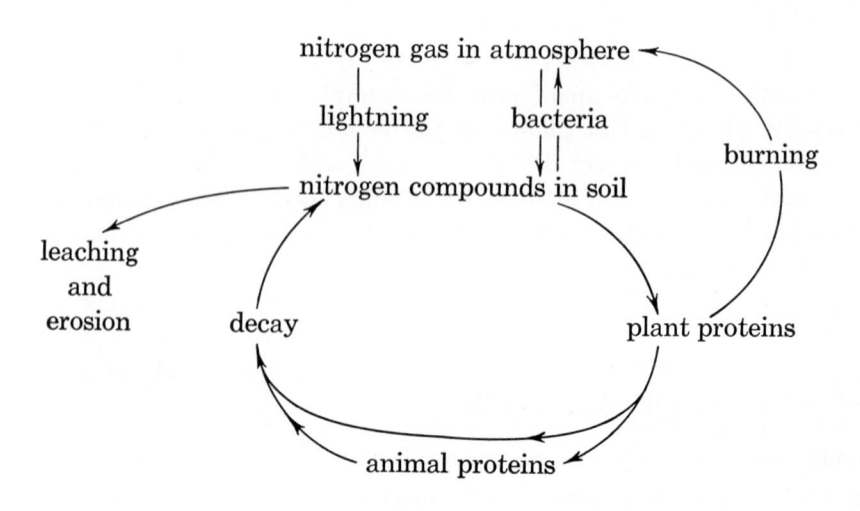

Nitrogen fertilizer for this sugar beet crop is supplied by adding ammonia directly to irrigation water. This is one of the ways in which man is trying to bring the nitrogen cycle back into balance. (Shell Oil Co.)

KEY WORDS

ammonia	Chile saltpeter	nitride
ammonium hydroxide	explosives	nitrogen cycle
calcium carbide	fertilizers	nitrogen fixation
calcium cyanamide	Haber process	Rutherford (Daniel)

HIGHLIGHTS

Life as we know it is impossible without nitrogen. Nitrogen is present in all proteins and therefore is a part of all organisms. Most plants take nitrogen from the soil in solution, but the legumes can use atmospheric nitrogen because of certain nitrogen-fixing bacteria which live on their roots.

Nitrogen is a colorless, odorless, and tasteless gas, slightly less dense than air and slightly soluble in water. It does not burn and does not support combustion except for a few elements such as magnesium and calcium. Pure nitrogen can be prepared by heating a mixture of sodium nitrite and ammonium chloride. Nitrogen is an important ingredient of all complete **fertilizers** and is present in most **explosives.**

Ammonia is a colorless gas with a characteristically pungent odor and very soluble in water. It is prepared in the laboratory by heating a mixture of an ammonium salt, such as ammonium chloride, and a strong base, such as sodium hydroxide. This reaction is also the test for ammonium compounds.

Industrially ammonia is made by the destructive distillation of soft coal, by the **Haber process,** and by the **cyanamide** process. The

Haber process is a direct synthesis carried out in the presence of a catalyst at a carefully controlled temperature and a high pressure. It is an application of Le Châtelier's principle. The cyanamide process uses electric energy to bring about the reaction of **calcium carbide** and nitrogen.

Ammonia is used as a refrigerant and in solution as a cleansing agent. It is used also in making fertilizers and explosives.

QUESTIONS

1. Explain why nitrogen compounds are of great economic importance.
2. In what forms is nitrogen found in nature?
3. How is nitrogen separated commercially from the other components of the atmosphere?
4. Give one laboratory method for preparing nitrogen. Write the appropriate equation.
5. Write the equation for the reaction of nitrogen with magnesium. What practical application is made of this reaction?
6. Describe the conditions under which hydrogen and nitrogen unite to form ammonia in the Haber process. Explain, in terms of Le Châtelier's principle, why a high pressure is used.
7. Write the equation for the cyanamide process for nitrogen fixation.
8. What ions and molecules are present in a solution of ammonium hydroxide?
9. Explain the test for the ammonium ion. Write the equation.
10. Describe the nitrogen cycle in nature.
11. What practices of man have tended to bring the cycle out of balance?
12. How do the nitrogen dietary requirements of animals differ from those of plants?

CHAPTER 32

the oxygen compounds of nitrogen

Nitrogen forms a great many different types of compounds—probably more than any other element except carbon. This chapter will deal with its most important oxides and acids. They are

Formula	Common Name	Systematic Name
N_2O	Nitrous oxide	Dinitrogen oxide
NO	Nitric oxide	Nitrogen oxide
NO_2	Nitrogen dioxide	Nitrogen dioxide
N_2O_4	Nitrogen tetroxide	Dinitrogen tetroxide
HNO_3	Nitric acid	
HNO_2	Nitrous acid	

Nitric acid

Nitric acid is of great economic importance. Since it is essential in the manufacture of all modern military explosives except the nuclear bombs, no country could wage a war without an enormous supply of it. Nitric acid also enters into the manufacture of a large number of dyes, plastics, lacquers, and chemicals, as well as fertilizers.

Nitric acid was known to the alchemists, who called it **aqua fortis.**

Laboratory preparation of nitric acid

Nitric acid may be obtained by a method comparable to that used for hydrochloric acid. It is formed by heating a mixture of sodium nitrate and concentrated sulfuric acid.

$$NaNO_3 + H_2SO_4 \xrightarrow{heat} NaHSO_4 + HNO_3 \uparrow$$

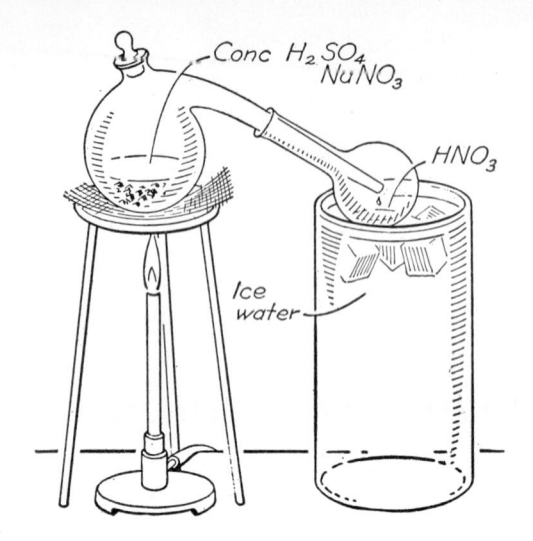

Fig. 32–1. Nitric acid may be prepared by heating sodium nitrate and concentrated sulfuric acid together. Because of its corrosive nature, an all-glass apparatus, such as that shown, is used in the laboratory for the preparation of nitric acid.

The nitric acid distills at 86°C. Because of the corrosive nature of nitric acid, the experiment should be performed in an all-glass retort as in Fig. 32–1. The receiver should be cooled in a water bath in order to condense the nitric acid vapors. Sulfuric acid is used for this purpose because it has a higher boiling point than nitric acid.

Commercial manufacture of nitric acid

The oldest commercial method for the manufacture of nitric acid is similar to the laboratory preparation given in the preceding section. Concentrated sulfuric acid is heated with sodium nitrate, obtained from natural deposits in Chile. A stainless steel retort is commonly used, since this is resistant to hot nitric acid and its fumes. The first reaction is the same as shown in the equation in the preceding paragraph. However, one of the products, sodium hydrogen sulfate ($NaHSO_4$), still has one replaceable hydrogen. By using a higher temperature, another molecule of nitric acid is obtained.

$$NaHSO_4 + NaNO_3 \xrightarrow{heat} HNO_3 \uparrow + Na_2SO_4$$

The second reaction is not normally obtained in the laboratory because at the temperature necessary the glass retort is apt to crack.

In the United States at present, most of the nitric acid is manufactured from ammonia by catalytic oxidation. This method is known as the **Ostwald process** after the German physical chemist who developed it. As you have seen in Chap. 31, page 350, when ammonia is burned it produces nitrogen and water vapor. However, if the oxidation takes place in the presence of a platinum (Pt) catalyst, the end product is nitric acid.

$$NH_3 + 2O_2 \xrightarrow{Pt\ catalyst} HNO_3 + H_2O$$

Fig. 32-2. The Ostwald process. A heated platinum wire continues to glow in a mixture of ammonia and air because it catalyzes the oxidation of ammonia to nitric acid.

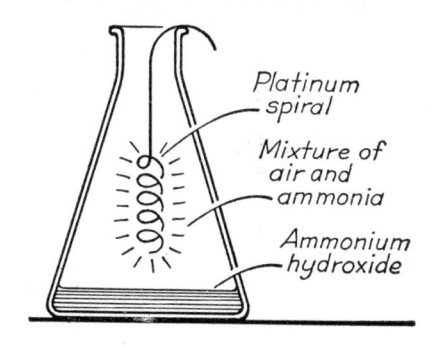

The ability of platinum to catalyze this reaction is easily demonstrated in the laboratory. Fill an Erlenmeyer flask partly full of concentrated ammonium hydroxide. Heat a piece of platinum wire coiled into a spiral, or a piece of foil, to red heat and quickly place it in the vapors above the liquid in the flask. The wire will continue to glow as a result of the heat liberated by the oxidation reaction. You will also observe the formation of a fog of nitric acid droplets.

In commercial practice a mixture of air and ammonia is passed over a screen-wire gauze of platinum metal maintained at about 800°C. The ammonia is almost completely converted to nitric acid. Because of the cheapness of this process and the low cost of ammonia produced by the Haber synthesis, this source of nitric acid is gradually replacing the older sulfuric acid-nitrate of soda process.

The economics of this source of nitric acid is interesting. Ammonia is produced from nitrogen of the atmosphere and hydrogen from water. This ammonia is converted into nitric acid by the use of air. (The catalyst, like the rest of the apparatus, is not used up in the process.) Hence over all we have

$$\text{Air} + \text{water} + \text{chemical know-how} \rightarrow \text{nitric acid}$$

Physical properties of nitric acid

Pure nitric acid is a colorless liquid. It boils at 86°C and freezes at −42°C. It is unstable and breaks down as shown in the following equation:

$$4HNO_3 \rightarrow \underset{\text{(yellow-red)}}{4NO_2} + 2H_2O + O_2 \uparrow$$

The nitrogen dioxide (NO_2) formed dissolves in the acid, coloring it yellow to red. Nitric acid which contains excess dissolved nitrogen dioxide is known as **fuming nitric acid.** It is used as the oxidizing agent in certain of the propellants used to launch satellites.

Commercial concentrated nitric acid contains 68 percent acid and 32 percent water. It is much more stable toward decomposition than the pure nitric acid. Strangely, its boiling point is 120.5°C. This acid is about $16M$ in concentration.

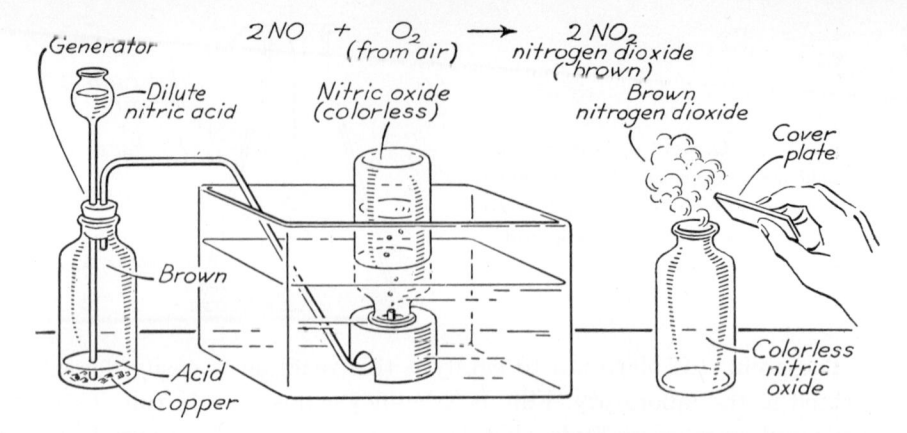

Fig. 32-3. Nitric oxide is formed by the action of dilute nitric acid on copper. On mixture with air, colorless nitric oxide is oxidized to brown nitrogen dioxide.

Chemical properties of nitric acid

Nitric acid is a powerful oxidizing agent. It attacks many of the nonmetals and all the metals except platinum, rhodium, iridium, and gold. The exact reaction depends on the metal, the concentration of the acid, and the temperature. In general, you should remember the following:

1. Concentrated nitric acid on a metal below hydrogen in the activity series gives a metal nitrate, nitrogen dioxide (NO_2), and water.

$$Cu + 4HNO_3 \text{ (concentrated)} \rightarrow Cu(NO_3)_2 + 2NO_2 \uparrow + 2H_2O$$

2. Dilute nitric acid on a metal below hydrogen yields a metal nitrate, nitric oxide (NO), and water.

$$3Cu + 8HNO_3 \text{ (dilute)} \rightarrow 3Cu(NO_3)_2 + 2NO \uparrow + 4H_2O$$

3. Nitric acid on a metal high in the activity series generally gives a mixture of reduction products ranging all the way from nitrogen dioxide to ammonium ion.

Reaction of nitric acid with organic compounds

Nitric acid reacts with certain classes of organic compounds to form nitrate derivatives. Thus with glycerin

$$\underset{\text{glycerin}}{C_3H_5(OH)_3} + 3HNO_3 \rightarrow \underset{\text{nitroglycerin}}{C_3H_5(NO_3)_3} + 3H_2O$$

(This is *not* an acid-base reaction, since glycerin is a non-electrolyte.)

In a similar way nitric acid acts upon cellulose (cotton or wood pulp) to form nitrocellulose, which is widely used as guncotton and in pyroxylin and some rayons (see Chap. 38, page 465).

With proteins, concentrated nitric acid reacts to produce a bright-yellow-colored substance called **xanthoproteic acid**. Hence skin, fingernails, wool, or silk turn yellow on contact with this acid. This reaction is used as a test for a protein. It can, for example, be used to determine whether a given textile contains wool or silk.

Many organic compounds can be ignited by the powerful oxidizing action of concentrated nitric acid. Thus if sawdust is heated in an evaporating dish and then moistened with concentrated nitric acid, it will catch fire.

$$\underset{\text{cellulose}}{C_6H_{10}O_5{}^*} + 6O_2 \rightarrow 6CO_2 + 5H_2O$$

* $C_6H_{10}O_5$ is the empirical, not the molecular, formula for cellulose.

The oxidation is started by the oxygen from the nitric acid.

Reaction of nitric acid with nonmetals

Sulfur is oxidized to sulfuric acid by boiling nitric acid. The reduction product may be nitric oxide or nitrogen dioxide depending on the concentration of the acid.

$$S + \underset{\text{(dilute)}}{2HNO_3} \xrightarrow{\text{heat}} 2NO \uparrow + H_2SO_4$$

Carbon yields carbon dioxide.

$$C + \underset{\text{(concentrated)}}{4HNO_3} \xrightarrow{\text{heat}} CO_2 \uparrow + 4NO_2 \uparrow + 2H_2O$$

Aqua regia

A mixture of concentrated nitric and hydrochloric acids is known as aqua regia (Latin: *royal water*). This name comes from the fact that the mixture will attack gold and platinum, metals which are not attacked by nitric acid alone. This is because the aqua regia contains chloride ions, the presence of which makes these metals more easily oxidized.

Nitrogen dioxide and nitrogen tetroxide

The brown gas formed by the action of copper on concentrated nitric acid is actually an equilibrium mixture of nitrogen dioxide (NO_2) and nitrogen tetroxide (N_2O_4).

$$\underset{\text{(pale yellow)}}{N_2O_4} \rightleftarrows \underset{\text{(dark brown)}}{2NO_2}$$

At room temperature it is impossible to have one without some of the other. Nitrogen dioxide is actually a dark brown gas, nitrogen tetroxide a light yellow gas. Increased temperature displaces the equilibrium to the right, indicating that the reaction from left to right is endothermic. The effect is easily demonstrated by collecting some of the gas in a closed test tube and cooling it with dry ice. As the gas is cooled, it becomes lighter in color; on rewarming, the intensity of the color increases again.

Either gas reacts with water to form nitric acid.

$$3NO_2 + H_2O \rightarrow 2HNO_3 + NO \uparrow$$

Nitric oxide

Nitric oxide (NO) is formed by the action of dilute nitric acid on a mild reducing agent such as copper (see Fig. 32–3, page 360).

$$3Cu + 8HNO_3 \rightarrow 3Cu(NO_3)_2 + 2NO \uparrow + 4H_2O$$

It is colorless and, unlike nitrogen dioxide, insoluble in (and does not react with) water. Consequently nitric oxide may be separated from nitrogen dioxide by bubbling through water.

With ferrous ion (Fe^{++}) nitric oxide produces ferrous nitroso ion [$Fe(NO)^{++}$] which is deep brown in color. The reaction can be used to identify nitric oxide. Generally, however, there is an easier method of recognizing it. At room temperature in contact with air nitric oxide is converted to nitrogen dioxide.

$$\underset{\text{(colorless)}}{2NO} + O_2 \rightarrow \underset{\text{(brown to red)}}{2NO_2}$$

The brown gaseous product is easily recognized.

The arc process for nitric acid manufacture

From the reaction between nitric oxide and air it is apparent that nitric acid is easily formed from nitric oxide by contact with air and water. If you had a simple method of making nitric oxide from air, this method could then be used for the manufacture of nitric acid.

The production of nitric acid from air is a chemical process found in nature. Lightning causes the formation of nitric oxide by direct combination of nitrogen and oxygen.

$$N_2 + O_2 \xrightarrow{\text{lightning}} 2NO$$

The nitric oxide is then changed into nitric acid according to the equation describing the oxidation of nitric oxide to nitrogen dioxide and the one for the reaction of nitrogen dioxide and water. The resulting nitric acid is eventually washed to earth by rain. This reaction may be the explanation for the peculiar acrid odor sometimes observed in the atmosphere following a flash of lightning which is generally at-

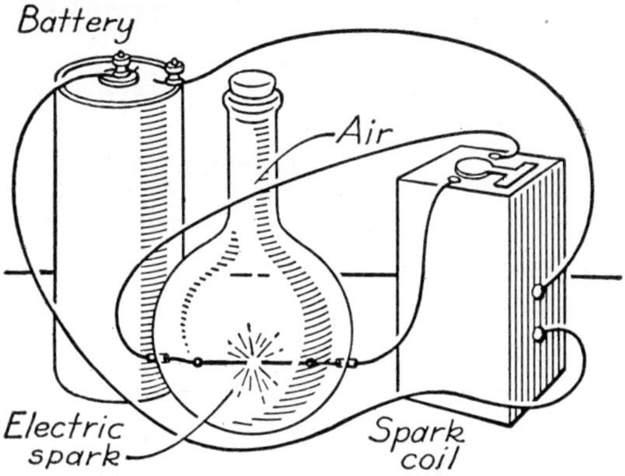

Fig. 32-4. A convenient laboratory apparatus for observing the formation of nitric oxide from air by an electric discharge.

tributed to ozone. It is estimated that 250,000 tons of nitric acid are produced in this way every 24 hr (see the nitrogen cycle, Chap. 31, pages 353 and 354). Unfortunately only a small part of this nitric acid falls on fertile soil and is utilized by plants.

The formation of nitric oxide and then nitric acid by the action of an electric discharge was first observed in 1779 by Joseph Priestley, who discovered oxygen. The formation of nitric acid by an electric discharge can be observed in the laboratory using an apparatus as shown in Fig. 32-4. The same method has been adopted for the manufacture of nitric acid. It is known as the **arc process.**

Industrially air is blown through an electric arc formed between copper or iron electrodes. At the temperature of the arc some of the air is converted into nitric oxide, which on cooling in contact with air and water produces nitric acid. The nitric acid is generally absorbed in limestone to form calcium nitrate, which is used as fertilizer.

$$CaCO_3 + 2HNO_3 \rightarrow Ca(NO_3)_2 + CO_2 \uparrow + H_2O$$

Although not as important in the United States as the Ostwald process, the arc process, which represents another method of nitrogen fixation, may eventually become very important here as electric energy becomes more plentiful. In the Scandinavian countries where electric energy is plentiful the process has been widely used for many years.

Nitrous oxide: laughing gas

Nitrous oxide is the gas used by the dentist as an anesthetic. It was first prepared by Joseph Priestley in 1772. Its physiological properties were first observed by Sir Humphry Davy (1799). When breathed, nitrous oxide produces various behaviors in different people. Some become violently excited and fight, whereas others cry or laugh. On account of the hysterical effect of nitrous oxide, it is known as **laughing gas.** It was first used as a dental anesthetic by the American dentist **Dr. Horace Wells** (1815-1848) in 1844. He had previously tried it on himself.

Nitrous oxide is prepared by gently heating ammonium nitrate.

$$NH_4NO_3 \xrightarrow{\text{heat}} N_2O \uparrow + 2H_2O$$

This reaction is highly exothermic. Furthermore, if the nitrous oxide becomes too hot, it decomposes exothermically. Consequently if ammonium nitrate is heated too hot, a violent explosion can result (see Chap. 31, pages 351 and 352). In actual laboratory practice you should heat pure ammonium nitrate just enough to cause evolution of the gas. Stop heating before the last of the ammonium nitrate has decomposed.

Nitrous oxide is collected by the displacement of warm water, since it is fairly soluble in cold water (60 volumes of gas in 100 volumes of water at 20°C).

Since nitrous oxide decomposes on heating (to yield oxygen and nitrogen), it is not surprising that it supports combustion. A burning splinter on introduction into a cylinder of the gas continues to burn. To distinguish between oxygen and nitrous oxide, mix the unknown gas with nitric oxide.

$$N_2O + NO \rightarrow \text{no reaction}$$
$$O_2 + 2NO \rightarrow 2NO_2$$
$$\text{(brown)}$$

Nitrous acid

To make salts of nitrous acid heat sodium or potassium nitrate.

$$2NaNO_3 \xrightarrow{\text{heat}} \underset{\substack{\text{sodium} \\ \text{nitrite}}}{2NaNO_2} + O_2 \uparrow$$

The acid is obtained in solution by adding dilute sulfuric acid to sodium nitrite solution. Pure nitrous acid is unstable, and attempts to obtain it from solution lead only to its decomposition products.

$$\underset{\text{(solution)}}{2HNO_2} \rightarrow NO_2 \uparrow + NO \uparrow + H_2O$$

The test for a nitrate

As you have seen, all nitrates are soluble; hence there is no precipitation test for this ion. The standard test for the nitrate ion (NO_3^-) is the **brown ring test.** The solution to be tested is mixed with ferrous sulfate ($FeSO_4$) solution. Holding the test tube containing these solutions at an angle of about 45 deg to the horizontal, concentrated sulfuric acid is poured into it. The more dense sulfuric acid will tend to form a layer on the bottom of the tube. If the unknown contains nitrate, a brown ring forms at the junction between the sulfuric acid and the solution under test.

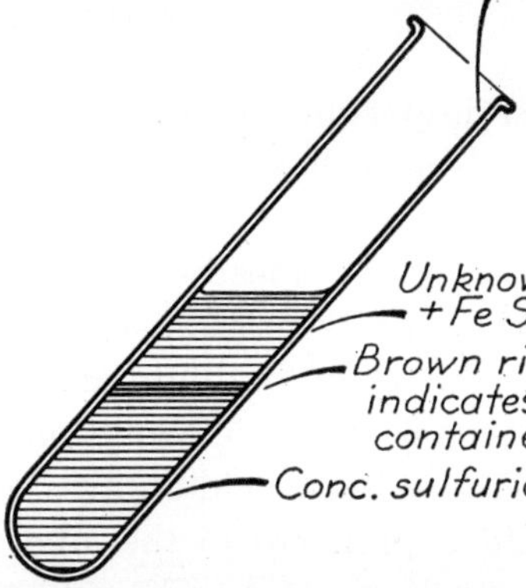

Fig. 32–5. The brown ring test for nitrates. If nitrate is present, a brown ring will form where the concentrated sulfuric acid contacts the test solution.

Pour conc. sulfuric acid down side of tube

Unknown solution + Fe SO₄
Brown ring indicates unknown contained NO_3^-
Conc. sulfuric acid

The explanation of the brown ring test depends on the fact that, where the sulfuric acid mixes with the test solution containing the nitrate ion, nitric acid is formed. The nitric acid reacts with the ferrous ion (Fe^{++}) forming nitric oxide.

$$3Fe^{++} + 4H^+ + NO_3^- \rightarrow 3Fe^{+++} + NO + 2H_2O$$

The nitric oxide reacts with the unchanged ferrous ion to form brown ferrous nitroso ion, $Fe(NO)^{++}$.

$$Fe^{++} + NO \rightarrow \underset{\text{(brown ring)}}{Fe(NO)^{++}}$$

Halogen compounds of nitrogen

The halogen compounds of nitrogen are all highly unstable, explosive compounds.

By adding a solution of iodine in aqueous potassium iodide to ammonium hydroxide, a precipitate of nitrogen tri-iodide (NI_3) is obtained. The resulting compound may be washed with alcohol, then dried. When dry, touching it with a feather causes it to explode.

Nitrogen trichloride (NCl_3), also known as **agene,** is formed in an analogous manner. It is an oily, unstable liquid. For 25 years it was used to bleach white flour in the United States. Recently it was found that dogs fed on flour so bleached developed running fits. Accordingly, in 1948, the Federal Food and Drug Administration outlawed its use for bleaching flour. Chlorine dioxide (ClO_2) is now being used in its place.

KEY WORDS

agene	brown ring test	Ostwald process
aqua fortis	fuming nitric acid	Wells
arc process	laughing gas	xanthoproteic acid

HIGHLIGHTS

The most important oxides of nitrogen are nitrous oxide, nitric oxide, and nitrogen dioxide. There are two important nitrogen acids: nitrous acid and nitric acid.

Nitrous oxide, the anesthetic, is a colorless gas, soluble in water.

Nitric oxide is a colorless gas only slightly soluble in water. It is prepared by the action of dilute nitric acid on copper.

Nitrous acid is unstable. Solutions of it can be prepared by the action of dilute sulfuric acid on nitrites.

Nitric acid is prepared in the laboratory by heating a mixture of concentrated sulfuric acid and a nitrate such as sodium nitrate. Commercially it is made by the **Ostwald process** in which ammonia is oxidized in the presence of a catalyst. Nitric acid is also made by the **arc process** in countries where electricity is available at low rates. Nitric acid is a strong oxidizing agent. Depending upon its concentration and other conditions, nitric acid reacts with most metals forming nitrates and various oxides, or ammonia. It is used in the manufacture of dyes, nitrates, nitrocellulose plastics, and various other organic compounds such as nitroglycerin, an explosive.

QUESTIONS

1. Give the names and formulas of four oxides and two acids of nitrogen.
2. Why is nitric acid of great economic importance?
3. Describe a laboratory method for making nitric acid. What type of vessel is used?
4. Describe a process occurring in nature by means of which nitrogen in the air is converted into nitric acid.
5. What three industrial methods are used to manufacture nitric acid?
6. What is fuming nitric acid?
7. What is aqua regia?
8. Write the reaction of concentrated nitric acid on copper.
9. Write the reaction of dilute nitric acid on copper.
10. Explain the relationship between nitrogen tetroxide and nitrogen dioxide.
11. What is laughing gas? Write the equation showing how it is prepared.
12. How is sodium nitrate converted into sodium nitrite?
13. Describe the test for a nitrate (NO_3^-).
14. What is agene? For what purpose was it formerly used? Why was its use discontinued?

CHAPTER 33

phosphorus

Phosphorus resembles nitrogen more closely than any other element. Both have principal valences of 5 and 3. Both form hydrogen compounds and oxygen acids. However, the resemblance between these two elements is not as close as between the various halogens. As with nitrogen, phosphorus is of great economic and biological importance because of its role in the metabolism of all living things.

History of phosphorus

In 1674 **Brand,** an alchemist of Hamburg, Germany, was searching for the "philosopher's stone." In one experiment he distilled a mixture of evaporated urine and sand (SiO_2). Collecting on a plate some of the vapor formed, he noted that it glowed in the dark. This substance was accordingly named *phosphorus* (from the Greek word meaning *I bear light*). Brand sold his secret to Krafft, who exhibited it at the court of Charles II in 1677, where it excited much interest and entertainment. About one hundred years later Brand's phosphorus was shown by Lavoisier to be one of the elements.

Occurrence of phosphorus

Phosphorus is found in nature only in the form of phosphates. The mineral apatite is $CaF_2 \cdot 3Ca_3(PO_4)_2$. Apatite occurs in small amounts in many rocks. There are large deposits of it in Canada. At the present time the chief source of phosphorus is phosphate rock, an impure tricalcium phosphate, $Ca_3(PO_4)_2$, believed to be of fossil origin. Deposits of this rock are found in Florida, Georgia, the Carolinas, Tennessee, Montana, Tunis, Algeria, and certain of the smaller Pacific islands.

Among living things, phosphorus occurs especially in milk, egg yolk, seeds, bones and teeth, nerves and brain, and muscle. The aver-

Crystals of apatite. (American Museum of Natural History)

age man's skeleton contains about 650 g of phosphorus, his muscles 72 g, his nerves and brain 6 g: a total of nearly 1.6 lb. In the process of tissue metabolism, the organic phosphorus compounds are broken up and the salts of phosphoric acid are excreted. To replace this tissue loss, as well as to provide for the building of bones and teeth, a steady and adequate supply of phosphorus is needed. This need continues even after the individual attains full growth and stature. Plants assimilate phosphorus from the soil in the form of phosphate ion ($PO_4^=$). For this reason phosphates are necessary fertilizers to maintain soil fertility. The best sources of phosphorus in human nutrition are milk and cheese, egg yolks, lean meats, and seeds (including nuts and grains).

Manufacture of phosphorus

The manufacture of the element phosphorus involves its reduction from calcium phosphate. The process used today is essentially the same as that used by Brand in his discovery of the element in 1674.[1] In the present process, phosphate rock is mixed with sand and coke and heated to a high temperature in an electric furnace.

$$Ca_3(PO_4)_2 + 3SiO_2 + 5C \xrightarrow{heat} 3CaSiO_3 + 5CO \uparrow + 2P \uparrow$$

In practice the charge, consisting of ground phosphate ore, coke, and sand, is fed continuously into the top of the furnace. Electric energy

[1] In Brand's experiment the evaporation of urine produced sodium phosphate and organic compounds. The latter on intensive heating produced carbon. Hence Brand probably carried out a reaction similar to the present-day process except that he used a sodium phosphate instead of calcium phosphate.

is passed through this charge. Because of the high electrical resistance of the charge, the necessary high temperature is obtained. Phosphorus vapor distills, leaving the furnace at the gas offtake (Fig. 33–1). When the phosphorus vapor is cooled, white phosphorus is formed. In phosphorus manufacture it is common practice to pass the vapor from the furnace directly into waiting railroad tank cars which are cooled by water. When a car is full of white phosphorus, it is sealed and the white phosphorus shipped directly to its consumer. There the white phosphorus is remelted and pumped out as a liquid. The calcium silicate ($CaSiO_3$) formed is known as slag. This material is withdrawn in a molten form from the bottom of the furnace through a tap hole provided for that purpose.

The role of sand: fluxes and slags

The process described in the preceding paragraph illustrates an important general principle frequently encountered in high temperature reductions—particularly in metallurgy. Since carbon is the actual reducing agent, why use the sand? Let us assume that calcium phosphate and carbon are heated without sand. Considering for a moment that tricalcium phosphate [$Ca_3(PO_4)_2$] is $3CaO \cdot P_2O_5$,

$$3CaO \cdot P_2O_5 + 5C \rightarrow 2P \uparrow + 5CO \uparrow + 3CaO$$

In this case the residue would be calcium oxide (CaO). Now calcium oxide in common with all metallic oxides has an exceedingly high melting point (mp 2707°C). Therefore, at the temperature of the furnace (1000 to 1200°C), it would not melt. This would result in coating the particles of ore on the outside with calcium oxide so that the carbon could not get to the tricalcium phosphate inside the particle (Fig.

Fig. 33–1. A cross section of the electric-arc furnace used in the manufacture of phosphorus. The process is essentially the same as that used by Brand, the discoverer of phosphorus.

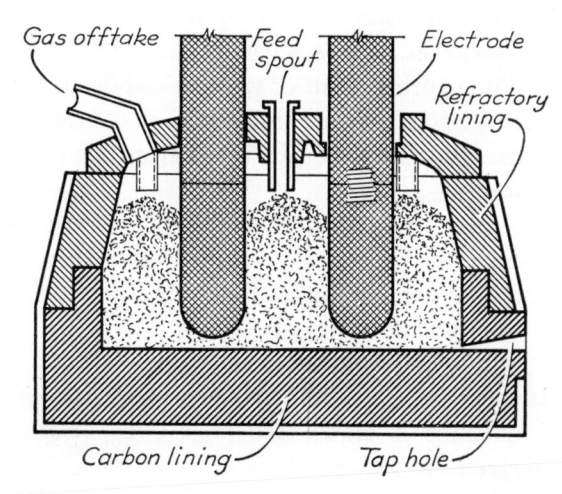

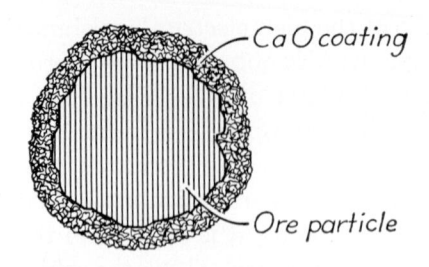

Fig. 33–2. If calcium phosphate and coke are heated without a flux, a surface layer of calcium oxide (CaO) is formed around the ore particles, which prevents the ore (calcium phosphate) from reacting further.

33–2). That is, the reaction would stop when only the phosphorus on the surface of the ore particles had been reduced. But if sand (SiO_2) is present, it reacts with the layer of calcium oxide to form calcium silicate.

$$CaO + SiO_2 \xrightarrow{heat} CaSiO_3$$
$$\text{(flux)} \qquad \text{(slag)}$$

The melting point of calcium silicate is much lower than that of calcium oxide. At the temperature of the furnace calcium silicate liquefies, drains off, and thereby exposes the unreduced ore until the entire particle is consumed.

In general, sand (and other acidic oxides) will combine with metallic oxides when heated. The result is a salt which, usually, has a lower melting point than either the sand or the metallic oxide. This salt is known to the metallurgist as a **slag**. In the case above, the sand is known as a **flux**. A flux is an agent used to convert an infusible oxide into a fusible slag. If sand were the material to be removed, then the flux would be a metallic oxide, commonly calcium oxide derived from limestone.

White phosphorus

Condensation of the vapor from the electric furnace yields white phosphorus. This is a waxlike white solid.

The melting point of white phosphorus is low (44°C), and it catches fire by spontaneous combustion on contact with air. White phosphorus must, therefore, be protected from air and is generally stored under water.

White phosphorous is highly poisonous, less than 0.15 g being a fatal dose. Even on contact with the skin white phosphorus produces painful, slow-healing burns. It should, therefore, never be handled with the fingers but only with tweezers.

White phosphorus is insoluble in water but dissolves in benzene, turpentine, olive oil, and especially carbon disulfide. Under proper conditions it glows (see page 372), from which fact its name was derived.

TABLE 33-1. Properties of red and white phosphorus

Property	Red P	White P
Odor	None	Garliclike
Toxicity	None	Very toxic
Behavior on contact with air	Ignites at 240°C	Glows, ignites at 30°C
Specific gravity	2.10 (variable)	1.84
Melting point	500–600°C (variable)	44°C
Solubility in CS_2	Insoluble	Soluble

Red phosphorus

This variety of phosphorus is a chocolate-brown powder which is not poisonous. It does not ignite on contact with air unless heated to 240°C. No special precautions are necessary in storing it. It is insoluble in water and carbon disulfide. Red phosphorus is made by heating white phosphorus in the absence of air to about 250°C.

The relationship between white and red phosphorus is similar to, but not exactly the same as, the allotropic modifications of sulfur. Red phosphorus is not a pure substance, since its properties are variable. It may possibly be a mixture (solid solution) of white phosphorus and another variety, **violet phosphorus.** Violet phosphorus is known to exist at exceedingly high pressures.

Chemical properties of phosphorus

Both red and white phosphorus show the same chemical properties, except that in general the reactions with the white variety are more rapid and more vigorous. In an excess supply of oxygen, either type of phosphorus burns to form a white solid, phosphorus pentoxide.

$$4P + 5O_2 \rightarrow 2P_2O_5$$
$$\text{phosphorus pentoxide}$$

If moisture is present, a fog (instead of a white solid) is obtained, consisting of minute droplets of liquid phosphoric acid.

$$P_2O_5 + 3H_2O \rightarrow 2H_3PO_4$$
$$\text{phosphoric acid}$$

For this reason white phosphorus is used in making smoke screens. In a limited supply of air phosphorus burns to phosphorus trioxide.

$$4P + 3O_2 \rightarrow 2P_2O_3$$
$$\text{phosphorus trioxide}$$

In a similar way, phosphorus unites with the halogens to form both pentahalide (for example, PCl_5) and trihalide (for example PCl_3).

With many metals phosphorus reacts to form phosphides (compare with nitrogen, Chap. 31, page 345). Thus with zinc:

$$3Zn + 2P \xrightarrow{\text{heat}} \underset{\substack{\text{zinc}\\\text{phosphide}}}{Zn_3P_2}$$

These phosphides are exceedingly poisonous. Zinc phosphide is widely used as a rodent poison—particularly to control mice in apple orchards.

The affinity of phosphorus for oxygen is very great. Hence with oxidizing agents such as potassium nitrate (KNO_3) and potassium chlorate ($KClO_3$) it gives violent explosions. Even red phosphorus has been known to explode while being mixed with potassium chlorate. *Such mixtures are exceedingly dangerous and should never be attempted.*

The glow of phosphorus

Robert Boyle (who discovered Boyle's law of gases) was the first to investigate scientifically the glow of phosphorus. He found that:
1. Phosphorus glows only in the presence of air.
2. The glow is exhibited by solutions of phosphorus in olive and certain other oils.
3. A very small quantity of phosphorus (1 part in 500,000) can be detected by the glow.

Other investigators later found that in pure oxygen at 1 atmosphere the glow does not occur below 27°C. At room temperature the glow can be produced by reducing the pressure of the oxygen to about 200 mm either by partial evacuation or by diluting the oxygen with an inert gas such as nitrogen.

Even today the complete explanation for the glow is not known. However, it is known that the glow represents the energy released by the slow oxidation of the phosphorus. Under these conditions this energy is liberated as cold, visible light instead of being liberated as heat energy, as is more common in chemical reactions.

The glow of phosphorus is shown in the following **"cold flame"** experiment. Place a few pieces of white phosphorus in a dry flask (Fig. 33-3). Then fill the flask with glass wool. Heat the flask on a water bath and pass a stream of dry carbon dioxide through the flask. The phosphorus vapor carried along with the gas is oxidized on contact with the air and produces a green "flame" at the top of the exit tube. The "flame" is so cold that one may hold a finger in it. This experiment should be carried out under a well-ventilated fume hood.

The word **phosphorescent** is now generally used to refer to a variety of cold light emission phenomenon. It does not necessarily mean that phosphorus is involved.

Fig. 33-3. The "cold flame" of phosphorus. This is a convenient laboratory setup for a demonstration of the glow emitted by phosphorus. The complete explanation of what causes phosphorus to glow is not known. However, it is known that the glow is caused in part, by the slow oxidation of the phosphorus. Under the conditions of the experiment, the energy produced by this oxidation is liberated as cold, visible light rather than heat. That this is so may be proved by holding a finger in the greenish flame at the top of the tube. Be sure to use a well-ventilated fume hood when conducting this experiment.

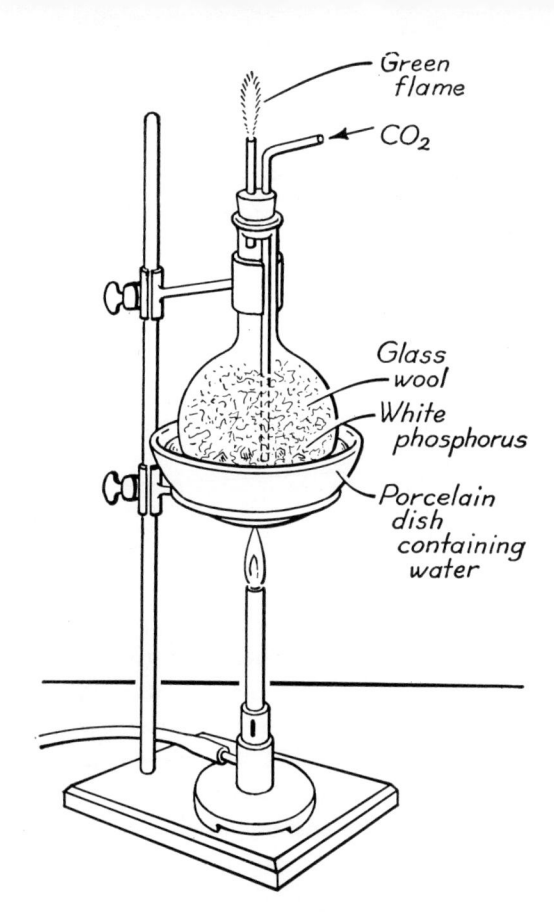

Uses of phosphorus

In war, white phosphorus is used to make smoke screens and as an incendiary. It is also used in high-explosive shells for firing against enemy troops. Such shells are said to be particularly demoralizing, since white phosphorus burns are both painful and slow-healing.

Much of the phosphorus now produced is converted into phosphates, which have many important uses. Most of the remaining production of phosphorus goes into the manufacture of matches.

Matches

It is said that the first matches invented (1812) consisted of a mixture of potassium chlorate, sugar, and sulfur molded onto the end of a stick. These matches were ignited by dipping them into a bottle of concentrated sulfuric acid. Matches containing white phosphorus, which can be struck by friction, came into use about 1830. Match-factory employees, however, who were exposed to white phosphorus, acquired a terrible, incurable phosphorus poisoning. The vapor enters the body through the teeth and eventually destroys the entire jawbone. As a result, all nations of the world have now either directly outlawed

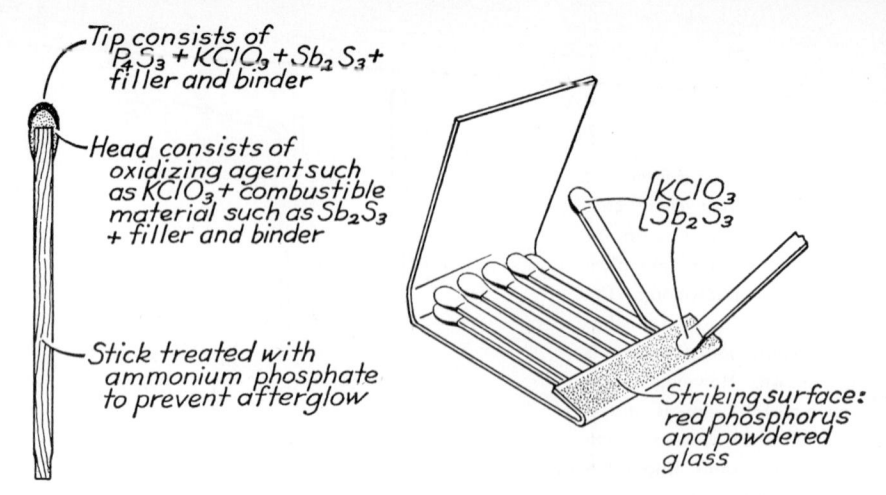

Fig. 33-4. The "strike-anywhere" match.

Fig. 33-5. The safety match.

the manufacture of white phosphorus matches or placed such a high tax upon them that their manufacture is unprofitable.

Modern matches are of two types: (1) the "strike-anywhere" variety, and (2) the safety match.

Figure 33-4 shows a diagram of the former. The matchstick is treated to prevent afterglow by soaking it in a solution of ammonium phosphate. The end on which the head is to be placed is treated with paraffin. The head is made up of a combustible material, such as antimony trisulfide (Sb_2S_3), together with an oxidizing agent, such as potassium chlorate, mixed with a filler (clay), and a binder (glue). The tip consists of a mixture of phosphorus sesquisulfide (P_4S_3) together with the mixture just described. Heat of friction causes the oxidizing agent in the tip to oxidize the phosphorus sesquisulfide, thus setting fire to the head of the match.

Safety matches are essentially the same except that the tip is omitted. Instead the surface for striking consists of a mixture of red phosphorus and powdered glass. The exact explanation for the kindling process is subject to question. It may be that the friction ignites a small bit of red phosphorus which ignites the head of the match.

Phosphorus-hydrogen compounds

The phosphorus compound analogous to ammonia is **phosphene** (PH_3). This gas is easily prepared by adding a phosphide (such as calcium phosphide, Ca_3P_2) to water.

$$Ca_3P_2 + 6H_2O \rightarrow 3Ca(OH)_2 + 2PH_3 \uparrow$$

Phosphene is a poisonous gas that burns on contact with air, producing a white smoke (water and phosphoric acid). Unlike ammonia, it has no basic properties. It is of no practical importance at present.

The acids of phosphorus

Unlike nitrogen, phosphorus forms several different acids in which it has a valence of 5.[1]

HPO_3 or $P_2O_5 \cdot H_2O$ metaphosphoric acid
$H_4P_2O_7$ or $P_2O_5 \cdot 2H_2O$ pyrophosphoric acid
H_3PO_4 or $P_2O_5 \cdot 3H_2O$ orthophosphoric acid

The differences between these acids are made clearer by structural formulas.

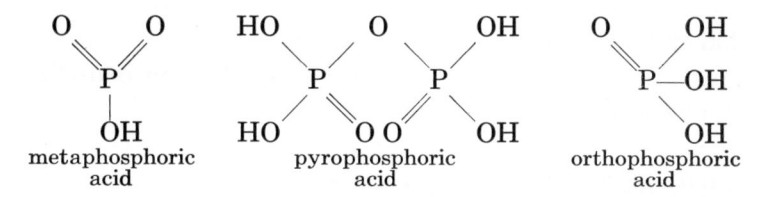

```
   O   O         HO   O   OH         O    OH
    \ //           \  ‖  /            \\  /
     P              P    P             P—OH
     |             /  ‖  \             /
     OH          HO   O O   OH        OH
 metaphosphoric      pyrophosphoric    orthophosphoric
     acid                acid               acid
```

The ability of pentavalent phosphorus to form several acids, while nitrogen forms only one (HNO_3, analogous to HPO_3), is due to the larger size of the phosphorus atom. Thus the phosphorus atom, which is a larger sphere than the nitrogen atom, has a larger surface, and there is room on it for the attachment of up to four groups (oxygen atoms or hydroxyl groups). The nitrogen, however, has room to attach only three. Since the atomic size increases as you progress downward in a group in the periodic table, the behavior of arsenic and antimony in this connection is even more involved than that of phosphorus.

The phosphoric acids and their salts are all important commercially. The most important is orthophosphoric acid.

Orthophosphoric acid

This acid is made by the addition of sulfuric acid to phosphate rock.

$$Ca_3(PO_4)_2 + 3H_2SO_4 \rightarrow 2H_3PO_4 + 3CaSO_4 \downarrow$$

The precipitated calcium sulfate is removed by filtration and the resulting solution is evaporated to remove the water. The commercial product is a sirupy liquid containing about 85 percent orthophosphoric acid and 15 percent water. It is such a weak acid that you can wash your hands in it without serious harm. Orthophosphoric acid ionizes in three steps:

$$H_3PO_4 + H_2O \rightleftarrows OH_3^+ + H_2PO_4^-$$
$$H_2PO_4^- + H_2O \rightleftarrows OH_3^+ + HPO_4^=$$
$$HPO_4^= + H_2O \rightleftarrows OH_3^+ + PO_4^\equiv$$

---

[1] It also forms acids in which the phosphorus shows a valence of 3. These *phosphorous acids* are analogous to nitrous acid.

Orthophosphoric acid is used in considerable quantities in making cola beverages and in making various phosphate salts.

Orthophosphoric acid is also obtained by burning phosphorus vapor from the electric furnace and the reaction of the resulting oxide with water.

$$4P + 5O_2 \rightarrow 2P_2O_5$$
$$P_2O_5 + 3H_2O \rightarrow 2H_3PO_4$$

Trisodium phosphate is made by neutralization of the acid. Solutions of this salt are rather alkaline as the result of hydrolysis (see Chap. 27, pages 306 and 307). For this reason and also because trisodium phosphate corrects water hardness, it is widely used as an ingredient of scouring powders and soap powders.

The acid salt, calcium dihydrogen phosphate [$Ca(H_2PO_4)_2$], is used in phosphate-type baking powders and self-rising flours (see Chap. 35, pages 404 to 406).

Pyrophosphates and metaphosphates

Salts of **pyrophosphoric acid** and **metaphosphoric acid** are becoming widely used as water softeners (see Chap. 45, page 583). (Calgon, a commercial water-softening product, is a sodium metaphosphate.)

Their preparation from orthophosphate is given by the following equations:

$$NaH_2PO_4 \xrightarrow{heat} \underset{\substack{\text{sodium} \\ \text{metaphosphate}}}{NaPO_3} + H_2O$$

$$2Na_2HPO_4 \xrightarrow{heat} \underset{\substack{\text{tetrasodium} \\ \text{pyrophosphate}}}{Na_4P_2O_7} + H_2O$$

$$Na_3PO_4 \xrightarrow{heat} \text{no reaction}$$

Phosphate fertilizers

You have already read about the importance of phosphates as fertilizers. The exact chemical form of the fertilizer is unimportant so long as it is a form which can dissolve and thereby enter the plant through its root hairs. Sometimes phosphate rock is ground up and used as such for fertilizer. This has the advantage of being low in cost but the disadvantage of being highly insoluble and hence only slowly available as plant food.

The standard phosphate fertilizer today is **superphosphate.** It is made by mixing phosphate rock with a calculated quantity of sulfuric acid. The mixture of the two resulting solids is sold as superphosphate. The reaction is

$$Ca_3(PO_4)_2 + 2H_2SO_4 \rightarrow \underbrace{Ca(H_2PO_4)_2 + 2CaSO_4}_{\text{superphosphate}}$$

The object of the sulfuric acid treatment is to convert the phosphate into calcium dihydrogen phosphate, which is soluble in water and hence available as plant food. This is the largest single use for sulfuric acid, about 25 percent of all produced being used in this way.

In commerce, superphosphate is generally sold as containing 20 percent available phosphorus calculated as phosphorus pentoxide (P_2O_5). It, therefore, has the disadvantage of containing a large percentage of inert material which adds considerably to the cost of transportation and handling. A more concentrated product is made by using phosphoric acid in place of sulfuric.

$$Ca_3(PO_4)_2 + 4H_3PO_4 \rightarrow 3Ca(H_2PO_4)_2$$

The product is sold as **triple superphosphate.**

Agricultural scientists still have much to learn about the most effective use of phosphate fertilizers. Although they are applied in soluble form, these phosphates react rapidly with materials in the soil. Thereby the soluble phosphates are converted into insoluble, unavailable forms. Hence much of the phosphorus applied to soils is never recovered in plant form. Since millions of dollars are spent annually for phosphorus fertilizers, the matter of how to apply them most efficiently is an unsolved problem of great importance.

Phosphorus and conservation

We are fortunate that the world's supply of phosphates is very large. Such supplies, however, are not inexhaustible. It is impossible to imagine our kind of civilization without adequate supplies of phosphorus for plant and animal growth. Man should, therefore, give thought to the **conservation** of phosphorus resources.

KEY WORDS

Brand	orthophosphoric acid	slag
"cold flame"	phosphene	superphosphate
conservation	phosphorescent	triple superphosphate
flux	pyrophosphoric acid	violet phosphorus
match	red phosphorus	white phosphorus
metaphosphoric acid		

HIGHLIGHTS

Phosphorus was discovered in 1674 by **Brand.** The source of the element is calcium phosphate. Phosphorus is an element essential for life; it is present in every cell of the body.

To obtain the element, a mixture of calcium phosphate, sand (the **flux**), and coke (the reducing agent) are heated in the electric furnace. Calcium silicate (the **slag**), carbon monoxide, and phosphorus are produced by the reaction in the furnace.

There are two common forms of phosphorus: white and red. **Red phosphorus** is the more dense and has a much higher melting point. **White phosphorus** is very poisonous and is soluble in carbon disulfide. White phosphorus has such a low kindling point that it takes fire when exposed to air at room temperature.

On burning, phosphorus becomes phosphorus pentoxide, which is soluble and combines with water to form phosphoric acid. There are three such acids: **metaphosphoric acid, pyrophosphoric acid,** and **orthophosphoric acid.** These acids are composed of one molecule of phosphorus pentoxide combined respectively with one, two, or three molecules of water.

Phosphorus is used in making smoke screens, matches, water-softening compounds, and fertilizers. The chief forms of phosphate fertilizers are **superphosphate** and **triple superphosphate.**

QUESTIONS

1. What element does phosphorus resemble most closely?
2. Why did Brand give the name phosphorus to the material he prepared in 1674?
3. In what minerals is phosphorus found in nature?
4. What biologic materials are rich in phosphorus?
5. Explain why man must have an adequate amount of phosphorus in his diet even after he has reached full stature.
6. How is phosphorus obtained from phosphate rock? Why is sand (SiO_2) employed in this process?
7. What precautions should be observed in handling and storing white phosphorus?
8. How do red and white phosphorus differ in their properties?
9. Which form of phosphorus is toxic?
10. Explain why phosphorus is useful for making smoke screens.
11. How is zinc phosphide made? For what is it used?
12. What kinds of chemicals should never be mixed with phosphorus?
13. Explain how a safety match differs from one of the "strike-anywhere" variety.

14. What is the name of the phosphorus compound analogous to ammonia?
15. Name and give the formula for three acids of phosphorus.
16. What is orthophosphoric acid used for?
17. What is superphosphate?
18. Why is there much research being carried on to learn more efficient methods of applying phosphates to the soil?

Suggested Projects for Unit Seven

1. Make a map of the world showing where pure sulfur and sulfur-containing minerals are found.
2. Find out how "pickling" is done. See whether you can locate an industry or factory where the process is used.
3. Farmers and gardeners are often advised not to apply complete fertilizers and hydrated lime to the same soil on the same day. (*Hint*: Most complete fertilizers contain an ammonium salt.) Why should these materials not be applied together?
4. Compute the weight of atmospheric nitrogen over your home property.
5. Find out why xanthoproteic acid is so named.
6. Make a list of materials that are phosphorescent.
7. Work out a test to distinguish between silver and platinum based upon information learned in this unit.
8. Learn the analysis or composition of some of the widely advertised all-soluble fertilizers.

UNIT EIGHT: King Carbon

CHAPTER 34

the forms of carbon

Carbon is the first member of Group IV*b*, which also includes silicon, germanium, tin, and lead. All these elements are characterized by four valence electrons. Although germanium, tin, and lead do form compounds in which they have a valence of 2, carbon, with the exception of carbon monoxide (CO), always forms compounds in which it shows a valence of 4.

In this chapter the properties and uses of elementary carbon will be considered. Later chapters will take up the study of the compounds of carbon.

Occurrence of carbon

Carbon compounds are found in all living things. Carbon is, therefore, as widely distributed on the earth as are living things or things that have been living. Vast quantities of carbon are found in coal and petroleum. In the mineral realm, metal carbonates, particularly limestone ($CaCO_3$) and dolomite [$CaMg(CO_3)_2$], are among our most common rocks. Carbon dioxide is found in the atmosphere surrounding the earth.

Pure and impure forms of carbon

Pure carbon in the uncombined form is found in nature as graphite and as diamond.

Such materials as charcoal, coke, coal, bone black, and carbon black are all impure varieties of carbon. Some of them are of great industrial importance.

In spite of its wide distribution, the percentage of the earth's crust (with its oceans and atmosphere) which is made up of carbon is only about 0.027 percent.

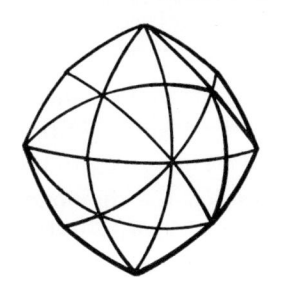

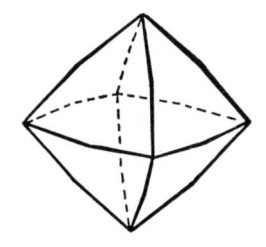

Fig. 34–1. Diamonds as found in nature.

Fig. 34–2. A cut diamond. The faces reflect light.

Diamond

The diamond is the hardest-known substance, either natural or man-made. Consequently, it cannot be scratched with any other material with the possible exception of boron carbide. That the diamond is pure carbon was proved by Davy in 1814 when he burned one. He found that only carbon dioxide and a trace of ash were formed.

Diamonds are formed from other varieties of carbon as a result of very high pressures and temperatures. They are formed deep within the earth, where the necessary pressures and temperatures exist, by crystallization of carbon from molten rock material. Hence diamonds are found either associated with the original **igneous rock**[1] from which they crystallized or sometimes in the sands of stream beds. In the latter case erosion has destroyed the original rock and the diamonds have been transported by water. Diamonds are found as rounded yellow "pebbles" in India, Brazil, Arkansas, and particularly South Africa. The principal commercial production is from the British Dominion of the Union of South Africa and the more recently discovered diamond fields of the Belgian Congo.

At the famous Kimberley mines of South Africa the diamond is found in the original rock (a weathered form of olivine) which runs in large columns (locally known as "pipes") downward through the earth. Masses of this rock are blasted out and allowed to weather, which causes it to crumble. The lighter material is washed away and the heavy residue is carried by water under pressure over a bed of grease. To this grease the diamonds adhere. The yield varies, but most of the rock yields less than 0.1 g of diamond per ton.

When found in nature, the diamond is not the brilliant, fiery stone with which the name is associated. The diamond crystals found in nature are commonly octahedral (Fig. 34–1) with worn and scratched faces. To make the gem stone, the crystal must be cut so that the maximum amount of the light entering the top of the stone is reflected from bottom faces back through the top (Fig. 34–2). The amount of

[1] Igneous rocks are the rocks formed by crystallization of molten rock material from deep within the earth.

this *reflected* light is greater for the diamond than, for example, a piece of glass the same shape because of the higher index of refraction of the diamond. The refractive index of diamond is 2.41. This gives it its characteristic brilliance. The fiery play of colors which the diamond shows is due to the relatively very large difference in its refractive index for red and blue light. The optical properties of the diamond, together with its chemical inertness, its hardness, and the rarity of large perfect stones, make it unique as a gem.

Diamonds vary in color all the way from white (colorless) to yellow, red, orange, green, blue, brown, and black. The dark-colored stones are of little or no value as gems but are useful industrially because of their hardness.

The diamond is sold by the **carat.** One international carat is equal to 0.200 g. The price varies widely according to the presence or absence of flaws, the size and color, and particularly the quality of the cut.

Although very hard, the diamond is brittle and can be cleft (split) along certain crystal planes with hammer and chisel. In converting a large raw stone into gem form, this cleaving is a matter of the greatest importance, since if the diamond is cleft along the wrong direction much of the value of the stone is destroyed. Experts carefully study the crystal faces of raw diamonds and from these locate the cleavage planes within the crystal. The desired cleavage plane is then marked on the diamond by a diamond saw. Diamond saws are high-speed metal disks impregnated with diamond dust. The diamond dust does the actual cutting. The diamond is then cleft by hammer and chisel.

One of the greatest operations of this kind was the cutting of the famous Vargas (named after the late President of Brazil) diamond in New York City. It is said that the cutter studied this stone for nearly two years, then, after marking it, came into his workshop one morning and with one blow of a mallet separated the stone into two pieces exactly as desired. Smaller stones may be cut with the diamond saw.

The specific gravity of diamond is about 3.5. Diamond is a nonconductor of electricity. Its heat conductivity is high and hence the diamond feels cold to the touch. This property is responsible for the slang term "ice" sometimes used by the underworld.

Some famous diamonds are shown in the photograph on page 383. The Kohinoor is now among the English crown jewels. Its history goes back to the fourteenth century when it was the property of the Rajah of Malwa. It originally weighed 186 carats but in 1852 was recut to increase its brilliance, the resulting stone being 106 carats. The Regent diamond was found in India in 1701. Originally it weighed 410 carats. At one time it belonged to Napoleon, who pledged it to secure a loan, and it is now in the Louvre in Paris. The Cullinan diamond, discovered

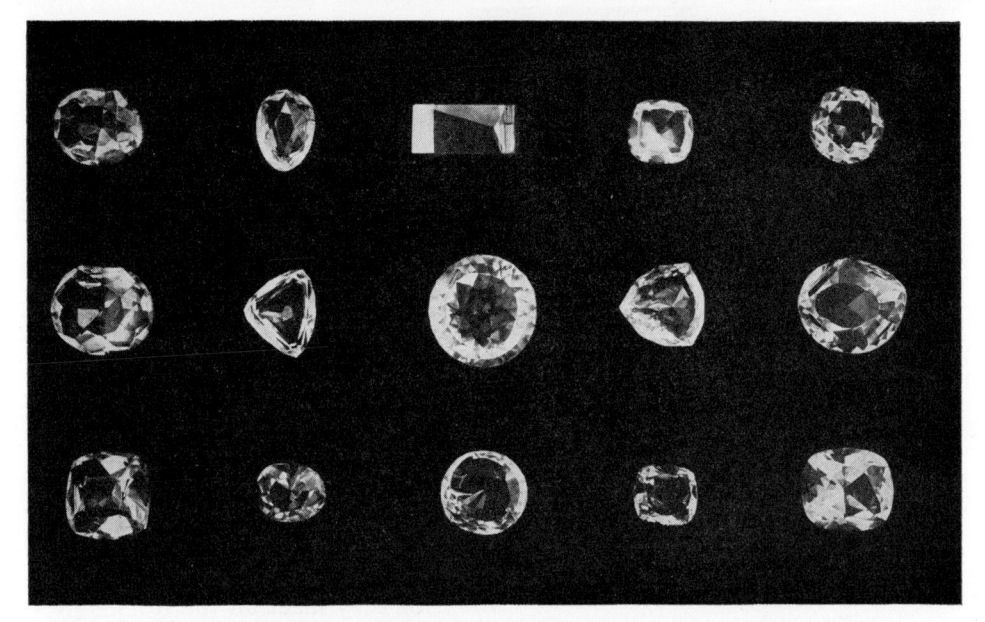

Models of famous diamonds. From left to right: top, Piggot, Sancy, Shah, Hope, Pasha of Egypt; middle, Kohinoor (second cut), Hassali, Great Mogul, Florentine, Kohinoor (first cut); bottom, Regent or Pitt, Eugenie, Orloff, Polar Star, Star of the South. (American Museum of Natural History)

in Kimberley in 1905, weighed 3032 carats (about $1\frac{1}{3}$ lb). The Hope diamond, 44.5 carats, is a fine blue stone and is famous for the superstition that it has brought misfortune to a long list of owners.

Industrial diamonds

Because of its hardness, the diamond is an important industrial tool. Black diamonds and diamond dust are used to coat grinding wheels for sharpening the very hard alloy cutting tools, such as those made of tungsten carbide. Certain metal wires, such as the tungsten wire for lamp filaments, are made by drawing through diamond dies. The hole in a diamond die retains its shape and size almost indefinitely. The cutting edge of bits used in drilling oil wells are diamond-tipped. A variety of diamond-tipped tools are used for cutting, drilling, and grinding operations. Because of uses of this type, diamonds are a strategic commodity and no nation can carry on its modern industrial operations without them.

Ever since the discovery that diamonds are composed of carbon, man has been fascinated by the possibility of making them. For some time enough has been known about their formation so that it is certain they could be formed from graphite if a sufficiently high temperature and pressure could be obtained. **Moissan** (1887) was the first to prepare diamonds experimentally. He dissolved charcoal in molten iron at 3500°C. When he plunged this molten iron into water, the carbon

Producing man-made industrial diamonds. They differ from natural diamonds only in color. (General Electric Company)

crystallized from the iron. As a result of the pressure produced by shrinkage of the metal, about twelve very small black or transparent diamonds were formed. In 1936 Professor J. W. Hershey, at McPherson College, Kansas, using the same procedure, produced a diamond 2 by 1 mm by 1 mm. The U.S. Bureau of Standards declared it to be of first quality. Recently the production of man-made industrial diamonds was announced by an American company. These are real diamonds for they meet all the tests.

Graphite

Graphite occurs in New York State, Canada, Siberia, and Ceylon. It was not until 1855, when graphite was first prepared from charcoal, that it was recognized as being an allotropic form of carbon. The industrial uses for graphite are so great that the natural supply is not equal to the demand. Much graphite is made from coke by the **Acheson process.** This process depends upon the fact that graphite is the stable allotropic form of carbon at ordinary temperatures and pressures. Hence if impure forms of carbon (such as coke) are heated in the absence of air to a very high temperature (3500°C), at which the carbon vaporizes, the vapor on cooling condenses to graphite crystals.

In the manufacture of graphite, coke or anthracite coal and sand (SiO_2) are heated in an electric furnace, out of contact with air. The heating is accomplished by passing electricity through the coke (see Chap. 33, page 369, on phosphorus furnace). The charge is heated for about twenty-four hours, thereby converting the coke to graphite. The sand may be considered as a catalyst.

Graphite consists of black, platelike crystals which on grinding give slippery scales. Therefore, rubbing the powder between the fingers produces a slippery, oily feel. Graphite is a good lubricant and is especially useful as lubricant where oil might attract dust, as in automobile door hinges, locks, and bicycle chains. Also, where a bearing develops a high temperature at which an oil would decompose, graphite can be used as a lubricant because it is very stable. Graphite may be suspended in water to form a lubricant known as Aquadag. Suspended in oil, graphite is known as Oildag.

Graphite, unlike diamond, is a good electrical conductor. This property makes it useful in the construction of brushes on electric generators and motors—an extensive and very important use. Because of its chemical inertness, graphite is used to make electrodes for many electrolytic operations, for example, in the electrolysis of sodium chloride. It would be difficult if not impossible to find another material which was at the same time a good electrical conductor and also resistant to the action of the liberated chlorine, as is graphite. Because of the same properties, graphite is used in making electrodes of dry batteries (see Chap. 52, page 673).

Mixed with clay and a binder, graphite is molded into thin cylinders and used in lead pencils, which, of course, contain no lead. The name graphite comes from the Greek word meaning *I write*. Lead also is soft enough to write on paper, and it is probably from this fact that the term "lead" pencil is derived.

Powdered graphite dusted onto a nonconducting material such as a wax or plaster of paris model causes the surface of the object to become conducting so that it can be metal-plated electrolytically. This is the principle in making the **electrotype** used in printing some books. In one process book plates are made by taking a cast in wax of each page of type, dusting the cast with graphite, and electroplating it with copper. This thin shell of copper type is then stripped off and the back strengthened by filling with a lead alloy. The actual printing is done from this electrotype. Thus the type itself is released and can then be used for setting other similar plates.

Because of its refractory nature, graphite is used for making crucibles for high-temperature metallurgy, as in the manufacture of crucible steel—a type highly prized for cutlery and tools and needles.

Graphite is not attacked by dilute acids or alkalis or halogens, nor is it soluble in any common solvent. Molten iron is one of the few known solvents for it. A mixture of potassium chromate (K_2CrO_4) and sulfuric acid slowly converts graphite to carbon dioxide. At about 700°C it burns in air.

The structure of diamond and graphite

The reason for the different properties of diamond and graphite can be understood in terms of the crystal structures of the two substances. In 1912 a German named von Laue discovered the technique by means of which x rays can be used to determine the arrangement of atoms within a crystal. This technique is often called **x-ray crystallography**. Although not generally known to the public, this discovery is judged to be, with the exception of nuclear fission, the most important scientific discovery made thus far in the twentieth century. The reason

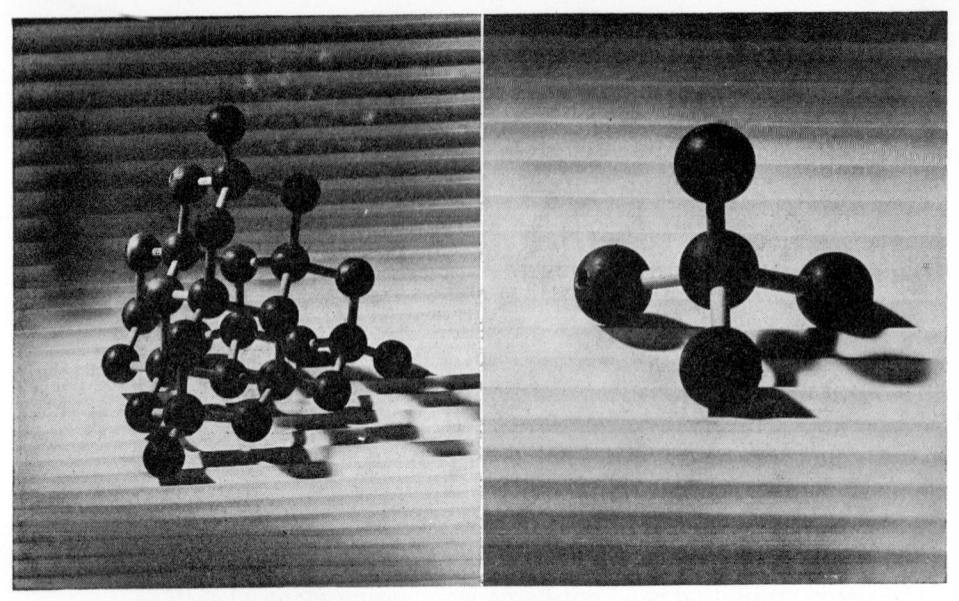

Models of a single diamond crystal (left) and of a diamond tetrahedron (right).

for the importance of this discovery is that these x-ray studies have shown that there is a strong correlation between the structures of solids and their chemical and physical properties. This discovery has led to stronger alloys, better electric insulators, better rubbers, longer-lasting textiles, and particularly to a clearer understanding of the nature of the forces which hold atoms together.

Although the actual technique for determining crystal structure by x rays is complex, some of the results are easily understood and appreciated. As an example the structures of diamond and graphite will be considered.

The unit of which the diamond crystal is made up can be considered as a carbon atom surrounded by four similar carbon atoms at the points of an imaginary four-sided pyramid. This four-sided pyramid is known as a *tetrahedron*. Each of these carbon atoms is in turn the center of another similar tetrahedron. Imagine this arrangement to be reproduced in the three different directions almost without limit. The result is a diamond crystal. A model of the crystal made with rods and balls is shown in the photograph (*a*) on this page. In this figure the balls represent carbon atoms, while the rods represent the forces holding the carbon atoms together. These forces are the covalence of the carbon atom, each of which shares an electron pair with each of four other carbon atoms. This is schematically shown in two dimensions in Fig. 34–3. Although this figure shows the way the carbon-to-carbon bonds are formed covalently, it is geometrically misleading because the structure is really three-dimensional as shown in the photograph (*b*). Every bond in the diamond crystal is thus the same. The distance

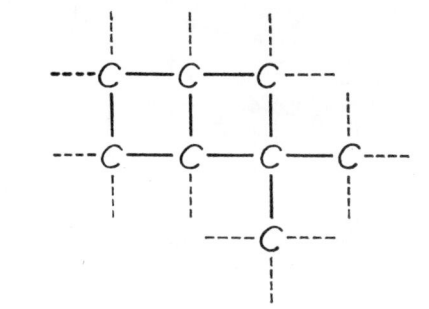

Fig. 34–3. A two-dimensional diagram of carbon-to-carbon linkages in a diamond.

from the center of each carbon atom to the centers of its four nearest neighbors is the same. X rays tell us this distance is 1.54 angstroms[1] ($= 1.54 \times 10^{-8}$ cm). There is no molecule unless one considers the entire crystal as a huge single molecule. (Such substances are called **macromolecules.**) Also, the carbon-to-carbon bond is a strong one. These two facts account for the hardness and chemical inertness of the diamond and for the fact that the properties of the diamond are the same in all three directions through the crystal. Note how these properties are the direct result of the valence characteristics of carbon according to which it tends to form four strong covalent bonds.

The structure of graphite is shown in Fig. 34–4. The carbon atoms form sheets composed of hexagons in which carbon atoms are bound to their neighbors by covalent bonds; every third bond is a double bond. (A double bond is one in which two pairs of electrons are shared between two atoms.) Thus

In graphite these layers of carbon atom hexagons extend throughout a single flake of graphite. The entire layer might be considered as a single molecule. The distance between all adjacent carbon atoms within a layer is the same, 1.42 angstroms. The layers are stacked one upon another; the distance between adjacent layers is 3.40 angstroms. The only forces which hold the layers together are the very weak van der Waals' forces (see Chap. 11, pages 99 and 100). The forces between layers are much weaker than the covalent forces holding the atoms

[1] One angstrom unit, Å, is 10^{-8} cm.

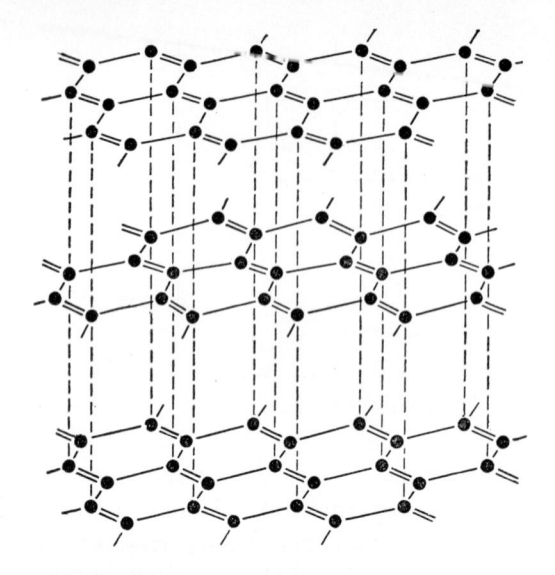

Fig. 34–4. Graphite consists of sheets of hexagons made up of carbon atoms. These sheets are piled one on top of another. A small section of a crystal of graphite is shown in this model.

together in a given layer. Hence the weak point of this structure is between layers. This is why graphite breaks into plates on grinding, and can be split into flakes of unlimited thinness. The layers of which graphite is composed easily slide over each other, giving graphite its slippery feel and lubricating qualities. But since the molecules (that is, the layers) are exceedingly large and the bonds holding the carbon atoms together within the layer are very strong, graphite is just about as inert to solvents and chemical action as is diamond.

Charcoal

Most charcoal is produced from wood. When wood is heated out of contact with air, various gases and liquids are driven off. This process is called **destructive distillation.** The volatile gases are nitrogen and some carbon compounds which are combustible. The liquids obtained are methyl alcohol (also called wood alcohol), acetic acid (wood vinegar), and acetone as well as wood tar. The residue in the still contains carbon as well as the minerals originally present in the wood. Because of the method of preparation, charcoal is extremely porous and presents very great surface areas. Because of its porosity, most varieties of charcoal will float. However, if charcoal is held under boiling water for a few minutes, the air is expelled from its pores and it will sink.

Charcoal finds limited use as a fuel because it burns without odor or flame. Tinners sometimes use it for heating soldering irons. Whereas charcoal formerly was produced as a by-product in the production of methyl alcohol and acetic acid, these substances are now made almost entirely by other methods. The chief use of charcoal at present is as an adsorbing agent. Bone black or animal charcoal is made by heating bones in the absence of air.

This man is wearing a gas mask to protect him against a poisonous gas, hydrogen sulfide. This gas will be adsorbed on the material in the canister on the man's hip. (Standard Oil Co.)

Adsorption

If some charcoal or bone black is sprinkled into a flask containing bromine vapor, the color of the bromine will disappear in a few minutes. If the charcoal is of the right kind, even the odor of bromine may disappear. On heating the charcoal, the bromine is again obtained. The charcoal is said to have *adsorbed* the bromine. Adsorption is an incompletely understood but important phenomenon. The adsorptive power of a material is determined by its chemical and physical nature —particularly the amount of surface area. Charcoal is impure graphite, but ordinary pure crystalline graphite shows little or no adsorptive power.

Most gas masks depend upon the adsorptive power of charcoal. In them, air is drawn through a canister packed with charcoal of high adsorptive power. Almost any gas which is near its liquefaction temperature will be adsorbed in this way. However, nitrogen and oxygen are not adsorbed at room temperature. This is because in general it is found that a gas is adsorbed more readily at temperatures close to its liquefaction point. Thus at room temperature, chlorine and bromine may be completely adsorbed, whereas oxygen and nitrogen are not. If, however, the charcoal is cooled to $-100°C$, the oxygen and nitrogen may be extensively adsorbed.

In World War I, in which gas warfare was introduced, all the gases used were of high boiling point. Gas masks packed with coconut charcoal were effective in adsorbing these gases. However, a poison gas such as carbon monoxide is not adsorbed at room temperature, and an adsorptive gas mask is of no protection against it.[1]

[1] There are gas masks for protection against carbon monoxide. They operate on the catalytic oxidation of carbon monoxide to carbon dioxide as the air passes over the catalyst.

An over-all view of a coke-coal plant. Both the main product and the by-products of the destructive distillation of coal are valuable. (Consolidated Edison Co.)

Charcoals also have the ability to adsorb certain high-molecular-weight compounds from solution. This is easily demonstrated by boiling a solution of the dye gentian violet with charcoal. On filtering the solution, it will be found to have been completely decolorized. The dye is held on the surface of the charcoal. White sugar manufacture involves the use of this principle. Juices from the cane or beet are boiled to remove water and cause the crystallization of crude sugar. This sugar is brown or yellow because it contains substances other than sugar which were originally present in the plant juice. It also contains some decomposition products of the sugar caused by the heating. At the sugar refinery the crude sugar is dissolved in water and passed through charcoal or bone-black filters. The colored constituents are removed by adsorption and very pure white sugar is crystallized from the remaining colorless solution by evaporation under reduced pressure.

Coal

Coal is derived by partial carbonization of vegetative matter. In past geologic periods certain plants became covered with sand and clay or even water. Under these coverings the plants were subject to bacterial decay in the absence of oxygen. Sinking into the earth, these plants were later subjected to high temperature and pressure in the absence of oxygen. The chemical processes occurring were similar to those in the destructive distillation of wood except that most of the

TABLE 34–1. Fuel values of common fuels

Fuel	Cal/g
Wood (seasoned oak, 13 percent water)	4000
Peat	1044
Lignite, brown	3364
Bituminous coal (Illinois)	6508
Bituminous coal (West Virginia)	7721
Anthracite coal (Pennsylvania)	7417
Charcoal	6626
Coke	6768
Petroleum (crude oil)	11000

volatile material was unable to escape because of the overlying layers of rock. The coal that is mined today in America and Europe was formed in this way during the Paleozoic geologic period some 300 or 400 million years ago. Coal is a complex mixture consisting largely of carbon compounds and free carbon. Depending on the amount of carbonization and length of the carbonizing process, the result may be **anthracite** (hard) **coal, bituminous** (soft) **coal,** or **peat.** Peat can be seen today in the process of formation in bogs. Anthracite coal contains a higher percentage of free carbon and less volatile matter than bituminous. Both have about the same fuel value, but anthracite produces less soot than soft coal and is therefore preferred for home heating. The fuel value of peat is lower because of its high water content. About ninety percent of the coal mined today is bituminous.

The destructive distillation of coal

When heated out of contact with air (destructive distillation), coal yields a host of different chemicals, and the residue in the still is **coke.** Coke is free carbon plus the ash of the original coal. The coking of coal is important both for the volatile products which are given off and for the production of coke. Formerly the operation was carried out solely for the purpose of obtaining coke, and the by-products were burned as they left the oven. The oven used was known as a beehive oven because of its shape. This wasteful process has now all but disappeared. Most coke is produced in such a manner as to collect all by-products (the by-product oven). The products are listed in Table 34–2.

Coal gas contains carbon-hydrogen compounds, carbon monoxide, carbon dioxide, hydrogen, nitrogen, and hydrogen sulfide. It is used largely for fuel. The **coal tar** is a veritable treasure chest of organic compounds, but the principal ingredients are benzene, toluene, naphtha, phenol, anthracene, and naphthalene. From these materials in coal tar, the chemist can make a wide variety of compounds ranging

TABLE 34–2. Products formed by distillation of one ton of average bituminous coal

Coal gas	11000 ft^3
Ammonia (separated as ammonium sulfate)	5 lb
Tar	12 gal
Coke	1300 lb

from vanilla flavoring and dyes to TNT. It is for this reason that one hears the expression "coal-tar dye" or "coal-tar flavoring." However, these so-called coal-tar products are not necessarily made from coal tar, since the starting materials can be obtained elsewhere, particularly from petroleum. The tars themselves, or parts of them, are used for road building, roofing, and other waterproofing materials.

Coke is used as a fuel, but its principal importance is as a source of carbon for metallurgical reduction, particularly in the making of pig iron from iron ore. When used in this way, coke must have the necessary strength to support the weight of the ore charge above it in the furnace. Hence its physical as well as its chemical properties are important.

Normally coking is carried out by heating coal to about 1000°C. It has been found that if the temperature is kept lower (about 600°C) a larger proportion of volatile matter is produced. Some of the liquids obtained in this process can be made into a good motor fuel. This **low-temperature carbonization** of coal will doubtless receive more attention in the future as our supplies of natural petroleum are used up.

The size of the coal deposits known to exist in America is very large. Geologists have estimated that these coal deposits are sufficient to supply all our fuel requirements for the next thousand years—assuming that the use of fuels continues at the present rate. Of course it is to be expected that the actual rate of fuel consumption will continue to increase as it has increased in the past. In any case there appear to be ample coal supplies to meet our requirements until science develops other sources of energy, such as the practical utilization of nuclear energy and the direct utilization of the sun's energy.

Carbon black

Carbon black is produced by burning natural gas (carbon-hydrogen compounds) in a deficient supply of oxygen, so as to produce a smoky flame. This smokiness is due to the presence of fine particles of unburned carbon. If the flame is directed toward a cold metal plate, most of the carbon particles adhere to it. In actual practice the plate rotates against a scraper which removes the carbon black as it collects, and the plate is cooled by a stream of water directed against the back of it.

Carbon black and lampblack (which is about the same thing) are used extensively in the rubber industry, particularly in making automobile tires. Their incorporation into the rubber greatly improves the tensile strength, abrasion resistance, and tear resistance of the tires. Ordinarily tire treads contain about one-third carbon black and two-thirds rubber. Ground in oil, carbon black is used as a black paint pigment. It is also the pigment in printer's ink. For this reason printer's ink is not bleachable with chlorine or anything else. Typewriter ribbons and some carbon papers contain carbon black, as do certain varieties of black shoe polish.

KEY WORDS

Acheson process	coal tar	low-temperature
adsorption	coke	carbonization
anthracite coal	destructive distillation	macromolecule
bituminous coal	diamond	Moissan
carat	electrotype	peat
carbon black	graphite	von Laue
charcoal	igneous rock	x-ray crystallography

HIGHLIGHTS

Carbon occurs in nature in two pure forms, **diamond** and **graphite,** and in various impure amorphous forms.

The diamond is the hardest substance known and one of the most valuable gems. The atoms in the diamond are arranged in tetrahedral fashion. The beauty and brilliance of the diamond depends partly upon the skill of the cutter. Industrial diamonds, including diamond dust and black diamonds, are used in making saws and drills.

In graphite the atoms are arranged in the form of sheets, which are free to slide over each other. Because of this fact, graphite is a good lubricant. Graphite is used in making lead pencils, generator brushes, and electrodes for dry-cell batteries and many electrolytic processes. It is also used for making **electrotype.**

Varieties of impure carbon include **charcoal, coke,** and lampblack or **carbon black.**

Charcoal is produced by the **destructive distillation** of wood. Because of its porosity and its large surface area, it is a good adsorbing agent and is widely used in gas masks and in refining sugar.

Coke is produced by distilling soft coal.

There are two forms of coal: **anthracite,** or hard, **coal** and **bituminous,** or soft, **coal.**

In the destructive distillation of wood, acetone and methyl or wood alcohol are also produced. In the destructive distillation of soft coal the by-products are coal gas, ammonia, and **coal tar.**

Carbon black is a product of the incomplete combustion of coal gas. It is widely used in the manufacture of rubber products, especially tires, and in paints and printer's ink.

QUESTIONS

1. How was it established that diamond is an allotropic form of carbon?
2. What conditions are necessary for the conversion of graphite into diamond?
3. How many grams are there in one international carat?
4. Why is the cut of a diamond important in determining its value?
5. How are diamonds cut?
6. What combination of properties makes the diamond unique?
7. List three industrial uses for diamonds.
8. Explain how graphite is made from coke.
9. Give three uses for graphite.
10. Explain in terms of its crystal structure why graphite splits into thin flakes.
11. Which of the following gases would you expect to be more completely adsorbed by charcoal, hydrogen or chlorine? Explain.
12. Explain the use of charcoal in refining sugar.
13. Why is anthracite coal preferred over bituminous for home heating?
14. Name four products formed by the destructive distillation of coal.
15. What is meant by the term low-temperature carbonization of coal? Why is it important?
16. How is carbon black made?
17. "Carbon black is a strategic commodity." Explain this statement.

CHAPTER **35**

some simple carbon compounds

Approximately 300,000 different carbon-containing compounds are known. This number is several times as many as the compounds formed by all the other known elements put together. The reason for this vast number of carbon compounds will be given in Chap. 36, page 414. A great many of these compounds are produced through the agency of living organisms—to mention a few: cellulose, the principal constituent of wood and cotton; cane sugar; and ethyl alcohol formed from sugar by the action of yeast. Consequently the study of carbon compounds came to be called **organic chemistry** and it is still known by that name.

Until 1828 it was believed that man would never be able to make, in the test tube, any of the carbon compounds produced by the metabolism of living things. This belief was disproved in 1828 by a German chemist, **Friedrich Wöhler,** who in that year synthesized **urea** [$CO(NH_2)_2$], an organic compound known to be present in urine. From this start organic chemists have succeeded in duplicating a great many, but by no means all, of the organic compounds formed by living things.[1] In addition they have produced many other carbon

[1] In this connection the word *synthetic* is sometimes a confusing one. To the chemist it means a compound made from its elements in the laboratory without the use of biological processes. Thus vitamin B_1 (thiamine) can be produced in the test tube. The product, which is chemically identical with the vitamin B_1 found in nature, is called synthetic vitamin B_1. On the other hand the newspapers and the public in general have come to use the term synthetic as meaning anything which will substitute for a natural product. Thus the many man-made rubbers, which are not chemically the same as natural rubber, are known to the public as *synthetic rubber*, meaning man-made substitute for natural rubber.

A three-dimensional model of a carbon tetrachloride (CCl$_4$) molecule. The black ball represents a carbon atom and the four light balls represent chlorine atoms. A diagram of the electronic structure of this compound is shown on page 397. (Fisher Scientific Co.)

compounds not found in nature. But some of these compounds are superior to natural products for man's purposes. An example is nylon, which for certain purposes is superior to any of the natural fibers—cotton, silk, or wool. Also, there are the newer man-made rubbers, which, although not chemical duplicates of natural rubber, are vastly superior to it for certain uses.

The chemical properties of carbon

The four valence electrons of carbon make it necessary for carbon to gain four more electrons or to lose its four in order to acquire an inert gas structure. Carbon never loses four electrons. The reason this process is impossible can best be understood by assuming for a moment that it does start to lose these four electrons (e^-). Such a process would occur stepwise, involving the following steps:

$$C^0 \rightarrow C^+ + 1e$$
$$C^+ \rightarrow C^{++} + 1e$$
$$C^{++} \rightarrow C^{+++} + 1e$$
$$C^{+++} \rightarrow C^{++++} + 1e$$

Before the last of the four electrons is lost, the positively charged carbon ion has a very high charge. Therefore, the electrostatic attraction between it and the remaining valence electron is so great that the electron cannot escape. You might answer this argument by thinking: Then carbon will lose just one or two or three electrons. But this would not give the atom an inert gas structure. Hence it loses none. This same effect makes the loss of four electrons by any other atom a very unlikely if not impossible process. A loss of four would be more likely to occur with an element farther down in the periodic table because in such a case the electrons would be farther from the nucleus. However, it is very doubtful if any atom ever loses more than three electrons.

Neither does carbon ever gain four electrons by electrovalent electron transfer. That is, it never forms the C≡ ion. The explanation for this is analogous to the explanation given above. **Carbon always enters into compound formation by the formation of four covalent bonds.** (The case of carbon monoxide, CO, is an exception which is not well understood.) Thus with the nonmetallic element chlorine, carbon tetrachloride (CCl_4) is formed.

$$\begin{array}{c} \ddot{:}\ddot{Cl}: \\ \ddot{:}\ddot{Cl}:C:\ddot{Cl}\ddot{:} \\ :\ddot{Cl}: \\ \ddot{} \end{array}$$

Carbon dioxide contains two double covalent bonds.

$$:\ddot{O}::C::\ddot{O}:$$

Carbon disulfide is similar to carbon dioxide.

In general any nonmetallic element can share one or more pairs of electrons with a carbon atom. Not all the bonds must be shared with atoms of the same element. Thus Freon 12 is

$$\begin{array}{c} :\ddot{Cl}: \\ \ddot{:}\ddot{Cl}:C:\ddot{F}\ddot{:} \\ :\ddot{F}: \\ \ddot{} \end{array}$$

Methyl (wood) alcohol is

$$\begin{array}{c} H \\ \ddot{\ }\ \ddot{\ } \\ H:C:O:H \\ \ddot{\ }\ \ddot{\ } \\ H \end{array}$$

Carbon disulfide

When you recall the structures of graphite and diamond (Chap. 34, pages 386 to 388) in which very large molecules exist by covalent bond formation between adjacent carbon atoms, you may not be surprised that each of these forms of carbon is very inert at ordinary temperatures. Sulfur and oxygen are among the few elements which combine directly with free carbon, and these require a high temperature.

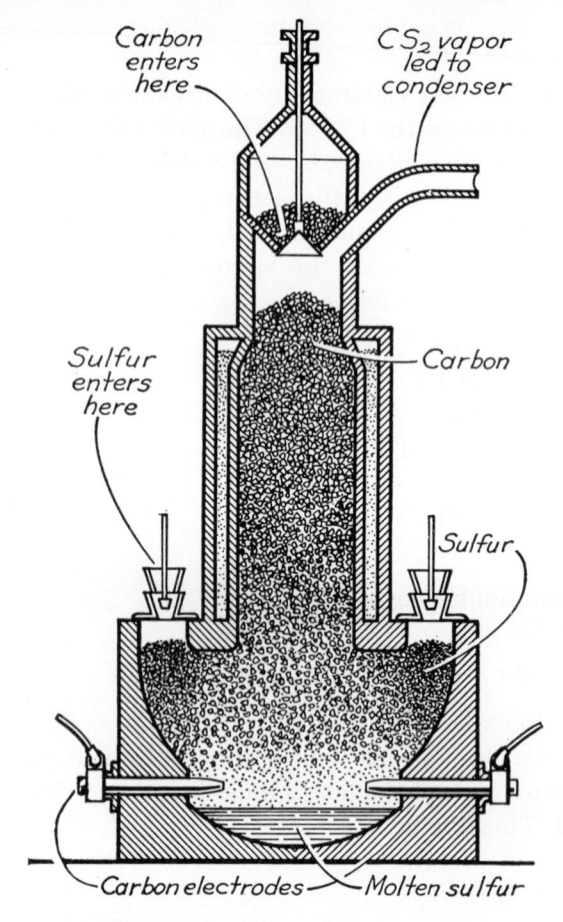

Fig. 35–1. The manufacture of carbon disulfide (CS_2). Heat is generated in the electric furnace by an electric current. The sulfur at the bottom of the electric furnace is vaporized and passes up through the hot carbon. The hot sulfur vapor and hot carbon unite to form carbon disulfide. The carbon disulfide vapor is condensed by being passed through cooled condensers.

Carbon disulfide is made by heating coke and sulfur in an electric furnace.

$$C + 2S \xrightarrow{\text{heat}} CS_2 \uparrow$$

The carbon disulfide is highly volatile (bp 46°C) and distills out.

Carbon disulfide is a heavy liquid (specific gravity 1.26) which forms highly combustible and toxic vapors. Because of this fact, great care should be exercised when using carbon disulfide in the laboratory. It is immiscible in water and is an excellent solvent for many water-insoluble substances, including fats, waxes, oils, rubber, white phosphorus, and sulfur.

Carbon disulfide is used as a solvent and in the manufacture of carbon tetrachloride. Large quantities are employed in the manufacture of rayon and cellophane by the viscose process (see Chap. 38, pages 363 and 364).

Carbon disulfide is sometimes used as a poison for rodents, such as prairie dogs, gophers, and rats, because when poured into a burrow, it rapidly evaporates, filling the den with heavy toxic fumes. It is used to

Carbon tetrachloride fire extinguisher. Carbon tetrachloride is a liquid that vaporizes easily, will not burn, and will not support combustion. For these reasons it is used to extinguish fires. When sprayed at the base of a flame, as shown in this photograph, carbon tetrachloride will vaporize and form a dense gas which excludes oxygen and smothers the flames. (Pyrene Manufacturing Co.)

kill moths in furs and weevils in stored grain (corn, wheat, and others). Its use here depends upon the fact that the poisonous carbon disulfide eventually evaporates completely and hence does not leave a toxic residue in the grain.

Carbon tetrachloride

Carbon and chlorine do not unite directly. Carbon tetrachloride is made by the reaction of carbon disulfide and chlorine.

$$CS_2 + 3Cl_2 \rightarrow \underset{\text{(bp 76.8°C)}}{CCl_4} + \underset{\text{(bp 135.6°C)}}{S_2Cl_2}$$

Both products of this reaction are liquids, but they are easily separated by fractional distillation because of the difference in their boiling points. The second product, sulfur monochloride, is used as a rubber solvent.

Carbon tetrachloride is a colorless liquid with a specific gravity of 1.59. It is immiscible with water and is a good solvent for the same types of substances that carbon disulfide is used to dissolve. Carbon tetrachloride is non-inflammable, which makes it a safer solvent than carbon disulfide. It is widely used in dry cleaning. Because carbon tetrachloride is not a fire hazard, it is commonly used at home in removing an occasional spot from the clothing. However, because of its toxicity, the practice may be dangerous.

Since the molecular weight of carbon tetrachloride is 154, the vapors have a much higher density than air. This fact together with its low boiling point and non-inflammability, make carbon tetrachloride suitable for use in fire extinguishers (Pyrene and others). Sprayed, as a liquid, at the base of a flame, the carbon tetrachloride evaporates quickly, forming a blanket of dense fumes which tend to exclude air from the fire. This type of extinguisher is particularly suited for fires in electrical machinery, where water might ruin the machinery. Other halogen derivatives of carbon are now used in the same way. Probably none of them is as efficient as liquid carbon dioxide for putting out fires (see page 403), but they have the advantage of being more easily stored since liquid carbon dioxide can be kept only under high pressure.

Although this is not commonly recognized, carbon tetrachloride is a toxic substance. It is not nearly so toxic as some other solvents, but there is good evidence that prolonged breathing of the vapor is very harmful. Serious, irreparable kidney damage may occur. Therefore, one should avoid the fumes of carbon tetrachloride as much as possible.

Silicon carbide

This substance, because of its hardness, is an important commercial abrasive. Silicon carbide is sold under the trade name of **Carborundum** and also, by certain companies, under its chemical name.

It is made by the reaction of sand and coke in an electric furnace.

$$SiO_2 + 3C \xrightarrow{\text{heat}} SiC + 2CO \uparrow$$

The furnace charge contains sawdust which, by decomposing, keeps the mass porous. The product of the furnace consists of coarse, iridescent crystals, which are crushed and sieved for size. The crushed crystals may then be mixed with a binder to form abrasive wheels ranging in size all the way from those used for grinding large metal castings to those used by the dentist in grinding a tooth preparatory to filling. Silicon carbide crystals are also cemented onto paper or cloth giving what is known as a *coated abrasive*. The most common coated abrasive is sandpaper in which the abrasive is quartz (SiO_2). Silicon carbide coated abrasives are much faster cutting and more durable than sandpaper and are used for grinding and polishing a wide variety of metals, plastics, and woods.

Although not as hard as diamond, silicon carbide approaches it in hardness, and it will scratch all but the hardest alloys. Its structure is similar to that of diamond in which every other carbon atom is replaced by an atom of silicon.

Boron carbide (B_4C) is harder than silicon carbide, but it cannot be used in grinding wheels because no satisfactory binder for it is known.

Carborundum, or silicon carbide, is useful because of its hardness. In this photograph an abrasive wheel of silicon carbide is being used to polish the surface of a metal alloy. (Carborundum Co.)

Occurrence and preparation of carbon dioxide

The presence of carbon dioxide in the atmosphere and its relationship to photosynthesis has already been mentioned. Because the density of carbon dioxide is greater than that of air, the gas tends to accumulate in wells and cisterns. Although not toxic itself, it may thereby exclude oxygen and cause death by suffocation. Consequently before descending into a well, it is a safe practice to test for oxygen by lowering a burning candle or lantern into the well.

Carbon dioxide is formed by slow bacterial decay of organic compounds and also by completely burning carbon and any of its compounds. Animals also produce it in the oxidation of their foods. Although each of these reactions differs in detail, the over-all reaction in each case can be represented by the oxidation of glucose.

$$\underset{\text{glucose}}{C_6H_{12}O_6} + 6O_2 \rightarrow 6CO_2 + 6H_2O$$

Carbon dioxide is also obtained by the fermentation of glucose by yeast (see Chap. 37, page 435).

All metal carbonates, except alkali carbonates, yield carbon dioxide on heating. The other product is the metal oxide if this is stable; otherwise it is the metal and oxygen. For example,

$$CaCO_3 \xrightarrow{\text{heat}} CaO + CO_2 \uparrow$$

In the laboratory the best method of preparing the gas is by the action of a strong acid (HCl) upon limestone lumps. The reaction is conveniently carried out in a Kipp generator.

$$CaCO_3 + 2OH_3^+ + 2Cl^- \rightarrow CO_2 \uparrow + 3H_2O + 2Cl^- + Ca^{++}$$

Small or large cylinders of liquefied carbon dioxide are available commercially at low cost.

Properties of carbon dioxide

The critical temperature of carbon dioxide gas is 31°C; hence it can exist under pressure as a liquid at room temperature. When cooled sufficiently, carbon dioxide forms a white solid, dry ice (see below). The gas is slightly soluble in water (1 volume of carbon dioxide in 1 volume of water at 15°C) with which it reacts to form the weak carbonic acid.

$$CO_2 + 2H_2O \rightleftarrows HCO_3^- + OH_3^+$$
$$HCO_3^- + H_2O \rightleftarrows CO_3^= + OH_3^+$$

For convenience the reaction of carbon dioxide and water is sometimes indicated as follows:

$$CO_2 + H_2O \rightleftarrows H_2CO_3$$

Actually there is no evidence that un-ionized H_2CO_3 exists.

Many of the uses of carbon dioxide depend on one or more of its specific properties; these will be discussed together. The largest industrial use is in the manufacture of sodium carbonate (page 557).

Dry ice

Although first prepared in 1835, dry ice was not manufactured commercially until 1924 when a plant was erected in Montreal, Canada. The first patent on the use of dry ice was taken out by Elsworthy, a British army doctor stationed in India.

As explained in Chap. 12, page 120, dry ice is made by the rapid evaporation of liquid carbon dioxide. A cylinder of liquid carbon dioxide obtained by compressing the gas at a temperature below 31°C is inverted and the liquid allowed to flow out through a small opening. Two effects contribute to its cooling: (1) the rapid boiling of the liquid on contact with the air and (2) the rapid expansion of the gas (Joule-Thomson effect). The result is that about 30 percent of the escaping carbon dioxide is cooled to the point of solidification. The other 70 percent is collected and reliquefied. This snow of carbon dioxide is then compressed into the familiar blocks of dry ice.

Dry ice has two advantages over ordinary ice. It is much colder and it passes directly to the gaseous stage leaving no messy liquid to be disposed of. When a piece of dry ice is placed in air, it sublimates at −78°C. That is, at −78°C its vapor pressure is equal to atmospheric pressure. Thus except that we do not speak of solids as boiling, we might say that −78°C is the boiling point of dry ice because it is

A fire extinguisher employing liquid carbon dioxide. This type of fire extinguisher puts out fires by smothering the flames in a blanket of carbon dioxide which keeps out oxygen. It is particularly valuable since there is no damaging residue left after the fire is extinguished. (Walter Kidde and Co., Inc.)

exactly comparable to a boiling point. If the solid is confined under pressure so that it cannot boil, then it melts at $-56.4°C$, but under normal atmospheric pressure the liquid is never formed. It has been said that carbon dioxide is one of those few substances that "has its boiling point colder than its melting point."

Most carbon dioxide for dry ice production is made by burning a specially selected grade of coal. Carbon dioxide obtained as a by-product in the production of alcohol from grain or molasses fermentation may also be used for the production of dry ice.

In addition to being used in the storage and transportation of ice cream and frozen foods, dry ice is sometimes used for shrink-fitting metal parts in machine assembly. Where an especially tight fit is required, one part, which fits into another, may be cooled in dry ice. This cooling shrinks it. The part is then fitted into the other part and, on warming to room temperature, the cooled part expands, thereby giving a tight fit.

Fire extinguishers

As mentioned in the section dealing with carbon tetrachloride, liquid carbon dioxide is the best type of fire extinguisher for certain types of fires, including electrical fires and oil fires. An extinguisher of this type contains the liquid carbon dioxide together with a valve and delivery tube, by means of which the liquid is blown onto the fire. The fire is extinguished because the carbon dioxide blankets out the air around it. Such extinguishers leave no damaging residue when used. However, they are not recommended for "trash" (that is, wood, paper, and so on) fires, since such fires will smoulder and may re-blaze after having been "put out" by liquid carbon dioxide. Nor are carbon dioxide extinguishers suitable for putting out magnesium fires (incendiary bomb).

Magnesium actually will burn in carbon dioxide.

$$2Mg + CO_2 \rightarrow 2MgO + C$$

The reaction is highly exothermic.

For trash fires, water or a **foamite** type of extinguisher is recommended. The latter consists of a solution of sodium hydrogen carbonate containing saponin. (The latter is a vegetable extract, added to produce a tough long-lasting foam.) A loosely stoppered bottle of sulfuric acid, or alum solution, is supported above the solution. When inverted, the acid produces carbon dioxide by reaction with the sodium hydrogen carbonate, thus forming large volumes of foam. The foam is forced out of the base of the extinguisher by the pressure generated.

Carbonated beverages

The use of carbon dioxide in beverages has been mentioned (see Chap. 14, page 155).

Water-type fire extinguisher. (Walter Kidde and Co., Inc.)

Carbon dioxide in baking

In making breads and pastries, the cook causes the bread to rise, thereby making it light. Most commonly this rising is caused by evolution of carbon dioxide within the dough.[1] In the so-called *raised breads* (or baker's bread) the formation of carbon dioxide is the result of yeast fermentation. It is for this purpose that yeast is used in such breads. The alcohol which is formed volatilizes on cooking.

$$C_6H_{12}O_6 \xrightarrow{\text{yeast}} 2CO_2 \uparrow + 2C_2H_5OH$$

Baking powder

Baking powder is a mixture of sodium bicarbonate (sodium hydrogen carbonate), starch, and a solid acid. When water is added the acid reacts with the bicarbonate. This reaction liberates carbon dioxide. There are three types of baking powders on the market which vary only in the nature of the acid used.

---

[1] There are certain exceptions, one of which is the beaten biscuit which used to be so well known in the South. In this, the cook pounds the dough with a mallet, thereby trapping air bubbles which on cooking expand and give some leavening action.

1. *Phosphate type.* In this type of baking powder the source of the acid is calcium dihydrogen phosphate, $Ca(H_2PO_4)_2$. When placed in water, calcium dihydrogen phosphate ionizes, furnishing hydronium ions.

$$Ca^{++} + 2H_2PO_4^- + 2H_2O \rightarrow Ca^{++} + 2HPO_4^= + 2OH_3^+$$

2. *Alum type.* Alum-type baking powders contain sodium aluminum sulfate, $NaAl(SO_4)_2 \cdot 12H_2O$. The active ingredient is the $Al_2(SO_4)_3$ which is acid by hydrolysis (see Chap. 27, page 307).

$$2Al^{+++} + 3SO_4^= + 12H_2O \rightleftarrows 2Al(OH)_3 + 6OH_3^+ + 3SO_4^=$$

3. *Tartrate type.* Tartrate-type baking powders contain potassium hydrogen tartrate (cream of tartar, $KHC_4H_4O_6$). This compound ionizes in solution as a monobasic acid.

$$K^+ + \underset{\substack{\text{hydrogen}\\\text{tartrate ion}}}{HC_4H_4O_6^-} + H_2O \rightarrow K^+ + OH_3^+ + \underset{\substack{\text{tartrate}\\\text{ion}}}{C_4H_4O_6^=}$$

In each case the hydronium ions formed by water and the acid react with the sodium bicarbonate, forming carbon dioxide and water.

$$Na^+ + HCO_3^- + OH_3^+ \rightarrow 2H_2O + CO_2 \uparrow + Na^+$$

If you want the complete equation for any given type of baking powder, you can obtain it by adding together this last equation with the one showing the ionization of the acid. Thus for the tartrate type of baking powder the total equation is obtained as follows:

$$\cancel{K^+} + HC_4H_4O_6^- + \cancel{H_2O} \rightarrow \cancel{K^+} + \cancel{OH_3^+} + C_4H_4O_6^=$$

$$\cancel{Na^+} + HCO_3^- + \cancel{OH_3^+} \rightarrow CO_2 + \cancel{2}H_2O + \cancel{Na^+}$$

$$\overline{HC_4H_4O_6^- + HCO_3^- \quad\quad \rightarrow C_4H_4O_6^= + CO_2 \uparrow + H_2O}$$

The various types of baking powders differ on the basis of the speed of reaction at room temperature. In general they are classified as follows: (1) tartrate type—quick acting, (2) phosphate type—medium speed, and (3) alum type—slow acting.

In using the tartrate type of baking powder, the batter should be put into the oven soon after mixing so that the gas will not be lost before baking. Some commercial powders contain a mixture of phosphate and alum. These mixtures produce some gas immediately on mixing into the batter as well as a slow steady evolution on baking (double-acting type).

The starch in baking powder serves two purposes: (1) to keep the mixture dry and thereby prevent deterioration on storage and (2) as a filler to allow the various types of baking powder to be so mixed that a tablespoon of each type will give the same amount of leavening action. The Federal Food, Drug, and Cosmetic Act requires that all baking powder shall contain at least 12 percent of its weight as available carbon dioxide.

Whenever baking soda (sodium hydrogen carbonate, $NaHCO_3$) is used by the cook, it is necessary also to use an acid. The acid is commonly provided by adding sour milk, which furnishes lactic acid to liberate the carbon dioxide. Obviously the correct amount of acid is quite important, and since the lactic acid content of the milk may vary, you can see that much depends upon the skill and luck of the cook.

Much has been written in the form of commercial advertising about the relative merits and demerits of the various types of baking powders. This concerns mainly the claim of competing manufacturers that one or more of the products formed by a certain type of baking powder is harmful for human consumption. However, there is at present no real evidence that any of the types is at all harmful when consumed in the quantities used in baking.

Chemical properties of carbon dioxide

Carbon dioxide gas is exceedingly stable, but as noted above, very active metals will burn in it, forming a metal oxide and free carbon. When carbon dioxide is bubbled into basic solutions, carbonates are formed. Thus with a solution of calcium hydroxide:

$$Ca(OH)_2 + CO_2 \rightarrow CaCO_3 \downarrow + H_2O$$

Since calcium carbonate is insoluble, this reaction can be used as a *test* for carbon dioxide.

Preparation of carbon monoxide

Carbon monoxide is a poisonous gas which does not occur naturally. It is almost always formed, however, during the burning of coal or wood in a furnace or open fireplace. Figure 35–2 shows a sectional diagram of a coal furnace. The bottom draft supplies oxygen which on contact with the coal at the bottom of the grate forms carbon dioxide.

$$C + O_2 \rightarrow CO_2 \uparrow + \text{heat}$$

As this hot carbon dioxide passes up through the bed of coal, it reacts with the coal to form carbon monoxide.

$$CO_2 + C \xrightarrow{\text{heat}} 2CO \uparrow$$

The hot carbon monoxide reaches the top of the fuel layer where, on

Fig. 35–2. How carbon monoxide forms in a coal furnace. Air entering the bottom combines with carbon, forming carbon dioxide. This hot gas travels up through the bed of coal, reacting to form carbon monoxide. In a properly operating furnace, air entering near the top of the furnace causes this carbon monoxide to burn and form carbon dioxide.

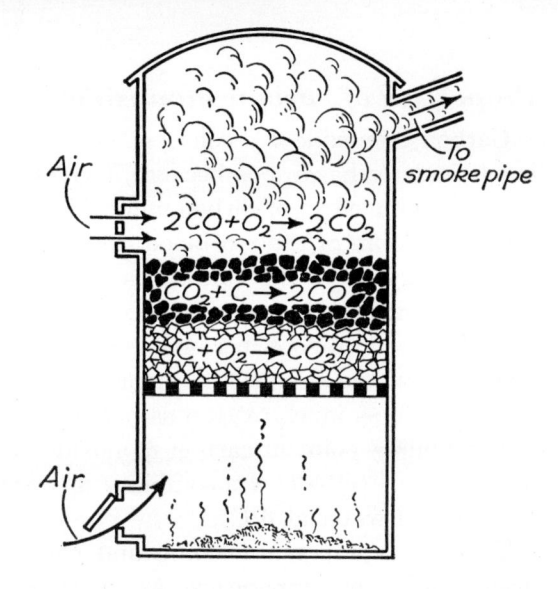

mixing with additional air entering through the top draft, it burns with a blue flame, forming carbon dioxide.

$$2CO + O_2 \rightarrow 2CO_2 \uparrow$$

If the furnace is leaky or the draft improperly adjusted, the carbon monoxide may fail to burn and may escape into the room. Every year many people are asphyxiated by carbon monoxide from defective furnaces.

The presence of carbon monoxide in automobile exhaust fumes has been mentioned earlier (see Chap. 7, page 57).

Carbon monoxide is made industrially by reaction of red-hot coke and steam.

$$C + H_2O \rightarrow \underbrace{CO \uparrow + H_2 \uparrow}_{\text{water gas}}$$

The resulting mixture, known as **water gas**, has high fuel value. It is frequently mixed with coal gas (see Chap. 34, page 391) to increase the heating value of the latter when used for municipal fuel gas.

Carbon monoxide is also manufactured by burning coal in a limited supply of air. The result is mainly a mixture of carbon monoxide and nitrogen which is called **producer gas**. It is sometimes used as a fuel. (The nitrogen of course is merely a diluent.[1])

Pure carbon monoxide can be formed by adding concentrated sulfuric acid to formic acid (HCO_2H).

$$HCO_2H \xrightarrow[\text{(concentrated)}]{H_2SO_4} CO \uparrow + H_2O$$

[1] A diluent is an agent used for dilution.

Properties of carbon monoxide

Carbon monoxide is a colorless, odorless gas of extreme toxicity. It is particularly hazardous because it gives no warning of its presence. The poisoning effect of carbon monoxide is due to its combination with the hemoglobin of the red blood cells, thereby preventing them from carrying oxygen to the various parts of the body. First symptoms of carbon monoxide poisoning are dizziness, nausea, vomiting, and headache. The victim soon becomes unconscious and death may quickly follow. First aid consists of artificial respiration and supplying the patient with as much oxygen as possible.

The boiling point of carbon monoxide is $-190°C$; its critical temperature is $-139.5°C$. Its solubility in water is low (0.035 volume in 1 volume of water at $0°C$).

The gas is not acid-forming and generally speaking is not very reactive at room temperature. As mentioned earlier, it is not adsorbed by charcoal at room temperature. Consequently it is difficult to construct a gas mask which will give protection against carbon monoxide. The one in use is based on the fact that a mixture of certain metal oxides will catalyze the oxidation of carbon monoxide to carbon dioxide by air at room temperature.

$$CO + air \xrightarrow[\text{catalyst}]{\text{room temperature}} CO_2$$

At high temperatures, carbon monoxide is an excellent reducing agent and is widely employed commercially in the reduction of metal oxides. An example is its use in the blast furnace process.

$$Fe_2O_3 + 3CO \rightarrow 2Fe + 3CO_2$$

In most metallurgical operations the carbon monoxide is formed in the reduction chamber by incomplete combustion of coke.

Carbon monoxide has a remarkable property of forming gaseous compounds with certain metals, such as iron, cobalt, and nickel. These are known as **metal carbonyls.** Examples are:

$Fe(CO)_5$ iron carbonyl
$Ni(CO)_4$ nickel carbonyl

The formation of carbonyls by passing carbon monoxide over the metal is sometimes employed in separating two metals which occur together in nature, as in the refining of nickel.

Iron carbonyl is employed in the manufacture of very fine iron powder like that used in powder metallurgy and tape recorders. The gaseous iron carbonyl is decomposed by heating to a very high temperature. This precipitates from the gas finely divided metallic iron.

Test for carbon monoxide

Formerly canaries were used to test air suspected of containing carbon monoxide. If a canary died, it was assumed that the air contained carbon monoxide.

A chemical test is now used. The reagent is a mixture of iodine pentoxide (I_2O_5) and concentrated sulfuric acid adsorbed on an inert base such as pumice. In the presence of carbon monoxide the mixture turns green to an extent that depends on the concentration of carbon monoxide.

KEY WORDS

baking powder	Carborundum	producer gas
boron carbide	dry ice	silicon carbide
carbon dioxide	foamite	urea
carbon disulfide	metal carbonyl	water gas
carbon monoxide	organic chemistry	Wöhler
carbon tetrachloride		

HIGHLIGHTS

Since 1828 when **Wöhler** first synthesized **urea** from its elements, more than 300,000 compounds of carbon have been studied. Many new carbon compounds are synthesized each year. Theoretically many more millions are possible. One reason for these great numbers of compounds is that carbon can combine with itself and in entering compounds the carbon atom forms four covalent bonds with many elements and radicals.

Among the simpler carbon compounds are **carbon disulfide, carbon tetrachloride, silicon carbide, carbon dioxide,** and **carbon monoxide.**

Carbon disulfide and carbon tetrachloride are both volatile liquids and good solvents for fats, oils, waxes, and free halogens. Carbon disulfide is also an excellent solvent for sulfur and phosphorus. Carbon tetrachloride is non-inflammable and forms a heavy vapor, making it a good fire-extinguishing agent. It is also widely used in dry cleaning. Its fumes are very poisonous. Silicon carbide, or Carborundum, is nearly as hard as diamond and is widely used as an abrasive.

Carbon dioxide is a product of combustions, oxidations, fermentation, and decay. The **foamite** and soda-acid fire extinguishers are devices for generating carbon dioxide. **Baking powders** are mixtures of baking soda and a substance which acts as an acid on contact with water. The three kinds are the phosphate, alum, and tartrate types.

Carbon monoxide is produced by the incomplete combustion of carbon compounds or by the reaction of carbon and carbon dioxide. It is present in the exhaust fumes of the automobile. Many people die each year because they do not appreciate the danger of this compound.

QUESTIONS

1. What element forms the greatest number of known compounds?
2. Why is the study of carbon chemistry called *organic chemistry?*
3. Explain two different ways in which the term *synthetic* may be used.
4. Who synthesized the first organic compound?
5. What type of valence does carbon always show?
6. Why does carbon never have electrovalence?
7. Draw electron structure diagrams of CCl_4, CO_2, CF_4, and CH_3OH.
8. What two common nonmetals combine directly with carbon?
9. Does chlorine combine directly with carbon? How is carbon tetrachloride made?
10. What are the uses for carbon tetrachloride?
11. Why is carbon tetrachloride more suitable for dry cleaning than gasoline?
12. How is silicon carbide made? For what purposes is it used?
13. Give three different ways in which carbon dioxide may be formed.
14. Explain a good laboratory source of carbon dioxide.
15. Explain how dry ice is manufactured.
16. Describe three different types of fire extinguishers.
17. What type of fire extinguisher is best for fires in electrical machinery? Why?
18. Would you prefer a liquid carbon dioxide or a foamite extinguisher for trash fires? Explain.
19. Describe the three types of baking powders.
20. What is meant by a double-acting baking powder?
21. What is baking soda?
22. Describe a test for carbon dioxide.
23. Describe two common sources of carbon monoxide in everyday life.
24. Why is carbon monoxide a more treacherous poison than hydrogen sulfide?
25. What is water gas? For what is it used?
26. What is producer gas? For what is it used?
27. What are the first symptoms of carbon monoxide poisoning?

CHAPTER 36

the hydrocarbons, fuels, and petroleum

The ability of carbon to form such a large number of compounds is due to the fact that it can share electrons, not only with any other nonmetal but also with itself. This fact makes possible the formation of chains of carbon atoms linked to each other with covalent bonds. For illustration

$$\cdot \overset{..}{C} : \overset{..}{C} : \overset{..}{C} : \overset{..}{C} : \overset{..}{C} \cdot$$

The covalent bonds are more commonly represented by a dashed line than as shown above.

$$-\overset{|}{\underset{|}{C}}-\overset{|}{\underset{|}{C}}-\overset{|}{\underset{|}{C}}-\overset{|}{\underset{|}{C}}-\overset{|}{\underset{|}{C}}-$$

The remaining valence bonds on each carbon atom can "hook on" any nonmetal. Furthermore, there seems to be no limit to the length of the carbon chain which can exist. These facts together with one more fact given in the section "Structural Formulas" (page 414) make the number of carbon compounds which are theoretically possible extremely large. As stated earlier, about 300,000 have been studied already, but this is only a small fraction of the total number which can exist. Organic chemistry is, like many other branches of science, a field in which the most important discoveries are to be made some time in the future.

Organic chemists classify carbon compounds

Although a student beginning the study of organic chemistry may feel it a hopeless task to learn about the properties of so many compounds, this is by no means the case. Most of the organic compounds fall into a few classes. The chemical properties of all members of a given class are very similar, and their physical properties are also closely related to each other. Examples of such classes are the *hydrocarbons*, the *alcohols*, and the *organic acids*. In this book the properties and uses of some of the most important classes of organic compounds will be considered. In this chapter you will learn about the hydrocarbons.

The paraffin hydrocarbons

These organic compounds are, as the name implies, made up entirely of carbon and hydrogen. The simplest such compound is methane, CH_4, one of the main constituents of natural gas. The structural formulas of methane and other members of the paraffin hydrocarbon series are shown below.

```
        H
        |
    H—C—H               CH₄         methane
        |
        H

     H   H
     |   |
   H—C—C—H              C₂H₆        ethane
     |   |
     H   H

    H  H  H
    |  |  |
  H—C—C—C—H             C₃H₈        propane
    |  |  |
    H  H  H

   H  H  H  H
   |  |  |  |
 H—C—C—C—C—H            C₄H₁₀       butane
   |  |  |  |
   H  H  H  H
```

Note that each higher member of the series is formed by replacing one of the hydrogen atoms by another methyl (—CH_3) group.

Note also that the formula for any member of the series is C_nH_{2n+2}, where n is the number of carbon atoms in the molecule.

There seems to be no actual limit to the length of the carbon chain which can exist in this type of hydrocarbon. One containing 94 carbon atoms and having the formula $C_{94}H_{190}$ has been synthesized.

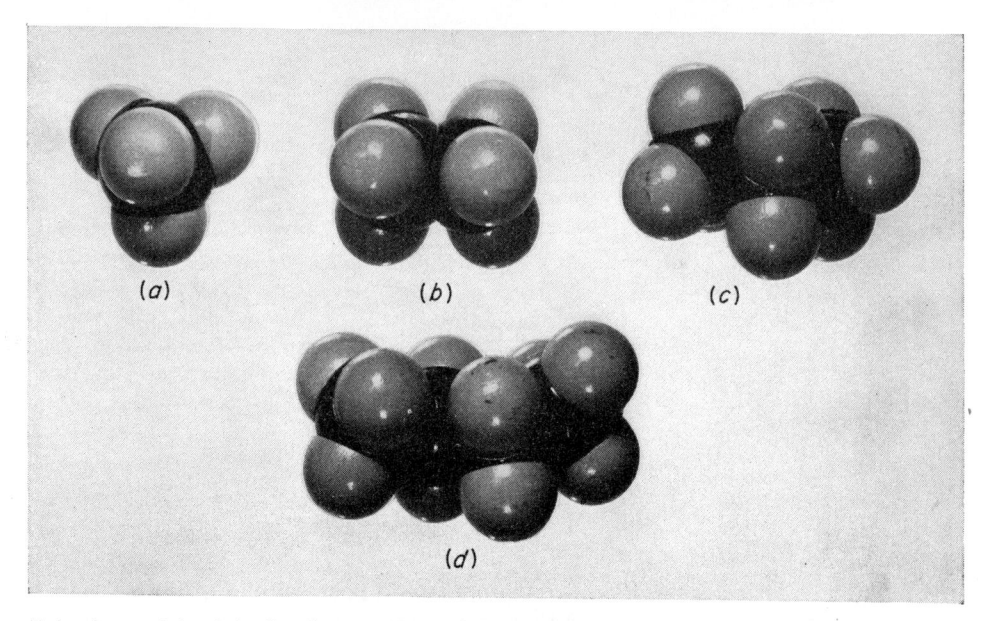

Molecular models of the first four members of the paraffin hydrocarbon series. Methane (a), ethane (b), propane (c), butane (d). (Fisher Scientific Co.)

Properties of paraffin hydrocarbons

Table 36-1 gives properties of some members of the paraffin hydrocarbon series. You will observe that the boiling point and the melting point increase with increasing molecular weight. Those compounds up to butane, C_4H_{10}, are gases at room temperature, from pentane, C_5H_{12}, to about hexadecane, $C_{16}H_{34}$, the paraffin hydrocarbons are liquids, and higher members of the series are solids. Many compounds

TABLE 36-1. Some normal paraffin hydrocarbons[a]

Molecular formula	Name	Boiling point, °C	Melting point, °C	State at room temperature and normal pressure
CH_4	Methane	−161.5	−184	Gas
C_2H_6	Ethane	−88.3	−172	Gas
C_3H_8	Propane	−42	−188	Gas
C_4H_{10}	Butane	−0.6	−135	Gas
C_5H_{12}	Pentane	36	−130	Liquid
C_6H_{14}	Hexane	69	−94	Liquid
C_7H_{16}	Heptane	98	−90	Liquid
C_8H_{18}	Octane	126	−57	Liquid
$C_{18}H_{38}$	Octadecane	317	28	Solid
$C_{19}H_{40}$	Nonadecane	330	32	Solid

[a] Normal hydrocarbons are those in which the carbon chain is not branched (see page 415).

Molecular models of the structural isomers of butane. Left, normal butane. Right, isobutane. You can see the structural formulas for these compounds on page 415. (Fisher Scientific Co.)

of this series are found in natural gas and petroleum. Ordinary "paraffin" wax is a mixture of higher-molecular-weight compounds of this series. The compounds in "paraffin" wax contain mostly 20 to 40 carbon atoms per molecule.

Chemically the paraffin hydrocarbons are quite stable. Their most important reaction is that all members of the series burn to form carbon dioxide and water, thereby liberating large amounts of energy. Compounds from this group furnish our most important liquid and gaseous fuels—gasoline, fuel oil, and others. This point is discussed more fully later in this chapter.

All the hydrocarbons are non-electrolytes, insoluble in water but soluble in each other.

Structural formulas

Formulas like those given on page 412 for the first four members of the paraffin hydrocarbon series are known as *structural formulas*. They are an attempt to show the location of every atom in the molecule with respect to every other atom. Actually the molecules are three-dimensional and a more accurate representation of the structures of the molecules is shown in the photograph on page 413. However, chemists still find it very convenient to make use of the two-dimensional structural formula. The reason for this is that there is more than one possible structure for compounds having some of these formulas, and these differences can be shown in two-dimensional figures.

The study of organic chemistry is something like solving a mathematical puzzle.

Consider the following puzzle. You have 4 balls, each with 4 hooks on it. You have 10 smaller balls, each with 1 hook. How many different ways can you hook these balls together, using all 14 balls and all hooks on each ball? You will eventually conclude that there are only two different ways. They are

```
    H   H   H   H
    |   |   |   |
H—C—C—C—C—H
    |   |   |   |
    H   H   H   H
```

and

```
    H   H   H
    |   |   |
H—C—C—C—H
    |   |   |
    H   |   H
    H—C—H
        |
        H
```

To the organic chemist the 4 large balls having 4 hooks each are carbon atoms. The 10 smaller ones with 1 hook each are hydrogen atoms. And hooked together they represent the molecular formula of butane, C_4H_{10}. But since there are two ways of hooking the atoms together, there are two *different compounds* having the formula C_4H_{10}. They are said to be **structural isomers**.

```
    H   H   H   H
    |   |   |   |
H—C—C—C—C—H    normal butane, bp −0.6°C
    |   |   |   |
    H   H   H   H
```

```
    H   H   H
    |   |   |
H—C—C—C—H    isobutane, bp −10°C
    |   |   |
    H   |   H
    H—C—H
        |
        H
```

Structural isomers have the same molecular formula but different structural formulas and different properties. The number of isomers of a given formula increases very rapidly with the number of carbon atoms in the molecule. For pentane, C_5H_{12}, there are 3. For eicosane, $C_{20}H_{42}$, calculations show there are 366,319 possible isomers!

The olefin series of hydrocarbons

The **olefin hydrocarbon** series of carbon-hydrogen compounds contains a double bond between adjacent carbon atoms. A double bond is the sharing of two pairs of electrons between the atoms. The first member of the series is *ethylene* (or ethene).

$$H:C::C:H \quad \text{or} \quad \underset{H}{\overset{H}{\diagdown}}C=C\underset{H}{\overset{H}{\diagup}}$$

ethylene

The next is *propylene* (or propene).

$$\underset{H}{\overset{H}{\diagdown}}C=\underset{H}{\overset{H}{|}}C-\underset{H}{\overset{H}{|}}C-H$$

The type formula for compounds of this series is C_nH_{2n} where n is the number of carbon atoms in the molecule.

Ethylene occurs in natural gas and is formed in petroleum refining. It can be prepared by heating ethyl alcohol and concentrated sulfuric acid.

$$H-\underset{\boxed{H}}{\overset{H}{\underset{|}{C}}}-\underset{\boxed{OH}}{\overset{H}{\underset{|}{C}}}-H \xrightarrow[150°C]{\text{concentrated}~H_2SO_4} \underset{\text{ethylene}}{C_2H_4} + H_2O$$

ethyl alcohol

Ethylene is used as an anesthetic. For this use, it has many points in its favor but one serious disadvantage. Mixtures of ethylene and oxygen, as they must be administered to the patient, are very explosive. Even a spark from static electricity on the operating table has been known to ignite such mixtures.

Ethylene is also employed in the artificial ripening of fruit, particularly oranges and lemons. Although colorless itself, ethylene causes the production of "tree-ripened color" in the skin of prematurely picked oranges and lemons.

Reactions of olefins

Olefins are more reactive than the paraffin hydrocarbons. Since they can add a nonmetal, olefins are sometimes called **unsaturated** hydrocarbons. They will react with halogens:

$$\underset{H}{\overset{H}{\diagdown}}C=C\underset{H}{\overset{H}{\diagup}} + Br_2 \rightarrow H-\underset{Br}{\overset{H}{\underset{|}{C}}}-\underset{Br}{\overset{H}{\underset{|}{C}}}-H$$

dibromoethane

Under proper conditions two olefin molecules will react with themselves:

$$\begin{array}{c} H \\ \diagdown \\ C=C \\ \diagup \quad \diagdown \\ H \quad\quad H \end{array} \begin{array}{c} H \\ \diagup \\ C=C \\ \diagdown \quad \diagup \\ H \quad\quad H \end{array} + \begin{array}{c} (H) \\ \diagdown \\ \diagup \\ H \end{array} \rightarrow H-\overset{H}{\underset{H}{C}}-\overset{H}{\underset{H}{C}}-\overset{H}{C}=C\begin{array}{c} H \\ \diagup \\ \diagdown \\ H \end{array}$$

The resulting product, which still has a double bond, can react with another molecule of ethylene or of itself, and so on. In this way *very large* molecules can be formed. Some of our most important plastics as well as synthetic rubbers are produced by reactions of this type (Lucite, polystyrene, polyethylene, and others; see Chap. 39). A reaction of this kind in which two or more molecules of the same type combine with each other is called **polymerization**.

The acetylene series of hydrocarbons

The **acetylene hydrocarbon** series is characterized by the presence of a triple bond between carbon atoms. The first member is acetylene (or ethyne).

$$H : C ::: C : H \quad \text{or} \quad H-C\equiv C-H$$
acetylene

The next member is propyne.

$$H-C\equiv C-\overset{\overset{\displaystyle H}{|}}{\underset{\underset{\displaystyle H}{|}}{C}}-H$$
propyne

Acetylene, the most important compound of this type, is made by adding water to calcium carbide. Calcium carbide is formed by heating limestone and coke in an electric furnace.

$$CaCO_3 + 3C \xrightarrow{\text{electric furnace}} \underset{\text{calcium carbide}}{CaC_2} + CO_2 \uparrow + CO \uparrow$$

$$CaC_2 + 2H_2O \rightarrow Ca(OH)_2 + \underset{\text{acetylene}}{C_2H_2} \uparrow$$

Acetylene burns with the liberation of much heat. The oxyacetylene torch is widely used in welding because it produces such a high temperature. Furthermore, acetylene is very reactive. It will add halogens, polymerize, and undergo many other types of reactions. For this reason a great many other organic compounds can be made from it. When one reads in the newspaper that a certain new organic compound is "made from limestone, coal, and water," it usually means the compound has been made from acetylene.

The ring hydrocarbons

All the hydrocarbons considered so far have been open-chain types. In the ring type of hydrocarbons the ends of the chain are linked together. The most important ring hydrocarbon is benzene, C_6H_6. Its structure is

$$\begin{array}{c} H \\ | \\ C \\ H-C \diagup \diagdown C-H \\ H-C \diagdown \diagup C-H \\ C \\ | \\ H \end{array}$$
benzene

Benzene is not to be confused with benzine, which is a name given to a mixture of the more volatile open-chain hydrocarbons.

Benzene is a colorless liquid which boils at 80°C. It is obtained by the distillation of coal tar, which contains about 1.6 percent benzene. Benzene can also be made from petroleum.

Toluene is methyl benzene ($CH_3C_6H_5$).

$$\begin{array}{c} H \\ | \\ C \quad H \\ H-C \diagup \diagdown C-C-H \\ H-C \diagdown \diagup C \quad H \\ C \quad H \\ | \\ H \end{array}$$
toluene

Toluene also is a colorless liquid which may be obtained from coal tar or made from petroleum.

Organic compounds containing the **benzene ring** are called **aromatic** compounds. This does not necessarily mean that all such compounds have pleasant odors. Those organic compounds containing only open chains of carbon atoms are called **aliphatic** compounds. This name comes from the fact that fats are open-chain carbon compounds.

A section of the Elk Basin, Wyoming, oil field. (Standard Oil Co.)

Naphthalene ($C_{10}H_8$) may be considered as two benzene rings attached to each other; thus

$$\text{naphthalene}$$

Naphthalene is a white solid. Its odor is familiar to most people, since it has been widely used as moth balls. It also is obtained from coal tar.

Petroleum

Crude natural petroleum is a complex mixture of many organic compounds but contains mainly hydrocarbons. Petroleum is found widely distributed over the earth. At the present time the principal producing regions are the United States, Canada, Venezuela, the Near East (Iran and Iraq), and Russia. In the United States, the most important petroleum-producing states are Texas, California, Louisiana, Oklahoma, Kansas, and Illinois.

The history of the development of the petroleum industry in America is almost a complete history of the country for the last hundred

Petroleum refinery equipment and storage tanks at the Sarnia refinery in Ontario, Canada. (Standard Oil Co.)

years. This is because petroleum has been closely related to many of the political, economic, and technological events of the last century.

Long before the white man came, the American Indians knew of certain spots where they could collect oil which had seeped from the earth. They used it as a healing oil. As the country west of the Alleghenies was being settled by the white men, one of their pressing needs was for salt—without which man cannot live. In attempting to locate a supply of salt, some of the pioneers dug wells, hoping to strike brine rather than fresh water. In 1829 a Pennsylvanian named Kier found one of his brine wells suddenly flowing oil. Instead of abandoning the well which was now ruined as a source of salt, he resourcefully started to bottle the crude oil and sell it as a medicine. Although the curative powers of crude petroleum are surely questionable, it is said that he did a very good business peddling his "petroleum, or rock oil."

About this time a sample of Kier's oil came to the laboratory of one James Curtis Booth. In 1830 Booth was one of the few chemically trained persons in America. For this period he was well trained, having studied under the German chemist Friedrich Wöhler, who synthesized the first organic compound. Booth distilled some of Kier's rock oil and found that one of the products was an oil highly satisfactory for illumination (what we now call *kerosene*). Thus the era of kerosene lamps came into existence. This was a particularly timely discovery because up to this time man had depended for illumination mainly on candles, coal oil from the distillation of coal, and whale oil; and whales were beginning to be scarce. Kier, acting on Booth's advice, set up a crude still for distilling his petroleum. By 1858 he was selling weekly in New York "100 barrels of carbon oil at 62½ cents per gallon."[1] The result was a tremendous business in kerosene for illumination and, as Haynes[1] had said, "In five years the oilcan became a familiar object from Pittsburgh to St. Petersburg and in ten years from Pekin to LaPaz." In the meantime a more complete analysis of petroleum had been made by **Professor Benjamin Silliman** of Yale University, one of the most eminent chemists of his day. Acting on his advice, a group of men set out to drill an oil well at Titusville, Pa. In 1859 they struck oil at about 69 ft. (Modern oil wells are sometimes 15,000 ft deep.) This was the first well drilled for the purpose of producing petroleum.

Distillation of petroleum

When crude petroleum is distilled, the low-molecular-weight hydrocarbons, having lower boiling points, come off first, followed by those having higher boiling points. The various fractions obtained are classified as shown in Table 36-2.

TABLE 36-2. Products from distillation of petroleum

Fraction	Compounds present	Boiling range, °C
Gas	CH_4 to C_4H_{10}	
Petroleum ether (naphtha, benzine)	C_5H_{12} and C_6H_{14}	35–70
Gasoline	C_7H_{16} to C_9H_{20}	70–200
Kerosene	$C_{10}H_{22}$ to $C_{16}H_{34}$	200–300
Light fuel oil	$C_{15}H_{32}$ to $C_{19}H_{40}$	300–380
Lubricating oils	$C_{20}H_{42}$ and above	
Petroleum jelly (vaseline)		
Paraffin	High-molecular-weight hydrocarbons	Not distilled
Tar		

The various fractions are used in the following ways:

Gases are used as fuel, sometimes transported by pipeline and sometimes compressed to a liquid and transported and sold in steel cylinders (Essotane, Pyrofax, and others). Much of the gas associated with crude petroleum escapes from the ground as the well is drilled. In the past a great deal of this gas was wasted by burning because there was not enough demand for it in the neighborhood of the well. Now it is being transported by pipeline as far as New York City and New England, where it is used as fuel. Some of the gas is coming East through the Big Inch pipeline built during World War II to bring petroleum from Texas to New York.

[1] From William Haynes, *This Chemical Age*, Alfred A. Knopf, Inc., New York, 1942.

A crew of workmen laying a high-pressure natural gas pipeline in Tomball, Tex. Natural gas is now piped all the way to New York from gas fields as far away as Texas and Louisiana. (Standard Oil Co.)

With a change in the carburetor, some natural gases can be used to operate automobile engines, and certain trucks now use butane.

Petroleum ether is sometimes used in dry cleaning and as a solvent in the laboratory. Because of its volatility, it is a very real fire hazard in the home. Most of it is used as motor fuel by mixing it with the higher boiling fractions of petroleum especially for winter gasoline. Addition of petroleum ether makes for easier cold-weather starting.

Gasoline, of course, is used mostly as a motor fuel.

Kerosene, which formerly was used as an illuminating oil, is now used mainly for heating and to replace gasoline in large tractors. It is also converted into gasoline by cracking (see below).

Light fuel oil is used in home heating and in diesel engines or it is converted into gasoline.

Lubricating oil is used for engine lubrication.

Petroleum jelly serves as a base for medicinal ointments and is used in lubricants (greases).

Paraffin is utilized for candles, waterproofing, and other things.

Tar is used in road building, waterproofing, and roofing.

Cracking

On the average, 100 gal of crude oil will yield on straight distillation about 25 gal of naphtha and gasoline and 15 gal of kerosene. In the beginning of the petroleum industry the demand was almost entirely for kerosene for illumination. The internal-combustion engine was unknown, and there was no demand for the gasoline necessarily produced as a by-product of kerosene production. The stuff was a nuisance, difficult to dispose of. But about the beginning of the twentieth century, with the invention of the horseless carriage, the demand for

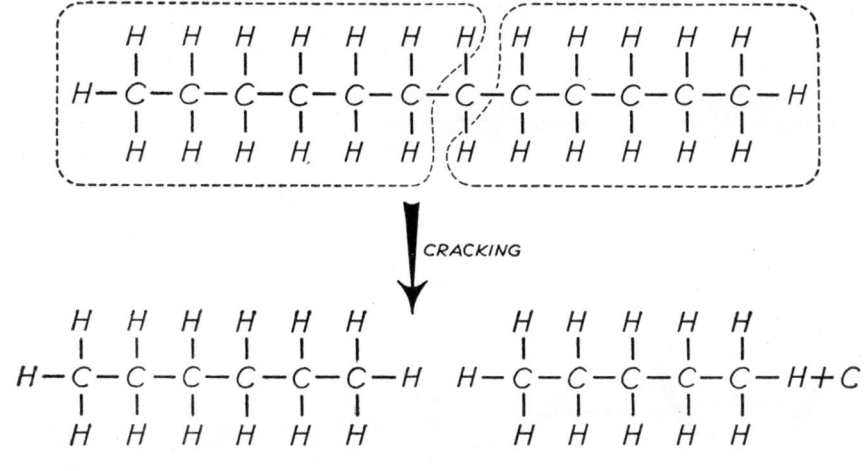

Fig. 36-1. An illustration of the cracking of higher-molecular-weight molecules to yield compounds suitable for automobile fuel.

gasoline began to increase. The demand has increased steadily ever since then and the end is not yet in sight. Even by 1910 the demand for gasoline was greater than the demand for kerosene, and the disposal of the kerosene and higher products began to be a problem.

The problem was solved by cracking, by means of which these higher boiling fractions are converted into gasoline. Cracking is sometimes described as making little molecules out of big ones. If a compound, such as dodecane, $C_{12}H_{26}$, which is too nonvolatile to be used for gasoline, is heated to 500 or 600°C, the molecule breaks down into smaller fragments. A typical reaction is

$$\underbrace{C_{12}H_{26}}_{\text{(unsuitable for gasoline)}} \xrightarrow{500°C} \underbrace{C_6H_{14} + C_5H_{12}}_{\text{(suitable for gasoline)}} + C$$

Both these smaller molecules are suitable for use as gasoline. By cracking the higher hydrocarbons, the yield of gasoline may be 40 to 50 gal per 100 gal of crude oil. At present the demand for both fuel oil and gasoline is large and the demand changes with the season. Modern petroleum refineries change seasonally the proportions of these two products produced by cracking and thus follow the market demand.

Polymerization

By polymerization, a reaction opposite to cracking, low-molecular-weight gaseous hydrocarbons can be combined with each other to form products usable as gasoline. The process requires special conditions and catalysts, which will not be described here. The point is that the petroleum industry can now convert these gaseous hydrocarbons into

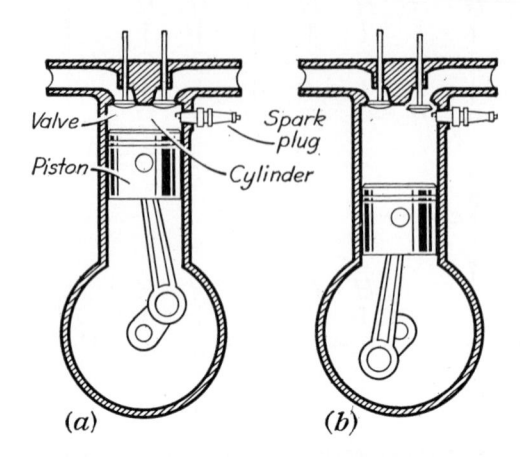

Fig. 36–2. A simplified drawing of a one-cylinder gasoline engine with the piston in two positions: in (a) the piston is up, and in (b) it is down.

gasoline. In fact a modern petroleum refinery, if it is desired, can now produce about 100 gal of gasoline from 100 gal of crude oil. This is a comforting margin of safety in time of war, when there is great demand for gasoline. But if many refineries were to go on such a program, there are many homes that would be cold as the result since many homes use fuel oil and many use gas for heating purposes.

What goes on inside a gasoline engine?

The power which a **gasoline engine** delivers is derived from the energy released in the oxidation of gasoline. The carburetor introduces, into the cylinder (Fig. 36–2) of the engine, an explosive mixture of gasoline vapor and air. The piston moves upward, thereby compressing this fuel charge. An electric discharge at the spark plug then ignites this compressed charge. The energy from this combustion causes heating and expansion of the gases produced, thereby pushing the piston down. After discharge of these burned gases by the proper arrangement of valves, the process is repeated. It has long been known that the greater the extent of compression of the fuel charge the greater the amount of power delivered by the engine per gallon of gasoline. The **compression ratio** of an engine is the ratio of the volume of the cylinder before compression to its volume after compression. Thus a high-compression-ratio engine is desirable because such an engine is more efficient. In fact the principal difference between the engine in a present-day model automobile and that in a 1930 model is that the former has a higher compression ratio and is thus more efficient. Most present-day model automobiles have a compression ratio of about 7.50:1. It is estimated that, if this ratio could be increased to 12:1, fuel consumption would drop 35 to 40 percent. A drop in fuel consumption is to be desired both for individual economy and for national conservation.

Antiknock gasolines

High-compression engines knock badly with certain types of gasoline, and in engine designing this sets a limit to the compression ratio. Hence a more efficient engine requires not only a higher compression ratio but also an improved fuel on which to operate.

It has been found that, in general, straight-chain hydrocarbons are the worst knock-producers (this is true because they burn more rapidly). Branched-chain hydrocarbons are less knock-producing. To set up a scale for comparing the antiknock ratings of different fuels, the compound normal heptane, which knocks very badly when used in an engine, was assigned an antiknock rating of zero. The branched-chain hydrocarbon, isooctane, which has excellent antiknock qualities, was assigned a rating of 100.

Normal heptane: CH_3–CH_2–CH_2–CH_2–CH_2–CH_2–CH_3 — antiknock rating 0

Isooctane: (structural formula shown) — antiknock rating 100

The fuel to be rated is run in a standard test engine and in that way compared with mixtures of the two above standards. A gasoline which has, for example, an **octane rating** of 85 has the same antiknock qualities as a mixture composed of 15 percent normal heptane and 85 percent isooctane.

How can the octane rating be increased?

Knocking of a fuel is caused when it burns too rapidly in the combustion chamber. It was found by Thomas Midgley (1889–1944), of the General Motors Research Laboratory (who also developed Freon for refrigeration), that **tetraethyllead** [$Pb(C_2H_5)_4$], added to fuels in quantities of about 0.001 percent, increased their octane rating. That is because this compound reduces the rate at which the fuel burns. Now practically all gasoline on the market has some tetraethyllead in it. The octane rating can be increased also by making a gasoline which contains a higher proportion of branched-chain hydrocarbons. Modern petroleum chemists have found that in polymerization and

Testing unit for high-octane fuels. This is a view from the control panel to the inner cell where the aviation motor is housed. (Standard Oil Co.)

cracking, certain catalysts tend to cause formation of branched-chain compounds. Both these factors affecting the octane rating are employed in present-day gasoline manufacture in an attempt to make gasoline with the highest octane rating that is practical.

Airplane fuel

The fuel requirements of an internal-combustion piston engine used for an airplane are even more exacting. Speed, performance, rate of climb, engine weight, and fuel consumption all depend upon the compression ratio of the engine, and hence a high-octane fuel is required. During World War II the Air Force used 100-octane fuels commonly, and in some cases their fuels even went above this in octane number. Such fuels are not only much more expensive to make but also rather more wasteful of petroleum than the lower-octane fuels which are commonly used for automobiles.

Present-day jets and other non-piston-type engines which are now being employed in increasing numbers in airplanes do not have such exacting fuel requirements. In fact some of them will operate efficiently on 65-octane gasoline or even on kerosene.

Internal-combustion engines of the future

Because everyone in the United States is vitally concerned with motor transportation, the efficiency of the automobile engine is a matter of great interest and importance to every citizen. In no other country in the world are such good automobiles available to such a large percentage of its population. For this we must give credit not only to the automobile industry itself but also to the petroleum industry. The development of this industry necessarily paralleled the development of the automobile industry. If automobile engines of present design are to have their efficiency still further stepped up by increased compression ratio, gasolines of higher octane ratings than are at present available will be required to run them. Although the petroleum industry could make them, such fuels would cost much more than present-type fuels. Therefore, the cost per mile to the motorist would probably be as great as, or greater than, the present cost. Some automobile and petroleum engineers believe that the efficiency of the internal-combustion engine of the future will be increased by a complete redesign of the engine rather than by using fuels of much higher octane rating than at present.

Other products from petroleum

While the American public thinks of petroleum as a source of fuel only, it is actually a source of a great many organic compounds of wide application outside the field of fuels. The starting materials used in making the most important synthetic rubber (buna S or GRS) are obtained from petroleum. TNT (trinitrotoluene), the most widely used military explosive, requires toluene for its manufacture. Although some toluene is obtained in the coking of coal, it was found during World War II that the supply from this source was not great enough. Much of the toluene used during World War II was made from petroleum. Even glycerin, which used to be obtained entirely from animal fats and oils, is now made from petroleum, as are the newer "soapless soaps" and a host of other organic products.

The world's petroleum resources

There is no agreement among the experts as to just how much more petroleum remains within the earth to be tapped and used by man. New fields are being discovered every year and the proved resources of petroleum (those known to exist underground) are greater today than ever before. Yet America used around *three billion barrels* of petroleum in 1956. At such a rate of consumption, the *proved* resources of the world would supply us for only a few years. Of course, no one knows with certainty just how much more petroleum remains to be discovered. However, the prospect for a continued supply, even at the present rate of consumption, is not bright. The consensus of expert opinion in the petroleum industry, as summarized by a congressional committee in 1947, was to the effect that by 1967 petroleum production in the United States would have declined because of depletion of supply to about half our present rate of consumption. Two courses of action are called for: (1) conserve our fuel resources, particularly our natural supply of liquid fuels, and (2) seek new sources of liquid fuels. Fortunately there are two other possible sources of liquid fuels.

Retorting plant for producing petroleum from oil shale. (U.S. Bureau of Mines)

Petroleum substitutes

1. The oil shales. In Utah, Wyoming, and particularly Colorado, there are great deposits of **oil shale.** These are shale rocks which contain a considerable amount of organic matter, probably of vegetable origin. Similar oil shales are found in Scotland. When these oil shales are heated in the absence of air, a liquid fuel distills off which can be refined almost exactly as is crude petroleum. Except for its higher cost, shale oil is a perfectly good substitute for natural petroleum. On the average, less than one barrel of oil is obtained per ton of shale distilled. The U.S. Bureau of Mines has built a plant near Rifle, Colo., which has proved that these oil shales can serve as a practical source of liquid fuels. The cost of shale oil, although higher than the cost of natural petroleum, is not unreasonably so. In addition we can expect the cost to be reduced if large-scale production goes into effect. To be sure, some problems remain to be solved. One of the largest is the disposal of the ash remaining after distilling out the oil. This ash amounts to nearly a ton per barrel of oil produced. It is estimated that we may eventually obtain 350 billion barrels of oil from this source. This would leave enough ash to "cover the entire state of Colorado to a depth of 10 ft." Large-scale production of shale oil would yield as a by-product large amounts of ammonia, which, being salable, would reduce the cost of the oil.

2. *The hydrogenation of coal.* Since our coal supplies are still vast and since liquid fuels can be obtained from coal, in the long run we shall probably obtain much more oil from coal than from shale. Two processes for obtaining liquid fuel from coal are now receiving serious study by research chemists and engineers with the view of making them as economical as possible.

a. The Bergius process. The **Bergius process** was discovered by the German engineer, Friedrich Bergius, in 1913. Powdered coal is mixed with tar, from a previous run, to make a thick paste. A catalyst of tin chloride or iron oxide is added, and the resulting mixture is heated with hydrogen gas at a pressure of several thousand pounds per square inch. Under these conditions part of the coal is converted to gaseous and liquid hydrocarbons. One ton of coal yields about 140 gal of an oil which can be refined as crude petroleum is refined. Discovery of a more effective catalyst would greatly cheapen the process.

b. The Fischer-Tropsch process. In the **Fischer-Tropsch process**, a mixture of carbon monoxide and hydrogen is passed over a catalyst of certain metal oxides, where they combine, forming liquid and gaseous hydrocarbons and water. The nature of the reaction may be represented by the general equation

$$n\text{CO} + (2n + 1)\text{H}_2 \rightarrow \text{C}_n\text{H}_{2n+2} + n\text{H}_2\text{O}$$

By controlling conditions, the process can be made to yield predominantly low or predominantly high-molecular-weight hydrocarbons as desired for fuel or lubrication. Carbon monoxide and hydrogen (water gas) can be obtained from coke (see Chap. 35, pages 406 and 407), coal, natural gas—in fact almost any carbonaceous material. Recently construction was begun on a Fischer-Tropsch plant in Texas to utilize natural gas in this way. This is a particularly promising process since our supplies of natural gas are very large.

TABLE 36–3. Estimated cost of gasoline synthesized from various raw materials, relative to cost of gasoline from natural petroleum[a]

Source	Cost to make, cents per gallon
From crude petroleum	12.2
Natural gas by Fischer-Tropsch	15.0
Oil shale	22.5
Indiana bituminous coal by Fischer-Tropsch	22.5

[a] Eugene Ayres, "The Fuel Problem," *Scientific American*, vol. 181, December, 1949.

KEY WORDS

acetylene hydrocarbons	cracking	petroleum
aliphatic	Fischer-Tropsch process	polymerization
antiknock gasoline	gasoline engine	Silliman
aromatic	octane rating	structural isomer
benzene ring	oil shale	tetraethyllead
Bergius process	olefin hydrocarbons	unsaturated
compression ratio	paraffin hydrocarbons	

HIGHLIGHTS

The tendency of carbon atoms to form straight, branched, and closed chains partly explains why there are so many carbon compounds. It also explains why there are so many compounds (isomers) with the same empirical formula but with different structural formulas.

The **aliphatic** or open-chain hydrocarbons include (1) the single-bond paraffin series (C_nH_{2n+2}), (2) the double-bond olefin series (C_nH_{2n}), and the triple-bond acetylene series (C_nH_{2n-2}).

The simpler paraffins include the constituents of natural gas and gasoline. The olefins combine with the halogens. Olefin molecules also combine with each other, a process known as **polymerization.** Acetylene is the starting point of a great many important industrial organic compounds.

Among the **aromatic** or ring hydrocarbons are benzene, toluene, and naphthalene, which are all parent compounds of huge numbers of other synthetic compounds.

Petroleum or crude oil is distilled fractionally to produce such products as natural gas, petroleum ether, gasoline, kerosene, fuel oil, lubricating oil, petroleum jelly, paraffin, and tar. Because of the ever-increasing demand for more gasoline, high-molecular-weight hydrocarbons such as kerosene are heated to 500°C to break them into smaller molecules—a process known as **cracking.** The addition of small amounts of **tetraethyllead** increases the **octane rating** of a gasoline and therefore gives it better antiknock qualities. Automobile engines of better design and with more favorable **compression ratios** such as 12:1 may be expected in the future.

Because the present-known resources of petroleum are far from inexhaustible, future sources may be expected to include hydrocarbons distilled from **oil shales** and those produced by the hydrogenation of coal by the **Bergius** and the **Fischer-Tropsch processes.**

QUESTIONS

1. What property of the carbon atom enables this element to form such a large number of compounds?
2. Give the names and formulas of the first four members of the paraffin series of hydrocarbons.
3. What is the type formula for a paraffin hydrocarbon?
4. Would you expect the following compounds to be liquids, solids, or gases at room temperature: C_2H_6, C_7H_{16}, $C_{25}H_{52}$?
5. How many compounds are there with the molecular formula C_4H_{10}? Explain.
6. What is ethylene? How does it differ from ethane?
7. What is acetylene? How is it made?
8. Give the names and formulas of two ring-type hydrocarbons. From what source are they obtained?
9. Name and describe the uses for the various fractions obtained by distilling petroleum.
10. What is cracking? Why is it important?
11. Why is the compression ratio of an internal-combustion engine important?
12. Explain why the petroleum industry and the automobile industry must work together in developing more efficient internal-combustion engines.
13. Why is tetraethyllead added to most gasolines?
14. What is meant by the octane rating of a fuel?
15. Name three important commodities made from petroleum in addition to fuels and lubricants.
16. What are oil shales? Why are they of great potential importance?
17. Describe the Bergius process for hydrogenation of coal.
18. Describe a process by means of which water gas may be made into liquid fuels.

CHAPTER **37**

some other organic compounds

The characteristic formulas of classes of organic compounds other than the hydrocarbons (Chap. 36) can best be understood by considering them as derived from the hydrocarbons by replacement of one or more hydrogen atoms by other atoms. This, however, does not mean that all these compounds can actually be produced in the laboratory by starting with hydrocarbons, although some of them can be produced in this way. The systematic arrangement of organic compounds into classes is of great importance. It permits the chemist to predict what reactions many organic compounds will undergo, since compounds in the same class usually react similarly.

Type formula of alcohols

To most people the word alcohol means either wood alcohol or grain alcohol. Actually these two compounds are only the first two members of a whole class of organic compounds. An alcohol differs from a hydrocarbon in that one or more hydrogen atoms on the hydrocarbon have been replaced by the hydroxyl ($-OH$) group. Thus

$$\begin{array}{cc} \text{H} & \text{H} \\ | & | \\ \text{H}-\text{C}-\text{H} & \text{H}-\text{C}-\text{O}-\text{H} \\ | & | \\ \text{H} & \text{H} \\ \text{methane} & \text{methyl (or wood) alcohol} \\ & \text{or} \\ & \text{methanol} \\ & [methan(\text{e}) + (\text{alcoh})ol] \end{array}$$

and

```
    H H                H H
    | |                | |
H—C—C—H          H—C—C—O—H
    | |                | |
    H H                H H
   ethane         ethyl (or grain) alcohol
                          or
                   ethanol [ethan(e) + (alcoh)ol]

       H H H
       | | |
   H—C—C—C—O—H
       | | |
       H H H
   propanol (from propane + alcohol)
```

If we let R represent any hydrocarbon less one hydrogen (that is, $-CH_3$ or $-C_2H_5$, and so on), then the type formula for any alcohol is

$$R-OH$$

Properties of alcohols

Alcohols always have higher boiling points than the corresponding hydrocarbons. This is true because the presence of the hydroxyl group causes the molecule to become **polar**. A polar molecule, instead of being electrically symmetrical, as are the hydrocarbons, acts as though it has a positive charge on one end of the molecule and a negative charge on the other end.

This type of compound is not to be confused with ions, which have a net positive or negative charge. A polar molecule has zero *net* electrical charge. But because some of the electrons are drawn more closely to some of the atoms in the molecule than to other atoms in the molecule, the polar molecule has what amounts to a positive and a negative end. In the case of the alcohols, the electrons are drawn more closely to the oxygen than to the hydrogen or the R group.

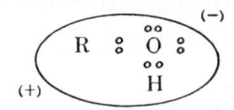

This makes the oxygen somewhat negative and the other end of the molecule in effect positive. Polar molecules line up plus end to minus end and are held together by electrostatic forces of attraction.

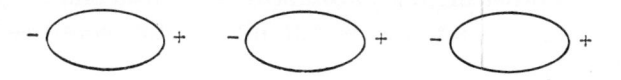

Because of these electrostatic forces exerted between them, polar molecules have less tendency to vaporize than corresponding nonpolar molecules. This is why the alcohols have higher boiling points than the corresponding hydrocarbons, in which such electrical forces are absent.

Water also is a polar compound for the same reason. Hence the alcohols are more soluble in water than the corresponding hydrocarbons. Methanol, ethanol, and propanol are completely miscible with water. In general, the other alcohols show decreasing solubility in water with increased length of the hydrocarbon chain. The boiling points also increase with the molecular weights.

Chemically, the alcohols are *not* bases because they do not dissociate. That they are not electrolytes can be demonstrated by testing their conductivity either alone or in water solution (see Chap. 27, page 294).

The alcohols burn forming carbon dioxide and water. For example,

$$2CH_3OH + 3O_2 \rightarrow 2CO_2 \uparrow + 4H_2O$$

By less drastic oxidation they can be converted into aldehydes and organic acids (see pages 439 and 442).

Methanol

This important alcohol was formerly produced entirely by the destructive distillation of wood (see Chap. 34, page 388), hence its common name, *wood alcohol*. This extravagant method of preparation, which requires about one cord of wood to produce 2.5 gal of alcohol, has largely been replaced by a synthetic process discovered in Germany about 1925. In this process, water gas is heated to 400°C in the presence of a catalyst of zinc and chromium oxides at a pressure of 50 atmospheres:

$$CO + 2H_2 \rightarrow CH_3OH$$

The yield is almost 100 percent. The product, *synthetic methanol*, is of course identical with that purified from wood distillation. The development of this synthetic method greatly reduced the price and increased the use of methanol. Today about 90 percent of all the methanol consumed is produced in this way. The other 10 percent is produced as a by-product in the production of wood charcoal. Large amounts of industrial hydrogen are used in the manufacture of synthetic methanol.

Methanol is a good solvent for gums, resins, and shellac and is used in industry for this purpose. It is also used as the starting point for making many other organic substances, since it is relatively inexpensive. Large amounts are used as automobile antifreeze (see Chap. 15, page 162).

Methanol is very poisonous. If taken internally, it acts on the optic nerve, producing blindness. One should avoid as far as possible breathing its vapor.

Ethanol

This compound has been produced by man since the earliest days of history by the **fermentation** of fruit juices and grains. As mentioned earlier, yeast produces an enzyme, *zymase*, which catalyzes the conversion of glucose into ethanol and carbon dioxide.

$$C_6H_{12}O_6 \xrightarrow{zymase} 2C_2H_5OH + 2CO_2$$

Starch, from grain or potatoes, may be used to produce ethanol if another enzyme, *diastase*, is also present. Diastase is formed by sprouting barley which is called *malt* after it has sprouted. Diastase is capable of catalyzing the conversion of starches into maltose. Maltose can be converted into glucose by another enzyme, *maltase*, also present in yeast. The glucose can then be fermented into alcohol and carbon dioxide by zymase. Overall the conversion may be written

$$\text{Starch} \xrightarrow{malt} \text{maltose} \xrightarrow{yeast} \text{ethanol} + \text{carbon dioxide}$$
(from grain, potatoes, and others)

Ethanol is also produced by yeast fermentation of blackstrap molasses, a by-product of the cane-sugar mills.

Waste wood products such as sawdust, planer shavings, and the waste from paper mills are all partially convertible into glucose, which can be fermented to form ethanol. In the latter part of the 1940s a plant was built to manufacture ethanol from the waste products of certain western United States lumber mills. The plant operated satisfactorily but closed down because on a cost basis it could not compete with alcohol from other sources, especially from molasses.

Ethylene, C_2H_4, a by-product of petroleum refining and also found in natural gas, can be converted into ethanol.

$$\underset{\begin{array}{c}H\ H\\|\ \ |\end{array}}{H-C=C-H} + H_2O \xrightarrow{H_2SO_4} \underset{\begin{array}{c}|\ \ |\\H\ OH\end{array}}{\overset{\begin{array}{c}H\ H\\|\ \ |\end{array}}{H-C-C-H}}$$

Fruit juices contain sugars which are fermentable into ethanol. This is the basis of all wine making. Beer and whisky are generally produced by fermenting grains, although at times both have been made from potatoes. Some beverage alcohol is produced from molasses fermentation, particularly that which goes into rum.

Left, the tops of vessels in which grain is fermented to alcohol. Right, alcohol is distilled in these columns. (Joseph E. Seagram and Sons, Inc.)

By proper purification procedures, usually distillation, pure ethanol can be obtained from any of the above sources. Which of the methods will be used for commercial production depends on relative costs and availability of the various starting materials.

Properties and uses of ethanol

Ethanol is a colorless, volatile liquid, boiling at 78.5°C. It is a good solvent for many organic substances which are not soluble in water. Commercial ethanol is 95.5 percent ethanol and 4.5 percent water. The 100 percent variety is known as *absolute alcohol.*

Ethanol is a very important commodity in industrial chemistry. It is widely used as a solvent for making perfumes and flavorings (vanilla, lemon extract, and others) as well as smokeless powder, shellac, varnish, celluloid, hair tonic, mouthwash, and after-shave lotion. Ethanol is used as a starting material for making organic compounds. It forms the basis of certain automobile antifreezes (see Chap. 15, page 162).

When a small amount of soap or calcium acetate is dissolved in alcohol, the solution sets to a jellylike mass (or gel). This is the way certain types of canned heat, such as Sterno, are made.

Ethanol can be used as a satisfactory motor fuel when mixed in certain ratios with gasoline. In certain countries of the world which are less favorably supplied with natural petroleum than the United States, it is so used. In this country, its present cost is too high for it to compete with gasoline as a motor fuel. A group called the *Chemurgic Council*[1] urges the production of ethyl alcohol from various farm products, hoping to find thereby a use for surplus farm commodities.

In the trade the concentration of alcohol-water solutions is given in terms of its *proof*, which is two times the percentage of alcohol by volume. Thus a 90-proof alcohol solution is 45 percent alcohol by volume.

The physiological effects of ethanol

Alcoholic solutions are used medicinally for "alcohol rubs" (see Chap. 12, page 115). In addition to producing a local cooling effect, the alcohol acts as an astringent by closing the pores of the skin, thereby tending to prevent sweating.

Many people mistakenly believe that ethanol when taken internally acts as a stimulant. Actually it depresses the central nervous system, thereby dulling the senses and decreasing the speed of reaction from a nervous impulse. For this reason alcohol is the cause of many automobile and industrial accidents.

It is also believed that alcohol taken internally increases the body temperature. What it actually does is to produce a temporary feeling of warmth by increasing the flow of blood to the skin, thereby causing the body to lose heat at a rate greater than normal.

Large amounts of alcohol taken internally are irritating to the stomach and when taken into the stomach interfere with normal body physiology.

Denatured alcohol

Because of the possible use of ethanol as a beverage, the United States government places a heavy tax on pure ethanol or water solutions containing it. At present the tax is over $20 per gallon, which is many times the cost of making the alcohol itself. In order not to interfere with nonbeverage uses of ethanol, the government allows the tax-free sale of ethanol mixed with other chemicals which make it unsuitable as a beverage. Such mixtures are known as *denatured alcohol*. Many different denaturing agents are used, depending on the use to which the alcohol is to be put. The most common denatured alcohol contains 10 percent of methanol or of methanol plus a small amount of a hydrocarbon. Others, such as those used in the cosmetic industry (after-shave lotions, hair tonics, and so on), contain less toxic denaturants.

[1] The Chemurgic Council is concerned in general with industrial utilization of farm products.

Other alcohols

Some of the higher alcohols are also important industrially. Certain of those containing up to eight carbon atoms are used as solvents. Lauryl alcohol ($C_{12}H_{25}OH$) is used in making some of the numerous detergents. The alcohols containing 20 to 30 carbon atoms are waxy solids. Beeswax contains certain of these higher alcohols, as does carnauba wax. Carnauba wax is the product of a Brazilian tree and is highly prized, because of its hardness, for making durable floor wax, automobile wax, and shoe polish.

The polyhydric alcohols

So far mention has been made only of alcohols which contain one hydroxyl (−OH) group per molecule. You may ask: Can there be more than one hydroxyl group per molecule? Yes, there can be, provided that there is not more than one hydroxyl group on any one carbon atom.

Ethylene glycol is an important polyhydric alcohol. Its formula is shown below.

$$\begin{array}{c} CH_2OH \\ | \\ CH_2OH \end{array}$$
bp 197°C

Ethylene glycol is the base of the best permanent antifreezes (Prestone, and others). It is made from ethylene gas. When taken internally, ethylene glycol is highly poisonous.

Glycerin (or glycerol) is the analogous trihydric (three hydroxyl group) alcohol.

$$\begin{array}{c} CH_2OH \\ | \\ CHOH \\ | \\ CH_2OH \end{array}$$
glycerin

Glycerin is present in combined form in all plant and animal oils and fats, such as cottonseed oil, lard tallow, and others. It is a colorless, very viscous liquid boiling at 290°C. Unlike ethylene glycol, glycerin is not toxic and of course, being a component of all body fats, it is intimately involved in human metabolism.

Glycerin is hygroscopic and is sometimes used on shredded coconut to keep it moist. For the same reason it is used in making a nondrying ink for pads used with rubber stamps and in making hand lotions. Its use as an antifreeze has already been mentioned (see Chap. 15, page 162).

Glycerin has a sweet taste which is characteristic of all polyhydric alcohols including ethylene glycol (see carbohydrates, pages 450 to 452). For this reason it is used in candy making.

Formerly all the glycerin was obtained as a by-product of soap-making. Now some of it is made synthetically, starting with petroleum.

Aldehydes

If a coil of copper wire is held in a flame, it becomes coated with black copper oxide. If this wire, while still hot, is held in the vapors of methyl alcohol, the wire is reduced to the metal and methyl alcohol is converted into formaldehyde.

$$Cu\boxed{O} + H-\underset{H}{\overset{H}{C}}-O-\boxed{H} \rightarrow H-\underset{\text{formaldehyde}}{\overset{H}{C}=O} + Cu + H_2O$$

Aldehydes are characterized by the presence of the group

$$-\overset{H}{\underset{}{C}}=O$$

The type formula for these compounds is

$$R-\overset{H}{\underset{}{C}}=O$$

where R is a hydrocarbon radical. Formaldehyde is the first member of the series. The second is acetaldehyde:

$$CH_3\overset{H}{\underset{}{C}}=O$$
$$\text{acetaldehyde}$$

Aldehydes are formed by the partial oxidation of the corresponding alcohol. This oxidation is actually the removal of hydrogen from the alcohol,—hence the name aldehyde [*al*(cohol) *dehyd*(rogenation)].

Formaldehyde is a gas. Its water solution, known as formalin, is used as a disinfectant and antiseptic. It is used for preservation of biological specimens and in embalming fluid. Large amounts of formaldehyde are used in the manufacture of certain plastics, such as bakelite.

Formaldehyde is made commercially from methanol in much the same way as described in the first equation in this section. In actual practice a mixture of oxygen and methanol vapor is passed over a copper catalyst.

Ketones

Almost everyone has encountered one of the ketones in his daily living. The first member of this series is acetone, which is used as a solvent in making nail polish, nail polish remover, varnish remover, and certain types of ammunition (cordite).

$$H_3C-\overset{\overset{O}{\|}}{C}-CH_3$$
acetone

The type formula is

$$R-\overset{\overset{O}{\|}}{C}-R'$$

where R and R' are hydrocarbon radicals which may be the same or different from each other.

Acetone is a volatile liquid, boiling at 56°C. It is now produced mainly by fermentation of starch by special types of bacteria. Acetone is also formed in small amounts in the destructive distillation of wood. It is used mainly as a solvent and in making certain types of ammunition (cordite).

At the start of World War I the fermentation method was unknown. Britain and America badly needed acetone for the making of cordite, and it was impractical to produce the necessary quantities of the liquid from wood distillation. A Jewish chemist, **Dr. Chaim Weizmann,** working at the University of Manchester, England, developed the fermentation method for acetone during World War I. He thereby gave the Allied Nations a great new source of this important commodity and in so doing possibly influenced the course of the war. Haynes in his book *This Chemical Age*[1] relates that the British Prime Minister summoned Dr. Weizmann to London to express the gratitude of the British Empire for his discovery. He was offered money and honors, which he refused. Finally he told the Prime Minister that the only thing he wanted was a national home for the Jewish people. History records the fact that when the state of Israel was established in the late 1940s, this same Chaim Weizmann was its first president.

The organic acids

Anyone who has been stung by a bee or a sea nettle has been introduced to the first member of the organic acid series. The active substance in both cases is *formic acid*. Its name, in fact, is derived from the Latin word for ant (*formica*).

$$H-\overset{\overset{O}{\|}}{C}-O-H$$
formic acid

[1] William Haynes, *This Chemical Age*, Alfred A. Knopf, Inc., New York, 1942.

Stearic acid is an organic acid containing 18 carbon atoms in a chain. It is a waxy solid, insoluble in water, and is used as an ingredient of many shoe polishes, waxes for wood and metal, and cosmetics.

All organic acids contain the carboxyl group

$$\begin{array}{c}\text{O}\\\|\\-\text{C}-\text{O}-\text{H}\end{array}$$

The type formula is

$$\begin{array}{c}\text{O}\\\|\\R-\text{C}-\text{O}-\text{H}\end{array}$$

The organic acids are electrolytes. The hydrogen attached to the oxygen is ionizable. The second member of the organic acid series is the familiar acetic acid:

$$\begin{array}{c}\text{O}\\\|\\\text{CH}_3-\text{C}-\text{O}-\text{H}\\\text{acetic acid}\end{array}$$

This ionizes as a weak acid:

$$CH_3COOH + H_2O \rightleftarrows CH_3COO^- + OH_3^+$$

The next member is propionic acid:

$$CH_3CH_2COOH$$
propionic acid

Formic acid is a liquid boiling at 101°C. Acetic acid boils at 118°C and propionic acid at 141°C. In general, the boiling and melting points of the organic acids increase with increasing molecular weight. Those acids containing more than nine carbon atoms are solids at room temperature. As with the alcohols, the solubility in water of organic acids decreases with increasing molecular weight. Stearic acid ($C_{17}H_{35}COOH$) is a white, waxy solid which melts at 69°C and is insoluble in water.

All those organic acids above propionic, which are sufficiently volatile to have odors, have very disagreeable ones. Butyric (C_3H_7COOH) acid is present in rancid butter, Limburger cheese, and perspiration.

Certain of the acids of this type, combined with glycerin, make up vegetable and animal fats and oils. Hence this series of acids is called the **fatty acid** series. The fatty acids are characterized by having only one acid group per molecule.

In general, the fatty acids are formed by oxidation of the corresponding alcohol (see the illustration with acetic acid in the following paragraph).

Acetic acid

Acetic acid is the active component of vinegar. Ethanol is converted into acetic acid by the oxygen of the air in the presence of a certain microorganism (*Bacterium aceti*) often called *mother of vinegar*.

$$O_2 + CH_3CH_2OH \xrightarrow{\text{mother of vinegar}} CH_3COOH + H_2O$$

In apple cider vinegar, the alcohol is derived by fermentation of the sugars in apple juice. White vinegar is usually an aqueous solution of pure acetic acid. The law requires that the acetic acid content of vinegar shall be at least 4 percent.

Acetic acid is also formed in small amounts by the destructive distillation of wood. Most of it is now made synthetically, starting with acetylene.

Acetic acid is an important industrial chemical. It is used in producing a large number of organic chemicals, as a solvent, and in making the acetate type of rayon.

Other organic acids

A wide variety of organic acids are found in natural products, particularly in fruits, where they are partly responsible for the taste of the fruit. Many of these acids contain more than one carboxyl group (—COOH) per molecule. Some also contain the hydroxyl (—OH) group, and therefore are alcohols as well as acids.

Of the acids listed in Table 37–1, citric and malic acids are readily utilized by the body as foodstuffs. Citric acid is particularly important since it is always present in the blood stream and is closely related to calcium metabolism. Besides occurring in food, it is formed within the body from other compounds.

Oxalic acid is poisonous. Taken in large quantities, it will cause death, probably as a result of precipitating calcium ion from the blood

If these healthy sheep should happen to nibble on the leaves of a weed, halogeton, they would be doomed. Soon they would choke up, grow weak and die. Halogeton is poisonous because its leaves and stems contain oxalic acid. (Standard Oil Co.)

stream. When consumed in small quantities, it interferes with the absorption of the calcium in the diet by precipitating calcium oxalate in the intestinal tract. Because of this, spinach, swiss chard, and so on, which contain it, are not nutritionally as good "greens" as are kale and turnip greens, dandelion, and certain others which do not contain significant amounts of oxalic acid. A certain weed, halogeton, is becoming a serious problem to the ranchers of the Southwest. Animals which graze on this weed soon become weak and die because halogeton contains appreciable amounts of oxalic acid in its leaves and stem.

Citric acid is used extensively in making various carbonated beverages and hard candies. The latter are mostly citric acid, sugar, and flavoring.

TABLE 37–1. Some organic acids of fruits and vegetables

Name	Formula	Occurrence
Malic	CH_2COOH $\mid$ $CHOHCOOH$	Widespread in fruits and vegetables, especially in apples from which it gets its name
Citric	CH_2COOH $\mid$ $C(OH)COOH$ $\mid$ CH_2COOH	Citrus fruits, practically all fruits and vegetables (also in milk)
Tartaric	$CHOHCOOH$ $\mid$ $CHOHCOOH$	Grapes only
Oxalic	$COOH$ $\mid$ $COOH$	Spinach, beet greens, swiss chard, rhubarb, purslane, poke, and halogeton

Esters

Esters can be considered to be compounds formed by a reaction between an acid and an alcohol. This reaction is called **esterification.** If ethanol and acetic acid are boiled in a test tube containing some concentrated sulfuric acid, a fruity odor is soon observed. This odor is due to the ester formed.

$$\underset{\text{acetic acid}}{CH_3CO\boxed{OH}} + \underset{\text{ethanol}}{\boxed{H}OC_2H_5} \xrightarrow[\text{(concentrated)}]{H_2SO_4} \underset{\substack{\text{ethyl acetate}\\ \text{(an ester)}}}{CH_3\overset{\overset{O}{\|}}{C}-O-C_2H_5} + H_2O$$

Although esterification may seem similar to the neutralization of acids with bases, careful study has shown that esterification and neutralization are quite different. For one thing, in esterification the alcohol does not ionize; for another, the esterification reaction is slow, while acid-base neutralization is very rapid; furthermore, as indicated in the equation, the OH came from the acid and only the H came from the alcohol. Esters are not saltlike, since they do not ionize. The function of the sulfuric acid is to take up the water formed, thereby causing the esterifications, which are all reversible, to go further to the right.

In general, the formula for an ester is

$$R-\overset{\overset{O}{\|}}{C}-O-R'$$

where $R-\overset{\overset{O}{\|}}{C}-$ = radical from acid
$-O-R'$ = radical from alcohol

Esters are named according to the acid and alcohol from which they are derived. For example, the one shown above is ethyl acetate.

$\underbrace{CH_3COO}_{\substack{\text{(from}\\ \text{acetic}\\ \text{acid)}}}\underbrace{CH_3}_{\substack{\text{(from}\\ \text{methanol)}}}$ methyl acetate

$CH_3COOC_3H_7$ propyl acetate
$C_3H_7COOC_2H_5$ ethyl butyrate

Esters are widely distributed in nature. The odors and flavors of many flowers and fruits are due to them. It is interesting to note that, although the organic acids themselves may have disagreeable odors, the esters, if they are volatile enough to have an odor, almost always have a pleasant odor.

A number of esters, such as those listed in Table 37–2, are manufactured in preparing artificial flavors and perfumes.

TABLE 37–2. Some esters of fruits

Name	Formula	Odor
Amyl acetate	$CH_3COOC_5H_{11}$	Pear
Isoamyl acetate	$CH_3COOC_5H_{11}$	Banana
Methyl butyrate	$C_3H_7COOCH_3$	Pineapple
Octyl acetate	$CH_3COOC_8H_{17}$	Orange
Amyl butyrate	$C_3H_7COOC_5H_{11}$	Apricot

Some of the lower-molecular-weight esters are important solvents in the manufacture of automobile lacquers (which frequently smell like bananas). Such a lacquer consists of a solution of a cellulose derivative dissolved in a volatile ester. When spread or sprayed on a surface, the ester quickly evaporates, leaving a thin, tough film of the cellulose compound.

Some of the high-molecular-weight esters, which are solids, are the principal constituents of natural waxes. Carnauba wax contains a large amount of ceryl cerotate, $C_{25}H_{51}COOC_{26}H_{53}$, the ester of cerotic acid, $C_{25}H_{51}COOH$, and ceryl alcohol, $C_{26}H_{53}OH$.

The esters of glycerin

All the natural animal and vegetable fats and fatty oils are esters of glycerin and acids of the fatty acid (page 442) series. One of the principal constituents of beef tallow is glyceryl stearate. This is the ester of glycerin and stearic acid ($C_{17}H_{35}COOH$).

$$\begin{array}{c} CH_2OOCC_{17}H_{35} \\ | \\ CHOOCC_{17}H_{35} \\ | \\ CH_2OOCC_{17}H_{35} \end{array}$$
glyceryl stearate

Glyceryl stearate is a white fat melting at 71°C. Natural fats and oils are mixtures of various glyceryl esters.[1] The fatty acids present in largest amounts, however, are:

Stearic acid $C_{17}H_{35}COOH$
Oleic acid $C_{17}H_{33}COOH$ (this acid has one double bond in the carbon chain)
Palmitic acid $C_{15}H_{31}COOH$
Linoleic acid $C_{17}H_{31}COOH$ (this acid has two double bonds in the carbon chain)

[1] For simplicity the triglycerides are here referred to as having all three fatty acid radicals the same. Actually it is believed that much natural fat consists of mixed triglycerides in which two or even three different fatty acids are present.

TABLE 37-3. The main glycerides of natural fats and oils

Name	Formula	Melting point, °C
Glyceryl stearate	$(C_{17}H_{35}COO)_3C_3H_5$	71
Glyceryl oleate	$(C_{17}H_{33}COO)_3C_3H_5$	17
Glyceryl palmitate	$(C_{15}H_{31}COO)_3C_3H_5$	65
Glyceryl butyrate	$(C_3H_7COO)_3C_3H_5$	Below 0
Glyceryl linoleate	$(C_{17}H_{31}COO)_3C_3H_5$	Below 0

Note that oleates and linoleates have much lower melting points than the stearates and palmitates. This is in some way related to the presence of an ethylene-type double bond in the acid parts of these molecules. Glyceryl esters of unsaturated fatty acids always have lower melting points than the **saturated**[1] compounds of comparable molecular weight. That is, the only difference in the formulas for glyceryl stearate and glyceryl oleate is two hydrogen atoms in the fatty acid radical, and this causes the difference in melting points which is noted. There is no essential difference between a vegetable fat and a vegetable oil except melting point. In general, a fat is solid at room temperature, whereas a fatty oil is liquid at room temperature. Whether a substance is a solid or a liquid at room temperature is determined by the proportions of the various fatty acids present. Thus tallow and butter are solids, or fats, at room temperature because of their high proportion of stearates and palmitates. Olive, cottonseed, and soybean oils are liquids, or oils, because of their high proportion of oleates and linoleates (Table 37-4).

We have seen that liquid oils can be hardened by hydrogenation (Chap. 8, page 72). This is because hydrogen can add to the double bond, thereby converting an unsaturated ester to the saturated type.

$$3H_2 + \underset{\text{glyceryl oleate}}{(C_{17}H_{33}COO)_3C_3H_5} \xrightarrow[200°C]{Ni} \underset{\text{glyceryl stearate}}{(C_{17}H_{35}COO)_3C_3H_5}$$

This is the basis of the manufacture of vegetable shortenings.

An interesting problem in livestock feeding results from the above facts. Soybeans are excellent hog feed, causing rapid and efficient growth. But the pork fat produced by hogs fed on soybeans has a high proportion of unsaturated glycerides and accordingly is "softer" (that is, has a lower melting point) than that to which the housewife is accustomed. Consequently for the highest market grade of pork the hogs can be fed only a limited amount of soybeans. Of course, this

[1] A saturated compound is an organic compound which has no double or triple carbon-to-carbon bonds.

These hogs must be fed primarily on corn although soybeans are an excellent feed for them. This is because soybeans have a higher percentage of unsaturated glycerides so that the fat of soybean-fed hogs melts at a lower temperature than that of corn-fed hogs. (Standard Oil Co.)

objection to "soft" pork is entirely prejudice because actually such pork is fully as nutritious as that from an animal fed on corn, which produces a harder fat.

TABLE 37-4. Approximate compositions of some fats and oils, in percent

Name	Glyceryl oleate	Glyceryl stearate and palmitate	Glyceryl linoleate	Others
Beef tallow	25	75		
Butter fat	39	53		8[a]
Olive oil	70	25	4	
Cottonseed oil	25	25	47	3
Linseed oil	18	8	30	44[b]
Soybean oil	33	7	52	8

[a] Mainly glyceryl butyrate.
[b] Largely glyceryl linolenate (linolenic acid, $C_{17}H_{29}COOH$, has three double bonds in the carbon chain).

Drying oils

Although they may serve similar purposes, an oil paint is quite different from shellac or lacquer.[1] The latter two consist of solids dissolved in a suitable solvent which evaporates, thereby depositing a film of the original solid. Oil paints are essentially mixtures of pigments and "drying oils." They "dry" as a result of the oxidation and polymerization of the oil present. The oxidation and polymerization product

[1] Shellac is an alcoholic solution of gum shellac, a gum secreted by certain insects on certain trees. It comes mainly from Asia. Lacquers are less definite, but most of them, as explained earlier, are synthetic derivatives of cellulose dissolved in a volatile solvent.

The large tanks shown here are used for the catalytic hydrogenation of vegetable oils. Usually the process is carried to the point where the liquid oils become semisolid. The products of hydrogenation are used as solid vegetable shortenings and as butter substitutes. (Procter and Gamble Co.)

is a tough, protective film. Linseed oil and tung oil are the best drying oils for use in paints. Although the actual chemical process of drying is not completely understood, it is known to involve the addition of oxygen to the double bonds present and also polymerization (see Chap. 36, page 417) through these double bonds. Thus linseed and tung oils are good drying oils because of their high percentage of highly unsaturated fatty acids.

Linseed oil is obtained from flax seed. Raw linseed oil dries slowly. If it is first boiled with lead oxide, the resulting so-called *boiled linseed oil* dries much more rapidly. So-called *driers* used in paints are catalysts which accelerate the oxidation process.

Turpentine (a hydrocarbon obtained from southern pine), or a mineral oil, is generally also present in an oil paint. These materials serve to dilute and thin the linseed oil, causing it to spread more easily. They also aid penetration into the wood, thereby anchoring the paint. On drying, the turpentine actually evaporates.

Oleomargarines

The oleomargarines are mixtures of various animal and vegetable fats or partially hydrogenated vegetable oils of such consistency as to resemble butter. To give a flavor more nearly resembling butter, skim milk is commonly incorporated in oleomargarines. With the proper dye they may be colored to resemble butter in appearance. The main reason for the sale of oleomargarines is that they can be produced much more cheaply than real butter. In certain states special laws levy taxes on, and regulate, the sale of colored margarines.

The hydrolysis of esters

The formation of an ester from an acid and an alcohol is a reversible reaction. When heated with water or steam an ester is hydrolyzed into its corresponding acid and alcohol. For example, if glyceryl stearate is heated with steam, glycerin and stearic acid are formed.

$$(C_{17}H_{35}COO)_3C_3H_5 + 3H_2O \rightarrow C_3H_5(OH)_3 + 3C_{17}H_{35}COOH$$
$$\text{(steam)} \qquad \text{glycerin} \qquad \text{stearic acid}$$

Fat used for deep frying may hydrolyze in this same way because of the water contained in the food. That is why the fat becomes rancid. The rancidifying of butter is due to the liberation of free butyric acid from the glyceryl butyrate. Certain aged cheeses (page 442) acquire characteristic odors and flavors for the same reason. In these cheeses, however, the change is a desired one.

Soapmaking

Common soap is a sodium salt of a high-molecular-weight fatty acid. If a fat or oil is boiled with sodium hydroxide solution, the same reaction (hydrolysis) occurs as with water. Except in this case, instead of the free acid the sodium salt of the acid is obtained.

$$(C_{17}H_{35}COO)_3C_3H_5 + 3NaOH \rightarrow C_3H_5(OH)_3 + 3C_{17}H_{35}COONa$$
$$\text{glyceryl stearate} \qquad\qquad\qquad \text{sodium stearate}$$
$$\text{(a soap)}$$

Since a soap is produced this type of reaction is called **saponification.**

Commercially, soap is made by boiling animal or vegetable fats and oils with sodium hydroxide. When the reaction is complete, both products are in water solution. Salt (NaCl) is added, which causes the soap to precipitate and float to the surface. The soap is skimmed off, partially dried, and coloring matter and perfume added as required. Glycerin is obtained by distillation of the water solution left behind.

Fats containing a large proportion of saturated fatty acids make the best soaps. Cottonseed oil does not make a good soap. But hydrogenated cottonseed oil makes as good a soap as tallow. The cleansing action of soaps is discussed in Chap. 42, pages 534 and 535.

Soapless soap

Today many detergents sold for commercial and household use do not contain any soap as this term is defined above. These detergents are sodium salts of the sulfuric acid derivatives of some of the higher (10-or-more carbon-atom) alcohols. One of the most common is sodium lauryl sulfate [$CH_3(CH_2)_{11}OSO_3Na$], formed by treating lauryl alcohol with sulfuric acid and neutralizing the product with sodium hydroxide. These higher alcohols are made from natural fats and oils by catalytic hydrogenation. For some, but not all, types of washing they are superior to soaps. They do not react with hard water as soaps do.

The ethers

The most common ether is diethyl ether (C_2H_5—O—C_2H_5), which is used as an anesthetic. The type formula for an ether is

$$R—O—R'$$

In diethyl ether R and R' are both ethyl groups,—C_2H_5. Diethyl ether is formed by heating ethyl alcohol with concentrated sulfuric acid at 135°C.

$$C_2H_5\boxed{OH + H}OC_2H_5 \xrightarrow[135°]{H_2SO_4} C_2H_5—O—C_2H_5 + H_2O$$

It has a boiling point of 35°C and is highly inflammable. It is only very slightly soluble in water.

The chief industrial use of ethers is as special solvents.

The sugars

It has already been pointed out that compounds containing more than one —OH have a sweetish taste. The sugars all contain several hydroxyl groups.

Glucose (grape sugar) is probably the most common sugar in nature. It occurs in the blood of animals and in the juices of many fruits. Its molecular formula is $C_6H_{12}O_6$.

$$\begin{array}{c} CH_2OH \\ | \\ CHOH \\ | \\ CHOH \\ | \\ CHOH \\ | \\ CHOH \\ | \\ CHO \end{array}$$
glucose

Glucose is both an aldehyde and an alcohol.

Sucrose (cane sugar or beet sugar), $C_{12}H_{22}O_{11}$, can be thought of as a compound between glucose and *fructose* (another six-carbon-atom sugar). On treatment with dilute acid solution, sucrose yields equal quantities of glucose and fructose.

$$\underset{\text{sucrose}}{C_{12}H_{22}O_{11}} + H_2O \xrightarrow{\text{acid}} \underset{\text{glucose}}{C_6H_{12}O_6} + \underset{\text{fructose}}{C_6H_{12}O_6}$$

The mixture of equal parts of glucose and fructose is called *invert sugar*.

Lactose (milk sugar), $C_{12}H_{22}O_{11}$, is found in cows' and human milk. It can be split to yield one molecule of glucose and one of *galactose* (still another six-carbon sugar).

Starch

Starch and cellulose, together with the sugars, are commonly referred to as carbohydrates. The name is due to the fact that all these substances contain hydrogen and oxygen in the ratio of 2:1.

Starch, $(C_6H_{10}O_5)_x$,[1] is found chiefly in the roots and seeds of plants. Although starch from different sources varies somewhat, all starches consist of very large molecules. These large molecules are formed by hooking together many molecules of glucose. This is accomplished by the elimination of water between two molecules of glucose. When boiled with water containing an acid, starch is hydrolyzed into glucose.

$$(C_6H_{10}O_5)_x + xH_2O \xrightarrow{\text{acid}} xC_6H_{12}O_6$$
$$\text{starch} \qquad\qquad\qquad\quad \text{glucose}$$

This is the way in which corn sirup (Karo, and others) is made: Cornstarch is boiled with dilute hydrochloric acid and the resulting solution, after neutralizing the acid, is concentrated by evaporating part of the water.

When dry starch is heated to 250°C, a material called *dextrin* is obtained. The water solution of dextrin is used as an adhesive (for example, on postage stamps). Dextrin appears to be made of molecules composed of many glucose units but smaller than starch. Dextrin has a somewhat sweetish taste. Some dextrin is formed on the surface when a slice of bread is toasted.

Starch is an important source of energy in human and animal metabolism. In the body it is broken down into glucose, in which form it may be absorbed and oxidized by the body.

Cellulose

Cellulose forms the framework of many of the members of the plant kingdom. It is the principal constituent of wood. Examples of pure cellulose are filter papers and cotton fibers. Cellulose, $(C_6H_{10}O_5)_z$,[2] has the same empirical formula as starch, and its molecules also are composed of glucose units. Its molecule differs from starch, however,

---

[1] The x is to indicate that starch is composed of very large molecules made up of many $C_6H_{10}O_5$ units.

[2] The z indicates that cellulose is also composed of many $C_6H_{10}O_5$ units, but not the same number that starch contains.

in two ways: (1) The glucose units are linked together in cellulose in a slightly different way from the linkage in starch. (2) The number of glucose units in the cellulose molecule is not the same as in molecules of the starches.

Like starch, cellulose is converted into glucose on boiling with acid solution.

$$(C_6H_{10}O_5)_z + zH_2O \xrightarrow{acid} zC_6H_{12}O_6$$
$$\text{cellulose} \qquad\qquad\qquad \text{glucose}$$

The reaction is slower than the corresponding starch reaction. Furthermore, this reaction cannot be brought about in the body of man or *most* other animals. Hence cellulose is not digestible by most animals. An exception is found in the case of cattle and sheep (ruminants), which have in their intestinal tracts certain bacteria that are capable of converting cellulose into glucose. These animals can then utilize the glucose as a nutrient. It is for this reason that cattle and other ruminants are able to utilize roughage for feed while other animals cannot. Certain insects (termites, silverfish) can also digest cellulose. Such insects may be very destructive.

Glucose for industrial purposes can be made from cellulose. The process has been sucessfully carried out in Germany for a number of years. Since glucose can be used as a food for man or livestock or can be fermented into ethanol (page 435), the process represents a potential method of utilizing sawdust and planer shavings, which otherwise would be wasted.

Economic poisons

Most people generally think of poisons as having only negative value and as things which should be avoided. However, this is not the case when insects, vermin, and noxious weeds threaten man's food supply and sometimes his very existence. By the development of selective poisons, chemistry has given man an exceedingly effective weapon in his fight to control these enemies which have plagued him from prehistoric times.

The idea of using poisons to control these natural enemies is not new. For many years, compounds of lead and arsenic as well as those extracted from plants, such as nicotine from tobacco and rotenone from derris root, have been used as **insecticides.**[1] But, thanks to newly discovered compounds, more progress has been made in the field of economic poisons during the last two decades than was made in all the preceding years of history.

[1] Insecticides are insect-killing materials.

The use of DDT to control the potato bug has approximately doubled the yield of potatoes per acre. This is but one of many ways in which chemistry improves man's food supply. This field of potatoes in Idaho is being sprayed with DDT. (Standard Oil Co.)

DDT

The common name DDT is an abbreviation of the systematic chemical name of this substance, which is dichloro-diphenyl-trichloroethane. Its formula is

$$\text{Cl}-\underset{\underset{\text{H}}{\overset{\text{H}}{\text{C}}}=\overset{\text{H}}{\underset{\text{C}}{\text{C}}}}{\text{C}}\cdots\underset{\underset{\text{Cl}}{\overset{\text{H}}{\text{C}}}}{\text{C}}-\overset{\text{H}}{\underset{|}{\text{C}}}-\underset{\underset{\text{H}}{\overset{\text{H}}{\text{C}}}=\overset{\text{H}}{\underset{\text{C}}{\text{C}}}}{\text{C}}\cdots\text{C}-\text{Cl}$$

The almost miraculous powers of this compound to control such disease-carrying insects as the housefly, body louse, and mosquito were discovered during World War II. Perhaps the most dramatic example of its effectiveness occurred just after the Allied invasion of Italy. At this time an outbreak of typhus occurred in Naples. This terrible disease, which threatened not only the Italian civilian population but also the Allied armies as well, was known to be carried by the body louse. The allies flew tons of DDT into Naples and, by liberal dusting of the body and clothing of a large percentage of the population, quickly brought the typhus under control. This was the first time in history that an outbreak of typhus had been brought under control so quickly.

Although its value as an insecticide was only recently discovered, DDT has been known for a long time. The compound was first prepared by a graduate chemistry student in a European university in 1874. No value was attached to the compound until 1937 when Paul Müller, working for the J. R. Geigy Co. in Switzerland, discovered its insecticidal value. (Patents on the use of DDT in the United States are owned by the Geigy Co.)

DDT is now made in hundreds of tons yearly in the United States. It is produced from benzene, chlorine, ethyl alcohol, and sulfuric acid. Although the cost of production varies with economic conditions, it was around 50 cents per pound in 1950.

The remarkable success of DDT in controlling houseflies when it was first used is well known. DDT is now known to have two disadvantages which were not recognized when it was first discovered: (1) Flies develop a resistance to it, so that now many strains of flies in most of the United States can tolerate the compound. (2) It is quite toxic to man. Thus, when dairy cows are sprayed with DDT, the compound will show up in the milk in quantities small but dangerous when such milk is consumed regularly. For this reason the use of DDT in dairy barns is now generally discouraged.

Another striking example of the effect of a remote scientific discovery on economic conditions is given by the potato-growing industry in the United States. By using DDT spray to control the potato beetle, the yield of potatoes per acre has been approximately doubled. For this reason DDT was largely responsible for the great surpluses of potatoes which the United States experienced in the latter 1940s.

Although toxic to warm-blooded animals, DDT is relatively much more toxic to insects. It acts on insects both as a stomach poison (that is, when eaten by the insect) and also as a *contact* poison. In the latter case the insect is killed by crawling over a surface covered with the insecticide. DDT is highly effective against the corn borer, Japanese beetle, and gypsy moth. Because of its effectiveness against the mosquito, DDT has played an important role in the control and eradication of malaria.

Other insecticides

The discovery of DDT was particularly important because it was the first example of a synthetic organic chemical which proved practical for the control of insects. With this fact to go on, chemists have synthesized other insecticides which are more suitable for control of certain insects than is DDT. There is now reason to believe that only a beginning has been made in this field and that even more effective insecticides, which are less toxic to man, will be discovered in the future. Hexachlorobenzene (sometimes called Gammexane, or 666) was developed by the British. Its formula is $C_6H_6Cl_6$. It is effective against the same type pests as DDT. Chlordan (a complex chlorinated hydrocarbon) is an effective insecticide against grasshoppers, aphids, and livestock pests. Methoxychlor (which is identical with DDT

A public health worker spraying an insecticide on the walls of a house to kill the anopheline mosquitoes which carry malaria. As a result of such treatment, malaria is rapidly dying out as an important disease in this country. (U.S. Public Health Service)

except that the methoxy group, —OCH$_3$, replaces each of the chlorines attached to the benzene ring) is particularly effective against houseflies which have acquired resistance to DDT. Pyrethrum is an insecticide which has been used for many years and originally could be obtained only from the powdered flowers of the pyrethrum plants which grow in the Near East. The active ingredient of pyrethrum has been discovered, and this compound is now being synthesized on a commercial scale in the United States.

Continued research in the field of economic poisons will continue to aid man in his war against destructive and disease-bearing insects.

The weed killers

Almost as spectacular as the insecticides is the progress made in controlling weeds. **Herbicides** (that is, plant-killing chemicals) have long been known, but the problem in controlling weeds is to kill the weeds without harming the useful plants. Since a weed is defined as "a plant out of place," the problem of finding a chemical which will kill one type of plant and not harm another type would seem almost hopelessly difficult. Yet real progress has been made in this direction. Most of this progress is based on the discovery that the compound known as 2,4-D (actually 2,4 dichloro-phenoxy-acetic acid), derived from acetic acid, will kill most broad-leaved plants without killing the grasses. Since the grasses include the important grain crops, corn, wheat, oats, barley, and rye, it is possible to use a spray of 2,4-D to control weeds in these crops. Thus 2,4-D not only has become a chemical useful for maintaining a nice lawn by selectively killing dandelion, broad-leaf and narrow-leaf plantain, and other lawn weeds, while not harming the desirable bluegrass, redtop, and fescue; but it has also

Honey mesquite infests millions of acres of rangeland, hides cattle gone wild, and crowds out grazing grass. It is being mastered by 2,4,5-T. This photograph shows mesquite brush before and after treatment with this herbicide. (Monsanto Chemical Co.)

become a chemical of great economic importance in food production.

$$\text{2,4-D}$$

An amazingly small amount of 2,4-D is capable of killing a plant. Thus only about 0.2 lb of this substance dispersed in water makes sufficient spray to kill the weeds in an entire acre of corn or wheat. Because of this fact and the fact that the chemical may also kill desirable shrubbery, considerable care must be exercised in applying the spray lest it be carried by the wind and kill desirable plants.

A similar compound, known as 2,4,5-T (2,4,5 trichloro-phenoxyacetic acid), is remarkably effective in killing brush such as elm, gum, hawthorn, maple, oak, poison ivy, and so on. Its use has largely replaced other more expensive methods of controlling brush along highways, railroads, and high-tension-line rights of way. The compound has proved a boon to cattlemen on the Western range lands for control of mesquite and other shrubby growth which tend to crowd out the grass.

Rat poisons

Property-destroying, disease-carrying rats have been one of the major scourges of mankind from the beginning of history. In the United States many millions of dollars' worth of property are destroyed every year by rats, to say nothing of the public-health menace which they constitute. At home in either the city or the country, or aboard ship, the rat has so far defied all attempts by man to eradicate him. That he is exceedingly able to look out for himself can be attested by anyone who has ever tried to trap or poison him.

ANTU (the chemical name is alpha-naphthyl-thiourea) was discovered at Johns Hopkins University to be an effective rat poison.

$$\text{ANTU structure}$$

The chief disadvantages of ANTU are that it is exceedingly toxic to other animals and that rats getting less than a lethal dose build up an immunity to it which lasts several weeks. One pound of this substance can kill as many as 200,000 rats.

Compound 1080 (sodium fluoracetate) developed by the U.S. Fish and Wildlife Service is also very deadly to rats. Like ANTU, however, it is extremely poisonous to other animals and hence is dangerous for the untrained person to use.

Warfarin was discovered in 1950 by the University of Wisconsin Alumni Research Foundation (whence its name). It is very toxic to rats but relatively nontoxic to other animals. Moreover, rats cannot detect it in food which they eat. Altogether Warfarin appears highly promising and is being manufactured in large quantities.

KEY WORDS

alcohols	esters	herbicide	polyhydric alcohols
aldehydes	ethers	insecticide	saponification
economic poison	fatty acids	ketones	saturated
esterification	fermentation	polar	Weizmann

HIGHLIGHTS

It will be helpful to learn the type formulas of the various classes of organic compounds treated in this chapter. The R and R' each stands for an alkyl radical, which is a univalent group made by removing one hydrogen from an aliphatic hydrocarbon. R and R' may be the same radical or different radicals. For example, CH_3 is simply methane with one hydrogen removed.

Class	Type Formula for Compounds without a Central C Atom
Alcohol	R—O—H
Ether	R—O—R'

Class	Type Formula for Compounds with a Central C Atom
Aldehyde	$\begin{array}{c} R \\ \vert \\ C{=}O \\ \vert \\ H \end{array}$
Ketone	$\begin{array}{c} R' \\ \vert \\ C{=}O \\ \vert \\ R \end{array}$
Acid	$\begin{array}{c} R \\ \vert \\ C{=}O \\ \vert \\ OH \end{array}$
Ester	$\begin{array}{c} R' \\ \vert \\ C{=}O \\ \vert \\ OR \end{array}$

A few generalizations concerning organic compounds may be made. Among these are (1) The solubility of alcohols and organic acids in water decreases with an increase in molecular weight and (2) in general, boiling points and melting points increase with increasing molecular weight.

QUESTIONS

1. In what ways are alcohols similar to, and in what ways are they different from, bases?
2. How does the boiling point of an alcohol compare with the boiling point of the corresponding hydrocarbon? Why?
3. Why did methyl alcohol come to be called wood alcohol?
4. What is the other name for grain alcohol?
5. How is synthetic methanol produced?
6. By what method is most ethanol produced?
7. What is meant by 100-proof alcohol?
8. What is denatured alcohol? Why is it prepared?
9. From what sources is glycerin obtained?
10. What is glycerin used for?
11. What is ethylene glycol? Why is it not used as a sweetening agent?
12. What is acetone?
13. From what sources is acetic acid obtained?
14. Why is kale a more nutritious "green" than spinach?
15. What is an ester?
16. Where are esters found in nature?
17. In general, what causes the variations observed in the melting points of the natural oils and fats?
18. How is cottonseed oil converted into a solid fat? What use is made of this solid fat?
19. How does a paint differ from a lacquer or shellac?
20. What are the best "drying" oils?
21. How is fat converted into soap?
22. Explain how waste planer shavings and sawdust may be converted into ethyl alcohol.
23. What are the disadvantages of DDT in the control of houseflies?
24. State the difference between neutralization and esterification.

CHAPTER 38

some giant molecules

made by nature

So far you have encountered a few things which are made up of giant molecules, among them diamond, graphite, starch, and cellulose. In this chapter you will learn about some others. Materials composed of giant molecules are very important to man, among other reasons because such materials furnish him with food, clothing, and shelter as well as with rubber and the host of things known as *plastics*.

Although some substances composed of very large molecules are used as fuels and foods, the great majority of them are valued for certain *physical properties* which they possess: Among these are elasticity, toughness, tensile strength,[1] durability, and other properties. For the most part, the science of giant molecules, which is among the newest branches of science, has shown that the physical properties of these materials are the direct result of the unusual shape and large size of the molecule. Substances composed of giant molecules are known to scientists as **high polymers.**

Cellulose and its derivatives

Some of the properties of **cellulose** have already been given. Cellulose is one of many high polymers found in nature. It may be thought of as consisting of units of glucose (see Chap. 37, page 450) tied end to end in this way

- - -☐—☐—☐- - -

where each  —☐— represents a glucose unit —$C_6H_{10}O_5$—.

[1] The student may consider that the tensile strength is that force applied at the ends of a material necessary to rupture the material.

Left, wood chips are screened for size before pulping. Right, cooking liquor is pumped into the digester which is filled with wood chips. (Standard Oil Co.)

Studies show that in cellulose from wood these chains composed of glucose units are from 0.0001 to 0.0002 cm in length. Although still small compared with things we can handle, they are enormously large compared with molecules of gases and liquids. The molecular weight of such a cellulose molecule may be as great as 500,000. In a fiber of cellulose from wood or cotton these long molecules lie parallel to each other and are placed end to end like a bundle of pencils of unequal lengths held in one's hand. Each glucose unit has alcohol (—OH) groups on it. These groups are polar (see Chap. 37, page 433) and cause one cellulose molecule to attract its nearest neighbors in adjacent chains of the bundle of threadlike molecules making up the fiber. For these and other reasons cellulose is *insoluble* and *infusible*, and the fiber has good tensile strength.

Paper and pulp

One hundred and fifty years ago paper was made almost entirely from cotton rags and linen. Now almost all paper is made from wood. Wood consists essentially of bundles of cellulose fibers (two-thirds) cemented together with an adhesive called **lignin** (one-third). In papermaking the fibers are torn apart and into short lengths, then matted together in a thin sheet. The wood may be disintegrated in two ways: (1) by mechanical grinding and (2) by chemically dissolving the lignin.

1. Mechanical grinding furnishes the cheapest and lowest grade of paper. After removal of the bark from the logs, they are held against rapidly revolving grinding stones which shred the log into fine fibers. All the lignin remains in the fibers. The fine wood fibers are floated

The dry end of the Fourdrinier, a papermaking machine. (Standard Oil Co.)

off in a stream of water. This thin suspension of fibers in water is called the *paper stock* and is converted into the final sheet, as explained in the section "Production of Paper." Newsprint and wallpaper are made of ground wood.

2. Chemical **pulp** is more nearly pure cellulose. Logs, cut into chips by high-speed knives, are cooked under pressure with calcium acid sulfite [$Ca(HSO_3)_2$] solution. This solution dissolves the lignin, leaving nearly pure cellulose fibers, which can then be converted into paper stock by grinding and suspending in water. The product of cooking with $Ca(HSO_3)_2$ is called sulfite pulp. Other substances are sometimes used to dissolve the lignin. Soda pulp is made by cooking with sodium hydroxide solution. Soda pulp is made mostly from poplar wood. Purified cellulose formed in these ways may be converted into paper, rayon, cellophane, plastics, or explosives. Kraft paper, the heavy brown wrapping paper, is made from pulp formed by cooking the wood chips with sodium sulfide. This process is known commercially as the *sulfate process* because the sodium sulfide is derived from sodium sulfate by reduction. Kraft paper is also used for towels and cartons. The discovery, by **Dr. Charles Herty** of Georgia, of a method whereby the resinous southern pines could be made into paper stock has resulted in the development of extensive paper industries in the South. For that section of the country this discovery was of great importance because formerly southern pine was considered too resinous for papermaking. Today one-third of all United States paper is produced in the Southeast. Moreover, because of the climate, more cellulose can be grown per year per acre in the South than in other sections of the United States.

Production of paper

From whatever source the paper stock is produced, the paper sheet is formed by straining out the cellulose fibers on a wire screen to give a layer of matted fibers. This fiber mat is then passed between a series of heated rollers which compact it, squeeze out the water, and finally dry it. In modern papermaking the operations are continuous so that a continuous stream of paper stock goes into one end of the mill and a continuous strip of dry paper comes off the other end.

Paper made simply as described would be like filter or blotting paper. In order to increase its strength and give paper some measure of waterproofness, various **sizing agents** are added to the stock before forming the sheet. The most common sizing agent is rosin dissolved in sodium hydroxide solution. The rosin solution is followed with alum solution, which causes the precipitation of rosin on the individual fibers of the stock. As the sheet later passes over the heated rolls, the rosin melts and cements the various fibers together. Newsprint is very lightly sized; a note paper for writing with ink must be more heavily sized. Most paper used for books and magazines is also "filled." Filling involves adding a pigment, such as white china clay, calcium carbonate, or titanium dioxide, which makes the paper more opaque, gives it a smoother surface, and improves the printing qualities. The "slick" paper magazine is an example of paper of this kind.

Rayon and cellophane

As pointed out earlier, cellulose, as such, is insoluble and infusible; hence its physical form cannot be changed except by mechanical processes like grinding. However, in 1892, two English chemists discovered how to make a compound of cellulose which is water soluble and which can also easily be reconverted into cellulose. Their discovery is the basis for the present-day manufacture of rayon and cellophane by the **viscose process.** In this process, purified cellulose from cotton

Fig. 38–1. A drawing showing the principle of the machine used in the regeneration of cellulose from viscose to form rayon thread.

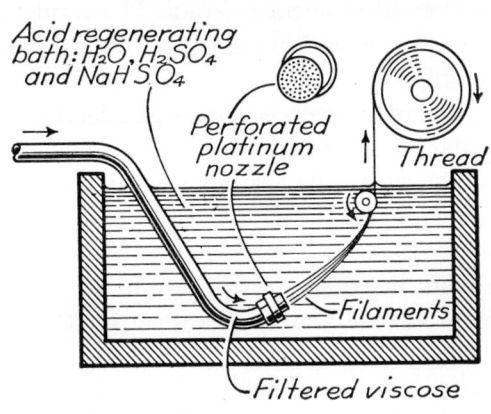

or wood pulp is treated with a sodium hydroxide solution and carbon disulfide. A chemical reaction occurs which converts the cellulose into a thick viscous liquid known in the trade as viscose. A solution of this liquid is squirted through fine holes in a nozzle called a *spinneret*. On the other side of the spinneret is a solution of sulfuric acid.[1] As the viscose comes into contact with the sulfuric acid, it is decomposed and the cellulose regenerated.

$$\text{Cellulose} + \text{NaOH} + \text{CS}_2 \rightarrow \text{viscose}$$

$$\text{Viscose} + \text{sulfuric acid} \rightarrow \text{cellulose}$$

Thus, if the viscose is squirted through a round hole, a round fiber, *viscose rayon*, sold under various trade names, is the result. If squirted through a long slit, a sheet of *viscose cellophane* is obtained. Both products are chemically cellulose and differ only in physical form.

In making rayon, the fibers from the spinneret are at once twisted into a thread and wound on a spool. If threads are cut in short lengths, carded, and spun, *staple rayon*, a material desirable for suits, textiles, and so on, is produced.

Rayon fibers have a high luster like that of silk. A dull luster can be obtained by adding a pigment, such as titanium dioxide, to the viscose before forming the fiber.

About sixty-five percent of all rayon made in the United States in 1945 was made by the viscose process.

Artificial straw for hats, imitation horsehair, cellulose "sponges," and other products are also made by the same process. The only difference is in the physical form the viscose has when it strikes the sulfuric acid bath.

Cellulose acetate

If purified cellulose is treated with acetic acid or acetic acid anhydride, some of the hydroxyl groups on the cellulose molecule are converted to acetate esters. The resulting product, known as *cellulose acetate*, differs from cellulose in that it is soluble in acetone and also fusible.

Celanese rayon is made by dissolving cellulose acetate in acetone and forcing the resulting solution through a spinneret into a warm current of air, where the acetone rapidly evaporates. This leaves a continuous filament of cellulose acetate. This is then spun into thread in the same way as viscose rayon. In some ways acetate rayon is superior to viscose rayon; in other ways, it is inferior. Acetate rayon has a higher luster than viscose and retains its strength better when wet. Acetate rayon

---

[1] Modern methods of rayon manufacture generally use acid salts, such as sodium hydrogen sulfate, $NaHSO_4$, to supply the acid.

Clothing of nature-made and man-made fibers. Left to right, viscose rayon dress, acetate rayon gown, nylon nightwear, orlon sweaters, dacron suit. (E. I. du Pont de Nemours & Co.)

is more difficult to dye, but special dyes have been developed for it so that it is now available in almost all colors. One of the disadvantages of acetate rayon is that it is soluble in acetone. If fingernail polish or nail-polish remover comes in contact with acetate rayon, it will dissolve. Furthermore, it melts on heating and should never be ironed with a hot iron (melts above 275°F). The fibers have good resistance to creasing and wrinkling.

Cellulose acetate dissolved in a volatile solvent makes a good lacquer which is used for coating wallpaper, leather, and metal and for sealing bottles and the like.

Cellulose acetate granules heated under pressure can be molded into a variety of shapes and objects. The substance itself is transparent and colorless, but colored plastics can be obtained by mixing the proper pigments with the molding powder. Like cellophane, thin sheets of cellulose acetate are used for wrapping. A few of the trade names under which cellulose acetate, in varied forms, is sold are Kodapak, Lumarith, Tenite I, Vue-Pak, and Vue-Lite.

Cellulose nitrate

This material is formed in a manner analogous to cellulose acetate. Cotton linters or sulfite pulp is treated with a mixture of nitric and sulfuric acids. The nitric acid reacts with the hydroxyl groups on the cellulose, forming cellulose nitrate. Depending on conditions, this product may be used for making celluloid, rayon, smokeless powder, or guncotton.

If all the hydroxyl groups are allowed to react with the nitric acid, the product is highly explosive and constitutes *military guncotton*. This material is used as a propellant powder. A somewhat less completely nitrated cellulose is used in making smokeless powder for rifles.

Raw cotton can be put to many uses besides the actual production of cotton cloth. It can be used to produce cellulose acetate, cellulose nitrate, and mercerized cotton. (Standard Oil Co.)

Also, when mixed with nitroglycerin, this material is blasting gelatin.

A still lower degree of nitration produces a product which, although highly inflammable, is not explosive. This product is about as soluble in organic solvents as cellulose acetate is and can be used in much the same way for making lacquer, rayon, and other materials. However, its inflammability is a serious disadvantage, and the manufacture of cellulose nitrate rayon in the United States has been discontinued. When it was being made into rayon, there were several cases in which a woman's dress burned up rapidly and completely when someone accidentally touched it with a cigarette.

Cellulose nitrate, mixed with camphor and alcohol, is a plastic material which, on evaporation of the solvent, hardens. It is known as *celluloid* and is still used to make pencils and pens. Celluloid was the forerunner of all modern plastics. It was discovered in 1868 by **Hyatt**, of Albany, N.Y., who was looking for a substitute for ivory for making billiard balls. Both cellulose nitrate and cellulose acetate are used as photographic film base—the latter in the "safety" film.

Mercerized cotton

Mercerized cotton is formed by treating cotton thread with concentrated sodium hydroxide solution. After stretching, the thread is washed and dried. The result is a thread of higher gloss and greater strength and one which takes a dye better than ordinary cotton.

Proteins

Giant molecules of protein have furnished several of the most important fibers used by ancient and modern man. The most important of these are silk and wool. Silk, however, is more restricted in its uses and of less importance as a textile fiber than wool. It differs from wool in its external structure and properties. When it is spun from the cocoon, silk consists of two filaments stuck together by a gluelike substance.

Wool is a general term. It is used most commonly in referring to the fleece of the sheep, but it also covers the fleeces of the angora goat, the alpaca, the camel, the cashmere goat, the llama, and the vicuña. These different wools vary in texture and length of the fiber. They may be fine or coarse and from ½ to 12 in. long, but their molecular structure is essentially the same.

Wool

Wool, silk, animal hair, and muscle fibers are composed of large molecules of *protein* which contain the elements carbon, hydrogen, nitrogen, sulfur, and oxygen. When treated with dilute alkali, all proteins are hydrolyzed into **amino acids.** There are about twenty-one different amino acids known to be the building blocks of the various proteins. All amino acids, however, can be considered as derivatives of the fatty acids. For example, one of the amino acids has the structure

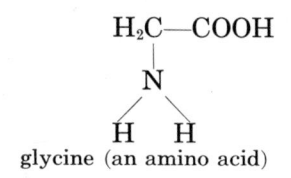

$$H_2C-COOH$$
$$|$$
$$N$$
$$/ \ \backslash$$
$$H \quad H$$

glycine (an amino acid)

Glycine is thus a substituted acetic acid.

All amino acids have at least one carboxyl (—COOH) group and one amino (—NH$_2$) group. Some of the amino acids also contain sulfur.

In protein molecules these amino acid building blocks are hooked one to the other by combination of the carboxyl group of one with the amino group of another.

The fibers used in this photograph all consist of giant molecules produced by nature. The drapes, curtains, and chair covering are of rayon. The stuffing of the chair is horsehair, and the rug is wool, both protein fibers. (E. I. du Pont de Nemours & Co.)

Wool is known to consist of very long chains of molecules having a unit structure shown at left below (*a*).

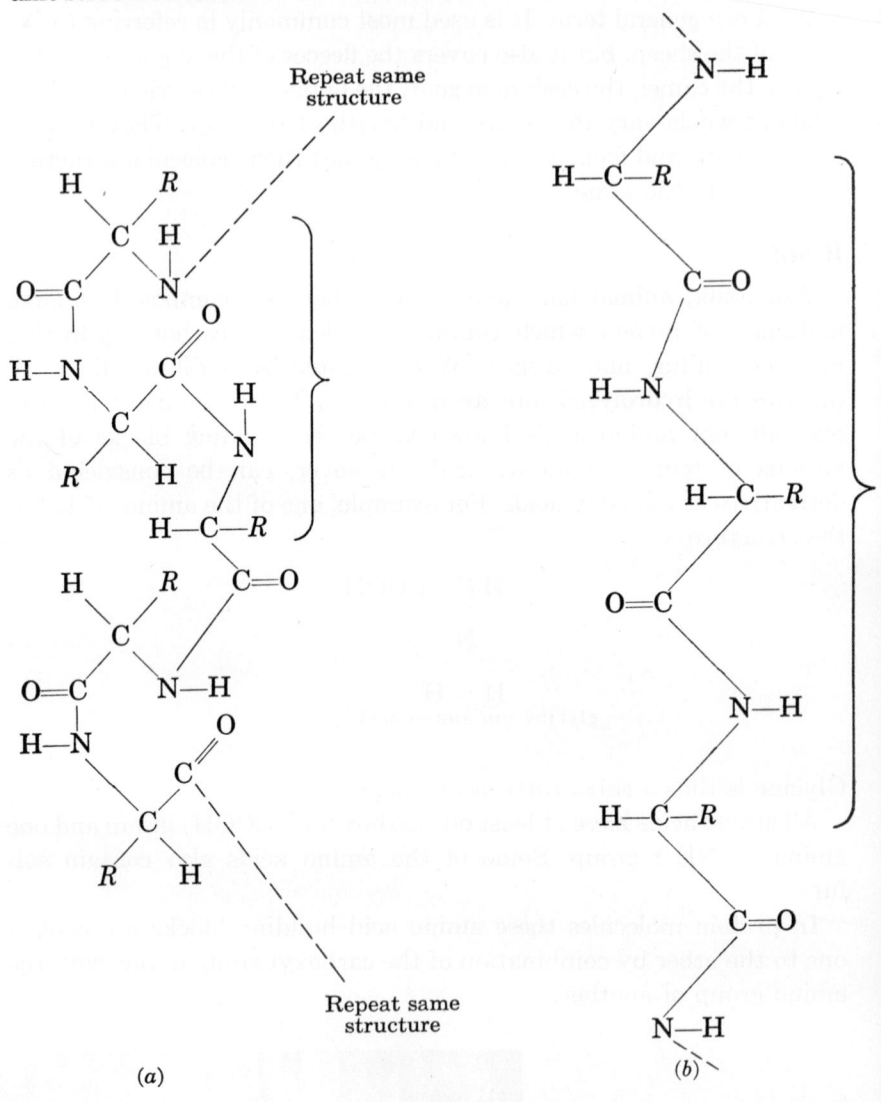

(*a*)

(*b*)

Now it is well known to anyone who has washed a pair of wool socks in hot water that wool can undergo shrinkage of as much as fifty percent. Further, a wool fiber when wet can be stretched to double its original length. In fact, the elasticity and resilience of wool are among its most important properties when used as a textile.

You should realize that in the structure *a* shown above each single bond shown corresponds, in a mechanical sense, to a single pin joining the two atoms together. You can then see that each atom can rotate

468

with respect to the one to which it is joined by a single bond. If structure *a* is pulled out at both ends, it can uncoil *without breaking any bonds or changing any bond angles* to yield structure *b*.

This coiling and uncoiling is what causes the elasticity and shrinking of wool. This fact was discovered by the use of x rays to determine the structure of wool fibers. The change is catalyzed by heat and moisture. Hot water and harsh (that is, alkaline) soap are particularly prone to shrink wool.

An actual hair or wool fiber consists of a bundle of chains, made up of the units shown in *a* or *b*, lying parallel to the long direction of the fiber. The various chains are tied together by atoms of sulfur which are hooked to carbon atoms in two different chains:

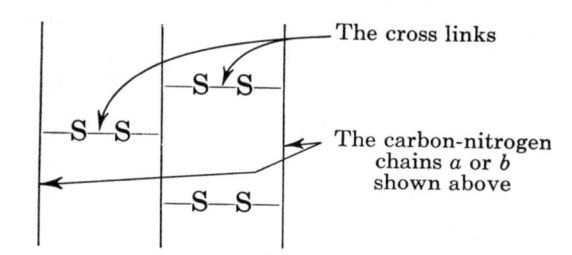

Sweaters made of wool are popular articles of clothing. (Sears Roebuck Co.)

The curling of human hair is also the result of the coiling and uncoiling of the units which make up the chain. If the hair is dampened and wound around a curling iron, the moisture allows the various chain units to coil as necessary to adjust themselves to the binding of the fiber. However, such a curl does not last long, especially on a damp day, because the individual units tend to re-establish their original shape. The various permanent waves involve first breaking the cross links in the hair fiber, then causing a part of the chains to coil and thereby become shorter, and finally re-establishing new cross links which set the curl and make it permanent. This is accomplished in the machine wave by treating the hair with dilute alkali and moisture, winding it around a curling iron, and heating it. The cold permanents employ special chemical reagents which break the **sulfur cross links,** then re-establish the cross links after curling, thereby setting the wave.

Although it has not been proved, it presumably is true that people with naturally curly hair have genes that normally produce fibers in which some of the chains are shorter, because of being coiled, than those lying next to them.

469

Synthetic wool

Casein, the principal protein obtained from milk, is similar to, but not identical with, wool in composition. Casein can be converted into a textile fiber which is used in a manner similar to rayon. Some of it is sold under the trade name of Aralac. Casein is converted into fibers by dissolving it in sodium hydroxide solution, extruding it into an acid bath which precipitates the protein, and then hardening it with formaldehyde. Several million pounds of casein fiber are made in the United States annually. Protein from soybeans and peanuts can be made into similar fibers.

Natural rubber

The word *rubber* at present is not a very definite term, since it is used to include various materials both natural and synthetic which have reversible elasticity. The natural rubbers are obtained from trees, shrubs, and vines which grow in the tropics. Usually the plant yields a liquid known as *latex* which consists of small droplets of the rubber dispersed through a water solution. Some of the sources are

Bully tree	yields	balata	
Gutta-percha tree	yields	gutta-percha	
Guayule shrub	yields	hevea rubber	common natural rubber
Hevea tree	yields	hevea rubber	

It is not known who discovered and first applied the useful mechanical properties of rubber. Joseph Priestley (see Chap. 6, page 46) in 1770 discovered its use for erasing lead-pencil marks, from which the present name rubber is derived. Before 1839 and the discovery of vulcanization by **Charles Goodyear,** rubber was little more than a curiosity. Today rubbers are as indispensable to our economy as coal and oil.

Almost all the natural commercial rubber is produced from the hevea tree, which is a native of Brazil. Transplanted by the British and Dutch into Malaya and the East Indies, the tree grew so well in its new home that before World War II, 98 percent of all natural rubber was produced in the Far East. Attempts are now being made to grow more natural rubber in this hemisphere, both by developing the wild rubber trees of Brazil and by developing plantations of other rubber-producing plants, especially guayule.

The hevea tree is tapped by cutting the bark of the tree and collecting the latex which oozes out. At the plantation the rubber is coagulated by adding acetic or formic acid to the latex. The slabs of raw rubber so obtained are washed and then squeezed between *rolls*

Rubber, since the discovery of vulcanization, has been one of the most important of nature's giant molecules in the advance of civilization. Modern transportation would be impossible without rubber. This photograph shows rubber tires hard enough to support 10,000 gal of water plus the weight of this huge truck, but elastic enough not to crack. (Firestone Tire & Rubber Co.)

to remove the solution. The slabs are then air-dried to produce *crepe rubber* or hung in smokehouses to produce as *smoked sheets*.

This crude crepe or smoked-sheet rubber is shipped to the rubber factory, where it is converted into the desired final product. The conversion generally involves addition of reinforcing agents which improve the strength and wear resistance of the rubber. Carbon black (see Chap. 34, page 392) is the most important reinforcing agent. Zinc oxide is also widely used. Almost all rubber is also vulcanized.

Raw, unvulcanized rubber changes with the weather. It is brittle when cold, soft and sticky when hot. These changes are largely overcome by vulcanization, which is still done in much the same way as it was done by its discoverer, Charles Goodyear (see Chap. 28, page 321). The amount of sulfur used determines the hardness of the product.

Hevea rubber is a hydrocarbon having an empirical formula C_5H_8. The molecules are long chains built up of these C_5H_8 units:

$$-\begin{vmatrix} & H & H & CH_3 & \\ & | & | & | & \\ -& C - C - C = C - \\ & | & | & | \\ & H & H & & H \\ & & C_5H_8 \text{ unit} & \end{vmatrix} \begin{vmatrix} H & H & CH_3 \\ | & | & | \\ -C - C - C = C - \\ | & | & | \\ H & H & & H \end{vmatrix} \begin{vmatrix} H & H & CH_3 \\ | & | & | \\ -C - C - C = C - \\ | & | & | \\ H & H & & H \end{vmatrix}-$$

Normally these chains are not straight but are coiled in random fashion, each chain being coiled differently. When stretched, the chains uncoil and elongate. When the tension is released, the molecules re-coil and the chunk of rubber assumes its original shape.

Although the nature of vulcanization is not yet completely understood, it is believed that sulfur combines with the double bonds in two adjacent chains, thereby cross linking the chains together in a way analogous to the cross linking of the chains in a wool fiber.

KEY WORDS

amino acid	Goodyear	Hyatt	sizing agent
casein	Herty	lignin	sulfur cross links
cellulose	high polymer	pulp	viscose process

HIGHLIGHTS

Nature's giant molecules may have a molecular weight of half a million or more. Among the sources of a host of man-made materials are wood, wool, **casein,** and rubber.

Wood is mainly **cellulose.** From cellulose are made paper, celluloid, cellophane, cellulose acetate, cellulose nitrate, and mercerized cotton.

The ability of wool to stretch and shrink depends upon the coil-and-spring arrangement of its molecules. Casein is one source of synthetic wool.

Natural rubber is a hydrocarbon which, after treatment with sulfur and carbon black, is used in making thousands of products.

QUESTIONS

1. How are the $C_6H_{10}O_5$ units arranged in cotton or wood?
2. How is the paper stock used for newsprint prepared?
3. What is sulfite pulp? For what purposes is it used?
4. What is meant by "sizing" paper?
5. What is the difference between viscose rayon and cellophane?
6. What is viscose?
7. Describe how viscose rayon is made.
8. What are the disadvantages of a textile made of cellulose acetate?
9. Why is cellulose nitrate rayon no longer made?
10. What is mercerized cotton?
11. What are the units in a protein such as wool called?
12. Describe the structure of natural rubber.
13. How is the elasticity of natural rubber explained?
14. What is vulcanization?

CHAPTER 39

some man-made giant molecules: synthetic plastics and rubbers

The exact way in which nature is able to put together the atoms in the giant molecules discussed in the last chapter is still unknown. None of these natural polymers, except possibly Hevea rubber, have been made in the laboratory. Chemists have made many other high polymers which serve a wide variety of purposes in the life of an average American. The average American may think of plastics as something used only to make nonessential gadgets, but the fact is that the modern synthetic plastics industry is indispensable to our present way of life. Without plastics, the *modern* radio, telephone, television, automobile, airplane, and electric motor would be impossible; to mention just a few of the industries which are dependent upon plastics. But, even at the present state of development of the plastics industry, there is reason to believe that tomorrow and the next day will bring forth even better plastics than we have today.

It is a common saying that for the first 75 years of the development of organic chemistry, chemists poured all their plastic discoveries down the sink. What is meant is that when a chemist systematically worked out the chemistry of the various classes of organic compounds, he would often obtain a tarry mass in the reaction flask. Because such tars are generally insoluble and nondistillable, they are not subject to purification as are ordinary organic compounds. Hence the chemist generally discarded the flask and perhaps recorded in his notebook,

Synthetic plastics are of great use both in the home and in industry. Left, this housewife is wrapping fresh corn in Saran for freezing. Right, nylon is added to the hemp in this rope for additional strength and longer wear. (E. I. du Pont de Nemours & Co.)

"The reaction produced a resinous mass of undetermined composition."

The modern synthetic plastics industry began in 1907 when **Dr. Leo Baekeland** was seeking a substitute for shellac. He discovered that a mixture of phenol and formaldehyde with a catalyst, when heated, produced a hard resin which could be molded with heat. The product, known as *bakelite*, has been manufactured ever since.

The structure of synthetic plastics

The basic structure of the synthetic plastics and rubbers is of the same type as those found in nature. That is, they consist of tremendously large molecules (high polymers). These large molecules are built up by linking together simple organic groups which make up the links in this long-chain molecule. Obviously each of the links must be capable of hooking chemically onto other links at each of its ends or no chain will form.

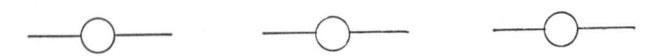

Greatly extended, this forms the chainlike large molecule. —O— represents a small molecule which is capable of reacting with other small molecules, thereby forming the chain.

Sometimes the starting material which reacts to form the plastic has three hooks on it, that is, three places to which other groups can attach themselves. In this case the chains will become cross-linked as wool is cross-linked with sulfur atoms (Chap. 38, page 469).

cross linking in high polymers

Whether long chains or long cross-linked chains are formed will depend on whether one starts with a material which has two or with one that has three reactive groups on it. Starting with a material with only two reactive groups, only chainlike polymers can be formed. If there are three reactive groups, then cross-linked chain polymers will form.

Classification of plastics

Plastics may be grouped into two classes: (1) thermoplastic polymers (that is, heat-softening) and (2) thermosetting polymers (that is, heat-setting).

1. **Thermoplastic** polymers are those which soften and can be molded by heating. These are composed of linear chains and have no significant amount of cross linking. Thermoplastic polymers are also soluble in appropriate solvents. Like sealing wax or paraffin, a thermoplastic polymer can be softened and reshaped as many times as desired. This is particularly important to the manufacturer because it makes

Veins of chrysotile asbestos in the serpentine matrix of rock. Asbestos is an example of an inorganic high polymer. (Johns-Manville Corporation)

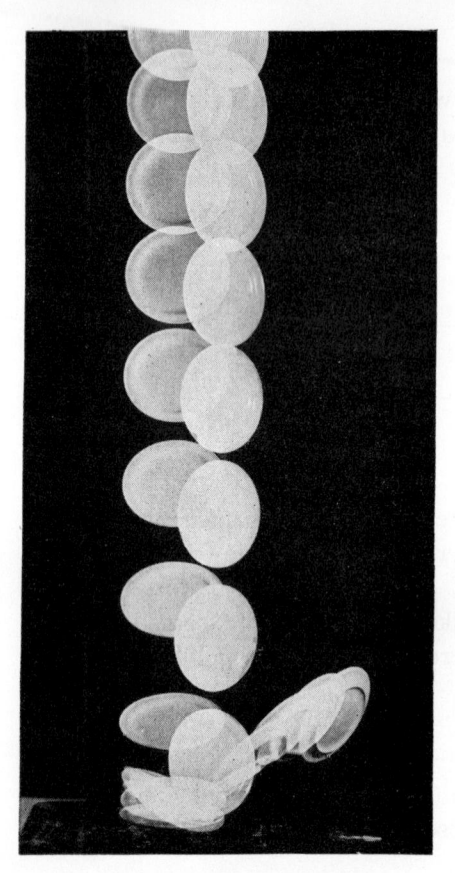

Melamine plastic dinnerware may be dropped without fear of breaking. (American Cyanamid Co.)

for simple fabrication processes. The solubility of thermoplastic polymers in organic solvents may sometimes be a disadvantage (as in the case of cellulose acetate rayon). Examples of thermoplastic polymers are natural unvulcanized rubber, nylon, cellulose acetate, Lucite or Plexiglas,[1] and Saran.

2. **Thermosetting** polymers are those which are formed by heating the reactants and which, once formed, *do not soften on heating*. They are in a sense like concrete which, once formed, cannot be re-softened. Thermosetting polymers are always cross-linked. Thermosetting resins are also insoluble in all solvents, although they may swell and become disintegrated in certain solvents. The reason for the infusibility and insolubility of these cross-linked polymers is easy to see. *The cross-linking makes the entire mass one big molecule*, and there is no point at which a solvent can penetrate the mass and separate it without breaking a chemical bond.

High polymers are not confined to organic chemistry. We have already encountered in diamond a similar high polymer which also is insoluble and infusible. Mica, portland cement, and asbestos are other illustrations from the inorganic realm.

A thermosetting plastic must either be made to assume the final desired shape while it is being formed, or it must be fabricated by sawing, drilling, turning, and so on, as wood is fabricated. Examples are bakelite, Beetle, and Melmac used for making dishes and jewelry.

There are many different commercial plastics. Those mentioned in this chapter are illustrative but by no means all that are known.

Polyethylene

This polymer is sold under the name of **polythene**. It is made from ethylene gas (see Chap. 36, page 416).

$$H_2C = CH_2$$
ethylene

---

[1] Lucite and Plexiglas are different trade names for the same product.

Under proper conditions of temperature and pressure (commercially from 500 to 3000 atmospheres) and in the presence of a peroxide catalyst, one of the bonds between the carbon atoms opens up

$$\begin{array}{c} H_2 \quad\quad H_2 \\ \diagdown \quad\diagup \\ C\!-\!C \\ \diagup \quad\diagdown \\ \text{(unstable)} \end{array}$$

forming an unstable molecule which combines with a similar molecule to form

$$\begin{array}{c} H_2 \; H_2 \; H_2 \; H_2 \\ |\;\;\;|\;\;\;|\;\;\;| \\ \text{---C---C---C---C---} \end{array}$$

which in turn can add on another ethylene group

$$\begin{array}{c} H_2 \; H_2 \; H_2 \; H_2 \; H_2 \; H_2 \\ |\;\;\;|\;\;\;|\;\;\;|\;\;\;|\;\;\;| \\ \text{---C---C---C---C---C---C---} \end{array}$$

It can be seen that the chain can grow indefinitely as long as there are unoccupied bonds on the end carbon atoms. In this way molecules of hydrocarbons containing hundreds of carbon atoms are produced. The result is a typical thermoplastic polymer.[1]

$$nC_2H_4 \xrightarrow{\text{catalyst}} \underset{\text{polythene}}{(C_2H_4)_n}$$

Where n = very large number

Polythene resins soften at about 110°C. They can be molded into sheets, bottles, bottle caps, tubing, rods, ice-cube trays, and many other items. Polythene is slightly flexible, has good resistance to moisture and most chemical reagents, and is an excellent electrical insulator. At the present time much of it is used for wire (and other electric) insulation and for making water pipe for underground installations.

Teflon

Replacing the hydrogen atoms in ethylene with fluorine atoms gives tetrafluoroethylene. This compound also will polymerize.

$$nC_2F_4 \xrightarrow{\text{catalyst}} (C_2F_4)_n$$

Where n = very large number

[1] The student may wonder why the reaction ever stops. Apparently the catalyst or some impurity eventually combines with the bonds on the end carbon atom, stopping the reaction.

Koroseal is a vinyl chloride plastic. Because it is waterproof it is used for electrical insulation, rainproof clothing, and many other purposes which require water resistance. This photograph shows a child's swimming pool made of Koroseal. (B. F. Goodrich Co.)

This thermoplastic is sold under the trade name *Teflon*. It is non-inflammable and has exceedingly good resistance to chemical reagents, being unaffected by concentrated acids, alkalis, and oxidizing agents. It also has a very high softening point, which makes it desirable for electrical insulation.

The vinyl chloride resins

Acetylene (see Chap. 36, page 417), treated with hydrochloric acid, yields **vinyl chloride.**

$$H-C\equiv C-H + HCl \rightarrow \underset{\underset{H\ \ H}{|\ \ |}}{H-C=C-Cl}$$
vinyl chloride

Vinyl chloride, it will be noted, is ethylene in which one hydrogen atom is replaced by a chlorine. Vinyl chloride polymerizes readily in a manner similar to ethylene.

$$n\text{C}_2\text{H}_3\text{Cl} \rightarrow (\text{C}_2\text{H}_3\text{Cl})_n$$
vinyl chloride   polyvinyl chloride

$$\underset{\text{(unit of polymer)}}{\left| \begin{array}{cc} H & H \\ | & | \\ -C-C- \\ | & | \\ H & Cl \end{array} \right|} \quad \begin{array}{cccccc} H & H & H & H & H & H \\ | & | & | & | & | & | \\ -C-C-C-C-C-C- \\ | & | & | & | & | & | \\ H & Cl & H & Cl & H & Cl \end{array}$$

Where n = very large number

Except for the cellulose derivatives, polyvinyl chloride is the most widely used thermoplastic resin. It is non-inflammable, insoluble in most organic solvents, moisture-resistant, nontoxic, odorless, and tasteless. It is not resistant to gasoline but resists weathering and most chemicals. Polyvinyl chloride itself is hard but when ground with certain organic liquids, which serve as plasticizers, it can be made into a rubbery material that does not crack on weathering.

Sold under many trade names, among them Koroseal and Geon, it is made into garden hose, heat-sealing moistureproof bags for frozen foods, tough electrical insulation, rainproof clothing, tents, shower curtains, gloves, aprons, upholstery fabrics, and many other things.

Polystyrene

Styrene is ethylene in which one of the hydrogen atoms is replaced with a benzene ring.

$$C_6H_5-\underset{H}{\overset{H}{C}}=\underset{H}{C}$$

styrene

Like ethylene, it polymerizes.

$$nC_6H_5CHCH_2 \rightarrow (C_6H_5CHCH_2)_n$$
styrene → polystyrene

(the unit)

Styron, a polystyrene plastic, is used a great deal for refrigerator parts, such as trays, compartment doors, control knobs and other interior portions. These plastic parts add to the performance and appearance of the refrigerator. Styron is also used for plastic wall tile, television windows, and lighting fixtures. (E. I. du Pont de Nemours & Co.)

Contact lenses made of Lucite. These lenses are worn next to the eyeball to correct defective vision. They are an improvement upon optical glass used for the same purpose because they weigh only 40 percent as much and are almost unbreakable and invisible. (E. I. du Pont de Nemours & Co.)

Polystyrene is a water-white, transparent thermoplastic solid. It is used for making bottle caps for mineral acids, storage battery boxes, and electrical insulators in radio and radar sets. Polystyrene has the ability to transmit light through a curved section, thereby "bending it around corners." This makes it useful for illuminating aircraft and automobile instrument panels and signs. It is used as the nonglass layer in shatterproof glass.

Lucite and Plexiglas

So far we have considered only resins formed by polymerizing ethylene or a compound derived from ethylene by replacing one or more of the hydrogen atoms by a halogen or a benzene group. One other important group of resins is also of this type. These resins are known as the **acrylic polymers,** but we can best consider them as derived from ethylene. The starting material is **methyl methacrylate:**

$$\begin{array}{cc} H & COOCH_3 \\ | & | \\ C\!=\!C \\ | & | \\ H & CH_3 \end{array}$$

methyl methacrylate

The material is ethylene in which one hydrogen is replaced by the ester group, —$COOCH_3$, and another (on the same carbon) is replaced by a methyl group, —CH_3. Methyl methacrylate is a colorless liquid which will polymerize, in the manner of ethylene, when warmed with a peroxide catalyst.

$$----\overset{\overset{H}{|}}{\underset{\underset{H}{|}}{C}}-\overset{\overset{COOCH_3}{|}}{\underset{\underset{CH_3}{|}}{C}}-\overset{\overset{H}{|}}{\underset{\underset{H}{|}}{C}}-\overset{\overset{COOCH_3}{|}}{\underset{\underset{CH_3}{|}}{C}}-\overset{\overset{H}{|}}{\underset{\underset{H}{|}}{C}}-\overset{\overset{COOCH_3}{|}}{\underset{\underset{CH_3}{|}}{C}}-\overset{\overset{H}{|}}{\underset{\underset{H}{|}}{C}}-\overset{\overset{COOCH_3}{|}}{\underset{\underset{CH_3}{|}}{C}}----$$
(the unit)

The plastics based on methyl methacrylate are crystal clear, light in weight, tough, and durable. They may be sawed, drilled, turned, and polished. They also "bend light around corners." Dilute acids and alkalis do not affect them, but they are soluble in acetone, esters, and hydrocarbons.

Methyl methacrylate plastics are used in airplane windshields, bomber blisters, safety goggles, dental plates, and costume jewelry. Probably their greatest disadvantage is that they scratch easily.

Nylon

The word *nylon* was originally coined by the E. I. du Pont de Nemours & Co. to refer to a group of nitrogen-containing organic polymers. Because of the high quality of some of these products, the word nylon in some European countries now has come to mean anything—particularly if made in America—of modern origin and high quality. Few products of the chemist's test tube have so struck the fancy of man or proved so versatile as nylon.

Nylon is a product of the research laboratory of du Pont. Its development was due to **Dr. W. H. Carothers** (1896–1937) and his co-workers at du Pont, who did much of the pioneering work upon which the present-day synthetic resin industry is based.

The late Dr. Wallace Hume Carothers, who invented nylon, shown at work in his laboratory. His invention was considered of such importance that a laboratory, the Carothers Research Laboratory, at the du Pont Company's experimental station was named in his honor. (E. I. du Pont de Nemours & Co.)

Top, molten nylon emerges from slot in lower end of autoclave, at upper left, and is solidified on wheel in the form of a plastic ribbon. This passes over the smaller guide wheel and as it comes off is broken into flake. Bottom, the nylon flake pours from hoppers into a storage barrel. (E. I. du Pont de Nemours & Co.)

Top left, nylon filaments are extruded from tiny holes in a spinneret. All these filaments will be wound together to form nylon yarn. Top right, the nylon yarn is baked in large "twist setting ovens" before it is wound on spools and cones. Bottom, finished yarn is wound on cones ready for use by knitters and weavers. (E. I. du Pont de Nemours & Co.)

Nylon is formed by reacting a dibasic organic acid, **adipic acid**, $(COOH)(CH_2)_4(COOH)$, with **hexamethylenediamine**, $NH_2(CH_2)_6NH_2$.

$$HOOC-(CH_2)_4-\overset{O}{\underset{\|}{C}}-\boxed{OH + H}-\overset{H}{\underset{|}{N}}-(CH_2)_6-NH_2$$

↑ acid
(another molecule of diamine reacts here)

diamine

↑
(another molecule of acid reacts here)

The result is a long chain composed alternately of units from the acid and from the diamine. The molecular weights in nylon are around 10,000. The resulting structure is similar to, but not the same as, silk and wool. However, no cross linking of chains exists as in wool. Nylon is therefore thermoplastic and can be molded or drawn into fiber.

In making nylon thread, the plastic in chip form is melted and forced through spinnerets. The resulting filaments harden quickly on cooling and are directly wound on bobbins. The thread is then stretched and thus permanently elongated to four times its original length. This thread forms the textile fiber with which the public is familiar. This elongation is necessary since, before elongation, the fibers have no elasticity. The stretching produces changes in the structure of the fiber and gives it the remarkable degree of elasticity combined with high tensile strength for which nylon is so famous. This is the reason that nylon has such great resistance to wear and tearing.

Nylon has only moderate resistance to strong acid reagents but is resistant to alkalis, organic acids, and organic solvents. It melts at 253°C. It does not have as good resistance to sunlight as could be desired. The low moisture absorption of nylon is somewhat of a disadvantage in textiles, since garments made of it do not absorb perspiration as readily as cotton, wool, or rayon. On the other hand this property causes nylon to dry quickly after laundering. Obviously nylon should not be ironed with a hot iron.

The use of nylon in textiles is known to everyone. What is not so commonly known is its use as a resin. It can be heat-molded as is any other thermoplastic resin. Rope, military powder bags, tennis-racquet string, surgical sutures, sails, parachutes, and paint-brush bristles are among the many articles made from it.

Textile fibers in the trade are identified by the **denier.** Denier is the weight in grams of 9000 m of the fiber.

TABLE 39-1. Tensile strength of some textile fibers

| | Tenacity in grams per denier ||
	Dry	Wet
Nylon 66	5	4.5
Silk	4.6	3.9
Viscose rayon	1.8	0.9
Acetate rayon	1.5	1.0
Wool	1.5	1.2

Orlon

This more recently introduced synthetic fiber (production started in 1950 by du Pont) is made by polymerizing **acrylonitrile** (C_2H_3CN). After formation, the fibers are stretched as in the case of nylon. The result is a fiber of very high tensile strength with excellent resistance to sunlight, outdoor exposure, acids, solvents, and mold (that is, mildew, and so on). Orlon fiber can be woven into a material resembling silk, or, by cutting the fiber into short pieces and spinning, a yarn resembling wool can be produced.

$$\begin{array}{c|cc|cc}
 & H & H & H & H \\
 & | & | & | & | \\
- & C - C & - & C - C & - \\
 & | & | & | & | \\
 & H & CN & H & CN \\
\end{array}$$

(chain unit in Orlon)

Synthetic rubber

Up until the Japanese attacked Pearl Harbor in 1941, almost all the rubber used in America was natural hevea rubber produced in the Far East. With this supply cut off, America was in a desperate situation. This country could no more fight a modern war without rubber than it could without explosives. Fortunately the scientists and technologists of this country were able to design and build plants which produced such great quantities of natural rubber substitutes that there was never any serious shortage of "rubber." The importance of this fact is not always recognized by the public, but it is true that without a rubber supply the United States and its Allies could never have won World War II.

Although there are many synthetic materials which serve as rubber substitutes, the principal synthetic rubbers are three in number: (1) buna S rubber, also known as GRS rubber; (2) butyl rubber, also known as GRI rubber; and (3) neoprene, also known as GRM rubber. (These code letters were assigned during World War II, and the first two stand for *G*overnment *R*ubber.)

Buna S rubber

Buna S, or **GRS,** rubber is formed by polymerizing styrene (see page 479) and **butadiene,** C_4H_6.

$$\underset{\text{butadiene}}{\begin{array}{c} H\ H\ H\ H \\ |\ |\ |\ | \\ C{=}C{-}C{=}C \\ |\quad\quad\ \ | \\ H\quad\quad\ \ H \end{array}} + \underset{\text{styrene}}{\begin{array}{c} H\ H \\ |\ | \\ C{=}C \\ |\ \ | \\ H\ C_6H_5 \end{array}} \xrightarrow{\text{catalyst}} \text{buna rubber}$$

The polymerization comes about somewhat like the polymerization of ethylene and styrene also discussed on page 477. It is carried out in the presence of soap solution and the resulting polymer is much like natural latex. The polymer is processed and vulcanized in much the same way as natural latex. Recently, it has been found that this polymerization can be carried out at temperatures as low as $-40°C$ with improvement in the quality of the rubber. Most of the buna S rubber now produced, which in 1949 amounted to 375,000 tons, is this **"cold rubber."**

The raw materials for this type of rubber are hydrocarbons which can be made from petroleum.

GRS rubber is far superior to natural rubber in resistance to aging, and tires and tubes made of it hold air better than those of natural rubber. It has about the same tensile strength and abrasion resistance as natural rubber. Its chief disadvantage is that tires made of GRS rubber heat up more than is desirable—a fact which limits its use in truck tires. It does not resist the action of oils and greases any better than natural rubber, and this is not very well.

GRS is a general-purpose rubber and is produced in greater quantity than any of the other synthetic rubbers. It is used for almost all the same purposes as natural rubber.

Butyl rubber

Butyl, or **GRI,** rubber is formed by polymerizing two ethylenic hydrocarbon gases, butadiene and **isobutylene.** It is far superior to natural rubber for certain purposes, particularly for inner tubes of automobile and truck tires. The tubes give long service and hold air better than those of natural rubber. But such tubes cannot be repaired with a "cold patch." GRI rubber is not suitable in general for tire treads.

Neoprene

The type of synthetic rubber called neoprene is formed by the polymerization of **chloroprene.**

$$\begin{array}{cccc} H & & H & H \\ | & & | & | \\ C=C&-&C=C \\ | & | & & | \\ H & Cl & & H \end{array}$$
chloroprene

Chloroprene is made from acetylene and hydrogen chloride. Hence this rubber may be said to come from limestone, coke, salt, water, and chemical know-how.

Neoprene is better than natural rubber in its resistance to organic solvents. For this reason gasoline hoses are most commonly made of neoprene rather than of natural rubber. (E. I. du Pont de Nemours & Co.)

Neoprene is similar to natural rubber except that it has much better resistance to oils, greases, and organic solvents in general. Its principal uses are in the manufacture of flexible hoses for handling petroleum products, for a lining in petroleum storage tanks, and for electrical insulation where the insulation is exposed to oil, as well as for shoe soles and gloves similarly exposed.

TABLE 39–2. Comparative resistance of natural and synthetic rubbers[a]

	To high temperature	To aging	To outdoor exposure	To solvents
Natural hevea rubber	Poor	Poor	Poor	Poor
Buna S rubber	Good	Excellent	Fair	Fair
Butyl rubber	Poor	Excellent	Excellent	Poor
Neoprene	Good	Good	Excellent	Excellent

[a] From A. X. Schmidt and C. A. Marlies, *Principles of High-Polymer Theory and Practice*, McGraw-Hill Book Co., Inc., New York, 1948, p. 514.

KEY WORDS

acrylic polymers	Carothers	neoprene, or GRM
acrylonitrile	chloroprene	polythene
adipic acid	cold rubber	styrene
Baekeland	denier	thermoplastic
buna S, or GRS	hexamethylenediamine	thermosetting
butadiene	isobutylene	vinyl chloride
butyl, or GRI	methyl methacrylate	

HIGHLIGHTS

Compounds made up of long linear chains of molecules constitute the **thermoplastic** polymers. An example is Lucite.

Compounds made up of both linear and cross-linked chains of molecules constitute the **thermosetting** plastics. An example is bakelite.

The following plastic materials are related by the fact that they are all polymers of ethylene or a substituted ethylene:

Polyethylene $(C_2H_4)_n$
Teflon $(C_2F_4)_n$
Polyvinyl chloride $(C_2H_3Cl)_n$
Polystyrene $(C_2H_3 \cdot C_6H_5)_n$
Orlon $(C_2H_3 \cdot CN)_n$
Lucite (Plexiglas) $(C_2H_2 \cdot CH_3 \cdot COOCH_3)_n$

Nylon consists of linked chains of **adipic acid** and **hexamethylenediamine** molecules.

The synthetic rubbers are polymerization products:

Buna S   butadiene and styrene
Butyl   butadiene and isobutylene
Neoprene chloroprene and chloroprene

QUESTIONS

1. What is meant by a thermoplastic resin? Give one example.
2. What is meant by a thermosetting resin? Give one example.
3. How does a thermoplastic resin differ in structure from a thermosetting resin?
4. What is polyethylene? From what is it made? What are some uses for it?
5. What are the special advantages of the plastic known as *Teflon?*
6. What are some of the objects made from polyvinyl chloride resins?
7. Is nylon thermoplastic or thermosetting?
8. Name some objects, other than textiles, that are made of nylon.
9. What are the advantages of buna S rubber over natural rubber? What is its chief disadvantage?
10. What special property makes neoprene highly useful for certain purposes?

CHAPTER 40

chemistry and nutrition

Of all the different ways in which the applications of chemistry influence the life of civilized man, probably none are of as great potential importance as the applications of chemistry to human nutrition. This is particularly true for future generations.

Students now enter American colleges taller and yet younger than were their parents and other predecessors when they entered the same colleges thirty to forty years ago. This is shown consistently by all the available records, and is true of both boys and girls. There has not been any known change in proportions of racial stocks which could account for the differences. The explanation is to be found not in inheritance in the biological sense but in a social inheritance—the increase of scientific knowledge and its use in the betterment of conditions of living.[1]

One of the principal ways in which this increased scientific knowledge of life has contributed to the betterment of conditions of living is through a knowledge of the ways in which the diet influences the health and general condition of the individual.

Broadly speaking, research has shown two facts:

1. Certain specific disorders of the body are caused by a deficiency of certain food factors in the diet. For example, about twenty years ago it was shown that scurvy, a condition which has affected man since the earliest days of history, is due to a lack of **ascorbic acid** ($C_6H_8O_6$) in the diet and that scurvy can be cured by adding a proper amount of this compound to the diet. Many other "diseases" are now known actually to be **nutritional deficiency** conditions which are curable by proper diet.

2. Even though a diet is adequate in the sense that it prevents nutritional diseases, in some cases the diet may nevertheless be subject

[1] Quoted from H. C. Sherman and C. S. Lanford, *Essentials of Nutrition*, 3d ed., The Macmillan Co., New York, 1951, p. 1.

Animals in a nutrition laboratory. (U.S. Bureau of Human Nutrition and Home Economics)

to improvement to the benefit of the individual concerned. In other words most people, even in America, who are living on what was previously considered to be a good diet, are not getting the best possible diet in terms of their general health and length of life. Animal feeding experiments have shown that the life span of the albino rat can be increased by 10 percent by improvement of a diet even though the diet is already adequate in the sense that normal animals can be raised on it for an unlimited number of generations. Not only can the life span be increased, but this increase comes largely during that part of the individual's life which Professor Sherman of Columbia University has called the "period of the prime." That is, proper dietary improvement produces faster growth in the young, earlier maturity, and a later-than-normal senility. Moreover, these well-nourished individuals pass some of their vigor and robust health on to their offspring. There is reason to believe that these findings with laboratory animals apply also to human beings, and it is easy to see the tremendous importance they can have for present and future generations.

The functions of food

Food nourishes the body in three ways:

1. It provides materials which the body can burn to yield energy for body activities and to heat the body.

2. It provides the building materials of which new body tissues may be formed or with which existing body tissues may be maintained or repaired.

3. It provides materials which directly or indirectly regulate or control body processes.

To do this, food should supply the following classes of substances: (*a*) water, (*b*) carbohydrates, (*c*) fats, (*d*) proteins, (*e*) mineral elements,[1] and (*f*) vitamins.

Some of these substances serve the body in one, some in two, and some in all three of the ways listed above. For example, carbohydrates function almost exclusively as sources of energy. Fats, on the other hand, serve both as sources of energy and as essential body-building materials. Proteins are particularly important as body-building materials, since every cell contains protein and many active tissues, such as muscles, are largely protein and water. But protein also serves as a source of energy and can in fact take over this entire function if carbohydrates and fats are lacking. And furthermore, from proteins are formed many of the body's most important regulatory substances, including enzymes and some hormones.

The mineral elements, or ash constituents, obviously can contribute nothing directly to the supply of body energy, since they offer no oxidizable residues. They are important as structural components of the body (for example, the calcium, magnesium, and phosphorus which give bones and teeth their rigidity) and as constituents of body regulatory agents (for example, iodine in thyroxine and iron in hemoglobin).

The vitamins function in such small amounts that they cannot contribute significantly to the energy supply or to the body structure. But they are important in controlling both the processes by which other foodstuffs yield energy in the body (several of the vitamins are active components of enzymes involved in respiration) and the processes of body growth (for example, vitamin D controls bone development).

Nutrition standards

Nutrition concerns itself with the problem of supplying through the diet the factors which the body needs for life, maintenance, and growth. Nutrition asks first: What elements or chemical compounds are needed? Then: How much of each one is needed, and how much more may be desirable? And finally: From what selection of foods can these desired materials be obtained?

Nutrition is such a new and rapidly developing science that a final answer to these questions is not possible in all cases. But already

[1] Nutritionists use the term *mineral* in a less precise way than other chemists. Nutritionists mean the elements remaining in the ash when food is burned when they speak of minerals.

scientists have established that improvement of the diet may improve health and well-being to a far greater extent than was thought possible even 20 years ago. At the same time, since about the start of World War II, a concerted effort has been made to bring together scientific knowledge (and expert judgments where our knowledge is not yet complete) regarding human nutritional needs, and to present it in a form which the average individual can understand and apply to his own case. To help make this possible, the Food and Nutrition Board of the National Research Council presents a table of "Recommended Daily Dietary Allowances." A recent revision of this table is reproduced as Table 40–1.

You are not expected to memorize these values; but you may be interested to refer to them as the individual nutrients are discussed in the paragraphs which follow. You may also want to compare the recommended allowances of the nutrients with the amounts present in common foods (Table 40–2, page 505).

Calories

The body can burn carbohydrates, fats, and proteins practically interchangeably as sources of energy for its activities. Since, in general, carbohydrates and fats are less expensive than proteins, they are apt to supply 85 or 90 percent of the calories in typical American diets. If the total intake of energy-yielding foods exceeds the energy requirement, the excess food is converted into body fat and stored as such. But though the body can change fat, carbohydrate, or protein into body fat, there are certain unsaturated fatty acids (linoleic, $C_{17}H_{31}COOH$, and arachidonic, $C_{19}H_{31}COOH$) which the body needs for normal functioning but cannot form. These are, therefore, called the **nutritionally essential** fatty acids, and the diet should contain them in amounts corresponding to about 1 percent of the total calories. These acids occur in small amounts in the fats of many foods and (as we saw in Chap. 37, page 446) they are likely to be more plentiful in food oils than in solid fats.

Proteins

Proteins are made up of very large molecules, some with molecular weights running into the hundreds of thousands. Examples of proteins are egg albumin and casein, a protein from milk. Although there are many different proteins in nature, all of them are made up by combinations of amino acids (Chap. 38, page 467). There are about 21 different amino acids found in natural proteins. That is, all the different proteins in nature are made up by different combinations of these 21 types of protein building blocks.

TABLE 40-1. Recommended daily dietary allowances[a]

	Calories	Protein, g	Calcium, g	Iron mg	Vitamin A value, IU	Thiamine, mg	Riboflavin, mg	Niacin, mg	Ascorbic acid, mg	Vitamin D IU
Man (weight 65 kg, height 170 cm)										
25 years	3200[b]	65	0.8	12	5000	1.6	1.6	16	75	
45 years	2900	65	0.8	12	5000	1.5	1.6	15	75	
65 years	2600	65	0.8	12	5000	1.3	1.6	13	75	
Woman (55 kg, 157 cm)										
25 years	2300[b]	55	0.8	12	5000	1.2	1.4	12	70	
45 years	2100	55	0.8	12	5000	1.1	1.4	11	70	
65 years	1800	55	0.8	12	5000	1.0	1.4	10	70	
Pregnant (3rd trimester)	Add 400	80	1.5	15	6000	1.5	2.0	15	100	400
Lactating (850 ml daily)	Add 1000	100	2.0	15	8000	1.5	2.5	15	150	400
Infants[c]										
0–1 month[d]										
1–3 months (6 kg, 60 cm)	kg × 120	kg × 3.5[c]	0.6	6	1500	0.3	0.4	3	30	400
4–9 months (9 kg, 70 cm)	kg × 110	kg × 3.5[c]	0.8	6	1500	0.4	0.7	4	30	400
10–12 months (10 kg, 75 cm)	kg × 100	kg × 3.5[c]	1.0	6	1500	0.5	0.9	5	30	400
Children										
1–3 years (12 kg, 87 cm)	1200	40	1.0	7	2000	0.6	1.0	6	35	400
4–6 years (18 kg, 109 cm)	1600	50	1.0	8	2500	0.8	1.2	8	50	400
7–9 years (27 kg, 129 cm)	2000	60	1.0	10	3500	1.0	1.5	10	60	400
Boys										
10–12 years (35 kg, 144 cm)	2500	70	1.2	12	4500	1.3	1.8	13	75	400
13–15 years (49 kg, 163 cm)	3200	85	1.4	15	5000	1.6	2.1	16	90	400
16–20 years (63 kg, 175 cm)	3800	100	1.4	15	5000	1.9	2.5	19	100	400
Girls										
10–12 years (36 kg, 144 cm)	2300	70	1.2	12	4500	1.2	1.8	12	75	400
13–15 years (49 kg, 160 cm)	2500	80	1.3	15	5000	1.3	2.0	13	80	400
16–20 years (54 kg, 162 cm)	2400	75	1.3	15	5000	1.2	1.9	12	80	400

[a] Data are from *Food and Nutrition Board, National Research Council*, 1953. In planning practical dietaries, the recommended allowances can be attained with a variety of common foods which will also provide other nutrient requirements less well known; the allowance levels are considered to cover individual variations among normal persons as they live in the United States subjected to ordinary environmental stresses. . . .

[b] These calorie recommendations apply to the degree of activity for the reference man and woman. . . . For the urban "white-collar" worker they are probably excessive. In any case, the calorie allowance must be adjusted to the actual needs of the individual as required to achieve and maintain his desirable weight.

[c] The recommendations for infants pertain to nutrients derived primarily from cow's milk. If the milk from which the protein is derived is human milk or has been treated to render it more digestible, the allowance may be in the range of 2 to 3 g per kg. There should be no question that human milk is a desirable source of nutrients for infants even though it may not provide the levels recommended for certain nutrients.

[d] During the first month of life, desirable allowances for many nutrients are dependent upon maturation of excretory and endocrine functions. Therefore no specific recommendations are given.

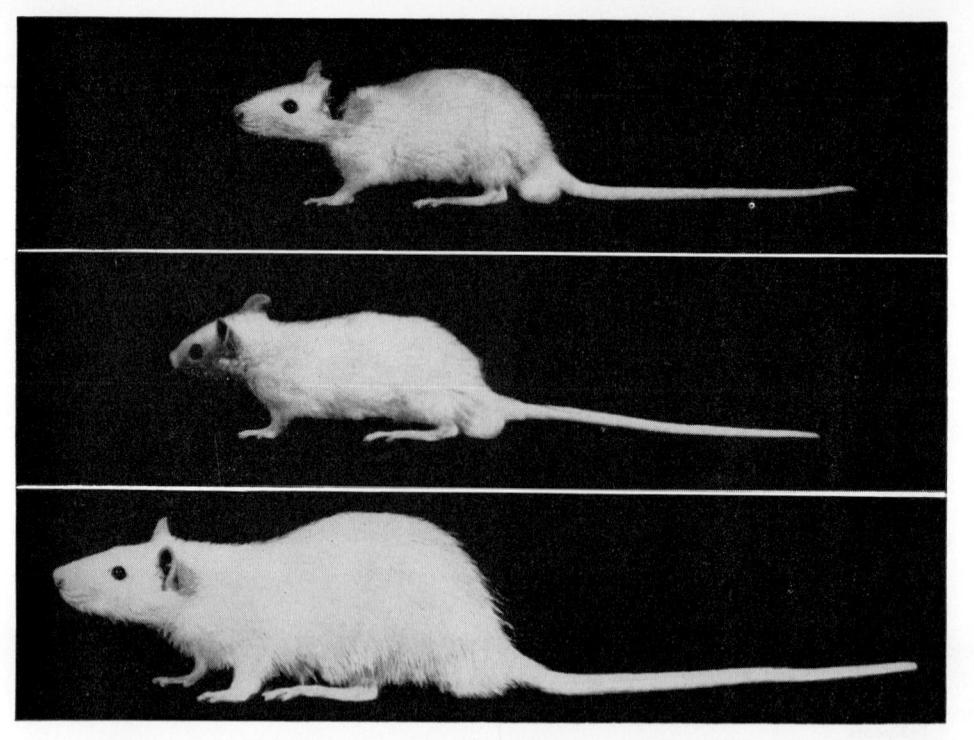

Top, a rat fed a diet low in all proteins. Middle, a rat fed a diet only low in essential amino acids. Bottom, a rat fed a diet high in essential proteins. The bottom rat is in the best condition. (U.S. Bureau of Human Nutrition and Home Economics)

In the process of digestion, the protein in food is broken down, by means of enzymes, into amino acids. These amino acids pass through the walls of the intestinal tract into the blood stream, where they are carried to the various tissues of the body. These amino acids may be used by the body in any one of three ways: (1) to form new protein or "repair" existing protein (for example, muscle tissue), (2) to form new substances, such as enzymes or hormones, and (3) as a source of energy. In this case the nitrogen is removed and excreted (as urea and ammonium salts) and the remainder of the amino acid is burned to carbon dioxide and water. Thus proteins can serve as sources of energy in body metabolism.

Feeding experiments show that there is a difference in the food value of different proteins. Some, such as gelatin, will not sustain life when fed as the sole source of protein in a diet which otherwise is good, whereas others, such as casein or the protein from wheat, will. This difference is due to the fact that of the 21 different amino acids which the body contains, 10 must be supplied in the diet because the body cannot make these. The other 11 can be made in the body by the transformation of other amino acids; hence these 11 need not be supplied *as such* by the food. However, the former group of 10 amino acids must be supplied in the food for normal growth to occur. For this reason they are referred to as nutritionally essential, and the remaining 11 amino acids are called nutritionally non-essential. A protein which lacks one or more of these essential amino acids will not support normal growth, and lack of certain of them causes eventual death.

Each protein differs from every other protein in the exact proportions of the different amino acids which it contains. When new protein is being formed, as in a growing child, the food protein which is most efficiently used is that which supplies the essential amino acids in most nearly the same proportion as they will occur in the newly formed protein. The proteins of eggs, milk, and meat are most efficiently used for growth. For the grown individual, the kind of protein is less important, especially if several different kinds are included so that one may supply amino acids which another lacks. The protein intake recommended for various individuals will be found in Table 40–1 and the amounts supplied by typical foods, in Table 40–2.

Chemists have not learned to synthesize proteins; hence, directly or indirectly, all animals are dependent upon plants for their source of protein (see Chap. 31, page 353). Plants are more self-sufficient than animals[1] in the sense that they can form proteins from simple inorganic nitrogen compounds in the soil.

Protein and livestock nutrition

In livestock feeding, essentially the same considerations apply as given above for human beings. Swine and poultry require a diet containing one or more proteins which together supply their nutritionally essential amino acids in the proper ratio. Protein sources for such feeds are corn (which contains about 10 percent protein), wheat (which contains about 12 percent protein), oats, soybean meal, grass, alfalfa or other legume meal, milk protein, plus fish or meat scrap.

The ruminants (cattle, sheep, goats) differ from other animals in that they can manufacture (probably by means of the bacteria which their intestinal tract contains) from any protein in their diet all the amino acids which they require. Hence cattle can live and thrive on a single source of protein which would not serve to sustain swine or poultry. In fact it is common practice to winter beef cattle on the Western ranges on grass hay, which supplies very little protein, and cottonseed meal. The latter protein source, although excellent for cattle, would not alone sustain poultry or swine.

More recently it has been found that cattle (and presumably other ruminants) can even convert the simple nitrogen compound urea

[1] One exception is the ruminants which are mentioned below.

[CO(NH$_2$)$_2$] into protein. When this was first observed, it was a rather startling discovery because up until then it had been believed that only plants could convert simple nitrogen compounds into protein. However, it is presumably through the agency of bacteria in the intestinal tract that cattle convert urea.

In any case this discovery is a matter of considerable practical importance. During and after World War II, urea was fed in quantity to cattle as a substitute for soybean and cottonseed meals, which were scarce then. Since urea can be produced much more cheaply (from carbon dioxide and ammonia) than most vegetable proteins, its use may in the future have considerable effect on our food supply.

The mineral elements

It is not known with certainty how many mineral elements are essential to normal human body functioning. This is because some mineral elements may be required in very small quantities, and experimentally it is quite difficult to conduct feeding experiments in which the last traces of certain mineral elements have been removed from the diet.

It is known that the following 13 mineral elements are essential:

Phosphorus	Sodium	Iodine
Calcium	Magnesium	Cobalt
Potassium	Iron	Zinc
Sulfur	Manganese	
Chlorine	Copper	

The mineral elements may function in three different ways, namely: (1) as constituents of the skeleton (that is, bones and teeth) to give it rigidity, (2) as constituents of the soft tissues (for example, sulfur is contained in most proteins, iron is an essential constituent of hemoglobin), and (3) as constituents of certain body regulators (inorganic salts themselves are important body regulators, for example, through their effect on osmotic pressure; and, in addition, certain of the mineral elements are contained in more complex regulatory compounds, as iodine in thyroxine, cobalt in vitamin B$_{12}$, and so on).

Phosphorus

Phosphorus is an essential constituent of every known cell in the body. In the human adult nearly 90 percent of the total phosphorus content of the body is in the skeleton. The mineral matter of the skeleton is mainly a double salt between tricalcium phosphate and calcium carbonate. Altogether about 1.6 lb of phosphorus are contained in the skeleton of a 150-lb man. Most of the remaining phosphorus is combined with protein in the cell nuclei. Some phosphorus is present in the body fluids.

Lean meat, milk, and grain products are good sources of phosphorus in the human diet. As with nitrogen, human beings and other animals normally obtain most of their phosphorus directly or indirectly from plants. The plants assimilate phosphorus from the soil. (Animals can, however, use the phosphorus of simple phosphates if these are fed to them.) Since a large proportion of the soil in the United States is deficient in phosphorus, the application of phosphate fertilizers (see Chap. 33, page 376) becomes a matter of extreme importance not only for the farmer but for every citizen. This is because it is now known that plants grown on a soil deficient in phosphorus are themselves phosphorus-poor. Such plants then fail to supply the normal amount of phosphorus to the animals consuming them.

Calcium

A normal 150-lb adult has about 3.3 lb of calcium in his body. About 99 percent of this is in the bones and teeth. If the diet of a young, growing individual is poor in calcium, then that individual obviously cannot build strong, sound bones and teeth. Calcium is also a necessary constituent of the body fluids and is regularly excreted from the body. Hence if a mature individual whose bones and teeth are already fully formed lives on a diet poor in calcium, the body fluids will remove calcium from the skeleton, with consequent weakening of the bones. This is particularly likely to occur in females during reproduction and lactation, when the mother has to supply the calcium requirement of herself and her offspring.

Experiments conducted at Columbia University by **Professor Henry C. Sherman** and his co-workers over the past 30 years have shown a most striking relationship between calcium intake on the one hand and rate of growth and length of life on the other. These experiments have shown that a diet consisting principally of whole wheat and dried milk is adequate for normal growth, maintenance, and reproduction of the white (albino) rat for as many as 72 generations. (This translated to human terms corresponds to a strain of individuals whose ancestors for 2000 years have been raised on the same known, adequate diet.) When young rats of such ancestry are placed on a diet exactly the same except containing extra calcium (as calcium carbonate), a remarkable change is noted. It is found that the individuals getting the extra calcium grow faster, mature earlier, have better mineralized skeletons at maturity, and live longer than their brothers or cousins which are getting the standard diet. The effect of this higher calcium intake is transmitted into the next generation in that the offspring of

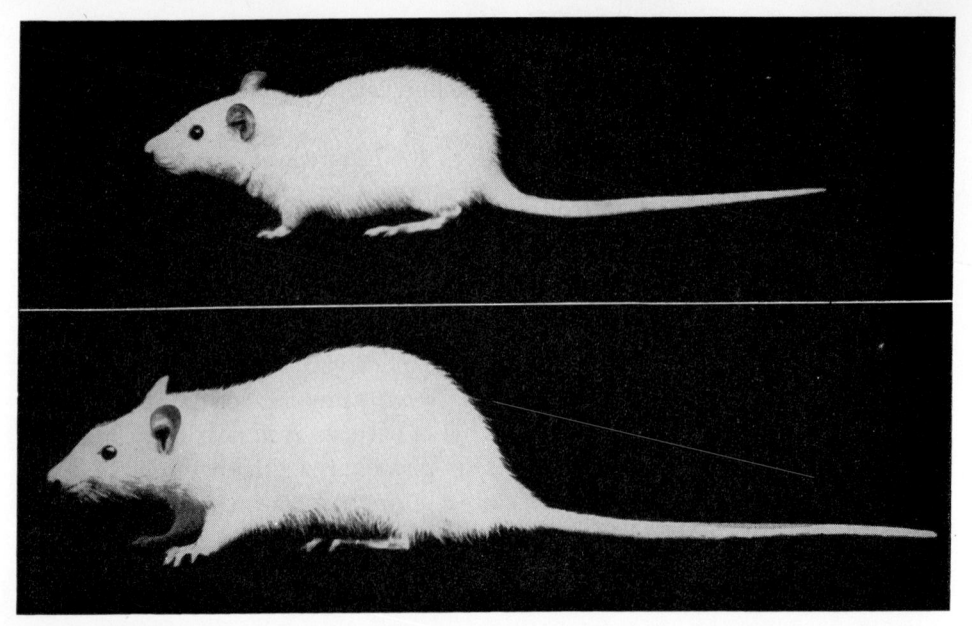

Top, a rat fed a diet low in calcium. Note the short stubby body due to poorly formed bones. Bottom, a rat fed a diet sufficient in calcium. This rat has reached full size and its bones are well formed. (U.S. Bureau of Human Nutrition and Home Economics)

the individuals receiving extra calcium are better calcified at weaning age than are the offspring of animals not receiving extra calcium. There is sound reason for believing that the results can also be applied to human beings.

Of calcium sources in the human diet, milk and cheese are particularly important, and they furnish many other desirable food factors in addition to calcium. Other good sources are eggs and green leaves such as broccoli, cabbage, lettuce, and kale. That spinach, beet greens, and swiss chard contain oxalic acid which interferes with calcium absorption has already been mentioned.

As yet there is no definite evidence that plants grown on a soil poor in calcium contain a lower-than-normal percentage of calcium. However, it is well known that certain plants which absorb large amounts of calcium from the soil will not grow luxuriantly unless the soil is well supplied with calcium. Thus the legume forage crops are particularly good sources of calcium in animal feeding and it is these very crops which require a "well-limed" soil (see Chap. 27, page 304) for best growth. Since liming is generally done with either calcium hydroxide or calcium carbonate, it serves the purpose not only of adjusting the pH of the soil but also of enriching it with calcium, both of which are necessary. It is probably not just a coincidence that many of the regions famous for their livestock are located where the soil was formed by the weathering of limestone. Perhaps the best known is the Bluegrass region of Kentucky, long famous for its race horses.

Some other mineral elements

The normal 150-lb adult body contains about 0.006 lb of *iron*. Much of this iron is in the hemoglobin of the blood. A shortage of iron in the diet can produce **anemia.** However, you should note that other conditions also can cause anemia, and not all types of anemia can be corrected by taking iron.

Copper functions in the human body as an agent in the formation of hemoglobin.

Iodine is a constituent of thyroxine, $C_{15}H_{11}O_4NI_4$, a hormone manufactured by the thyroid gland, which regulates the rate of metabolism. Simple goiter is a condition in which the thyroid gland becomes enlarged due to its inability to obtain enough iodine. Simple goiter is preventable by increasing the iodine content of the diet (see Chap. 22, page 247). Other types of thyroid disturbance are known and you should not assume that all of them can be corrected with iodine.

Vitamin A

The existence of vitamin A was discovered in 1913 when scientists observed that experimental animals would grow and thrive, or stop growing and sicken, according to whether the only fat in the diet was butterfat or lard. These results indicated that the butterfat contained some factor in addition to fat which was essential to life. It was later shown that this vitamin A contained in butterfat was a colorless, fat-soluble compound of formula $C_{20}H_{30}O$. Vitamin A is known to be essential for growth and also for maintenance of normal condition in the body at all ages.

A high vitamin A intake during growth will lead not only to more

A farmer adding a bag of lime to a combination cultivator and fertilizer spreader which will spread it evenly over the soil. The calcium from the lime will be absorbed by the plants that grow in this soil. (Standard Oil Co.)

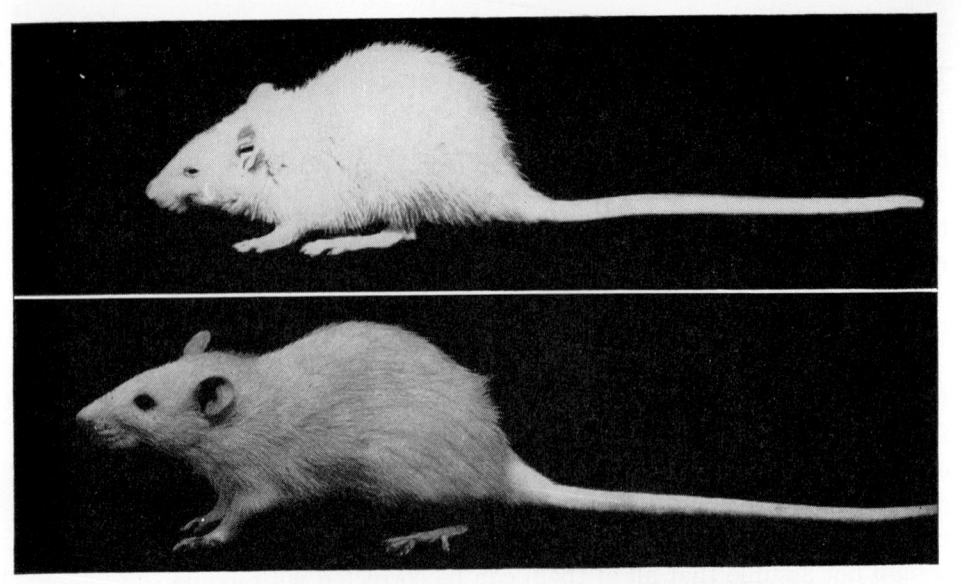

Top, a rat with a deficiency of vitamin A. Note the infected eyes and rough fur. Bottom, a rat with sufficient vitamin A. (U.S. Bureau of Human Nutrition and Home Economics)

rapid growth but also to better-formed bones and teeth, better muscular development, and a superior condition of the skin "like the sleekness of a well-conditioned farm animal." Abundant intake of vitamin A also favors longer life. A mild deficiency of vitamin A in human beings causes a certain dryness of the skin, reduces the resistance of the body to infection, and also produces night blindness. An individual suffering from night blindness has difficulty in adjusting his vision to decreased light. Extreme deficiency produces xerophthalmia, a condition of dry inflammation of the eyelid and outer surface of the eye which may lead to blindness.

Vitamin A is found in high concentration in fish liver oils. It is also found in eggs, liver, and butterfat. It is not found in plants, but among the natural coloring matter of green and yellow vegetation there are certain compounds which the body can convert into vitamin A and which are therefore called *provitamins A*. Thus carrots, leafy greens, and sweet potatoes are high in vitamin A *value*.

The yellow color of butter and cream is not vitamin A itself. However, part of this yellow-colored material is convertible into vitamin A in the body; hence it has vitamin A value. On the other hand one cannot judge the vitamin A value of milk, cream, or butter from its color because these products always contain at least some vitamin A as such and this is colorless. Furthermore, it is characteristic of different breeds of cows to give in their milk a different proportion of vitamin A (colorless) and the yellow substances (known also as **carotenes**) having vitamin A value. Thus Holstein cows give relatively more

A variety of foods that are high in vitamin A value. (U.S. Bureau of Human Nutrition and Home Economics)

vitamin A than carotene in their milk as compared with Guernsey or Jersey cows. Although the former may give a lighter-colored cream, it may contain just as much total vitamin A value as the cream from the latter two.

Because the body can use both vitamin A itself and the carotenes or provitamins A, it is customary to speak of the vitamin A *value* of foods instead of the vitamin A *content;* and this is expressed in international units rather than actual weights.

Vitamin A can be synthesized in the laboratory, and some synthetic vitamin A is now being manufactured on a commercial scale.

Vitamin B_1 (thiamine)

Extreme cases of **thiamine** deficiency result in **beriberi,** a nerve disease which first appears as a weakness and loss of muscular coordination in the feet and legs.

Thiamine is essential for growth and plays a part in the maintenance of appetite. With other substances in the body it forms an enzyme which is necessary for the oxidation of carbohydrates. The latter are, normally, the main source of the body's energy. Mild thiamine deficiency, insufficient to cause beriberi, may cause loss of emotional stability and loss of mental and physical efficiency.

Thiamine hydrochloride was first synthesized by **Dr. R. R. Williams** and his co-workers in 1934. It is a colorless crystalline substance having the formula $C_{12}H_{18}N_4SOCl_2$. Thiamine hydrochoride is now synthesized industrially in fairly large quantities.

Whole-grain cereals, beans, peas, peanuts, and pork muscle are good sources of thiamine in the diet. Whole-wheat bread is thus a good thiamine source. However, in making white flour, much of the thiamine-containing part of the grain is rejected. At the present time, most baker's white bread is **enriched bread,** which means that, besides other things, extra thiamine has been added to bring the thiamine content more nearly up to that of bread made from whole-wheat flour.

Riboflavin

This vitamin is a greenish-yellow water soluble solid having the formula $C_{17}H_{20}O_6N_4$. It is necessary for growth and also for the maintenance of health, efficiency, vigor, and resistance. Extreme deficiency of riboflavin in the diet leads to digestive disturbances, nervous depression, general weakness, poor condition of the eyes and skin, lessened vitality, and a shortened life.

There is evidence that higher-than-normal intake of riboflavin produces not only greater vitality and resistance to infectious disease but also a longer life by extending the period between the attainment of maturity and the beginning of old age. Milk, eggs, liver, wheat germ, green-leaf vegetables such as kale, and lean meats are good dietary sources of riboflavin. Riboflavin is one of the factors added to enriched flours, breads, and cereals.

Riboflavin is now produced synthetically on an industrial scale.

Other B vitamins

What was originally considered to be a single vitamin and named vitamin B actually consists of a number of different vitamins, including thiamine and riboflavin and several others.

One of these, **niacin** (or nicotinic acid) is found especially in liver, lean meats, fish, peanuts, and whole wheat.

Extreme deficiency of niacin causes **pellagra,** a disease characterized by rough, inflamed skin, mental and nervous disorders, inflammation of the tongue and mouth, and disorders of the digestive tract. Until fairly recently when the dietary cause of this disorder was recognized, pellagra was one of the most prevalent diseases of the southern United States.

Niacin is a water-soluble white solid having the formula $C_6H_5NO_2$. It is now made synthetically in large quantities, much of the synthetic product being used in enriching white flour, white bread, and certain breakfast cereals.

Also in the B group of vitamins are vitamin B_6 which enters into the formation of certain enzymes in the body; vitamin B_{12}, a cobalt-containing compound which is known to be essential for normal nutrition in man, chickens, and swine; folic acid; pantothenic acid; and an uncertain number of others which are less well known.

Vitamin C (ascorbic acid)

Vitamin C prevents scurvy. Since it is found principally in fresh fruits and vegetables, outbreaks of scurvy were particularly common among early sailors. Although it was recognized in the nineteenth century that citrus fruits would prevent scurvy among sailors, it was not until 1931 that the anti-scorbutic substance was actually isolated and identified by **King** of the University of Pittsburgh.

Vitamin C plays a role in keeping the teeth and gums healthy and in healing wounds. There are indications that a liberal intake of this vitamin also slows down the aging process.

Nutrition studies made on high school students in one of America's largest cities showed that 50 percent of these students did not get enough vitamin C in their diet for best health, although none of them showed scurvy.

Vitamin C is widely distributed in fresh fruits and vegetables. Good dietary sources are citrus fruits, tomatoes, strawberries, cabbage, and almost all raw green vegetables, especially green leaves and green pepper.

Vitamin C is destroyed by contact with oxygen of the air even at room temperatures. Cooking in contact with air destroys the vitamin even more rapidly because of the effect of temperature on the rate of the reaction. Because of this effect of air, it is desirable that vegetables be cooked in a covered pan, where the air is largely replaced by steam as the cooking water boils. Traces of copper or other heavy metals are active catalysts in speeding the rate of oxidation of vitamin C by oxygen. Also, food which is cooked with a pinch of soda (as is sometimes done to retain the bright color of green vegetables) loses its vitamin C content more rapidly than otherwise because the resulting decreased acidity causes more rapid oxidation of the vitamin C. Since vitamin C is readily soluble, it is better to cook vegetables in as small a volume of water as possible so as to minimize the fraction lost by solution.

Man is one of the few species for which the vitamin C content of the diet is important. Many species either have the ability to form this vitamin in their bodies or do not require it, so that in either case the result is that vitamin C does not have to be considered in the diet. This is true for poultry, swine, and cattle. The laboratory white rat also does not require it in the diet. For laboratory feeding experiments with vitamin C, the guinea pig which, like man, does require it, is used.

Vitamin D

This is the anti-rachitic vitamin. **Rickets** is a condition in which the growing bones do not calcify normally. Vitamin D is one of the agents concerned in the calcification of bones. If it is not present, proper bone formation cannot occur even though the body has sufficient calcium and phosphorus in the diet. Vitamin D is also of great importance to the formation of sound teeth. It has been shown that teeth that have developed in a body well supplied with vitamin D are more resistant to decay later in life than teeth that have developed under conditions of vitamin D deficiency.

Vitamin D is found in fish liver oils, from which it is produced commercially (for example, the livers of the cod and halibut). Eggs are also a good source.

In 1924 it was discovered that there are certain substances in the body and in many natural foods which are converted into vitamin D by **irradiation** with ultraviolet light from sunlight or other suitable sources although they themselves contain no vitamin D. Thus it is not necessary to consume vitamin D in the diet, provided one's skin is exposed to a sufficient amount of sunlight or other proper source of ultraviolet radiation. The photochemical reaction in which vitamin D is formed by sunlight occurs very close to the surface of the skin and probably does not occur appreciably where the skin is covered with layers of clothing. These facts account for the well-known observations that rickets is more common in winter and in the higher latitudes and among people with darker pigmentation of the skin. It should also be noted that ordinary window glass stops almost all the ultraviolet radiation of the sun, but special glasses are now made which transmit the ultraviolet.

Besides fish oils, liver, and eggs, milk is one of the few natural foods which contain vitamin D. The vitamin D content in cows' milk varies greatly, apparently depending somewhat on the cows' diet and their exposure to sunlight. However, the vitamin D content of milk can be increased by irradiation, and for some years irradiated evaporated milk has been on the market. Fresh milk in which the vitamin D concentration has been increased artificially is now available on many markets.

Vitamin D must also be considered in the feeding and management of many farm animals, such as cattle, swine, and poultry.

Vitamin K

Vitamin K is the name given to a substance which aids in the clotting of blood and thereby helps prevent hemorrhages. Vitamin K is especially abundant in green leaves.

TABLE 40–2. Composition of foods: nutrients per 100 grams edible portion[a]

Food	Calories	Protein, g	Calcium, mg	Iron, mg	Vitamin A value, IU	Thiamine, mg	Riboflavin, mg	Niacin, mg	Ascorbic acid, mg
Almonds	597	18.6	254	4.4	0	0.25	0.67	4.6	Trace
Apple	58	0.3	6	0.3	90	0.04	0.03	0.2	5
Bacon	630	9.1	13	0.8	0	0.38	0.12	1.9	0
Banana	88	1.2	8	0.6	430	0.04	0.05	0.7	10
Beans, dried	338	21.4	163	6.9	0	0.67	0.23	2.2	2
Lima	128	7.5	63	2.3	280	0.21	0.11	1.4	32
snap or string	35	2.4	65	1.1	630	0.08	0.11	0.5	19
Beef, lean	182	19.5	11	2.9	0	0.08	0.17	4.7	0
Bread, white enriched	275	8.5	79	1.8	0	0.24	0.15	2.2	0
whole wheat	240	9.3	96	2.2	0	0.30	0.13	3.0	0
Broccoli	29	3.3	130	1.3	3500	0.10	0.21	1.1	118
Butter	716	0.6	20	0	3300	Trace	0.01	0.1	0
Cabbage	24	1.4	46	0.5	80	0.06	0.05	0.3	50
Carrots	42	1.2	39	0.8	12000	0.06	0.06	0.5	6
Chard	27	2.6	[b]	2.5	8720	0.06	0.18	0.4	38
Cheese, "store"	398	25.0	725	1.0	1400	0.02	0.42	Trace	0
cottage	95	19.5	96	0.3	20	0.02	0.31	0.1	0
Codfish	74	16.5	10	0.4	0	0.06	0.09	2.2	2
Eggs	162	12.8	54	2.7	1140	0.10	0.29	0.1	0
Grapefruit	40	0.5	22	0.2	Trace	0.04	0.02	0.2	40
Ham, smoked	389	16.9	10	2.5	0	0.70	0.19	4.0	0
Ice cream, commercial, plain	207	4.0	123	0.1	520	0.04	0.19	0.1	1
Kale	40	3.9	225	2.2	7540	0.10	0.26	2.0	115
Lettuce, head	15	1.2	22	0.5	540	0.04	0.08	0.2	8
loose leaf	15	1.2	62	1.1	1620	0.04	0.08	0.2	18
Liver, beef	136	19.7	7	6.6	43900	0.26	3.33	13.7	31
Margarine, fortified	720	0.6	20	0	3300	0	0	0	0
Milk, whole	68	3.5	118	0.1	160	0.04	0.17	0.1	1
Oatmeal, dry	390	14.2	53	4.5	0	0.60	0.14	1.0	0
Oranges	45	0.9	33	0.4	190	0.08	0.03	0.2	49
Peanut butter	576	26.1	74	1.9	0	0.12	0.13	16.2	0
Peas, green	98	6.7	22	1.9	680	0.34	0.16	2.7	26
Pepper, green	25	1.2	11	0.4	630	0.04	0.07	0.4	120
Pork, lean	357	14.5	8	2.2	0	0.70	0.17	3.8	0
Potatoes	83	2.0	11	0.7	20	0.11	0.04	1.2	17
Prunes	268	2.3	54	3.9	1890	0.10	0.16	1.7	3
Soybeans, dry	331	34.9	227	8.0	110	1.07	0.31	2.3	Trace
Spinach	20	2.3	[b]	3.0	9420	0.11	0.20	0.6	59
Sugar	385	0	0	0	0	0	0	0	0
Sweet potatoes	123	1.8	30	0.7	7700	0.09	0.05	0.6	22
Tomato	20	1.0	11	0.6	1100	0.06	0.04	0.5	23
Whole wheat	333	13.3	41	3.3	0	0.55	0.12	4.3	0

[a] Data from *Agriculture Handbook No. 8*, U.S. Department of Agriculture, 1950.
[b] Calcium not available to body because of oxalic acid present in food.

Vitamin E

Vitamin E is a compound, the structure of which is known, that is essential to reproduction in rats and probably other animals. It is found in wheat germ and is quite abundant in the seed oils, such as cottonseed, corn, and soybean oil. It has not been clearly shown to be essential for human beings.

Nutrients contributed by some common foods

In Table 40–2 below is shown the amount of each[1] nutrient (for which dietary allowances were given in Table 40–1) that is contained in 100 g of the edible portion of a number of common foods. Similar values for many other foods will be found in *Agriculture Handbook No. 8*, issued by the U.S. Department of Agriculture in 1950.

KEY WORDS

anemia	irradiation	pellagra	thiamine
ascorbic acid	King	protein	vitamin A
beriberi	niacin	riboflavin	vitamin D
carotene	nutritional deficiency	rickets	vitamin K
enriched bread	nutritionally essential	Sherman	Williams

HIGHLIGHTS

Foods serve the body in three ways: (1) as sources of energy to support the body's activities and keep it warm, (2) for the building of new body tissue, and (3) either directly as, or as sources of, regulatory substances which control body processes.

To meet these needs, the nutriment should contain the following substances or classes of substances:

Water
Carbohydrates
Fats, including the essential fatty acids
Proteins, providing the (10) **nutritionally essential** amino acids
So-called *mineral elements*, of which at least 13 are required
Vitamins: an assortment of chemically diverse organic substances
  including the 12 considered here and probably still others

These groups of foodstuffs serve in one, two, or all three of the ways listed above.

[1] Vitamin D is omitted because so few foods contain significant amounts of it and also because the need of normal adults for this factor may be met to a large extent (or completely) by exposure to sunlight.

Some of our knowledge of what the body needs comes from study of deficiency diseases—disorders which have long been known to mankind and which now are seen to arise from shortage of some specific substance in the body. For example, **beriberi** is a disease caused by lack of **thiamine** (vitamin B_1) in the diet; scurvy, by shortage of **ascorbic acid** (vitamin C); **rickets,** by too little **vitamin D; pellagra,** by lack of **niacin;** and goiter, by lack of iodine.

What is more important to most of us is the finding that, even when the diet is good enough to prevent any deficiency disease and to support normal health, it can still be improved, with resulting better growth, superior health, longer life, and other evidences of optimal nutrition.

QUESTIONS

1. How do the age and stature of students entering college today compare with those of 30 to 40 years ago? To what is this difference attributed?
2. What two broad generalizations about the relation of nutrition to health have been established by research?
3. Is it believed that most Americans get the best possible diet?
4. List the three functions of food.
5. List the six classes of substances which should be supplied in the food.
6. Which of the classes of substances referred to in question 5 can serve as sources of energy for the body?
7. What is meant by the term nutritionally essential amino acids?
8. Explain why all proteins do not have the same nutritional values.
9. How do cattle and other ruminants differ from poultry, swine, and man in their protein requirements?
10. What functions does phosphorus serve in the body?
11. What foods are good sources of phosphorus?
12. What functions does calcium serve in the body?
13. Explain why a diet adequate in calcium is necessary at all ages of the individual.
14. Why is the use of adequate phosphate fertilizers a matter which concerns not only the farmer but also the general public?
15. What two functions are served by liming soils?
16. Give one reason why iron is necessary in the diet.
17. What foods are good sources of iron?
18. What is the value of a high vitamin A value of the diet?
19. Explain why the vitamin A content of milk or butter cannot be judged by its color.

20. What foods are good sources of thiamine?
21. What advantages are gained by a high level of riboflavin in the diet?
22. Name two animals which require vitamin C in their diet.
23. What are the principal food sources of vitamin C?
24. Is scurvy always observed if an individual is not getting enough vitamin C?
25. What is the relation between vitamin D and bone development?
26. What is the relation between vitamin D and sunshine?

Suggested Projects for Unit Eight

1. On your vacation into the country next summer collect some natural methane. Learn how this can be done.
2. Make a collection of newspaper clippings reporting deaths due to carbon monoxide.
3. Collect all possible information concerning von Laue. Explain why his contributions to science are very important.
4. Write a report on Goodyear's discovery of vulcanization.
5. Find out the average cost of a one-carat diamond. You may benefit by knowing more about diamonds. What facts should one know before purchasing one?
6. Make up a menu for one day for yourself which fits your personal needs. Explain why each item is selected.
7. What is the most widely used pure organic compound?
8. List several greens that are good substitutes for spinach. Explain in what way they are better than spinach.

UNIT NINE: The Mineral Realm

CHAPTER 41

silicon

In preceding chapters you have seen that carbon compounds form the basis of all living things. It is a striking fact that **silicon,** the element chemically most similar to carbon, forms the backbone of the mineral realm.

Occurrence of silicon

Silicon makes up about 28 percent of the earth's crust. It is never found free in nature, but always in combination with oxygen, commonly as silicon dioxide (SiO_2) and otherwise as metal silicates. Silicon is, therefore, as widespread as rock and soil. The only common minerals which do not contain silicon are limestone ($CaCO_3$), dolomite [$CaMg(CO_3)_2$], and gypsum ($CaSO_4 \cdot 2H_2O$).

Small amounts of silicon are present in certain plants, notably bamboo, horsetail, and wheat straw. The feathers of some birds contain as much as 40 percent silicon dioxide. **Diatomaceous earth,** used in oil refining and in some scouring powders, is the skeletal remains of diatoms. It is nearly pure silicon dioxide, as are *natural sponges.*

Comparison of silicon with carbon

Since silicon is directly under carbon in the periodic table, the student will expect it to resemble carbon closely. Like carbon, silicon, with four valence electrons, always shows a *covalence of 4.* Furthermore, silicon will form covalent bonds with most other nonmetals, as carbon does. Thus we have such compounds as silicon tetrachloride ($SiCl_4$), analogous to carbon tetrachloride (CCl_4), and silane (SiH_4), analogous to methane (CH_4).

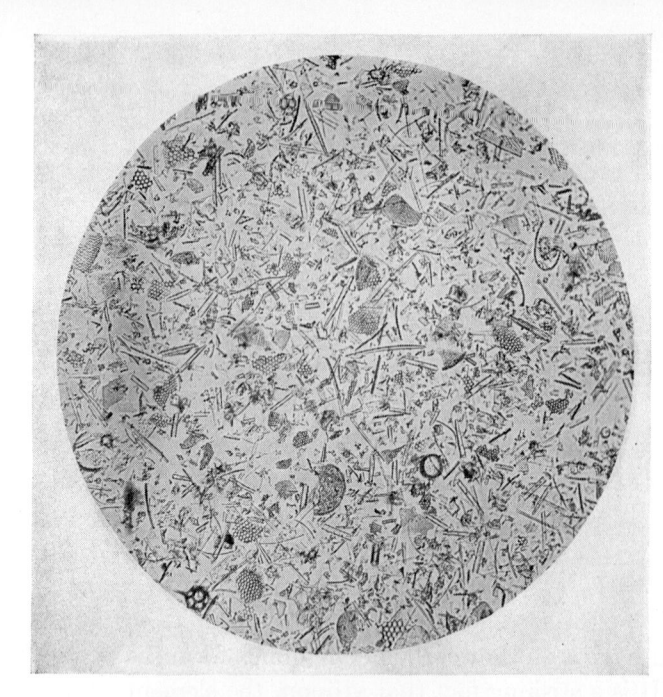

This photomicrograph of typical diatoms shows a view of the many delicate and intricate shapes found in the Johns-Manville deposit of diatomaceous silica at Lompoc, Calif. (Johns-Manville Corp.)

There are, however, two important ways in which silicon does *not* resemble carbon:

1. Silicon does not form stable silicon-to-silicon chains like the carbon-to-carbon chains which are the basis of organic chemistry. This fact may be remembered and understood by recalling that the nuclear charge of silicon is $+14$ and that of carbon is $+6$. This higher nuclear charge causes the silicon atoms to repel each other so strongly that silicon-to-silicon linkages are very unstable.

2. Silicon is unable to form a double bond with oxygen as carbon does (see pages 514 and 515).

Although it has been recognized for a long time that the compounds of silicon may be almost as varied as those of carbon, little real progress was made in understanding the chemistry of silicon until the last 25 years. In this period the structure of most silicate minerals was determined. In addition recent research, particularly that carried on at the General Electric Co. and the Dow-Corning Co., has shown that certain synthetic silicon compounds have properties which make them very desirable for special industrial uses (see pages 520 to 523).

Elementary silicon

Elementary silicon is made by the reduction of silicon dioxide by carbon in the electric furnace.

$$SiO_2 + 2C \rightarrow Si + 2CO \uparrow$$

Formerly scarce and expensive, silicon is now made on a large scale by this process and sells for only a few cents per pound.

The element silicon has a structure like diamond (see Chap. 34, pages 386 and 387) and is hard enough to scratch glass. Its luster is somewhat like graphite, but in color silicon more nearly resembles a metal. It melts at 1420°C.

Elementary silicon is used extensively in the steel industry. When added to steel in amounts up to 5 percent, it softens the steel and develops its magnetic properties. Such steels are desirable for making magnets and transformer cores. Steels containing 14.5 percent silicon (**duriron**) are highly resistant to acid corrosion and are used in making acid-resistant kettles, pipes, and drain lines. These steels are hard and very brittle. Some silicon is used as a deoxidizer (see Chap. 49, page 643) in making ordinary carbon steels. **Ferrosilicon,** which is made by reducing a mixture of iron oxide and silicon dioxide, is the source of much of the silicon used in the steel industry. When alloyed with aluminum, silicon improves the casting qualities of the latter.

Chemically silicon is not acted upon by any single acid, although it is attacked by a mixture of hot nitric and hydrofluoric acids and also by aqua regia. Silicon is readily attacked by alkali, even in the cold, forming a silicate and hydrogen.

$$Si + 2NaOH + H_2O \rightarrow Na_2SiO_3 + 2H_2 \uparrow$$

Either pure silicon or ferrosilicon will give this same reaction. It will be noted that the above reaction requires water as a reactant and it is a not unexpected fact that the reaction does not occur in the absence of water. Hence a mixture of dry silicon and sodium hydroxide, which do not react, will liberate hydrogen on the addition of water. The amount of hydrogen released depends on the amount of water added. Thus silicon and sodium hydroxide constitute a convenient portable source of hydrogen for use outside the laboratory. This mixture is used by the Armed Forces as a source of hydrogen for filling balloons for weather observation.

Silicon dioxide (silica)

Silicon dioxide, or **silica,** is very common in nature in the form of *quartz* (or rock crystal). Pure quartz is colorless. *Amethyst* is quartz colored purple because of the presence of a small amount of manganese. Rose quartz is pink, probably because of the presence of small amounts of titanium. Other colors of quartz are common, such as milky quartz, smoky quartz, and yellow quartz. Quartz is one of the most common minerals; ordinary **sand** (but not all sand) is made up of small quartz crystals. However, large, well-formed quartz crystals are found in quantity in only a few places in the world; and in order to supply the demand, it has been necessary to grow them in the laboratory.

A piece of a petrified tree stump. Silica has taken the place of the original cellulose that made up the tree by passing into the pores of the wood and being deposited there. At the same time, the wood fibers were dissolved. (American Museum of Natural History)

Onyx and *agate* are impure, generally banded, forms of amorphous (uncrystallized) silica, as is also *flint*. The latter, because it is hard and yet can be chipped to a sharp edge with other stones, played an important part in the implements fashioned by early man. *Opal* is amorphous silica containing variable amounts of water.

Silica is insoluble in water and in all acids except hydrofluoric (see Chap. 22, pages 250 and 251). But deep inside the earth, superheated water, especially if alkaline, dissolves it slightly. If this silica-bearing hot water reaches the surface of the earth, as it does at Mammoth Springs of Yellowstone or Great Geyser of Iceland, the silica is deposited in hydrated form at the mouth of the geyser. Or, underground, it may pass into the pores of buried wood where simultaneously the fibers of the wood are being dissolved and silica is deposited in their place. In this way **petrified wood** and other fossils are formed.

The melting point of quartz is approximately 1400°C. When melted and allowed to cool, quartz normally fails to recrystallize, so that it exists indefinitely at room temperature as a **supercooled liquid.** This supercooled liquid, although mechanically very rigid, differs from a true solid in two important ways:

1. There is no definite, completely orderly arrangement of the atoms (or molecules) which make up the substance.

2. The substance has no melting point, in the true sense of the word, since it is already a liquid although a very viscous one. Hence when it is heated, the supercooled liquid quartz gradually becomes softer as the temperature is raised (like molasses candy or pitch). This means it can gradually be softened and then worked and shaped; when recooled, it will retain that shape. A truly crystalline solid, on the other hand, passes sharply from solid to liquid at a definite temperature and does not go through an intermediate plastic condition. Thus the supercooled silica can be heated and shaped into beakers, crucibles, and other

shapes, whereas a true crystalline solid such as ice cannot be so worked. Glass also is a supercooled liquid.

Silica ware made as described in the preceding paragraph is very valuable for certain laboratory purposes. Beakers and crucibles made of silica ware can be heated to a much higher temperature without softening than those made of glass. They are resistant to almost all laboratory reagents except hydrofluoric acid and strong alkali. Most important, silica ware can stand drastic temperature changes without breaking. Thus a silica dish can be heated red hot, then plunged into cold water without breaking. This is true because the silica expands, or contracts, only very slightly with temperature change. A glass object treated in this way will, of course, break. The glass breaks on sudden cooling because the outside and inside cool at different rates. Thus strains are set up within the glass because of unequal rates of shrinkage of the glass on the outside and the inside. With silica ware, since there is very little shrinkage on cooling, not enough strain is set up to break the object.

Silica ware is transparent to ultraviolet rays, whereas ordinary glass is not. Therefore, it is used for making lenses and prisms for optical systems employing ultraviolet light and also for making *quartz mercury vapor lamps*. These are used in the laboratory as a source of ultraviolet light and in the home as sun lamps or health lamps.

Sections sawed from quartz crystals are employed as filters that permit the use of 12 speech channels on a single long-distance telephone unit. These quartz-crystal sections also have other industrial and military uses. Formerly the quartz for this purpose came mainly from Brazil. Because the demand became greater than the natural supply, research was undertaken to develop means of growing quartz crystals in the laboratory. Recently a successful method has been developed at the Bell Telephone Laboratories. Thus science has learned to duplicate another of nature's products, and the United States has become independent of a foreign source of another strategic commodity.

Quartz is harder than glass, being number 7 on the **Mohs' scale** of hardness.[1] It is used for making inexpensive sandpaper (the flint type). A better sandpaper is made by using garnets instead of sand.

Quartz is an ingredient of almost all soils. Its presence in soil tends

[1] The Mohs' scale of hardness is as follows:

1.	Talc	6.	Feldspar
2.	Gypsum	7.	Quartz
3.	Calcite	8.	Topaz
4.	Fluorite	9.	Corundum
5.	Apatite	10.	Diamond

Thus, for example, an object hard enough to scratch quartz but not hard enough to scratch topaz has a hardness between 7 and 8.

Quartz crystals. A group of large, well-formed quartz crystals such as those shown above is rarely found in nature even though quartz in other forms is very common. (American Museum of Natural History)

to improve drainage. Too much sand in a soil may be objectionable because of its poor ability to hold moisture and plant food. If water percolates through the soil, it carries out water-soluble plant food with it. Most of the good agricultural soils are mixtures of sand and clay with organic matter and may or may not contain limestone or dolomite.

Sandstone, consisting of quartz grains cemented together (commonly with calcium carbonate or iron oxide), is sometimes highly prized as a building stone. Sand is used in making brick and portland cement (see Chap. 47, page 618).

The structure of quartz

One of the surprising facts of elementary chemistry is that whereas carbon dioxide is a gas, its closest chemical relative, silicon dioxide, is a solid, melting above 1400°C. The cause of the difference has already been implied earlier. Carbon dioxide is made up of molecules, each of which contains one atom of carbon doubly bonded to two atoms of oxygen.

$$O = C = O$$

The resulting molecules have little attractive force for each other and hence the compound is a gas. Silicon never forms a double bond. Instead a quartz crystal consists of silicon atoms bonded by single bonds to four different oxygen atoms, each of the oxygens being bonded to two different silicon atoms. The idea, in two dimensions, is:

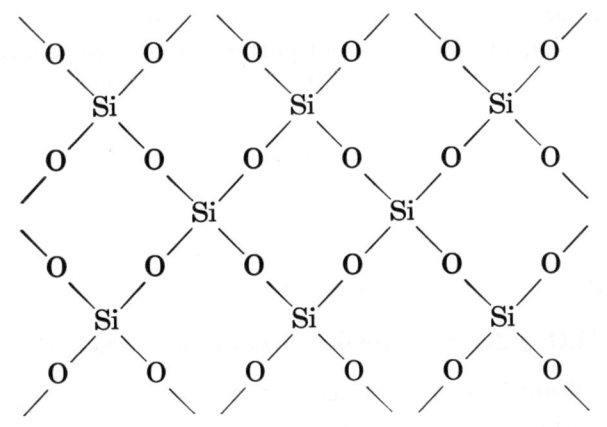

If you imagine such a structure in three dimensions[1] and continued throughout the entire crystal, you then have the structure of a quartz crystal. Like diamond, the entire crystal is one big molecule. The only bond in the crystal is the silicon-oxygen-silicon bond. It is the strength of this bond which gives quartz its high melting point, its lack of cleavage, and its chemical inertness.

Waterglass

Waterglass is the common name given to solutions of sodium silicate. Although silica differs greatly from carbon dioxide, it does resemble the latter in that it is weakly acid-forming. When silica is boiled with sodium hydroxide, sodium silicate is formed.

$$2NaOH + SiO_2 \rightarrow Na_2SiO_3 + H_2O$$

Sodium silicate may also be obtained by fusing sand and sodium carbonate.

$$Na_2CO_3 + SiO_2 \xrightarrow{\text{fused}} Na_2SiO_3 + CO_2 \uparrow$$

[1] Actually the unit of the structure is a tetrahedron of oxygen atoms (one at each apex) and a silicon atom in its center.

Fig. 41–1. The fundamental unit structure of quartz. Quartz is made up of silicon atoms and oxygen atoms. The silicon atoms (black) are attached to four oxygen atoms (light). Each of the oxygen atoms is attached to another silicon atom (not shown).

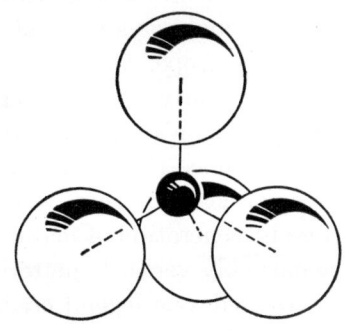

Various commercial sodium silicates are made, and some of them contain excess silica, mainly in colloidal suspension. Sodium silicate is used as an adhesive and strengthener for cardboard and corrugated cartons, as a cement for glass and pottery, and as an addition agent for soaps and scouring powders. It is also used in waterproofing concrete, for preserving eggs, and for many other purposes.

Silica gel

If strong acid is added to a sodium silicate solution, a gelatinous precipitate of silica and varying amounts of water is formed. (Silicic acid itself does not exist.) The unbalanced equation is

$$H_2O + Na_2SiO_3 + OH_3^+ \rightarrow SiO_2 \cdot xH_2O + 2Na^+$$

If the precipitate is formed under just the right conditions, a jelly is produced in which the precipitate entraps all the water of the solution. The product is known as **silica gel.** If heated to drive off the water, fine crystals of silica are formed. This partly dehydrated silica gel is an excellent *adsorbing agent* for water and many other substances (see Chap. 34, pages 389 and 390). It is used for removing moisture from the fluid employed in mechanical refrigerators. If this moisture were not removed, it might freeze and block the expansion valve. Silica gel is used for adsorbing the moisture from electronic assembly cabinets, which are sensitive to moisture; as an adsorbing agent for recovering valuable vapors, such as sulfur dioxide, nitrogen oxides, and organic solvents, from the waste gases of large industrial plants; and as a catalyst in petroleum refining. The silica gel can adsorb large amounts of a foreign substance, but also, when heated, gives back this material and is regenerated for re-use at the same time.

Glass

Few people stop to realize the importance of glass in their daily lives; yet the development of our present civilization would have been impossible without it. Astronomy, the mother of physics, could not have come into being without the telescope. For our knowledge of bacteria and ways of combatting disease, we are greatly indebted to the microscope. Countless millions of people would go through life blind or nearly so without glass spectacles. Window glass has greatly modified man's living habits, as have the forms of illumination developed since the candle. Considering these and the numerous other uses for glass in this twentieth century, you realize how much the present generation of mankind owes to the unknown discoverer of this remarkably versatile material. Although no one knows how glass was discovered, one legend credits it to certain Phoenician sailors. These

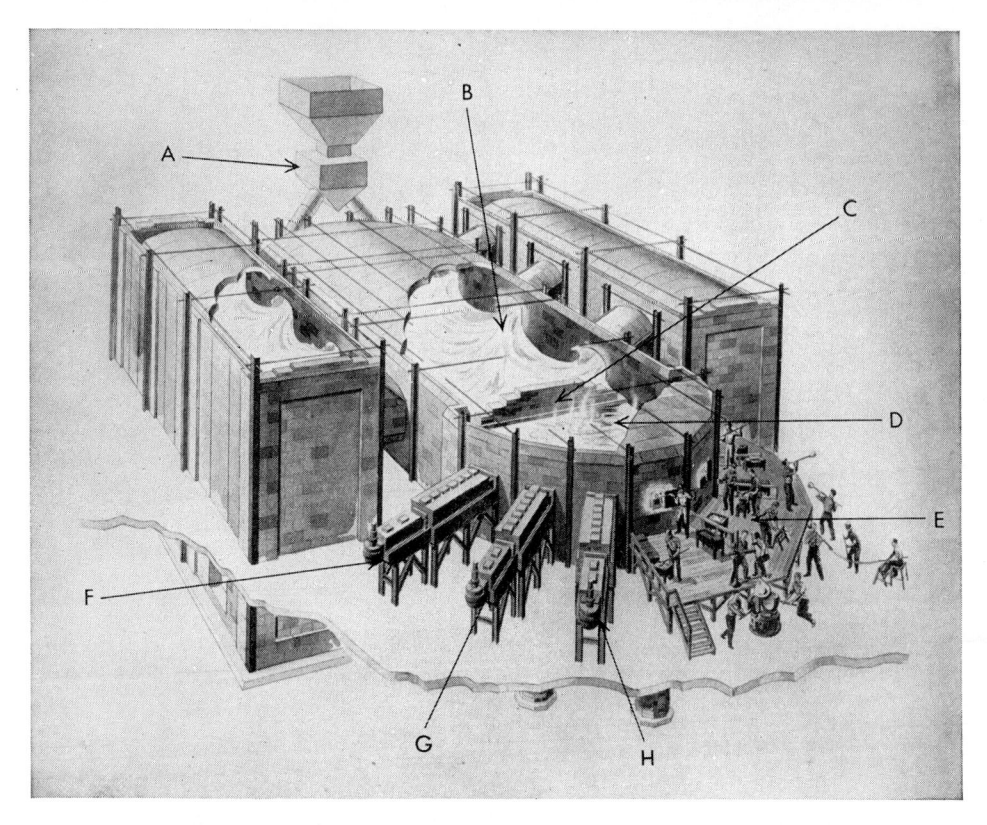

The manufacture of glass. A, raw materials are fed into the end of the tank. B, through ports, jets of flame shoot across the glass. C, the sandy mass subjected to this heat fuses and begins to flow. D, as the purified glass flows through the fining portion of the tank, the glass bubbles are removed. The glass is now ready for shaping. E, hand artisans gather some molten glass on the tip of a hollow iron pipe for shaping. F, a constant flow of molten glass is sent to spinning molds where certain blown-glass objects are shaped automatically. G, a stream of molten glass is divided into portions which go to an automatic press to make pressed glass. H, some molten glass is drawn into an endless tube. (Corning Glass Works)

sailors built a fire on a beach and used lumps of a naturally occurring sodium carbonate, which was part of their cargo, to support their kettles. It is entirely possible that glass was formed in this way—by the heating of the sodium carbonate, potassium carbonate from the wood ashes, and sand from the beach—because modern glass is formed in much the same way. Whatever its origin, glass was known to the Egyptians by 3500 BC. Glass found in tombs going back to this date has the same composition as some present-day glass! In fact little improvement in the art and science of glassmaking occurred from 3500 BC until 1900. All the glasses known today except common glass and flint glass have been developed during the last 50 years, mainly at the Jena glassworks in Germany and the Corning glassworks in the United States.

Pyrex glassware (left) and vycor glassware (right) are very useful in the laboratory because of their resistance to heat and to changes in temperature. (Corning Glass Works)

The making of glass

If sodium carbonate and sand are heated together to the fusion point, sodium silicate is formed (see equation, page 515). On cooling, this clear liquid crystallizes to a granular solid which is not glassy. The same thing occurs if another metal carbonate, such as calcium carbonate, is heated with silica. If, however, a mixture of sodium carbonate, calcium carbonate, and *excess* silica is heated, the silicates of sodium and calcium are formed, and the excess silica dissolves in the molten silicates. When this liquid is cooled, it fails to crystallize. The mass remains a liquid but becomes so viscous that at room temperature it is as rigid and hard as a true solid. Yet being a supercooled liquid, it has no melting point. When warmed sufficiently, it becomes plastic and hence can be worked and shaped, that is, it is a true plastic.

Common window glass and bottle glass are *soda-lime glass* made as just described: by heating calcium carbonate, sodium carbonate, and sand. Impurities in the sand will color the glass. The most common impurity is iron (Fe^{++}), which causes the green color frequently noticed in bottles, fruit jars, and telephone line insulators. The green color can be neutralized by adding a small amount of manganese dioxide or selenium to the melt. Soda-lime glass is known as *soft glass* because it is easily softened on heating. *Hard glass* is made by substituting potassium carbonate for the sodium salt. The potassium raises the softening temperature. *Flint glass*, used for lenses and prisms for optical instruments and for cut glass, is made from sodium carbonate, potassium carbonate, lead carbonate, boric oxide, and silica. Flint glass has a higher density and greater brilliance (because of a higher refractive index) than soft glass.

Heat-resisting glasses, developed by the Corning Glass Co. and sold under the name **pyrex**, contain about 12 percent boric oxide (B_2O_3) as well as a high percentage of silica. These borosilicate glasses have not only a higher softening temperature but also a lower temperature coefficient of expansion, which enables them to withstand more sudden temperature changes than ordinary glass. A great deal of the chemical laboratory apparatus is now made of pyrex. In this way heat-resistant glass has contributed to many technical developments of our times.

Articles made of **vycor** glass start out as a borosilicate glass and after shaping are given a heat treatment followed by an acid bath. By this treatment, most of the constituents of the glass, except the silica, are leached out, leaving a sort of "sponge" of silica which is a skeleton of the original object. When this silica sponge is heated, it shrinks about 15 percent, the pores are closed, and the final result is an object containing about 96 percent silica which has properties almost like fused silica itself.

The bulk of present-day glass is made by melting the ingredients in tanks lined with fire clay which hold several tons. By pouring the liquid into molds or stamping it with dies, *pressed glass* articles are made. Bottles are blown by taking some glass on the end of a pipe and blowing it into a mold of the desired shape. Most bottles and incandescent lamp bulbs are blown on automatic machines. Window glass is made by drawing a wide sheet of the liquid from the tank. The sheet hardens as it cools. *Plate glass* is made by extruding a sheet of the liquid between rollers which press it out to the desired thickness. It is then ground and polished to a smooth surface. *Foam glass* is made by frothing the liquid by generating a gas within it. This frothy liquid is then allowed to cool, whereupon it is cut into slabs. It can be sawed and nailed like cork or wood and is a good heat-insulating agent which is waterproof and rotproof. Because of its low density, foam glass is used in place of cork and balsa by the Navy. Glass fibers, drawn from the molten liquid, are spun into threads and woven into cloth. Such fabrics are used for filter materials, theater curtains, electrical insulation, and coats. Bakelite plastic laminated with fiber glass will withstand the impact of a .45 caliber pistol bullet and is much lighter than the amount of steel required to give the same protection.

Colored glass is produced by adding pigments to the melt. Chromium trioxide (Cr_2O_3) gives green glass, copper or cobalt oxide gives blue, selenium and gold give ruby red.

TABLE 41–1. Composition of various glasses, in percent

	Window	Flint optical	Pyrex chemical	Vycor
SiO_2	71–74	50–55	80.5–80.9	96.0
Na_2O	12–16	3–4	3.8	
K_2O		8–10	0.4	
CaO	8–12			
Al_2O_3	0.5–2.0		2.2	
MgO	0–5			
Fe_2O_3	0.1			
B_2O_3		1.5	12.9	4.0
PbO		30–35		

Nonreflecting glass is made by depositing a layer of magnesium or calcium fluoride on the surface of the glass. This may be done either by evaporating the fluoride and condensing it on the glass in a vacuum or by dipping the glass into a bath of hydrofluoric acid under controlled conditions. The thickness of the coating is critical—it must be about 0.000005 in. Lenses treated in this way (coated lenses) are now commonly used in cameras, projectors, binoculars, and other optical equipment. Coated lenses transmit more light under a given set of conditions than uncoated lenses. This is true because very little light is reflected from their surface. One naval officer said that by using coated elements in a submarine periscope instead of uncoated lenses it was possible for him to use his periscope one hour earlier in the morning and one hour later in the evening.

Laminated safety glass consists of a layer of transparent plastic sandwiched between two layers of plate glass to which it is cemented. Such a glass has greatly reduced the danger of cuts in automobile accidents. Many states now require it for automobile windows.

Silicones

Silicones refer to a remarkable group of synthetic silicon compounds which became available about 1944 largely as a result of research carried out by the General Electric Co. and the Dow-Corning Co. Silicones are in a sense a sort of chemical hybrid between carbon-containing organic compounds and inorganic silicon compounds.

One method for producing silicones starts with silicon and methyl chloride, which react in the presence of a copper catalyst:

$$2CH_3Cl + Si \xrightarrow{Cu} (CH_3)_2SiCl_2$$
methyl chloride   dimethyl dichlorosilane

The product, a colorless liquid, when treated with water, is converted into a polymer. The reactions are

$$(CH_3)_2SiCl_2 + 2H_2O \rightarrow (CH_3)_2Si(OH)_2 + 2HCl$$
$$\text{(unstable)}$$

The unstable product shown above reacts to form the polymer by splitting out water between adjacent molecules.

$$\begin{array}{ccc} CH_3 & & CH_3 \\ | & & | \\ HO-Si-O\boxed{H + HO}-Si-OH \\ | & & | \\ CH_3 & & CH_3 \end{array}$$

In this way, long chains are formed in which the unit is

$$\begin{array}{cccc} CH_3 & CH_3 & CH_3 & CH_3 \\ | & | & | & | \\ -Si-\boxed{\quad O-Si\quad}-O-Si-O-Si- \\ | & | & | & | \\ CH_3 & CH_3 & CH_3 & CH_3 \end{array}$$
$$\text{(chain unit)}$$

These open-chain compounds are oils (known as silicone oils), the viscosity of which changes very little with temperature. These silicone oils flow about as well at $-35°F$ as they do at $100°F$, something which is unheard of in a hydrocarbon oil. This property makes silicone oils highly suitable for hydraulic fluids, particularly in aircraft where extreme temperature changes are encountered. Silicone oils are good lubricants and more stable chemically than hydrocarbon oils. Hence they can be used to lubricate bearings at temperatures at which hydrocarbon oils will break down and form sludge. Small amounts of silicone oils mixed with hydrocarbon oils greatly reduce foaming of the hydrocarbon. Foaming has always bothered lubrication engineers.

Silicone resins can be formed in a manner analogous to the one used to form oils by starting with dimethyl dichlorosilane, $(CH_3)_2SiCl_2$, and methyl trichlorosilane, CH_3SiCl_3. The resins are similar in structure to the oils except that they are cross-linked.

$$\begin{array}{ccc} CH_3 & CH_3 & CH_3 \\ | & | & | \\ -Si-O-Si-O-Si- \\ | & | & | \\ O & CH_3 & O \\ | & CH_3 & | \\ -Si-O-Si-O-Si- \\ | & | & | \\ CH_3 & CH_3 & CH_3 \end{array}$$
$$\text{(unit of silicone resin)}$$

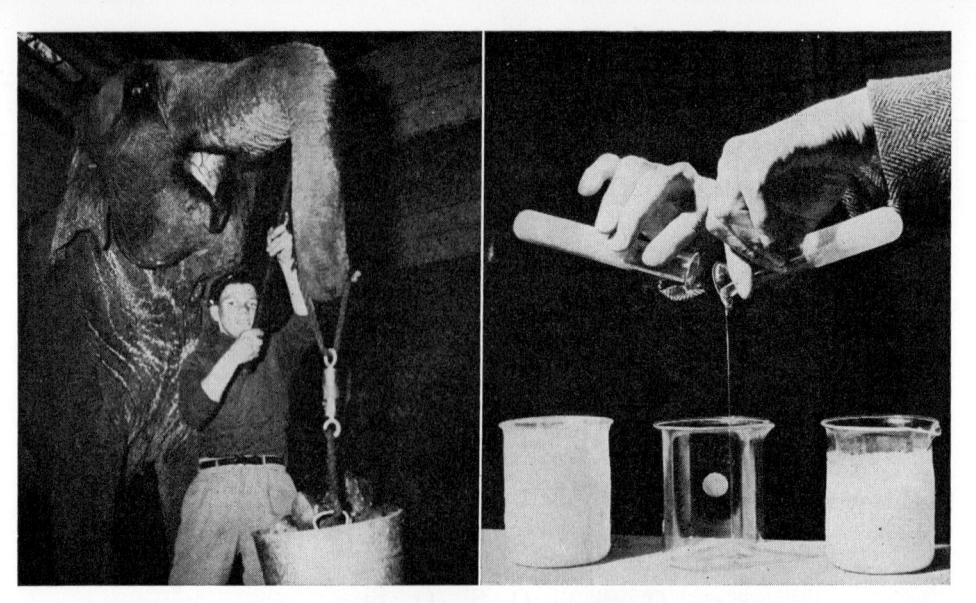

Left, a piece of silicone rubber bonded to two metal hooks is strong enough to support the tub full of rocks weighing about 300 lb that the elephant is lifting. This rubber keeps its elasticity at very high and low temperatures. Right, silicone oil flows at low temperatures which cause petroleum oils to solidify. (General Electric Co.)

These silicone resins will stand much higher temperature without decomposing than will organic resins. In a vacuum, samples heated as high as 550°C did not decompose. This fact is not altogether surprising, since we have seen that the silicon-oxygen bond is a very stable one and the only one found in quartz. The resins are well suited as electrical insulators. A piece of electrical machinery insulated with them can be operated at a higher temperature and a greater output than is otherwise possible. This is particularly important in aircraft, where high output and low weight are desirable. The resins are also being used now in automobile and furniture polishes.

Some of the cross-linked polymers are rubberlike. These silicone rubbers are useful because they remain rubbery over a much wider temperature range than other known elastic materials. One of the rubbers which does not melt or become sticky at 300°C is still rubbery at −55°C! Silicone rubbers are useful when heat stability of a rubber is of prime importance—as, for example, in making gaskets for the superchargers on aircraft engines.

Dimethyl dichlorosilane, the liquid referred to earlier, has the ability to waterproof a wide variety of materials. For example, although a piece of ordinary filter paper when exposed to its vapor for a few seconds shows no visible change, it becomes completely waterproof, so that water either rolls off it or stands on it in drops. The same result is obtained on cotton, wool, leather, silk, glass, and porcelain products. The water-repellent properties are known to be due to a reaction which forms a layer of silicone resin on the surface of the object. Hydrochloric acid is formed as a by-product. Although the process may have great potential value for waterproofing textiles, the most important application to date has been in waterproofing ceramic surfaces of insulators in electronic equipment. In airplanes brought from a high altitude to the warm humid atmosphere of a landing field, moisture may condense (by dew formation) on parts of the radio, thereby shorting them and causing the radio to go dead. Such parts waterproofed with silicone do not short out, and the radios so equipped, which otherwise would fade out, continue to operate. Ignition systems of aircraft and automobiles may be similarly waterproofed.

Although many practical applications have already come from these synthetic silicone compounds, there is reason to believe that only a beginning has been made in understanding silicone chemistry and that the most important discoveries concerning these compounds are yet to be made.

The silicate minerals

It has already been noted that a great many of the minerals found in nature are silicates. Although most of these minerals are of complex nature, a few simple facts stand out.

Feldspar is the most abundant mineral on the earth's crust, making up about 60 percent of it. The most common variety (orthoclase feldspar) has the formula $KAlSi_3O_8$. Some feldspars contain sodium and calcium in place of potassium. Pure feldspar is used in making porcelain and some is used as an abrasive. On weathering, feldspar is acted upon by carbonic acid-bearing waters and converted into a hydrogen aluminum silicate, which is **clay**.

$$2KAlSi_3O_8 + H_2CO_3 + H_2O \rightarrow \underset{\text{clay}}{H_4Al_2Si_2O_9} + 2K^+ + CO_3^= + 4SiO_2$$

This is the way most of the clay on the earth was formed. The potassium ion (K^+) leached from the feldspar eventually finds its way to the sea. The silica may be deposited as quartz crystals in crevices through which the water percolates.

Pure clay is a white powdery material highly prized for making high-grade china (that is, china clay). More commonly, the clay formed is mixed with iron oxide, giving the red clay so common along the eastern coast of the United States from New Jersey to Georgia. If the soil contains much organic matter the color of the iron may be obscured. Soils high in clay content may contain some unchanged feldspar and hence the weathering is still going on. Therefore, clay soils are generally much less likely to be deficient in potash than are those which are low in clay content.

KEY WORDS

clay	petrified wood	silicon
diatomaceous earth	pyrex	silicone resins
duriron	quartz	silicones
feldspar	sand	supercooled liquid
ferrosilicon	sandstone	vycor
glass	silica	waterglass
Mohs' scale	silica gel	

HIGHLIGHTS

Silicon is produced in the electric furnace by the reduction of **silica** with carbon. Silicon occurs mainly in a variety of forms of the oxide and in silicates. Silicon dioxide transmits ultraviolet light. Silicon is soluble in a mixture of nitric and hydrofluoric acids. It reacts with sodium hydroxide and water to form waterglass and hydrogen. Sodium silicate or **waterglass** is widely used. Silicon is used in making a number of steel alloys such as the acid-resisting **duriron.**

Feldspar ($KAlSi_3O_8$) is the most abundant mineral in the earth's crust. On weathering, it forms **clay** ($H_4Al_2Si_2O_9$).

Glass is a **supercooled liquid** of variable composition. Ordinary glass is made from a mixture of **sand,** limestone, and sodium carbonate. Optical glass and high-grade crystal ware are made from a mixture of sand, potassium carbonate, sodium carbonate, boric oxide, and lead oxide. Heat-resistant glass includes **pyrex** (borosilicate glass), fused quartz (pure silica), and **vycor** (acid-treated borosilicate glass). Other forms include foam glass, plate glass, fiber glass, nonreflecting, and laminated or safety glass.

Silicones are polymers of substituted silane molecules. The molecules are arranged in chains much as organic polymers. Some silicones are only slightly affected by wide-range temperature changes. At present silicones are widely used as lubricants, in aircraft, and as water-repellents.

QUESTIONS

1. In what forms of combination is silicon most commonly found in nature?
2. In what ways does silicon resemble carbon in chemical properties?
3. In what two ways does silicon differ from carbon in chemical properties?

4. How is elementary silicon prepared?
5. Give two uses for elementary silicon.
6. Explain how a mixture of silicon and sodium hydroxide may be made to liberate hydrogen.
7. Explain how petrified wood is formed.
8. In what ways is silica ware superior to glass for certain laboratory uses?
9. Name two reagents which attack silica.
10. Describe the structure of quartz and explain why this structure causes quartz to have physical properties very different from those of carbon dioxide.
11. For what purposes is partially dehydrated silica gel employed?
12. What raw materials are used in making ordinary glass?
13. List ten ways in which the use of glass improves your own standard of living.
14. What are the advantages of using nonreflecting glass for cameras and binoculars?
15. How is nonreflecting glass prepared?
16. List some uses for the silicone oils and resins.
17. How is clay formed?

Suggested Projects for Unit Nine

1. What can you learn about soil fertility by comparing the formulas of feldspar and clay?
2. Glassworking is a nice hobby. You should know a few techniques of glassworking. Find out what tools are needed and learn to make simple bends, delivery tubes, medicine droppers, and other simple objects.
3. What is bouncing putty?
4. What are the six crystal systems? In which one does quartz belong?
5. What is piezoelectricity? What does it have to do with silicon?
6. Learn how to make a silicate garden and explain how it operates.
7. Make a list of household and other common products containing silicones. (Look at the labels.)
8. What is a rhinestone?

UNIT TEN: Between Solutions and Mixtures

CHAPTER 42

colloids

The branch of chemistry which deals with colloids is one of the most important and least well understood of all branches of chemistry. Colloids are important because they are encountered frequently both in nature and in modern technology. The cells of animals and plants are colloidal; the red color at sunset and the blue color of a cloudless sky are due to colloidal dust particles in the atmosphere.

What is a colloid?

Although in many ways they are quite different, a colloid is somewhat like a solution, and one can best understand what a colloid is by comparison with a solution. As you have already learned, a solution consists of two components in which single molecules of one component are spread throughout the other. Thus in a sugar-water solution, single, individual molecules of the sugar are mixed throughout the water, just as nitrogen molecules are mixed with oxygen molecules in air.

Now suppose that you try to make a concentrated solution of sand in water. If you start with coarse crystals of sand and shake with water, the sand, which is insoluble, does not dissolve. You have obtained only a coarse mechanical suspension, and when you stop shaking, the sand settles to the bottom. The nearest you could come to such a solution (and it is very far from a true solution) is to grind the sand *very* fine and then shake it with water. If the sand particles are sufficiently fine, and other conditions are right, the particles may, on shaking, remain dispersed through the water and fail to settle out on standing. The result is a **colloid**. This colloid may appear similar to a solution. For example, the sand particles may be so fine as to be invisible to the naked eye, and the colloid may—like a true solution—

Crystals of amethyst are an example of a colloid in which a solid is dispersed in a solid. Amethyst consists of colloidal particles of manganese dispersed in quartz. (American Museum of Natural History)

appear homogeneous. Actually the dispersed material in a colloid consists of particles which are many times larger than simple molecules or ions and yet small enough so they do not settle out. This is the difference between a colloid and a true solution.

A colloid may be defined as a mixture of two components in which the particles of the dispersed component are intermediate in size between simple ions or molecules and the particles in coarse suspensions. As with solutions, many types of colloids are possible. Obviously, if the two components are soluble in each other, no colloid is possible. For example, no colloid of sugar and water is possible because on mixing, sugar and water form a true solution.

TABLE 42–1. Classification of colloids

Dispersed component may be a	Dispersed in a	Example
(Gas)	(Gas)	*Impossible:* only true solutions can form by mixing gases
Gas	Liquid	Foam, whipped cream, or whipped egg white
Gas	Solid	Pumice and certain other minerals
Liquid	Gas	Fogs and clouds
Liquid	Liquid	Milk, mayonnaise (these are called emulsions)
Liquid	Solid	Jelly
Solid	Gas	Smoke and dust in air
Solid	Liquid	Sand in water
Solid	Solid	Certain minerals, such as amethyst which is colloidal manganese in quartz (gold in ruby glass is sometimes classed under this group but actually glass is not a true solid)

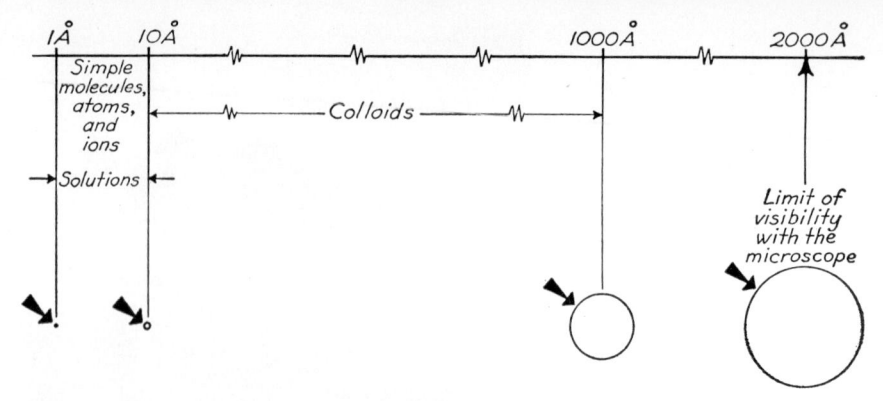

Fig. 42-1. Colloidal particles vary from those just too small to be seen with a microscope to those slightly larger than simple molecules. (1 angstrom, Å, = 10^{-8} cm)

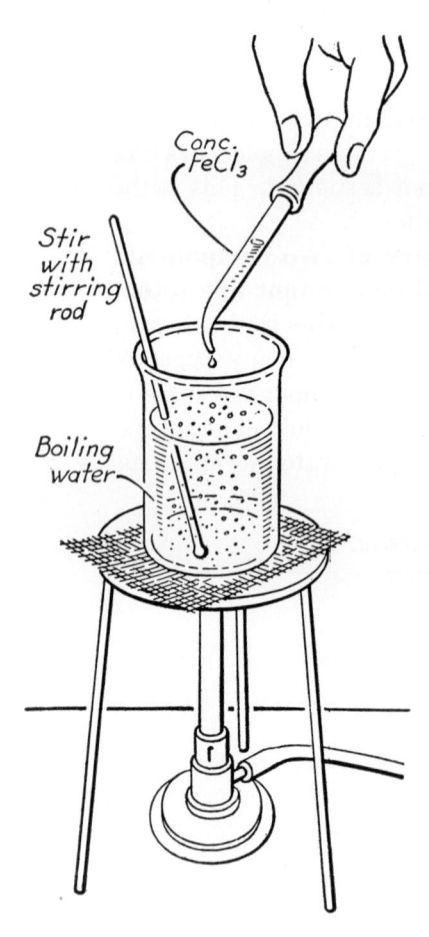

Fig. 42-2. A convenient setup for the preparation of a colloid of ferric hydroxide in water is shown in the drawing above.

How may colloids be prepared?

Various methods are used to prepare colloids, but all of them involve one of the following general methods: (1) making large particles small enough to become colloidally dispersed and (2) making ions or molecules react to form larger particles of colloidal size.

Grinding is commonly used to prepare colloids. A **colloid mill** in which solids are ground fine enough to become colloidal may be used. Thus finely ground graphite can be dispersed in oil or water to form a good lubricant. Sometimes the formation of a colloid is an undesirable consequence of fine grinding, as in a starch or flour mill where some of the fine starch becomes colloidally suspended in the air and thus becomes an explosion hazard (see Chap. 25, pages 278 and 279).

Cloud formation is an example of the second general method. When air containing water vapor is cooled, the moisture condenses on dust particles or gas ions which serve as condensation nuclei (see Chap. 30, page 338). The resulting particles of liquid or solid water may be of such size as to remain colloidal. If so, a cloud or fog, which consists of tiny droplets of water dispersed in air, is formed. If the particles of water become

528

Clouds are one of the most important colloids. They consist of tiny particles of liquid or solid water dispersed in air. These tiny particles of water will remain suspended in air as long as they are small enough. When they grow large, they fall to the earth as rain or snow (see pages 151–152). (Standard Oil Co.)

too large to remain colloidally suspended, they fall as rain or snow.

A simple laboratory experiment will illustrate this general method of forming a colloid. Prepare a concentrated solution of ferric chloride and add a few *drops* of this solution to a beaker containing about 150 ml of boiling water. Within a few seconds you will observe the formation of deep red colloidal ferric hydroxide. The explanation for the formation of the colloid is as follows: Ferric chloride is hydrolyzed by water.

$$Fe^{+++} + 3Cl^- + 6H_2O \rightarrow Fe(OH)_3 + 3Cl^- + 3OH_3^+$$
$$\text{(insoluble)}$$

The boiling increases the degree of hydrolysis, thereby rapidly forming insoluble ferric hydroxide which, instead of precipitating, remains colloidal. The color observed is due to this colloidal ferric hydroxide.

Colloidal dispersions of many metals can be made by electrically arcing wires of this metal under water. An apparatus such as that shown in Fig. 42–3 is used. When the arc is struck under water, some of the metal of which the wires are composed vaporizes. This vapor condenses in the water, leading to a colloidal dispersion of the metal in water. Beautiful ruby red dispersions of gold in water can be made in this way. If the wires are composed of silver a gray-to-yellow silver colloid can be obtained.

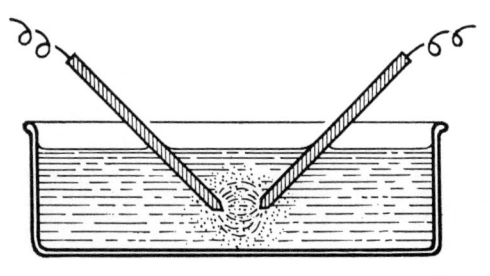

Fig. 42–3. Colloids of gold or silver dispersed in water may be prepared by arcing electrodes made of the metal under water.

Why colloidal dispersions do not settle out

A complete answer to why colloids do not settle out is a matter about which chemists have argued and disagreed ever since the Scot **Thomas Graham** made the first studies of colloids about one hundred years ago. Consider, for example, a white fleecy cirrus cloud, composed of minute droplets of liquid water. According to elementary principles of physics, these droplets of liquid water should be expected to fall to the earth under the action of gravity. Yet, as everyone knows, such clouds do not always mean rain. Or consider the smoke pouring from certain factory smokestacks. Why is it that the solid particles which make up this smoke do not fall rapidly to earth instead of remaining suspended in air? The main explanation is to be found in the phenomenon which is called **Brownian movement,** after the Scotch botanist **Robert Brown** (1773–1858), who discovered it in 1827.

Brownian movement can be observed by placing some of the smoke from a factory, or cigarette smoke, which is more easily obtained, in a cell under a microscope, as in Fig. 42-4. The smoke should be illuminated by a beam of light at right angles to the microscope. When the smoke is observed through this apparatus, it will be noted that the individual smoke particles move here and there completely at random (Fig. 42-5). The explanation for this erratic motion is that the smoke particles are being knocked around. This is a result of the smoke particles being struck by the *molecules* of gas in which they are dispersed. That is, a single gas molecule which we cannot see may strike one of the smoke particles, sending it off in a certain direction. Then some other molecule collides with it, sending it in another direction, and so on. That is, colloidal particles are small enough to be deflected by collision with a

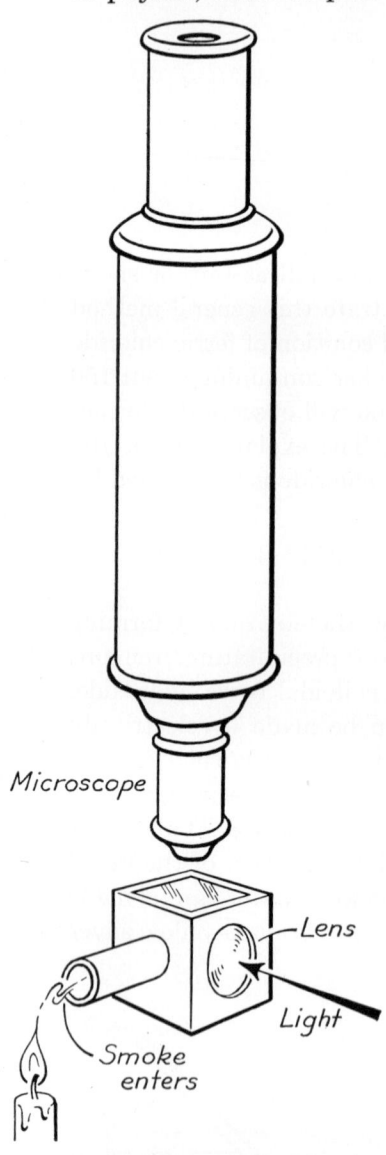

Fig. 42-4. A setup for observing Brownian movement in smoke.

Colloidal dispersions in water are precipitated by the addition of electrolyte. The graduated cylinder on the left contains ferric hydroxide colloid. The graduated cylinder on the right shows the same liquid 10 min after adding sodium sulfate to it. Note that the ferric hydroxide has precipitated and settled to the bottom.

single molecule of the medium in which they are dispersed. Thus a smoke particle in air may tend to settle out under the influence of gravity. But because of the numerous side detours it is forced to make as a result of molecular bombardment, the actual rate of settling of the smoke particle may be so slow as to be unnoticeable even after months. Thus Brownian movement is probably the principal reason why colloids do not settle out.

Observation of Brownian movement is also important for another reason. It affords a directly observable consequence of the kinetic energies of gas molecules. In observing Brownian movement, one is observing the direct effect of collisions of gas molecules. Hence its discovery and explanation were important in confirming the kinetic molecular theory.

A secondary effect in stabilizing colloids is based on the electrical charge which colloidal particles carry. It is known that most colloidal particles are charged. Probably all colloidal particles are charged, although the way they acquire their charges is different for different

Fig. 42–5. A schematic diagram showing the random Brownian movement of a colloidal particle.

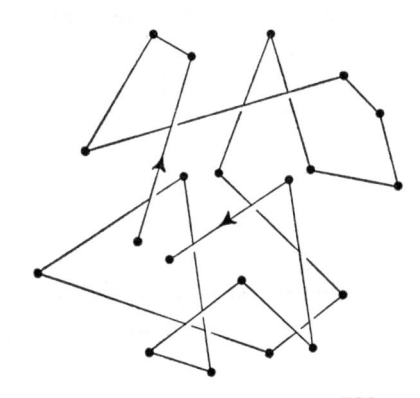

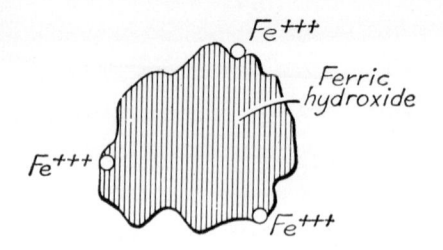

Fig. 42–6. Colloidal particles of ferric hydroxide are positively charged because they adsorb ferric ion (Fe^{+++}) on their surfaces.

colloids. Thus droplets in clouds probably acquire their charge by friction with the atmosphere. (When the charge flows off to the ground we call it *lightning*.) Colloidal particles in water, such as the ferric hydroxide mentioned earlier, become charged by adsorbing ions from the solution onto their surfaces (Fig. 42–6). Whatever the source of the charge, and this is a point about which chemists disagree among themselves, all particles in a given colloid have a charge of the *same* sign. These particles, therefore, repel each other. If they did not repel each other, the particles would clump together, making particles so large that Brownian movement would stop and hence the colloid would settle out.

How can colloids be made to settle out?

Sometimes the breaking up of a colloid is highly important—as, for example, in reducing the smoke nuisance in cities. Most methods for breaking up a colloid depend upon destroying the charges which the particles carry. An extremely simple, but ingenious and important, application of this is in the **Cottrell precipitator** for freeing gases of dust, smoke, liquid droplets, and other materials. In this apparatus the colloid is passed between a wire and a plate which are highly charged electrically by being connected to a source of direct current (Fig. 42–7). The charged smoke particles are attracted by the oppositely charged plate, where they are deposited.

This simple device is playing an important part in making our cities cleaner and in reclaiming materials which formerly were wasted as smoke. Examples are the reclaiming of zinc oxide from foundry smoke and of metal oxides from smelter flue gases.

Colloidal dispersions in water, such as the ferric hydroxide colloid, can be broken by adding an electrolyte. In this case the iron hydroxide particles have their positive charge neutralized by the negative ions of the electrolyte added. The resulting neutral particles of iron hydroxide clump together and settle out. Because it furnishes a negative ion of higher charge, sodium sulfate (Na_2SO_4) is more efficient in breaking up this colloid than sodium chloride (NaCl). Trisodium phosphate (Na_3PO_4) is still more effective.

The formation of deltas at the mouths of rivers—for example, the Mississippi or Nile deltas—is due partly to the same type of effect.

The material of which these deltas are composed is brought from upstream. Part of this material is in mechanical suspension but much of it is in colloidal dispersion. This material is deposited at the mouth of the river for two reasons: (1) the velocity of the water is reduced at the river's mouth, thereby causing the mechanically suspended matter to settle, and (2) more important, the ions of sea water cause the colloidal particles to settle out.

In the manufacture of soap (see Chap. 37, page 449), salt is used to cause the soap to separate from the water in which it is dispersed. Hides and skins, which are colloids, may be tanned by common salt,

A Cottrell precipitator would remove the dust, smoke, and droplets of liquid shown escaping from the stack in the foreground. (Western Precipitation Corp.)

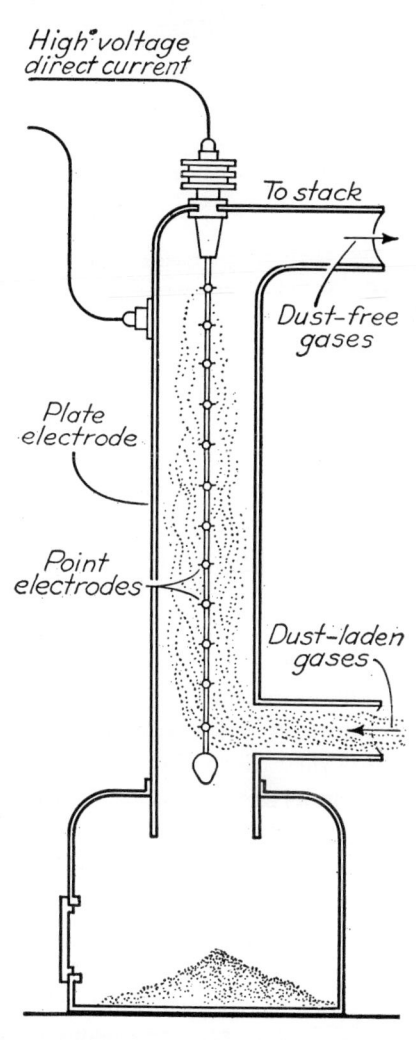

Fig. 42–7. The internal structure and operation of a Cottrell precipitator.

533

A latex emulsion coagulates when added to acetic acid. (Firestone Tire & Rubber Co.)

but tannin, a vegetable extract, or alum, works better. Both tannin and alum give ions of higher charge. Latex is a colloidal dispersion of rubber in water. It is coagulated and the crude rubber separated from it by adding acetic acid. Milk is a complex colloid. The protein, casein, is colloidally dispersed in sweet milk. As the milk sours because of bacterial action converting the milk sugar lactose into lactic acid, the casein separates out, and cottage cheese forms.

Emulsions

The name **emulsion** applies to a colloidal dispersion of one liquid in another. If kerosene and water are shaken together vigorously, a temporary dispersion is formed which separates into the two liquids as soon as shaking stops. If a little soap or detergent is added and the mixture is shaken vigorously, a milky-looking liquid which does not separate on standing is produced. A more effective means of emulsifying oil and water is by using an emulsifier which forces the liquids through very fine holes, thereby producing smaller dispersed droplets than can be produced by shaking or stirring. The emulsion obtained, if examined, will be found to consist of a dispersion of *oil droplets in a medium of water*. The soap or other **emulsifying agent** serves to stabilize the emulsion by coating the surface of the oil particles. This coating prevents the oil particles from coming together and forming drops large enough to settle out. All soaps or other emulsifying agents consist of long molecules, one end of which tends to dissolve in oil (the hydrocarbon end), while the other end tends to dissolve in water (the carboxyl end). As a result the soap tends to concentrate at the boundary between the oil and the water (Fig. 42–8).

The cleansing action of soap is explained on the same basis. The dirt to be washed out is a water-insoluble material which attracts one end of the soap molecules. The other end of the soap molecules tends to stay in the water. This anchors the dirt to the water so it can be floated off and washed away.

Mayonnaise is an emulsion of salad oil and vinegar. Unless an emulsifying agent is used, the oil and vinegar separate quickly. In real mayonnaise the emulsifying agent is egg yolk. In cooked salad dressings it may be flour or starch, with or without eggs; and in many commercial dressings it is a gum.

Milk is an emulsion of butterfat in a medium of water (which also contains dissolved solutes). The emulsifying agents are the milk proteins. As emulsifiers they are not very efficient, for as everyone knows, the cream normally begins to separate a few hours after the milk is withdrawn from the cow. If the milk is run through an emulsifier, the butterfat is broken up into smaller particles which do not separate nearly so quickly. The result is called **homogenized milk.** Goat's milk is a more stable emulsion than cow's milk. The cream does not separate from goat's milk on long standing.

The color of colloids

Many years ago, an Englishman, **Lord Rayleigh,** studied the effect of colloids on light that passes through them. He found, among other things, that when visible light passes through a colloid a certain

Fig. 42–8. A schematic diagram showing how soap acts as an emulsifier. Soap consists of a long molecule, one end of which tends to dissolve in water. Consequently in an oil-in-water emulsion, the soap tends to collect in the region between the oil and the water.

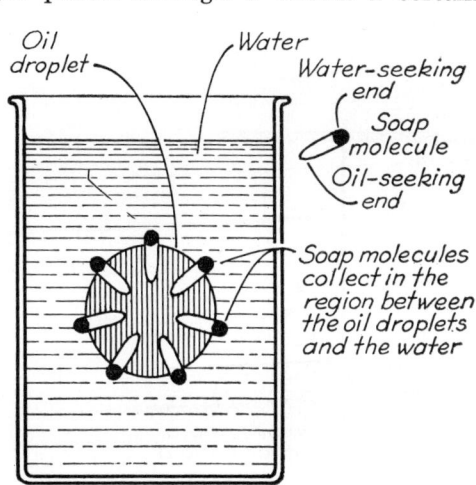

amount of the light is scattered by the colloid. Thus, in Fig. 42-9, if light passes through a cell containing smoke or fog, some of the light is scattered off to the sides and back in the direction of the source. This happens because the light is reflected from the surfaces of the individual colloidal particles. This is why dust particles are visible in a beam of light in an otherwise darkened room. Lord Rayleigh found that, other things being equal, the shorter the wave length of the light the greater the percentage of the light which is scattered. That is, a larger percentage of blue light is scattered than of green, and green in turn is scattered more than red. This fact has some important applications. The red color of the sun at **sunset** is due to the thick layer of dust and smoke in the atmosphere through which the sun's rays pass before reaching an observer on the earth. Because of the relatively greater scattering of the blue light, the sun's rays which have passed through the atmosphere are relatively richer in red and so appear red to an observer on earth. On the other hand, when the sun is high in a clear sky and an observer stands with his back to the sun, the sky appears blue because he now sees only that light which is being scattered by the atmosphere.

A yellow automobile fog light is better than a white one, because the white one, containing some blue and green, and other colors, causes more light to be scattered back into the eyes of the driver by the fog. This tends to blind the driver by glare. That a red light can be seen farther through the atmosphere than a blue light of the same intensity is well known. (This may have some bearing on the traditional use of red as a signal of danger.) For the same reason, sodium vapor lamps, which give off a single yellow color, are more effective in penetrating fog than a white, blue, or green light of the same intensity. Because of this, in some places sodium vapor lamps are being used to light highways.

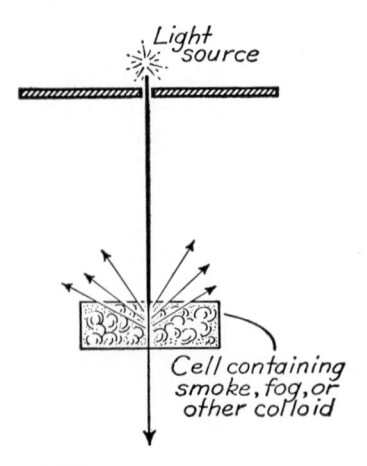

Fig. 42-9. When light passes through a colloid of any type, some of the light is scattered in various directions by the colloid.

KEY WORDS

Brown	colloid mill	Graham
Brownian movement	Cottrell precipitator	homogenized milk
cloud formation	emulsifying agent	Rayleigh
colloid	emulsion	sunset

HIGHLIGHTS

Colloids exist as dispersed particles intermediate in size between those of a solution and those of a suspension. On the basis of state of matter there are eight possible types of colloids.

Colloidal particles do not settle out, at least partly because of **Brownian movement**. The **Cottrell precipitator** is a device for removing the smoke and dust colloids from the atmosphere by neutralizing the charges on such particles. In a liquid, colloids may be removed by introducing an electrolyte.

Colloids scatter light of short wave length more than that of longer wave length. This relationship explains the fact that **sunsets** are generally rich in red, whereas the sky at midday may be blue.

QUESTIONS

1. How does a colloid differ from a solution and from a coarse suspension?
2. Give four illustrations of colloids.
3. What is meant by Brownian movement?
4. How does Brownian movement tend to keep colloids from settling?
5. What relation does electric charge have to the stability of a colloid?
6. How can smoke be separated from air?
7. How does the Cottrell precipitator help to promote clean cities?
8. What is an emulsion? How does soap stabilize an emulsion?
9. How is the cleansing action of soap explained?
10. What relation did Lord Rayleigh discover between color (or wave length) of light and its scattering by colloids?
11. Why does the sun seem redder at sunset than at noon? Is it actually redder?
12. Why can a red light be seen farther away on a foggy night than a blue light of the same intensity?
13. Is there any advantage of a yellow fog light over other colors? Explain.

Suggested Projects for Unit Ten

1. Learn how to make pyrophoric lead. This would make a fine demonstration for a science club. Be sure, however, that you can explain what it means as related to colloids. It is more than mere fireworks.
2. Find out how to make emulsions of waxes and cleaning solvents such as benzine or gasoline.
3. Learn all you can about deltas and give a report on them to the class. Explain why deltas are so called.
4. Demonstrate Brownian movement in smoke under a microscope. Or better, show it with a projecting microscope.
5. On the basis of colloids explain the remarkable color effects in the atmosphere produced by the volcanic eruption of Krakatoa in 1883.
6. Find out what laws your state has enacted to control atmospheric pollution.
7. Making mayonnaise is an excellent example of an emulsion. Explain the purpose of each ingredient used in the process.

UNIT ELEVEN: Metals

CHAPTER 43

the metals

The metals are second only to fuels in their economic importance to twentieth-century civilization. That metals have been equally important in preceding ages also is indicated by the fact that historians have named some of these eras after metals, for example, the *Age of Bronze*, or the *Age of Steel*. Our early ancestors had no knowledge of metals. Their first implements were fashioned of wood or stone. Gold, silver, and copper were the first metals known to man. This was because these metals occur free in nature. Gold and silver being rare and also soft were used chiefly for ornaments. Copper and bronze (an alloy of copper and tin) were used to fashion the first weapons and tools made of metal. The discovery of iron (before 3400 BC) resulted in its gradual replacement of bronze (by about 1500 BC). In addition lead was known to the Egyptians. All these metals are mentioned in the Old Testament.

About three-quarters of all the elements are classified as metals. Of this number only about one-third are of any great economic importance *at present*. The other two-thirds of the metals are not now important either because they are too rare in nature or because no practical uses for them are known. New discoveries, however, can rapidly change the value of a metal. This is well illustrated by uranium. Previous to the discovery of fission, uranium had few practical uses—the most important one being as a pigment in making yellow glass. Now it is the most sought-after metal in the world. We should realize that elements (including metals) unimportant today, may be of great practical value tomorrow. This is one of the things that come of living in an age in which scientific research is accorded the respect and importance that it now receives.

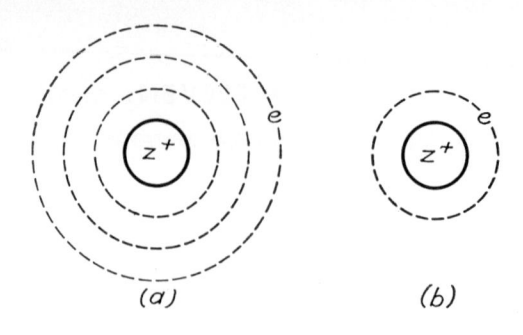

Fig. 43–1. Other factors being equal, an atom in which the valence electron is closer to the nucleus (b) will hold its electron more tightly than an atom in which the valence electron is farther away (a).

How do the metals differ from nonmetals?

The metallic elements as a group have both physical and chemical properties which distinguish them from the nonmetals. All the metals have a characteristic *metallic* luster and high heat conductivity. They are conductors of electric current and are malleable and ductile. The nonmetals, although not so uniform as a group, do not have the above properties. Chemically the metals tend to lose electrons, thereby forming positive ions. The nonmetals are electron receivers, forming either negative ions when they react with metals or covalent molecular compounds when they react with other nonmetals (for example, carbon dioxide). Also, nonmetallic oxides in water are acid, whereas metallic oxides in water are either basic or amphoteric. Table 43–1 gives a comparison between metals and nonmetals.

TABLE 43–1. Comparison of metals and nonmetals

Metals	Nonmetals
1. Shiny metallic luster	1. No metallic luster
2. Good electron conductors	2. Poor electron conductors (important exception, graphite)
3. Good conductors of heat	3. Poor conductors of heat
4. Malleable and ductile in solid state	4. Brittle in solid state
5. Tend to lose electrons in chemical reactions	5. Tend to gain electrons in chemical reactions
6. Oxides are basic or amphoteric	6. Oxides are acidic

The electron structure of metals

Most of the properties of metals, if not all, listed in Table 43–1 are due to the fact that **metals have loosely held electrons.** Two factors determine how tightly the valence-orbit electrons in an atom are held, and hence its metallic or nonmetallic properties. One factor is the electron structure of the atom with relation to the structure of the inert gases. That is, elements which have a structure of an inert gas plus one or two electrons always hold their valence electrons loosely and hence have the properties of typical metals. This includes all the elements in Groups Ia and IIa. The second factor is the size of the atom or actually the distance of the valence-orbit electrons from the nucleus. The farther these valence-orbit electrons are from the nucleus the more loosely they are held. That is, the larger the atom the more metallic its properties. You should recall that, within any one group, the atoms become larger as you read downward in the periodic table. Hence the metallic properties increase as you read downward within any one group. The effect of this second factor becomes noticeable in Group IIIb. The group starts with boron, a nonmetal. But the next element (progressing downward) is aluminum, which is a metal, as are all the others below aluminum in this group. In Group IVb, the first two members, carbon and silicon, are nonmetals; but the third element, germanium, has some of the properties of a metal. The metallic properties become more pronounced in the other elements of this group.

Because of the combination of these two effects, the metallic elements are found on the left and at the bottom of the periodic table. The nonmetals are found toward the right and upper part of the periodic table.

The crystal structure of metals

By means of x rays, the arrangement of the atoms in a crystal of metal can be determined. All the metals crystallize with a structure like that shown in Fig. 43–2 or another one very similar to it. That there are strong forces holding the atoms together is evident from the great tensile strength which certain metals have. A question often raised is: What holds the metal atoms together in the crystal? A possible, although incomplete, explanation is that the valence electrons lie midway between adjacent atoms in the manner shown below.

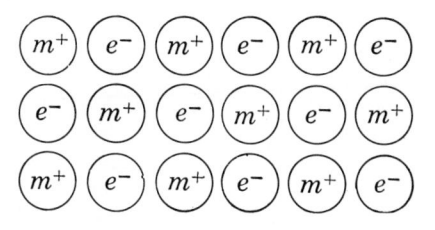

$$\begin{array}{cccccc}
(m^+) & (e^-) & (m^+) & (e^-) & (m^+) & (e^-) \\
(e^-) & (m^+) & (e^-) & (m^+) & (e^-) & (m^+) \\
(m^+) & (e^-) & (m^+) & (e^-) & (m^+) & (e^-)
\end{array}$$

The metal atoms can then be considered positively charged and the electrons as providing a cementing agent, binding the atoms together. This bond is referred to as a **metallic bond.** These mobile electrons could account also for the known electrical conductivity and the luster of metals. Unfortunately this theory cannot be verified by direct experiment because it is not possible to locate positions of electrons with x rays.

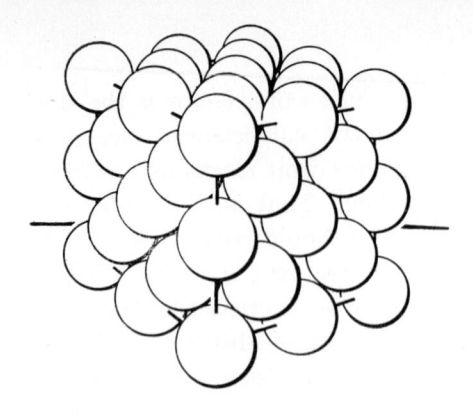

Fig. 43-2. A schematic diagram showing the formation in which the metals crystallize.

A survey of the physical properties of metals

Compact samples of all the metals have the same *metallic luster*. All of them, except copper and gold, have the same *silvery-white color* in large masses. In finely divided form, all are *velvety black* except aluminum and magnesium which in powder form are silvery white.

In *specific gravity* the metals vary widely. Lithium, scarcely more than half as dense as water, has a specific gravity of 0.53. Osmium has a specific gravity of 22.5, which is nearly twice as great as that of mercury (13.5).

The **tensile strength** is measured by the load which a wire of a given cross section can support. Iron has the greatest tensile strength of any element. The tensile strengths of certain elements are given in Table 43-2.

TABLE 43-2. Approximate tensile strengths of metallic elements after drawing into wire

Metal	Lb/in.^{2}
Iron	100,000
Copper	68,000
Silver	47,000
Aluminum	35,000
Gold	25,000
Zinc	25,000
Lead	3,000

The practical importance of iron is partly due to the high tensile strength of the alloys which it forms. Lead has such low tensile strength that it cannot be drawn into wire.

In *hardness* the metals vary widely from the alkalis which are butterlike to chromium which is hard enough to scratch glass.

The test of **malleability** is the thinness to which a piece of the

TABLE 43-3. Physical constants of the metals[a]

Metal	Specific gravity, 20°C	Melting point, °C	Boiling point, °C	Heat conduction[b]	Electrical resistance[c]	Hardness[d]
Aluminum	2.702	659.7	2057	0.504	2.828	2–2.9
Antimony	6.684	630.5	1380	0.044	41.7	3.0–3.3
Barium	3.5	850	1140			
Beryllium	1.85	1278	2970			
Bismuth	9.80	271.3	1560±5	0.019	119.0	2.5
Cadmium	8.642	320.9	767±2	0.222	7.54	2.0
Calcium	1.55	842–8	1240		4.6	1.5
Chromium	7.20	1890	2480		13.0	9.0
Cobalt	8.9	1495	2900		9.7	
Copper	8.92	1083	2336	0.918	1.69	2.5–3.0
Gold	19.3	1063	2600	0.700	2.44	2.5–3.0
Iron	7.86	1535	3000	0.161	10	4–5
Lead	11.343	327.4	1620	0.083	22	1.5
Lithium	0.534	186	1336±5		8.55(0°)	0.6
Magnesium	1.74	651	1107	0.376	4.6	2.0
Manganese	7.20	1260	1900		5.0	5.0
Mercury	13.546	−38.87	356.58	0.0197	95.78	
Molybdenum	10.2	2620±10	4800	0.346	5.7	
Nickel	8.90	1455	2900	0.142	6.844	
Palladium	11.40	1549.4	approx. 2200	0.168	11	4.8
Platinum	21.45	1773.5	4300	0.166	10	4.3
Potassium	0.86	62.3	760		6.1(0°)	0.5
Silver	10.5	960.8	1950	1.00	1.63(18°)	2.5–2.7
Sodium	0.97	97.5	880		4.3(0°)	0.4
Strontium	2.6	800	1150		24.8	1.8
Tin (β)	7.28	231.9	2270	0.155	11.5	1.5–1.8
Titanium	4.5	1800	Above 3000		3.2	
Tungsten (wolfram)	19.3	3370	5900	0.35	5.51	
Vanadium	5.96	1710	3000			
Zinc	7.14	419.47	907	0.265	5.75(0°)	2.5

[a] Data from *Handbook of Chemistry and Physics*, 39th ed., Chemical Rubber Publishing Co., Cleveland, Ohio, 1957–1958.

[b] The amount of heat in calories conveyed in 1 sec through a cube 1 cm on edge, when a temperature difference of 1°C exists between two opposite sides of the cube.

[c] Resistance in millionths of ohms by a cube of metal 1 cm on edge, data at 20°C except as otherwise noted.

[d] Mohs' scale of hardness (see Chap. 41, page 513).

metal can be beaten or rolled without cracking or splitting. Gold is the most malleable of all elements and can be beaten into sheets so thin that they are transparent. The following elements are in order of decreasing malleability: gold, silver, copper, tin, platinum, lead, zinc, iron, nickel.

Closely related to malleability is **ductility,** which is measured by

Metal ores. Top left, tungsten ores. Top right, nickel ore. Bottom left, chromium ore. Bottom right, tin ores and a tin-plated can. (American Museum of Natural History)

the thinness to which a wire of the metal can be drawn. Gold is the most ductile metal. A gold wire can be drawn so thin that 100 cm of it weighs only 0.0005 g. A wire this size and long enough to stretch all around the earth at the equator would weigh only 47 lb! Silver and copper also are very ductile. This fact is important in making copper wire and tubing, most of which is made by drawing of larger stock.

In the *melting points* of the metals there is a great variation. Mercury melts at $-39°C$ and tungsten (wolfram) at $3370°C$. The melting point of a metal not only determines the uses to which it can be put, but also influences the way in which it will be shaped. Aluminum (mp $660°C$) can be cast as a molten metal into prepared molds. Even pig iron, which melts above $1100°C$, is commonly cast into sand molds. But tungsten obviously cannot be cast. Nor can titanium, a metal in which there is a great deal of newly created interest. On the other hand, aluminum is obviously unsuitable for the construction of a jet engine, which calls for a metal of very high melting point. Many of the important uses of mercury depend upon the fact that it is a liquid at room temperature. Gallium, rubidium, and cesium are also liquid at temperatures not much above room temperature.

The *boiling points* of metals are sometimes important in determining their uses (see mercury, Chap. 48, pages 627 to 629) and also in purification of the metal. Mercury, cadmium, and zinc are purified by distillation. They have boiling points below $1000°C$.

TABLE 43-4. Ores of the common metals

1. Free or native metal
   - Gold   Silver   The platinum metals   Mercury   Copper
2. Oxides
   - Fe_2O_3 Hematite
   - Fe_3O_4 Magnetite
   - TiO_2 Rutile
   - SnO_2 Cassiterite
   - $Al_2O_3 \cdot xH_2O$ Bauxite
   - Cu_2O Cuprite
   - ZnO Zincite
3. Sulfides
   - ZnS Sphalerite
   - CdS Greenockite
   - Cu_2S Chalcocite
   - $CuFeS_2$ Chalcopyrite
   - PbS Galena
   - HgS Cinnabar
   - $NiS \cdot 2FeS$ Pentlandite (a source of nickel)
4. Carbonates
   - $PbCO_3$ Cerussite
   - $ZnCO_3$ Smithsonite
   - $MgCO_3$ Magnesite
   - $FeCO_3$ Siderite
   - $BaCO_3$ Barite
   - $SrCO_3$ Strontianite
   - $CaCO_3$ Calcite
5. Chlorides
   - $NaCl$ Halite
   - KCl Sylvite
6. Silicates[a]
   - $Be_3Al_2(SiO_3)_6$ Beryl

[a] Silicates are rarely used as ores because, without exception, it is difficult to extract the metal from them. Beryllium minerals are quite restricted in occurrence, hence there is no choice.

Although as a group the *electrical conductivity* of the metals is higher than that of the nonmetals, there is great variation in the electrical conductivity of the different metals. The best conductor known is silver, but copper is almost as good. This fact accounts for the enormous amount of copper used in the electrical industry. Mercury and bismuth are among the poorest of the metallic conductors. In general, the order of *heat conductivity* of the metals is the same as the order of electrical conductivity. Silver has the highest heat conductivity, and copper is next.

Occurrence of the metals in nature

Minerals found in nature from which the metals are commercially produced are known as ores. An **ore** is not always the most plentiful compound of a certain element because the cost of treating the ore to produce the metal must also be considered. Thus almost every square foot of soil in the world contains aluminum (as clay), but at present no metallic aluminum is produced from clay because the process is too expensive. Most of the metal ores contain the metal in one of the following forms: (1) uncombined (known as **native ore**), (2) as oxide, (3) as sulfide, (4) as carbonate, (5) as chloride, and (6) rarely, as silicate. The activity series, the periodic table, and the rules of solubility are helpful in remembering the forms in which the metals are found in nature. Thus one would not expect to find sodium or aluminum free in nature because these metals are too active. On the other hand the carbonates and sulfates of the alkaline earths (Group IIa), which are insoluble, are found widely distributed in nature. The occurrence of chlorides of the alkalis has already been discussed (see Chap. 22, pages 236 and 237).

The methods of extracting a metal from its ore

The branch of science which deals with the extraction of metals from their ores is **metallurgy.** Although the detailed procedure is different for each ore, certain general principles apply in every case.

The metal content of an ore as mined varies greatly. Iron ore containing less than 40 percent iron cannot be worked profitably, while much of the copper ore mined today contains less than 1 percent copper. The unwanted material mixed with the ore is called *gangue* (pronounced 'gang'). Gangue is usually silica or silicates.

In the case of an ore containing a large percentage of gangue, the first step after mining usually is **concentration** of the ore. The ore is finely ground, then shaken with water to wash off the lighter gangue. Sometimes an oil is added which adheres to the ore particles but not to the gangue. In this case air is then blown through the oil, water, and ore mixture. The oil forms a froth which rises to the surface, bringing the ore particles with it while the gangue falls to the bottom. This froth is skimmed off, thereby separating the ore from much of the gangue. This procedure is known as **flotation.** These newer techniques for concentrating ores have contributed much to the economical production of metals from low-grade ores. Since our high-grade-ore reserves are rapidly being used up, it is to be expected that methods for ore concentration will become more important as time goes on.

Treatment of native ores

The native ore is heated to melt the metal and allow it to drain away from the gangue. In the case of copper, a little carbon is added to prevent oxidation of the metal. A *flux* of limestone may be added. Its function is to convert the silica into a fusible *slag* (see Chap. 33, pages 369 and 370).

$$\underset{\text{(high melting)}}{SiO_2} + CaCO_3 \rightarrow \underset{\text{(easily fusible)}}{CaSiO_3} + CO_2 \uparrow$$

The liquid slag and molten metal ore are, like oil and water, immiscible; hence they are easily separated.

An open-pit copper mine. (Anaconda Copper Mining Co.)

Treatment of oxide ores

The majority of **oxide ores** are reduced with carbon. The general reactions may be written

$$MO + C \to M + CO$$

and

$$MO + CO \to M + CO_2$$

Where M = metal

This applies for iron, tin, zinc, and lead. The active metals such as magnesium and aluminum are not reducible by carbon. However, these active metals can be reduced electrolytically as described on page 548.

Sulfide and carbonate ores

The **sulfide ores** and **carbonate ores** must be converted to the oxide before they can be reduced.

Sulfide ores are heated in air. The reaction is[1]

$$2MS + 3O_2 \xrightarrow{\text{heat}} 2MO + 2SO_2 \uparrow$$

All the metal carbonates (except the alkalis) break down when heated.

$$MCO_3 \xrightarrow{\text{heat}} MO + CO_2 \uparrow$$

[1] HgS is an exception (see Chap. 7, page 58).

A close-up view of an electrolytic cell for the commercial production of magnesium. Metals such as magnesium, aluminum, and beryllium must be liberated by electrolytic metallurgy because they are so active that other metallurgical processes do not free them from their compounds. (Dow Chemical Co.)

Hence **roasting,** a metallurgical term meaning heating in an oxidizing atmosphere, will convert both sulfide and carbonate ores into oxides which can then be reduced.

Electrolytic metallurgy

We are indebted to electrolytic methods for many of the metals which now play an important role in our way of life—particularly the light metals, aluminum, magnesium, and beryllium.

These metals are all very active and their compounds so stable that it is either impossible or very expensive to reduce them by chemical reducing agents. By electrolyzing compounds of these metals under proper conditions, the metal is deposited at the cathode. The conditions required are (1) that the compound must be in a condition so that it can conduct an electric current and (2) that other substances more easily reduced must be absent. For the liberation of the active metals this means the electrolysis of a molten compound, since solid compounds are not electrolytic conductors (see Chap. 27, page 297). A water solution cannot be used because hydrogen, rather than the metal, will be obtained. For example, magnesium is produced by the electrolysis of molten magnesium chloride (see page 571), which gives magnesium at the cathode and chlorine at the anode.

$$MgCl_2 \text{ (molten)} \xrightarrow{\text{electrolysis}} Mg + Cl_2 \uparrow$$

Aluminum is produced by a similar, but not identical, process.

Aqueous solution electrolysis is important in the metallurgy of some of the less active metals. Thus copper is purified by electroplating it from a copper sulfate solution. Zinc and cadmium are sometimes reduced electrolytically from an aqueous solution.

Alloys

We live in an era sometimes referred to as the *Age of Steel*. To say ours is the Age of Iron would be incorrect because pure iron does not have the properties which make it suitable for constructing automobiles, locomotives, railroad rails, and the other numerous products made of steel. In fact iron is valued chiefly because it forms alloys. Pure iron is seldom encountered; all the various objects containing iron, whether steel or cast iron, are really alloys of iron and other elements.

An *alloy* may be defined as a material having the physical properties of a metal and containing a metal and one or more other elements, either metals or nonmetals. Alloys are generally prepared by fusing the elements together and cooling the melt. The properties of the alloy may be closely related to the properties of the pure elements which form it, or the alloy may have properties which are very different from those of its parent elements. Thus brass, an alloy of copper and zinc, has a yellow color somewhat intermediate between the colors of the two metals of which it is composed. But the American five-cent coin, which is an alloy of nickel (25 percent) and copper (75 percent), shows none of the color of the copper; nor is this alloy magnetic, although pure nickel is. Pure iron is soft and fairly ductile, but the addition of 0.1 percent carbon makes it hard and springy, that is, steel. One cannot predict with certainty the properties of an alloy from the properties of the pure elements.

Studies have shown that, structurally, alloys are of three types. These may be described as: (1) solid solutions, (2) compounds, and (3) mixed crystals.

1. Solid solution alloys. Such alloys are those in which only one type of crystal is present. An example is brass. In brass the crystal structure is the same as that of pure copper except that certain of the copper atoms in the structure have been replaced by zinc atoms.

2. Compounds. As strange as it may seem, there is good evidence that certain alloys involve compound formation between the alloying elements. Babbitt metal (used for bearings), an alloy of copper, antimony, and tin, contains the compounds $SbSn$ and Cu_3Sn. Just how these elements form compounds is not understood but the evidence that such compounds do form is quite clear. Carbon reacts with iron to form Fe_3C, for example, and this substance is present in carbon steels.

3. Mixed crystals. Microscopic examination of polished surfaces of many alloys shows them to be heterogeneous mixtures of two or more kinds of crystals. The individual crystals may be pure metals, compounds, or solid solutions.

Powder metallurgy

Powder metallurgy is a new technique for making alloys which has recently become important. Very fine powders of the metals are mixed and placed under very high pressure in a mold. The powder is heated, while under pressure, to a temperature slightly below the melting point. At this temperature the particles are welded together (that is, sintered). The result is a solid object of an alloy having properties different from either parent metal. The procedure is valuable for alloying metals which do not mix in the molten condition. It is also useful for those metals which melt at such a high temperature as to make ordinary methods of alloying impractical—as, for example, tungsten, tantalum, and molybdenum. Also, by this procedure highly complicated shapes can be produced without the difficulties of casting molten metal. Furthermore, highly porous alloys can easily be prepared by this technique. These porous alloys, which readily absorb oil, are used in certain engine bearings (that is, self-oiling bearings).

KEY WORDS

alloy	malleability	oxide ore
carbonate ores	metallic bond	powder metallurgy
concentration (of ore)	metallurgy	roasting
ductility	native ore	sulfide ores
electrolytic metallurgy	ore	tensile strength
flotation		

HIGHLIGHTS

Civilization advances in proportion to man's knowledge of the metals. Metals differ from nonmetals in having a higher luster and being better conductors of heat and electricity. All the metals except copper and gold are silvery white in color, but the fine powder of most metals is black. Metals vary greatly in specific gravity, tensile strength, melting point, and boiling point.

Metallurgy is the science that relates to reducing **ores** to their metals, and to the properties of metals and **alloys. Flotation** is widely used to **concentrate** ores in order that they may be reduced more efficiently. **Oxide ores** commonly are reduced by means of carbon. **Roasting** is the heating of an ore in an oxidizing atmosphere. Very active metals such as aluminum and magnesium are obtained by electrolytic processes.

Alloys are of three kinds: solid solutions, compounds, and mixed crystals. **Powder metallurgy** makes possible the economical fabrication of complicated objects of many metals.

QUESTIONS

1. What metals were first known to man? Why?
2. State six ways in which the metallic elements differ from the nonmetals.
3. What forces are believed to hold the atoms together in a crystal of a metal?
4. Which of the metals are not silvery white in large masses?
5. What is the color of the metals when finely divided? What two elements are exceptions?
6. Explain why the larger atoms tend to be more metallic than the smaller ones.
7. Which metal has the lowest density?
8. Which element has the highest tensile strength?
9. Which element has the highest electrical conductivity?
10. Describe the general method of treating an ore consisting of a native metal.
11. How are sulfide and carbonate ores treated to obtain the metal?
12. What kinds of metals require electrolytic methods in their metallurgy?
13. Do you expect the properties of an alloy to be related to the properties of the elements present? Cite some illustrations.
14. What is powder metallurgy? What are some advantages of this technique?

CHAPTER 44

the alkali metals

The elements of Group I*a* are known as the **alkali metals** because all of them form hydroxides which are strong bases. These metals are all very similar in physical and chemical properties. The free metals are soft and silvery white, with low melting points. They all have the electronic structure of an inert gas plus a single valence electron. They are, therefore, the most active metals known, since by losing this one electron they acquire the stable electronic structure of an inert gas. Thus the alkali metals always have an electrovalence of +1 in their compounds, and never show any tendency to share electrons with other atoms. The alkali metals should not be confused with the metals of Group I*b*, namely, copper, silver, and gold. The latter have very different chemical properties because of different electronic structure.

Properties of the alkali metals

The physical properties of the alkali metals are shown in Table 44–1. This group includes **lithium, sodium, potassium, rubidium, cesium,** and **francium.**

Notice that the radius of the atoms increases with atomic number. This is because of the increased number of orbits containing electrons. Most of the variations in physical properties can be remembered and explained on the basis of this difference in size of the atoms. Recall the theory given in Chap. 43, page 541, to explain the structures of metals. In the case of the alkalis, probably only one electron is loose enough to serve to bind adjacent atoms together; hence all these alkali metals are soft. But the softest one is cesium (francium has not been isolated) and the hardest is lithium, because the cementing electron is closest to the positive nucleus in the lithium and farthest away in cesium.

The shorter distance of the cementing electron from the nucleus of the lithium atom makes a more rigid structure than that in the corresponding structures of the larger atoms. Moreover, the melting points (Table 44–1), that is, the temperatures required to break down these crystal structures, also decrease as the radius increases, as would be expected from this theory.

The chemical activity, as measured by the tendency to lose an electron (sometimes called the **ionization potential**), increases

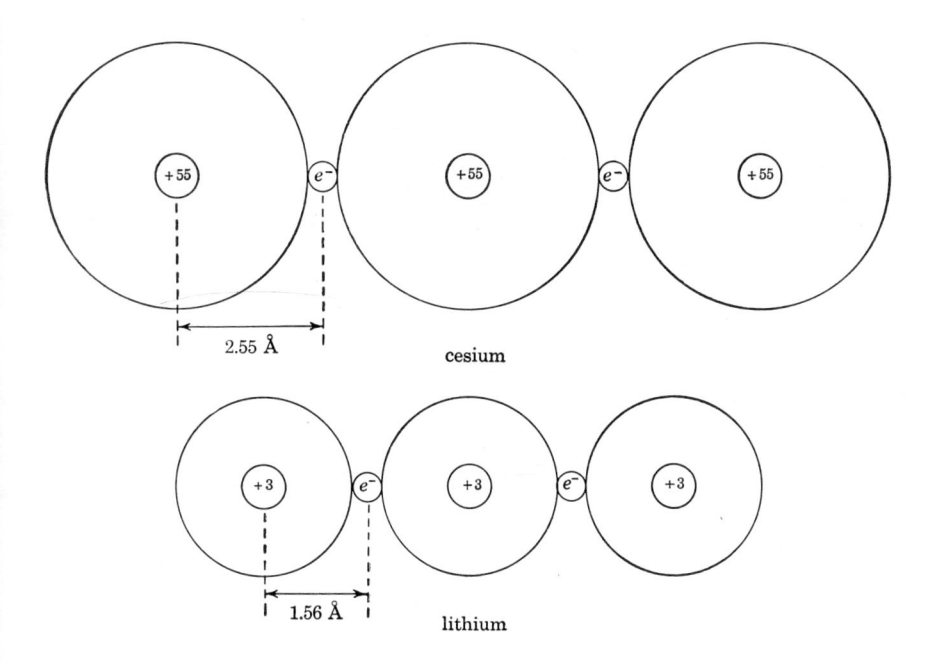

cesium

lithium

TABLE 44–1. Properties of the alkali metals

Property	Lithium	Sodium	Potassium	Rubidium	Cesium	Francium
Symbol	Li	Na	K	Rb	Cs	Fr
Atomic number	3	11	19	37	55	87
Electronic structure	2	2	2	2	2	2
	1	8	8	8	8	8
		1	8	18	18	18
			1	8	18	32
				1	8	18
					1	8
						1
Radius of free atom, angstroms (Å)	1.56	1.86	2.23	2.36	2.55	
Hardness	Decreases..→
Melting point, °C	186	97.5	62.3	38.5	28.5	
Tendency to lose an electron	Increases..→
Density, 20°C, g/cm³	0.53	0.97	0.86	1.53	1.87	

with increasing size of the atom. The explanation for this has already been given (see Chap. 21, pages 231 and 232, and Chap. 43, pages 540 and 541).[1]

The corresponding compounds of the different alkali metals are also quite similar. The principal differences are variations in solubility. Almost all these compounds are classed as *soluble*. Any of the compounds of the alkalis which are sufficiently insoluble to precipitate easily are noteworthy as tests for that alkali metal ion.

Occurrence of the alkali metals

Originally the alkali metals existed on the earth almost, if not entirely, as complex silicates—especially the feldspars (see Chap. 41, page 523) and the **micas**.[2] The weathering of these minerals and resulting leaching of the alkali metal ions has already been discussed (see Chap. 41, page 523). The formation of vast deposits of rock salt by evaporation of land-locked portions of the sea (see Chap. 22, page 236) has also been discussed earlier.

The relative abundance of the alkali metals is shown by Table 44–2.

TABLE 44–2. Occurrence of the alkali metals in nature

Metal	Estimated percentage of the earth's crust
Sodium	2.85
Potassium	2.60
Lithium	0.0004
Rubidium	0.000001
Cesium	0.0000001

Sea water contains 1.1 percent sodium ion (Na^+) and about 0.08 percent potassium ion (K^+). The principal commercial source of sodium is rock salt, which occurs rather plentifully in the United States. Elsewhere salt is sometimes obtained directly from sea water (see Chap. 22, pages 236 and 237). Although potassium is nearly as abundant in nature as sodium, potassium deposits of economic value

[1] In the presence of water the activity of lithium is greater than that of any of the other alkalis except cesium (and probably francium). This is due to the very strong tendency of the lithium ion (Li^+) to react with water, forming a hydrate $[Li(H_2O)_x^+]$. But in the absence of water the activity of the alkalis increases with increasing atomic radius as would be expected.

[2] Micas are a class of minerals of which common white mica (muscovite) is the best known example. They are complex aluminum silicates containing one or more alkali metals (and some also contain iron and magnesium).

A potash (potassium carbonate) filter. Potassium carbonate is made from the potassium chloride that is recovered from the brine of Searles Lake in California. Potassium chloride is also mined at Strassfurt, Germany, and Carlsbad, N.M. (American Potash and Chemical Corp.)

are much less abundant. This is true partly because potassium salts are more soluble than the corresponding sodium salts and hence, in the evaporated sea water, the potassium salts would be the last to crystallize. Further, the amount of potassium in sea water is much less than the amount of sodium. This is because clay particles tend to hold potassium ion by adsorption, thereby preventing it from reaching the sea. That is, clay soils are much more retentive of soluble potassium salts than they are of soluble sodium salts.

This latter fact is doubtless connected with the fact that plants in general contain about four times as much potassium as sodium. Animals, in their metabolism, excrete potassium and sodium in a more-or-less fixed ratio. Thus a herbivorous animal (that is, an animal that lives on plants), in excreting the large amount of potassium taken into the body as food, will tend to become sodium starved. This explains the well-known craving of cattle, deer, and other herbivores for salt, which they must have in order to live.

The principal sources of potassium at present are mines at **Strassfurt,** Germany, and at **Carlsbad,** N.M. and the brine from **Searles Lake** in California. This lake, located in the desert of southeastern California, appears to be a dry salt bed but, at a depth of 3 to 4 ft below the surface, brine is encountered. From this brine, pure potassium chloride can be obtained.

Lithium is found in nature mainly as lithium aluminum silicate minerals. Cesium and rubidium are very rare. Francium, which is not found in nature, was discovered by **Perey** in 1939 and named after his native country. Small amounts of the element were formed by nuclear bombardment. Francium is radioactive. One of the isotopes of potassium (K^{40}) found in nature is also radioactive, as is one of the natural isotopes of rubidium (Rb^{87}).

Preparation of the alkali metals

Sodium is the only alkali metal which is produced in any quantity. It is produced by the electrolysis of molten sodium hydroxide.

$$2NaOH \xrightarrow{\text{electrolysis}} 2Na + H_2 \uparrow + O_2 \uparrow$$
$$\text{(molten)} \qquad \text{(at cathode)} \quad \text{(at anode)}$$

This is the same method used by Davy who first prepared the metal in 1807.

Since sodium hydroxide is made from sodium chloride, attempts have been made to obtain sodium directly from salt. This can be done by electrolysis of molten sodium chloride (Downs' process).

$$2NaCl \xrightarrow{\text{electrolysis}} 2Na + Cl_2 \uparrow$$
$$\text{(molten)}$$

However, the high melting point of salt and the corrosive character of the chlorine at such a high temperature partly outweigh the advantage of a cheaper starting material.

Potassium and lithium are produced by analogous methods.

Properties and uses of the alkali metals

The alkali metals are so active that it is necessary to store them under kerosene in the laboratory. Sodium and potassium react violently with water, forming the hydroxide and hydrogen.

$$2Na + 2H_2O \rightarrow 2NaOH + H_2 \uparrow$$

In handling sodium in ton lots in industry, it has been found that the metal can be stored safely in 5 to 10 lb bricks, unprotected from air except by the corrosion film which naturally forms by oxidation of the outer surface of the brick. This mode of storage is *not* recommended for the laboratory.

Metallic sodium has good heat conductivity. It is used to partly fill hollow valves of aircraft engines, thereby replacing the steel, which is a poorer heat conductor. Because the sodium conducts heat away more rapidly, the valve is kept cooler than it would be if made of solid steel. Because it is cheap, metallic sodium has many possible applications as a heat transfer medium. When sealed in glass tubes with mercury or argon and vaporized with an electric current, sodium gives off a strong yellow light known as *sodium-vapor light*. This type of lamp is coming into use for lighting highways, bridges, and landing fields.

Metallic sodium alloyed with lead is used in the manufacture of tetraethyllead for addition to gasoline (see Chap. 36, page 425). Sodium is also used to manufacture sodium peroxide (Na$_2$O$_2$), sodium cyanide (NaCN), sodium hydride (NaH), and as a reducing agent for organic syntheses. It sells at a price per pound which is comparable with that of aluminum or copper.

A small amount of cesium is used in the manufacture of photoelectric cells. The use of cesium in these cells depends on the fact that cesium atoms hold their electrons so loosely that even visible light will eject them. One type of photoelectric cell is based on this principle. Fortunately this requires only a small amount of the metal.

Potassium, rubidium, and lithium metals have few uses outside the laboratory.

Sodium chloride

Rock salt is one of our most valuable mineral resources. It furnishes not only chlorine with its many essential uses (Chap. 22, page 241), but also sodium, many compounds of which contribute to our high standard of living.

Salt itself is a necessary food, not only for man, but for many animals (see page 555). In the United States we take salt for granted because it is so cheap, but in some other parts of the world obtaining even enough salt for the diet is a real problem. Salt is widely used in curing and preserving meats, particularly pork.

Sodium hydroxide

Electrolysis of salt solution yields sodium hydroxide and chlorine. Sodium hydroxide, known as *caustic soda* or *lye*, is used in enormous amounts in the manufacture of soaps (see Chap. 37, page 449), paper, leather, mercerized cotton, rayon and cellophane (see Chap. 38, pages 463 and 464), and scouring agents. It is also used in the refining of petroleum.

Sodium carbonate (soda ash)

The layman seldom hears of **sodium carbonate,** but if its manufacture were suddenly stopped, he would soon realize that something had happened to his way of life. Cheap glass, and all that that term implies, owes its existence to cheap sodium carbonate. Man has not always had cheap supplies of sodium carbonate. In the Middle Ages the glass factories of Bohemia and France depended upon sodium carbonate imported from naturally occurring deposits in Asia Minor and Spain. About the end of the eighteenth century, after England had cut off France's supply of this commodity, the French Academy offered a prize for the discovery of an inexpensive method for making sodium carbonate from common salt. The problem was solved by

Sodium carbonate is used by the ton in industry. Here you see a power shovel moving sodium carbonate in a storage building. (American Potash and Chemical Corp.)

Nicholas Le Blanc, physician to the Duke of Orleans. During the revolution Le Blanc's patents were confiscated, his factory destroyed, and his friend the duke guillotined; he himself committed suicide. Yet during the next 75 years his process supplied France and the rest of the industrial world with cheap sodium carbonate and thereby contributed greatly to economic and industrial development. Le Blanc's method has since been replaced, both in Europe and in America, by the more economical **Solvay** process.

The Solvay process was invented by the Belgian whose name it bears. Its success depends upon the fact that sodium hydrogen carbonate ($NaHCO_3$) can be precipitated by bringing together solutions of salt and ammonium hydrogen carbonate.

$$\underbrace{Na^+ + Cl^-}_{\text{brine solution}} + \underbrace{NH_4^+ + HCO_3^-}_{\text{(from ammonia and carbon dioxide)}} \rightarrow NaHCO_3 \downarrow + NH_4^+ + Cl^-$$

The precipitated sodium hydrogen carbonate (sodium bicarbonate) may be packaged and sold as *baking soda*, or made into *baking powder* (see Chap. 35, pages 404 to 406), but most of it is converted into sodium carbonate. This is done by heating.

$$2NaHCO_3 \xrightarrow{\text{heat}} Na_2CO_3 + CO_2 \uparrow + H_2O \uparrow$$

This reaction is a good laboratory source of carbon dioxide.

Ammonium hydrogen carbonate for the initial reaction is obtained by pumping carbon dioxide into ammonium hydroxide solution.

$$NH_4OH + H_2CO_3 \rightarrow NH_4HCO_3 + H_2O$$

The process is cheap and profitable because the ammonium chloride formed as a by-product of the first reaction mentioned is easily converted back into ammonia. This is done by heating it with lime.

$$2NH_4^+ + 2Cl^- + Ca(OH)_2 \rightarrow 2NH_3 \uparrow + Ca^{++} + 2Cl^- + 2H_2O$$

The ammonia is thus used over again. Lime is obtained by heating limestone and adding water to the calcium oxide produced.

$$CaCO_3 \xrightarrow{heat} CaO + CO_2 \uparrow$$
$$CaO + H_2O \rightarrow Ca(OH)_2$$

The first of these reactions as well as the heating of sodium hydrogen carbonate supplies the carbon dioxide used in the process.

The entire process thus converts salt and limestone into sodium carbonate. Calcium chloride is produced as a by-product.

$$\text{Salt and limestone} \xrightarrow{\text{by Solvay process}} \text{sodium carbonate and calcium chloride}$$

TABLE 44-3. The Solvay process

Raw materials	Primary products	By-products
Limestone	Sodium hydrogen carbonate	Calcium chloride
	or	
Salt	Sodium carbonate	
NH$_3$ to replace any lost in process		

The by-product, calcium chloride, is produced in greater quantity than can profitably be used and its disposal presents some difficulties.

Uses of sodium carbonate

Sodium carbonate is used in making glass, chemicals, soap, scouring powders, paper and pulp, water softeners, and fire extinguishers. Washing soda is $Na_2CO_3 \cdot 10H_2O$, hydrated sodium carbonate.

The fact that solutions of both sodium carbonate and sodium hydrogen carbonate are alkaline by hydrolysis has already been mentioned (see Chap. 27, page 306).

Other sodium salts

Sodium sulfate, a by-product of hydrochloric acid manufacture, is used in making certain types of glass and in making kraft paper. Sodium nitrate, which occurs naturally in Chile, is an important nitrogen fertilizer. Sodium cyanide, which, like all soluble cyanides, is very poisonous, is used in electroplating metals and in mining gold.

Potassium compounds

By far the most important fact about potassium is that it is used in large quantities in plant growth. Crop production, therefore, removes potassium from the soil (Table 44–4), and unless the soil is re-supplied with potassium, it will lose its ability to support plant growth.

TABLE 44–4. Amounts of potassium removed from the soil by crops

Crop	Yield per acre	Potassium removed, lb/acre
Tobacco	2000 lb	200
Corn	80 bu	38
Wheat	20 bu	14
Clover hay	2 tons	73

Natural deposits of soluble potassium compounds are decidedly limited. This gives rise to what has been called the *potash problem*, meaning the problem of how man will manage the earth's natural resources in order that there shall continue to be enough potassium compounds for growing all the required food.

Before World War I the world source of potassium was the Strassfurt, Germany, deposits. When these were cut off from the United States by war, the question of how to get potassium compounds to maintain a high rate of food production became a critical one. Exploration resulted in the discovery of the Searles Lake and Carlsbad deposits mentioned earlier in the chapter. From these sources potassium chloride is obtained. This is the form in which potassium is normally used as fertilizer, and potassium chloride also serves as the starting material for other potassium salts used in industry, agriculture,[1] or in the laboratory.

Although the world supplies of soluble potassium compounds are quite adequate for the present, there is no reason to assume that they will aways be so if our present wasteful practices continue. For this reason, we should give careful consideration to conserving potassium for essential uses. Particular consideration should be given to cutting down the losses of potassium which occur in soil erosion. The chemist can devise many substitute materials, but it is not to be expected that he can devise substitutes for potassium in plant and animal nutrition.

[1] Tobacco grown on land fertilized with potassium chloride yields an ash which has such a low melting point that it is unsuitable for making cigarettes. Tobacco fertilized with potassium sulfate yields an ash with a higher melting point. Consequently most tobacco fertilizer employs potassium sulfate. Potassium chloride is converted into the sulfate for this purpose by hydrochloric acid manufacture.

Plants use large amounts of potassium in growth. Therefore, potassium compounds must be added to the soil or it will lose its fertility. Potassium chloride is the compound most commonly used for potassium fertilizer. (Firestone Tire & Rubber Co.)

In this connection, one interesting practice has recently been started in New England. This section has long been known for its rocky fields and picturesque stone fences. Most of the rocks of New England contain large amounts of feldspars which are rich in potassium (see Chap. 41, page 523). By finely grinding the stones and spreading the rock flour on the soil, it appears that the potassium in these rocks becomes available to plants—slowly. Even so this slow supply is helpful in enriching the soil. It will be interesting to see whether this procedure proves a profitable source of potassium. If so, New England farmers will be able to dispose of some of their stones and at the same time enrich their soil as well as contribute to the conservation of soluble potassium resources.

Other potassium compounds

In most instances the properties of the corresponding sodium and potassium compounds are so similar that industrially they are interchangeable. In such cases sodium compounds are used because they are cheaper. However, there are a few uses, other than biological, in which sodium and potassium compounds are not interchangeable.

Potassium carbonate, when used to replace some of the sodium carbonate in glass, raises the melting point of the glass (see Chap. 41, page 518). *Black gunpowder*, made of potassium nitrate, sulfur, and charcoal, cannot be produced satisfactorily with sodium nitrate as a substitute for potassium nitrate. This is because the sodium salt absorbs moisture from the air too readily. *Potassium chlorate* is used in the laboratory for making oxygen and industrially for making matches and fireworks. The sodium salt is not satisfactory because, like sodium nitrate, it is too hygroscopic (absorbs water readily).

Compounds of lithium, rubidium, and cesium have few major uses.

Tests for sodium and potassium

All known sodium compounds are so soluble that *there is no satisfactory precipitation test for sodium ion*. Potassium ion forms a yellow precipitate when added to a solution of **sodium cobaltinitrite** [$Na_3Co(NO_2)_6$].

$$Na_3Co(NO_2)_6 + 3K^+ \rightarrow \underset{\text{potassium cobaltinitrite}}{K_3Co(NO_2)_6} \downarrow + 3Na^+$$

The test is a good one for potassium ion except that ammonium ion also gives a yellow precipitate with this reagent and hence must be absent from the solution being tested. This is best accomplished by evaporating the unknown to dryness and heating the residue to a dull red heat. Any ammonium salts present will evaporate (see Chap. 31, page 352), and the potassium salts, if any, will remain. Then the unknown can be dissolved in water and the reagent added.[1]

Potassium perchlorate ($KClO_4$) and potassium chloroplatinate (K_2PtCl_6) also precipitate when perchloric acid ($HClO_4$) or chloroplatinic acid (H_2PtCl_6) are added to solutions containing potassium ion.

The spectroscope

All the alkalis give characteristic colors when their compounds are heated in a bunsen flame. You can produce the flame colors best by dipping a platinum wire into a compound of the element and holding it in the flame. This is known as the **flame test.** The colors are:

Lithium	Red flame
Sodium	Yellow flame
Potassium	Violet flame
Rubidium[2]	Dark red flame
Cesium[2]	Blue flame

For sodium, the test is so sensitive that dust from the air contains enough sodium to give a yellow color to the flame. Touching a platinum wire to the hand will also pick up enough sodium to produce the color. The potassium flame color is much less intense, so that it normally cannot be observed if any sodium is present, as it usually is. If you view the flame through a blue cobalt glass, which does not transmit the yellow sodium color, the potassium flame can be observed even if the unknown contains sodium also (Fig. 44–1).

[1] Sodium cobaltinitrite solutions are unstable; hence the solutions should be prepared from the solid just before use.

[2] The names of these elements are based on the colors which they give: rubidium from the Latin *rubidus*, which means red, cesium from the Latin *caesium*, meaning blue-gray.

Fig. 44–1. The flame test for potassium. Because of the intense yellow color produced by sodium, it is necessary to observe the flame through a piece of cobalt (blue) glass. This procedure will show the violet flame produced by potassium.

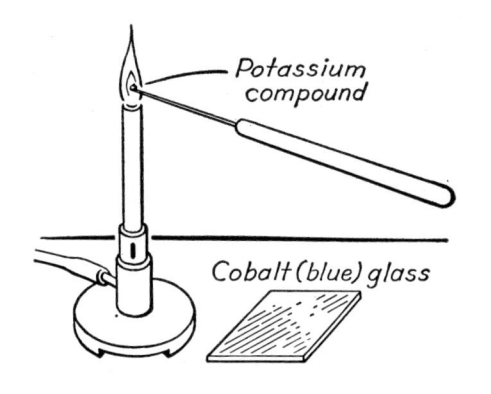

A more exact and reliable method for detecting the elements according to the color which they produce in a flame is by use of a spectroscope. This instrument consists essentially of a glass or quartz prism (Fig. 44–2) which breaks up the light passing through it into its component colors (that is, wave lengths). Thus in Fig. 44–2, if the source consists of light of three different wave lengths, the observer will see on the screen three images of the source, one for each of the colors present in the original source. This is known as a **spectrum.** In this way the colors due to different elements can be separated and the different elements recognized even though they all are present in the same sample. The spectrum of each element consists of certain colors (that is, wave lengths) characteristic of that element. These lines are as characteristic of an element as fingerprints are of a person, and no two elements give the same spectrum. The spectrum of the alkali and alkaline earth elements can be produced easily by heating the element or a compound in the bunsen flame. Most of the other elements must be heated in an electric arc to produce a spectrum. The spectrum of the gases can be produced from a gas discharge tube filled with the particular gas (like neon signs, Chap. 30, page 340). Since the colors of the lines of the spectrum determine their relative positions in the spectroscope eyepiece, it is possible to photograph the spectrum, rather than observe it directly. The lines on the resulting

Fig. 44–2. The principle on which the spectroscope works. Note that when passed through a prism, light is separated into its component colors.

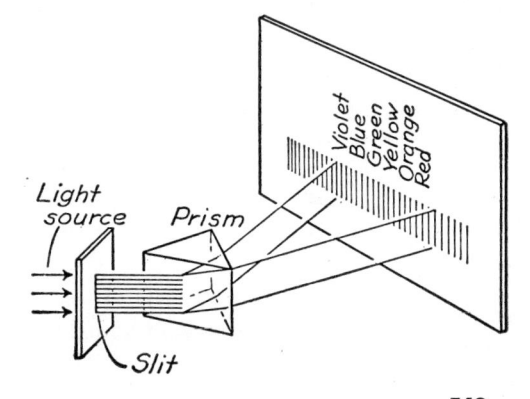

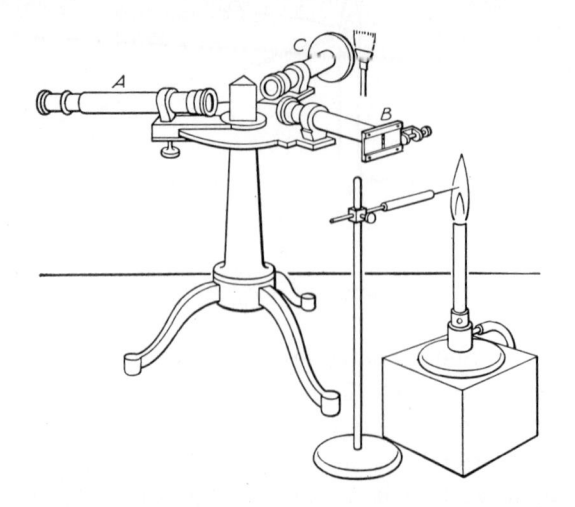

Fig. 44-3. A simple spectroscope. Light enters through B and is observed in eyepiece, A. Tube C contains a scale which can also be observed in A. The scale serves to locate the relative positions of different lines in the spectrum.

photograph can then be compared with similar spectrum photographs of known elements. In this way the elements present in an unknown can be identified. This procedure is known as *spectroscopic analysis*. Frequently it is a very rapid method of analysis and is widely employed in industry where many similar samples must be analyzed quickly, as in steel or aluminum metallurgy. Another advantage of spectroscopic analysis is that an analysis can be made with a very small sample. This is one reason why it is widely employed by law enforcement agencies such as the FBI and various state police crime laboratories.

KEY WORDS

alkali metal	Le Blanc	sodium
Carlsbad	lithium	sodium carbonate
cesium	mica	Solvay
sodium cobaltinitrite	Perey	spectroscope
flame test	potassium	spectrum
francium	rubidium	Strassfurt
ionization potential	Searles Lake	

HIGHLIGHTS

The alkali metals in the order of their increasing activity are **lithium, sodium, potassium, rubidium, cesium,** and **francium**. Lithium occurs mainly in a few complex silicates. Sodium occurs in salt (sodium chloride). Potassium occurs in feldspar, as the chloride in **Strassfurt,** Germany, and as brine in California. The other alkali metals are very rare.

The pure alkali metals are obtained by the electrolysis of their molten hydroxides or salts.

In the **Solvay** process for making sodium hydrogen carbonate and sodium carbonate, the starting material is salt and the by-product is calcium chloride. Potassium is essential for plant growth.

The test for potassium compounds is with **sodium cobaltinitrite.** The **flame tests** are also used in detecting the alkali metals. The **spectroscope** is an instrument for accurately observing the flame tests.

QUESTIONS

1. Explain in terms of their electron structures why the group Ia elements are the most active metals known.
2. Why are the group Ib metals less active than the alkalis?
3. Explain why the activity of the alkalis increases with increasing atomic number.
4. Explain how hardness and melting points of the alkalis change with atomic number.
5. In what types of minerals did the alkali metals originally occur in nature?
6. Which of the alkalis is most abundant in nature?
7. Explain why sea water contains so much more sodium than potassium.
8. Why must herbivorous animals have access to salt (sodium chloride)?
9. What are the principal commercial sources of potassium compounds?
10. What is meant by the potash problem? What relation does this problem have to the general subject of conservation?
11. How is sodium prepared commercially?
12. Describe the uses for metallic sodium.
13. Explain how salt is converted into sodium carbonate. What other raw materials are used and what is the by-product? Write the necessary equations.
14. Why is a cheap source of sodium carbonate essential?
15. Why is sodium nitrate unsuitable for replacing potassium nitrate in black gunpowder?
16. Describe a test for potassium ion.
17. Explain the use of the spectroscope in identifying the alkalis.
18. What is spectrography? Why is it important?

CHAPTER 45

the alkaline earth metals

The elements of Group IIa are known as the alkaline earth metals. This name is due to the fact that early chemists gave the name earth to any nonmetallic substance insoluble in water and unchanged by fire. Calcium oxide (quicklime) and magnesium oxide (magnesia), which give an alkaline reaction in water, thus became known as **alkaline earths.** When the periodic system was developed, the entire group became known by this name. The alkaline earth metals are **beryllium, magnesium, calcium, strontium, barium,** and **radium.** All of them are silvery-white metals.

Properties of the alkaline earth metals

The properties of the alkaline earth elements are shown in Table 45–1. Note that each is characterized by an electronic structure of an inert gas *plus* two valence electrons. Each element thus tends to lose two electrons and to form electrovalent compounds in which it always shows a valence of +2. The activity of the elements increases with the size of the atom, as would be expected (see Chap. 43, pages 540 and 541 and Chap. 44, pages 552 to 554). As a group, the alkaline earths are almost, but not quite, as active as the alkalis because, instead of having to lose one electron to attain a rare gas structure, each of these elements must lose two. However, barium is more active than the least active of the alkali metals. All the alkaline earth metals tarnish on contact with air because of oxidation. Calcium, strontium, and barium tarnish so rapidly that they should be stored in sealed containers.

Although harder than the alkalis, all except beryllium are soft enough to be easily cut or scratched with a penknife. Beryllium is hard

TABLE 45-1. Properties of the alkaline earth elements

Property	Beryllium	Magnesium	Calcium	Strontium	Barium	Radium
Symbol	Be	Mg	Ca	Sr	Ba	Ra
Atomic number	4	12	20	38	56	88
Electronic structure	2	2	2	2	2	2
	2	8	8	8	8	8
		2	8	18	18	18
			2	8	18	32
				2	8	18
					2	8
						2
Radius of free atom, angstroms	1.05	1.62	1.97	1.95	2.10	
Hardness	Decreases..→
Melting point, °C	1278	651	842	800	850	960
Tendency to lose electrons	Increases..→
Density, 20°C, g/cm^3	1.85	1.74	1.55	2.6	3.5	

enough to scratch glass. Note that the order of hardness is related to the diameters of the atoms just as in the case of the alkalis (see Chap. 44, page 552).

Beryllium and magnesium have properties which make them useful, in alloy form, as structural metals. Calcium, strontium, and barium are useful principally in compounds. Radium is, of course, very rare and of interest only because of its radioactivity.

Properties of compounds of the alkaline earth metals

Certain generalizations can be made about the properties of compounds of the alkaline earths which will be helpful in becoming familiar with them.

1. All the hydroxides are insoluble. Beryllium hydroxide is the least soluble, and the solubilities of the others increase in regular order, the most soluble being barium hydroxide.

2. All the carbonates are insoluble and easily precipitated from solution.

3. The sulfates of calcium, strontium, and barium are insoluble, the solubility decreasing in the order named. Beryllium and magnesium sulfates are quite soluble.

4. Beryllium hydroxide is a weak base; all the other hydroxides are strong bases.

5. All are above hydrogen in activity. The more active ones, barium, calcium, and strontium react with cold water to form the hydroxide

A crystal of beryl. This crystal, as you can see, is shaped like a hexagonal column. When crystals of beryl are transparent and emerald-green, they are the gem stone emerald. *When they occur as a transparent bluish-green stone, they are called* aquamarine. *(American Museum of Natural History)*

and hydrogen. Beryllium and magnesium react with steam to form the oxide and hydrogen.

$$Mg + H_2O \xrightarrow{heat} MgO + H_2 \uparrow$$

$$Ca + 2H_2O \xrightarrow{cold} Ca(OH)_2 + H_2 \uparrow$$

6. Heat converts all carbonates into the oxide and carbon dioxide.

$$MCO_3 \xrightarrow{heat} MO + CO_2$$

where M is any alkaline earth metal.

Occurrence of the alkaline earth metals

Of the alkaline earth group, calcium and magnesium are by far the most plentiful in the earth's crust. Table 45–2 gives the estimated percentages of the alkaline earth metals in the earth's crust.

TABLE 45–2. Occurrence of the alkaline earth elements in nature

Element	Estimated percentage of the earth's crust
Beryllium	0.00001
Magnesium	2.09
Calcium	3.63
Strontium	0.00019
Barium	0.05
Radium	0.000000000001

Beryllium occurs in nature only as a silicate. The most common beryllium mineral is **beryl**, $Be_3Al_2(SiO_3)_6$. It is a hard, green, yellow, or white mineral. Crystals of beryl are hexagonal columns. The transparent emerald-green crystals of beryl are the gem stone *emerald;* the bluish-green transparent variety is the semiprecious stone *aqua-*

A piece of asbestos. Asbestos is one of the naturally occurring complex magnesium-containing silicates. Others are talc and soapstone. These minerals are not used for the production of magnesium because magnesium is more easily obtained from magnesite, which is plentiful. (Johns-Manville Corp.)

marine. Most beryl crystals are opaque and valueless as gem stones. Single crystals of beryl 18 ft long and 4 ft in diameter have been found. However, generally, only a relatively small amount of beryl is found at one place. This fact increases the cost of producing beryllium.

Magnesium is found in nature as magnesite ($MgCO_3$) and dolomite [$CaMg(CO_3)_2$]. The former is used for producing the metal. Dolomite is a very common mineral, some mountain ranges being composed mainly of it. Talc and soapstone (the latter used for laboratory table tops), and also asbestos, are complex magnesium-containing silicates.

Magnesium ion is present in sea water. Although magnesium ion constitutes only 3.5 percent of the *dissolved solids* in sea water, the total amount of magnesium per cubic mile of sea water is 9 billion

In a cubic mile of sea water there are 9 billion pounds of magnesium. This provides an inexhaustible supply of the metal, and plants have already been set up to produce magnesium from this source. (Dow Chemical Co.)

pounds. The metal is now being produced from the sea water. In past geologic ages the evaporation of land-locked arms of the sea has occurred. The magnesium salts, which are very soluble, crystallized—if at all—later than the sodium chloride, and formed a layer on top of the rock salt. Commonly the magnesium salts crystallized out along with potassium chloride as the double salt *carnallite* ($KCl \cdot MgCl_2 \cdot 6H_2O$). This salt is found in the Strassfurt, Germany, deposits. Certain brine wells, such as those at Midland, Mich., contain as much as 10 percent magnesium salts.

Calcium is found in nature as calcium carbonate. The most common variety is limestone. Limestone and dolomite make up entire mountain ranges. The transparent variety of calcium carbonate is known as *calcite* or *Iceland spar*. These crystals are useful in studying polarized light. Pearl, coral, chalk, and oyster and egg shells are nearly pure calcium carbonate of organic origin. Gypsum, $CaSO_4 \cdot 2H_2O$, is also a common mineral. It is the "sand" of certain deserts in the western part of the United States. *Alabaster* is a variety of gypsum valued for its beautiful color banding and ease of carving. The occurrence of *fluorite* (CaF_2) and *apatite* [$3Ca_3(PO_4)_2 \cdot CaF_2$] has been mentioned.

Strontium and barium occur in nature as carbonates and sulfates. Radium is always found in uranium minerals as it is one of the intermediate products formed in the disintegration of uranium.

Preparation of the alkaline earth metals

Calcium, barium, and strontium can be prepared by the electrolysis of the molten chlorides or fluorides.

$$BaCl_2 \xrightarrow{\text{electrolysis}} Ba + Cl_2 \uparrow$$
$$\text{(molten)}$$

The metals of the alkaline earth group of greatest industrial importance are magnesium and beryllium.

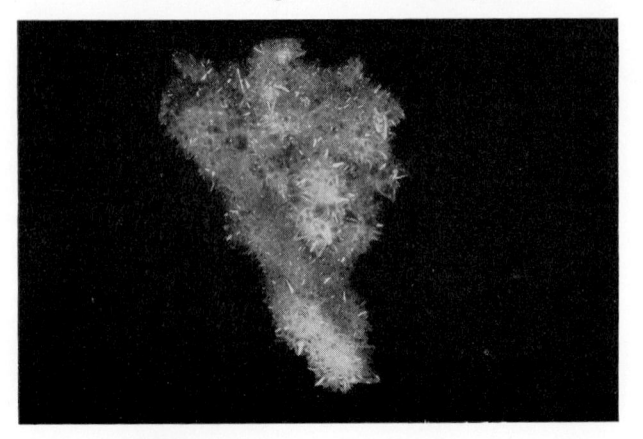

Crystals of calcite, or Iceland spar. This is a particularly beautiful form of calcium carbonate. The crystals are transparent and well shaped and are used to study polarized light. (American Museum of Natural History)

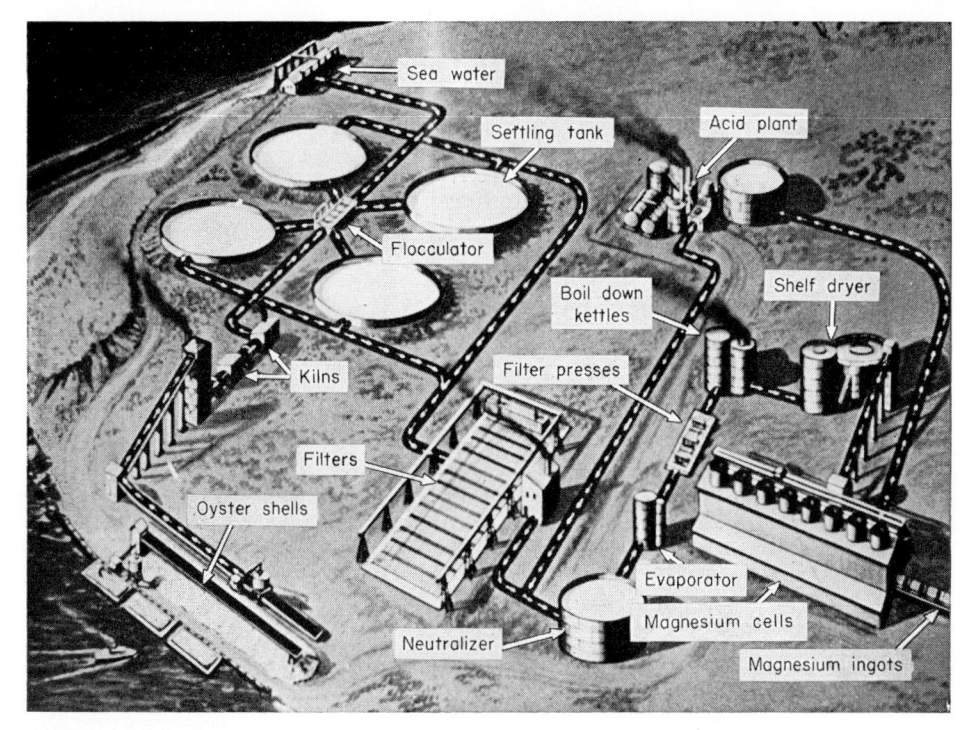

The layout of a plant for the production of magnesium from sea water. (Dow Chemical Co.)

Beryllium metal is prepared from beryl. Its manufacture is expensive for two reasons: (1) Beryl crystals are widely scattered over the surface of the earth with no large deposits in one place and (2) decomposition of the silicate is difficult.

The metal is produced by converting the beryllium in the beryl to beryllium fluoride (BeF_2) which is then electrolyzed in a solvent of molten sodium fluoride (NaF) and barium fluoride (BaF_2). The least active of the three metals present in the melt is beryllium; hence it is the one liberated.

$$BeF_2 \xrightarrow{\text{electrolysis}} Be + F_2 \uparrow$$
(dissolved in molten NaF and BaF_2)

Beryllium metal is quite expensive, but nevertheless it has certain important industrial uses. Most of the beryl used in producing it is shipped in from India and South America.

Magnesium is produced by the electrolysis of molten magnesium chloride.

$$MgCl_2 \xrightarrow{\text{electrolysis}} Mg + Cl_2 \uparrow$$
(molten)

Some magnesium chloride is produced from brine wells. Some of it is obtained from sea water by the following process: Sea water, pumped

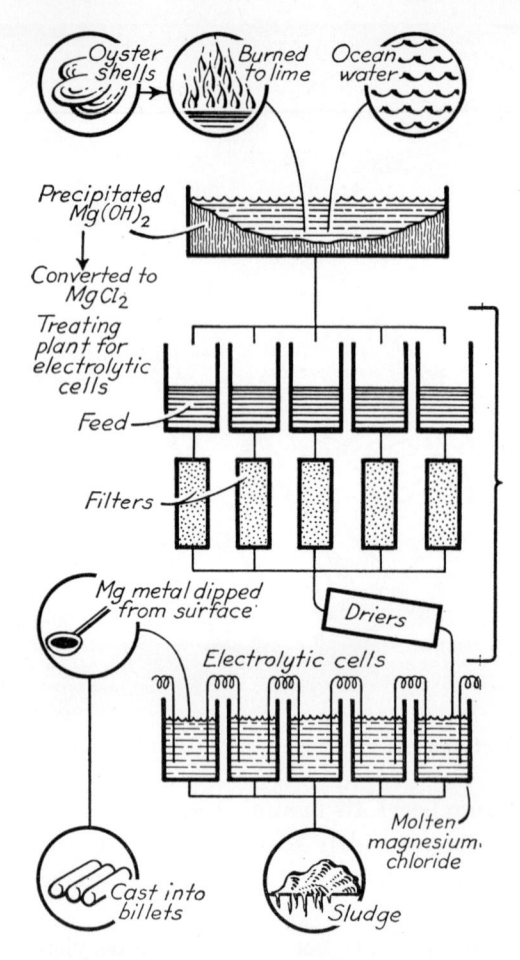

Fig. 45–1. An outline of the process by which magnesium is produced from sea water. Oyster shells are burned to produce lime. The lime is added to sea water and magnesium hydroxide [Mg(OH)$_2$] precipitates from this mixture. The magnesium hydroxide is separated from the other materials. Then it is converted to magnesium chloride (MgCl$_2$) by reacting with hydrochloric acid. The magnesium chloride is treated in electrolytic cells to liberate the free metal magnesium. (Dow Chemical Co.)

into shallow basins, is treated with calcium hydroxide to precipitate the less soluble magnesium hydroxide. The resulting precipitate is removed by filtration and converted into magnesium chloride by reaction with hydrochloric acid.

$$Mg^{++} + Ca(OH)_2 \rightarrow Mg(OH)_2 \downarrow + Ca^{++}$$
(sea water)

$$Mg(OH)_2 + 2HCl \rightarrow MgCl_2 + 2H_2O$$

The resulting magnesium chloride is electrolyzed to produce metallic magnesium. This process, although perhaps somewhat more expensive at present than making magnesium from certain other sources, is nevertheless a very significant one. It is a case of "mining the sea." In mining the sea, man has a natural resource which can never be exhausted. This is not the case with most of our important ore deposits of metals, some of which are already being exhausted. But from the sea man can, if necessary, produce magnesium metal for as many generations as he has need for it. The first plant operating on this process was built near Galveston, Tex., during World War II.

Another source of metallic magnesium is magnesite ($MgCO_3$). This is converted to the oxide, and the oxide is reduced with silicon:

$$\underset{\text{(magnesite)}}{MgCO_3} \xrightarrow{\text{heat}} MgO + CO_2 \uparrow$$

$$2MgO + Si \xrightarrow{\text{heat}} 2Mg + SiO_2$$

Magnesium oxide can also be converted to magnesium chloride by simultaneous treatment with carbon and chlorine:

$$MgO + C + Cl_2 \rightarrow MgCl_2 + CO \uparrow$$

The magnesium chloride is then electrolyzed to produce magnesium.

Uses of the alkaline earth metals

Beryllium, with a density of 1.85, is the lightest hard metal known. Although expensive (about $15 per pound in ingot form), the production of beryllium has greatly increased since it was started about twenty-five years ago. Most of the beryllium is used to form a copper-beryllium alloy containing about 2 percent beryllium, which is equivalent in physical properties to the hardest and toughest steels. These alloys do not spark when struck with a hard object and are, therefore, used to make mechanics' tools where explosive vapors are present (as in a petroleum refinery). Beryllium is also used to alloy with nickel and aluminum. Pure beryllium is quite transparent to x rays and is used for windows in x-ray tubes.

Magnesium is very important in forming light, strong alloys for airplanes, railway cars, busses, trucks, and innumerable other objects where lightness with strength is important. Although there are several hundred magnesium alloys known, the most important ones are those known as *Dow metals*.

TABLE 45–3. Composition of one Dow metal

Element	Percentage
Magnesium	88.9
Aluminum	9
Zinc	2
Manganese	0.1

When properly heat-treated, Dow metals have a tensile strength approaching iron and a density less than one-fourth as great. *Magnalium*, an alloy of aluminum and magnesium, contains up to about 30 percent of magnesium.

A boat made of aluminum is light enough for one man to carry. (Dow Chemical Co.)

It is reasonable to expect that the use of the light, strong alloys will greatly increase during the coming years and that magnesium alloys will become one of the most common structural metals.

Magnesium burns vigorously in air with the liberation of an intensely bright light. It was formerly used in photoflash bulbs and signal flares, but for this purpose it has been largely replaced by aluminum. Because of the ability of magnesium to combine not only with oxygen but also with nitrogen, it is used to de-gas electronic tubes (see Chap. 31, pages 345 and 346). During World War II the metal was widely used in incendiary bombs. In this connection, burning magnesium is very difficult to extinguish because the hot metal reacts with water to liberate hydrogen.

$$Mg + H_2O \rightarrow MgO + H_2 \uparrow$$

Magnesium will burn even in an atmosphere of carbon dioxide, liberating carbon.

$$2Mg + CO_2 \rightarrow 2MgO + C$$

Consequently no altogether satisfactory method for extinguishing magnesium incendiaries was ever developed. The best method was to cover the burning incendiary with sand.

Calcium has certain minor uses as an ingredient of bearing alloys.

Barium, on account of the ease with which it emits electrons, is used as an ingredient of an alloy for making filaments for electronic tubes.

Compounds of beryllium

Beryllium compounds are used in making some of the fluorescent powders employed in fluorescent light tubes. Beryllium compounds have a slightly sweetish taste and are highly toxic even when absorbed into the system through an open wound. Therefore, you should be aware of the danger of cutting yourself when disposing of old fluorescent lighting tubes. Where possible, these tubes should be disposed of without breaking them. Otherwise, you should wear gloves to avoid the possibility of a cut and thereby absorption of beryllium into the system. Such tubes also contain metallic mercury and the vapor of this substance is also toxic.

Compounds of magnesium

The oxides of all the elements of the alkaline earth group are notably high-melting. *Magnesium oxide* (magnesia) is used as a refractory lining for high temperature metallurgical furnaces. It is also used as an insulator for furnaces, hot water tanks, steam pipes, and other heating equipment. Unlike calcium oxide, the oxide of magnesium only very slowly combines with water.

Magnesium hydroxide, formed by adding sodium hydroxide to magnesium chloride solution and washing the resulting precipitate, is the familiar *milk of magnesia*.

$$Mg^{++} + 2Cl^- + 2Na^+ + 2OH^- \rightarrow Mg(OH)_2 \downarrow + 2Na^+ + 2Cl^-$$

This compound is a laxative, as are some other magnesium compounds, particularly epsom salts ($MgSO_4 \cdot 7H_2O$) and magnesium citrate (the magnesium salt of citric acid).

Magnesium hydroxide is also used in some tooth pastes and tooth powders. Its alkaline properties tend to neutralize mouth acids—one of the principal causes of tooth decay. It also has a mildly abrasive action, thereby polishing the teeth. Although a base, magnesium hydroxide is so insoluble that its saturated solutions are only mildly alkaline.

Calcium carbonate

The forms in which calcium carbonate occurs in nature have been mentioned above. **Limestone** is one of the most important natural resources and serves man in a surprisingly large number of ways. Its use in making glass and soda ash has already been mentioned. Since the earliest days, limestone has been used as a building stone. It is strong and durable but soft enough (its hardness is number 3 on the Mohs' scale) to be easily quarried and worked. Closely related is *marble*, also chemically calcium carbonate, formed from limestone by the action of heat and pressure below the earth's surface. Its value as a building stone and as a medium for carving statues is well known.

Thousands of tons of limestone, ground to a fine flour, are used yearly on the farms of America to correct soil acidity. As mentioned earlier, this limestone also serves the function of supplying to the soil the calcium so important in plant and animal nutrition (see Chap. 40, pages 497 and 498). The ability of calcium carbonate to correct soil acidity is due to the fact that it is a salt of a strong base and a weak acid and hence is hydrolyzed in solution.

$$CaCO_3 + 2H_2O \rightleftarrows Ca^{++} + 2OH^- + H_2CO_3$$

Most agricultural limestone is made from dolomite, which also supplies magnesium. The soil neutralizing ability of dolomite is about the same as that of calcium carbonate, but it has the additional advantage of supplying magnesium ion to the soil. Some soils, particularly those planted to apple trees, develop magnesium deficiency unless the element is supplied to the soil at regular intervals.

1. Lime. When heated to about 950°C, calcium carbonate decomposes into calcium oxide and carbon dioxide.

$$CaCO_3 \xrightleftharpoons{950°C} CaO + CO_2 \uparrow$$

This operation, known as the *burning of lime*, has been carried out since the days of the Roman Empire. A limekiln was built in America within fifty years of the landing of the Pilgrims. Early limekilns used wood to supply the heat. Modern ones use coal, gas, or oil (Fig. 45–2).

The product of the limekiln, calcium oxide (CaO), is known as **quicklime.** It reacts vigorously with water, forming calcium hydroxide or **slaked lime,** or *hydrated lime.*

$$\underset{\substack{\text{calcium oxide} \\ \text{(quicklime)}}}{CaO} + H_2O \rightarrow \underset{\substack{\text{calcium hydroxide} \\ \text{(slaked lime)}}}{Ca(OH)_2}$$

The energy liberated by the slaking of lime is so great that it has been known to start fires. Consequently calcium oxide should never be stored where water might get in contact with it. If allowed to stand in air, calcium oxide slowly reacts with moisture (see foregoing equation given) and carbon dioxide, forming a mixture of calcium hydroxide and calcium carbonate known as *air-slaked* lime.

$$CaO + CO_2 \xrightarrow{\text{room temperature}} CaCO_3$$

This latter reaction is simply the reverse of the reaction occurring in the limekiln.

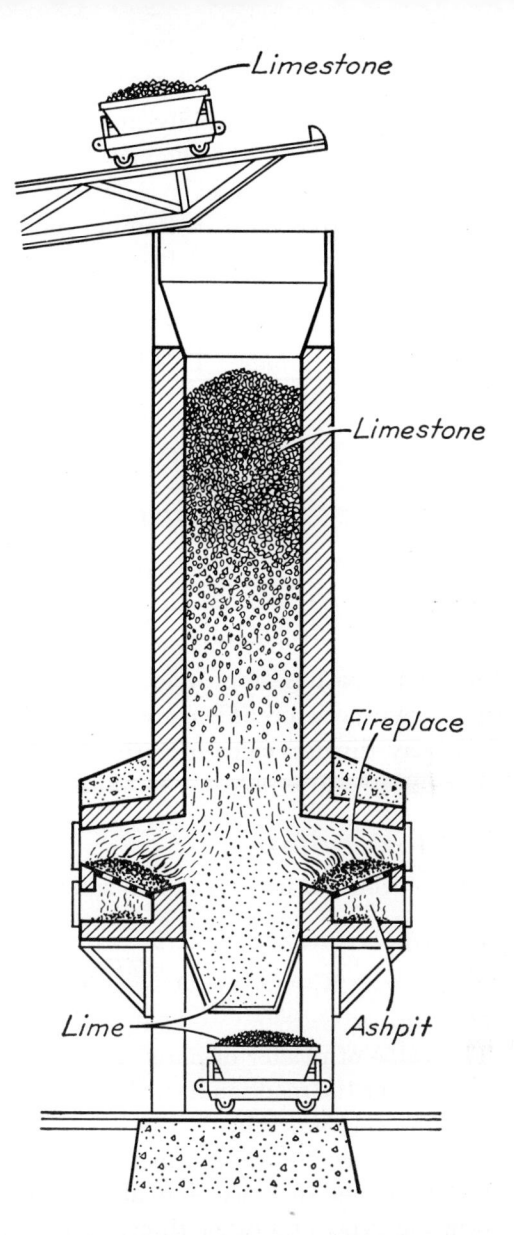

Fig. 45–2. A vertical section of a limekiln. The kiln works very simply. Lime (calcium oxide) is produced from limestone by heating the limestone in a type of oven called a *limekiln*. A limestone charge is added at the top. Heat is produced in the fireplaces in the sides of the kiln. At a temperature of 950°C the limestone (calcium carbonate) breaks down and loses carbon dioxide. As the limestone is converted to lime, it drops to the bottom of the kiln. The lime is removed from the bottom of the kiln in carts as shown.

2. Mortar. In the early days the principal object of burning lime was to obtain slaked lime for making **mortar.** If a mixture of slaked lime and sand is moistened with water to make a thick paste, it becomes almost jellylike. When allowed to stand, it slowly hardens, eventually becoming as hard as stone. From the days of the Romans until fairly recent times, mortar used for laying bricks, stone, and other building materials and also for plastering was made in this way. The reason for the hardening of mortar is still unknown. Almost all modern building mortars contain portland cement (see Chap. 47, page 618) as well as lime and sand. The portland cement causes the mortar to harden more rapidly and to be stronger than the older type.

Hydrated lime is the chemist's cheapest source of hydroxyl ion and is used as a base wherever the presence of the calcium ion is not objectionable. It is used in tanning hides, in refining sugar, in making sulfite paper and pulp, in bleaching powders, and for softening water.

Portland cement is made by heating limestone and clay (see Chap. 47, pages 618 and 619).

3. *Calcium carbide.* This is formed by heating limestone and coke in an electric furnace.

$$CaCO_3 \xrightarrow{\text{heat}} CaO + CO_2 \uparrow$$

$$CaO + 3C \xrightarrow{\text{heat}} \underset{\text{calcium carbide}}{CaC_2} + CO \uparrow$$

Calcium carbide forms acetylene on treatment with water (see Chap. 36, page 417). From this acetylene, many organic compounds can be made; hence limestone and coke become the starting materials for many synthetic organic compounds.

Finely divided calcium carbonate formed by precipitation is used as a cheap white pigment in paints and shoe cleaners.

Calcium sulfate

The principal use of calcium sulfate is in making **plaster of paris,** which is made by heating gypsum to 125°C.

$$\underset{\text{gypsum}}{2CaSO_4 \cdot 2H_2O} \xrightarrow{125°C} \underset{\text{plaster of paris}}{(CaSO_4)_2 \cdot H_2O} + 3H_2O \uparrow$$

The value of plaster of paris[1] is due to the fact that when it is mixed with water the reaction described in the foregoing equation is reversed and the mixture sets to a firm mass composed of gypsum crystals. Almost everyone knows about the use of this material for holding broken bones in place and also for making casts of coins, statues, printing type, and other things. For these latter uses, plaster of paris is particularly good, since on setting, it expands, thereby tending to fill every tiny crevice in the mold. What is not so commonly known is that large amounts of plaster of paris are made into wall board and lath for the inside of homes, stores, and offices. Gypsum has been called the most important building material except wood. Putting up gypsum board, available at almost all building supply companies, is much less expensive than the older method of plastering inside walls. These building boards are made by preparing plaster of paris from

[1] The name plaster of paris comes from the fact that the Montmartre gypsum quarries, near Paris, France, were one of the early gypsum sources.

The Luray Caverns in Virginia are an example of limestone solution caverns which are to be found elsewhere in this country and in other parts of the world. The caverns are formed by ground water dissolving limestone rock. The stalactites that you see hanging from the roof of the caverns and the stalagmites that grow up from the floor are formed by precipitation of calcium carbonate. (Luray Caverns)

gypsum, adding water, and sandwiching the plastic mass between two layers of heavy paper, where it hardens. Easily and cheaply installed, gypsum board can be painted or papered as desired. More than $100 million worth of gypsum board was used by the building industry in the United States in 1950.

Limestone solution caverns

If carbon dioxide is passed into a dilute solution of calcium hydroxide, calcium carbonate precipitates.

$$Ca(OH)_2 + H_2CO_3 \rightarrow CaCO_3 \downarrow + 2H_2O$$

If the addition of carbon dioxide is continued, the precipitate will dissolve. This is because the excess carbonic acid converts the calcium carbonate into calcium hydrogen carbonate, which is soluble.

$$\underset{\text{(insoluble)}}{CaCO_3} + H_2CO_3 \rightleftarrows \underset{\text{(soluble)}}{Ca(HCO_3)_2}$$

This reaction is reversible and the calcium exists in the soluble, bicarbonate form only so long as an excess of carbonic acid is present. Therefore, *anything which has the effect of removing some of this excess carbonic acid will cause reversal of the reaction and precipitation of calcium carbonate.* The reactions of solution and precipitation of calcium carbonate are among the most important occurring on the earth in the mineral realm. They account for the formation of vast *natural deposits of limestone* and also for the numerous *limestone solution caverns*, famous examples of which are Endless Caverns in Virginia, Howe Caverns in New York, and Mammoth Cave in Kentucky.

Solution caverns are formed by surface waters, which always contain carbon dioxide taken from the atmosphere. These surface waters seep downward through cracks in a limestone deposit and dissolve small amounts of the limestone or dolomite by reaction with it. The slow process, continued over long ages, eventually converts the crack into a huge cavern.

This water, carrying calcium hydrogen carbonate in solution, if tapped by a well is *hard*. Hard water is discussed on pages 581 to 584. If this calcium hydrogen carbonate bearing water flows into a region where the average temperature is higher, it will lose some of its carbon dioxide (see Chap. 14, page 156). This causes precipitation of calcium carbonate. Occasionally you find limestone being laid down in this way in the bottom of small surface streams or lakes. Agitation will remove dissolved gases. Therefore, if the calcium hydrogen carbonate bearing water passes over a waterfall, it may thereby lose carbon dioxide and form a deposit of limestone at the base of the waterfall. The greatest part of this calcium hydrogen carbonate bearing water eventually finds its way into the sea. There it loses some of its carbon dioxide. This occurs either because the average temperature of the sea water is higher or because the carbon dioxide is removed by organisms in the sea which need carbon dioxide to live. When the carbon dioxide is removed, calcium carbonate is precipitated. This precipitate settles to the bottom of the sea, where it gradually becomes compacted into limestone (or dolomite). This is the way in which almost all large deposits of limestone and dolomite were formed. Commonly you find fossil remains of sea organisms in the limestone. Clay, sand, and organic matter are carried to the sea mechanically in suspension by surface waters. For this reason these materials may also be found in limestone. This accounts for the fact that most natural limestone is not chemically pure calcium carbonate. The limestone and dolomite mountains that exist today were formed by geologic disturbances below the earth's surface which raised these ancient ocean bottoms to their present position high above sea level.

The **stalactites,** which hang from the ceiling, and the **stalagmites,** which grow from the floor, of a limestone cavern, are also formed by this same reaction. That is, after the cavern is formed, calcium hydrogen carbonate bearing water percolates through the overlying limestone and reaches the ceiling of the cavern. If carbon dioxide escapes before the solution drips to the floor, a stalactite is formed. If the solution drips to the floor before the calcium carbonate precipitates, a stalagmite is formed.

Scale formation in a boiler tube is caused by hard water. This scale formation decreases the efficiency of the boiler. Since the scale is a poor heat conductor, it may cause overheating if it occurs in the section of the boiler that comes in contact with the flame. (Permutit Co.)

Hard water

Hard water is water which contains in solution any or all of the following ions: calcium ion, magnesium ion, ferrous ion. Since all these ions produce about the same effect and all can be corrected by the same means, the discussion below will deal with calcium ion. You should bear in mind that the discussion applies equally to magnesium ion and ferrous ion.

Hard water is objectionable for many uses,[1] particularly for laundering, bathing, or making steam. Whenever soap is added to hard water, the calcium salt of the fatty acid precipitates as a curd or scum on top of the water.

$$2C_{17}H_{35}COONa + Ca^{++} \rightarrow (C_{17}H_{35}COO)_2Ca \downarrow + 2Na^+$$

sodium stearate 　　　　　　calcium stearate
(a soap)

No cleaning action of the soap is obtained until after enough soap has been added to precipitate all the calcium ion in the water. Not only does this waste soap, but the resulting calcium soap precipitate is a nuisance because it forms a ring in the bathtub. In laundering, this calcium soap precipitates in the fibers of the clothes, causing them to be dingy. Since the iron soaps are colored, they are particularly objectionable in this connection.

In making steam for industrial purposes, or for home heating, hard water causes the formation of scale on the inside of the boiler, just as it does in a teakettle. This scale is a poor heat conductor which decreases the efficiency of the boiler. The scale causes that part of the boiler in contact with the flame to get too hot. Eventually the boiler burns out and has to be replaced.

[1] However, its mineral content may make it beneficial for human and animal nutrition.

The method of correcting hard water depends somewhat on the compound of calcium which is present.

1. Temporarily hard water contains calcium hydrogen carbonate which it acquired in the way explained earlier. The name *temporary* is derived from the fact that heating the water causes the calcium to precipitate as calcium carbonate.

$$Ca(HCO_3)_2 \underset{}{\overset{heat}{\rightleftharpoons}} H_2CO_3 \uparrow * + CaCO_3 \downarrow$$

* Of course, carbonic acid is unstable and breaks down into carbon dioxide, which escapes as a gas, and water. See Chap. 35, page 402.

This condition is also called *bicarbonate hardness*.

2. Permanent or *sulfate hardness* is due to the presence of the metals as sulfates. Permanent hardness is caused by water passing through a deposit of gypsum which, although not very soluble, is sufficiently so to cause real water hardness.

Correction of hard water

As stated above, bicarbonate hardness can be corrected by boiling. This is generally impractical. Lime is commonly used in this case as a **water softener,** that is, a material which will correct water hardness. Boiler feed water is treated with lime and the precipitate allowed to settle before feeding it into the boiler.

$$\underset{(\text{"acid"})}{Ca(HCO_3)_2} + \underset{(\text{base})}{Ca(OH)_2} \rightarrow \underset{(\text{salt})}{2CaCO_3} \downarrow + 2H_2O$$

Of course the amount of lime added must be just the amount required to react with the bicarbonate present, as excess lime would be objectionable. Hence water treatment should be based on chemical analysis of the water. Lime is of no value in correcting sulfate hardness.

Sodium carbonate will correct both types of hardness.

$$\underset{\substack{(\text{sulfate}\\\text{hardness})}}{CaSO_4} + 2Na^+ + CO_3^= \rightarrow CaCO_3 \downarrow + 2Na^+ + SO_4^=$$

$$\underset{\substack{(\text{temporary}\\\text{hardness})}}{Ca(HCO_3)_2} + Na_2CO_3 \rightarrow CaCO_3 \downarrow + 2NaHCO_3$$

Sodium carbonate has for years been incorporated in laundry soaps and scouring powders to correct water hardness—hence the name *washing soda* for $Na_2CO_3 \cdot 10H_2O$.

Because lime is cheaper than sodium carbonate, it is generally used to correct bicarbonate hardness. A combination of lime and soda ash is used to soften billions of gallons of water annually.

Trisodium phosphate (Na_3PO_4) also softens water because it forms a very insoluble precipitate with calcium ion.

$$3CaSO_4 + 2Na_3PO_4 \rightarrow Ca_3(PO_4)_2 \downarrow + 3Na_2SO_4$$

Certain complex phosphates, particularly $Na_6P_6O_{18}$ (known as *calgon*) and sodium tripolyphosphate ($Na_5P_3O_{10}$), are good, but expensive, water-softening agents.

Ion exchangers

A modern method for softening water, which is gaining in popularity, depends upon a discovery made nearly fifty years ago. This uses certain naturally occurring minerals known as **zeolites,** which are complex sodium aluminum silicates. When these minerals come in contact with hard water, the sodium in the mineral changes places with the calcium ion in solution.

$$\underset{\substack{\text{(zeolite}\\\text{mineral)}}}{2NaZ} + \underset{\substack{\text{(hard}\\\text{water)}}}{Ca^{++}} \rightarrow \underset{\text{(solid)}}{CaZ_2} + 2Na^+$$

Where NaZ = sodium aluminum silicate

Thus by passing hard water through a cylinder packed with zeolite, all the ions responsible for water hardness are retained by the zeolite and replaced in solution by sodium ion. When the zeolite has been exhausted by having given up all its sodium ions, it can be **regenerated** by soaking in concentrated salt solution. That is, the preceding reaction is reversible.

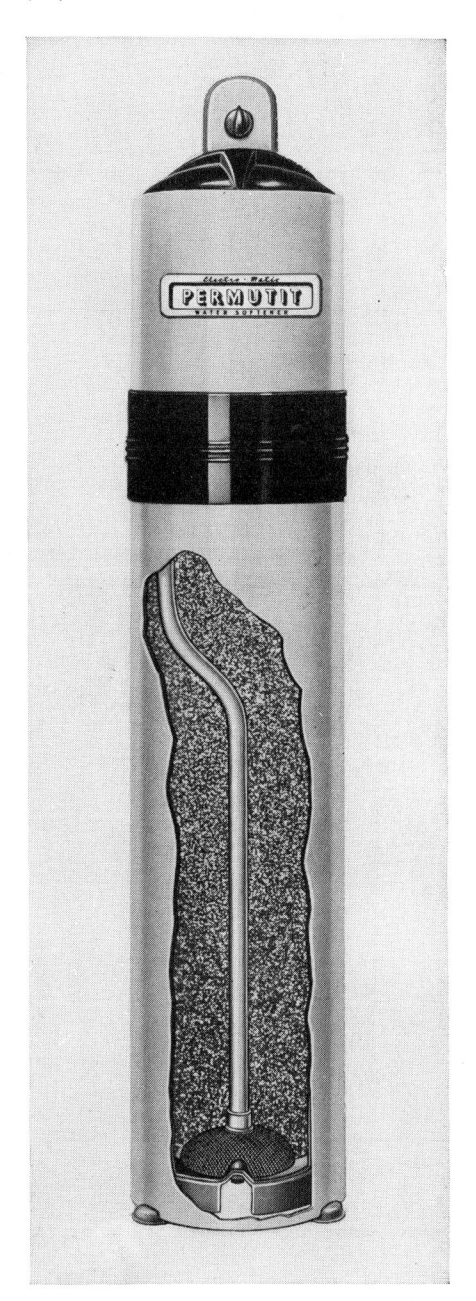

$$\underset{\substack{\text{(exhausted}\\\text{zeolite)}}}{CaZ_2} + \underset{\substack{\text{(concentrated}\\\text{brine)}}}{2Na^+ + 2Cl^-} \rightarrow$$
$$\underset{\substack{\text{(regenerated}\\\text{zeolite)}}}{2NaZ} + Ca^{++} + 2Cl^-$$

A zeolite-type water softener. (Permutit Co.)

The resulting calcium chloride can be flushed down the drain and the regenerated zeolite used over again. The demand for this type of water-softening mineral is greater than the natural supply of zeolite. Chemists have found how to make synthetic minerals which give the same result.

Water-softening installations based on this principle are found in thousands of homes and factories in the United States. The installation consists of a tank packed with zeolite through which incoming water must flow before reaching the tap or boiler. Such installations can be arranged so that regeneration is completely automatic. Hence properly installed, they require practically no attention other than periodically supplying the equipment with a bag of salt. Small portable installations for attaching directly to the faucet are available.

If home owners, in regions where water is hard, would all provide means of softening laundry and bath water, many millions of dollars' worth of soap would be saved annually. However, the waste of soap caused by hard water is not as great as it used to be. Synthetic detergents, that is, the so-called *soapless soaps* (see Chap. 37, pages 449 and 450), do not precipitate in hard water and clean just as well in hard water as in soft. The increasing popularity of these products is partly due to these facts.

Deionized water

It has been found that certain synthetic resins will exchange hydronium ion for any metal ion present in a solution.

$$\text{HResin (solid)} + \text{Na}^+ \text{(in solution)} + \text{H}_2\text{O} \rightarrow \text{NaResin (solid)} + \text{OH}_3^+$$

Analogous resins which will exchange hydroxyl ion for negative ions are also known.

$$\text{OHResin (solid)} + \text{Cl}^- \text{(in solution)} \rightarrow \text{ClResin (solid)} + \text{OH}^-$$

Thus by passing raw water over both of the above types of resins, positive and negative ions can both be replaced by hydronium ion and hydroxyl ion. These combine

$$\text{OH}_3^+ + \text{OH}^- \rightarrow 2\text{H}_2\text{O}$$

Hence such treatment will *deionize* the water. Installations based on this are now widely used in factories to purify water in place of the more expensive distillation process. The resins can be regenerated and used over again. Except that such systems do not remove dissolved gases, they are fully equivalent to distillation for water purification. Even sea water can be made drinkable by this method. Lifeboats and rafts are commonly equipped with small deionizing units for this purpose. During the water shortage crisis which confronted New York City in 1949 to 1950, it was suggested that this method might eventually have to be used to purify raw Hudson River water, which is quite salty near New York City, to furnish a water supply for the city. However, it does not appear that such a method is feasible for purifying large quantities of water because of the expense involved in regenerating the spent resin.

These resins do not remove bacteria. If resin deionizing units are used to prepare drinking water, other precautions, such as chlorination, should be taken to free the water of harmful bacteria.

Flame tests for the alkaline earths

Beryllium and magnesium compounds do not give characteristic colors in the bunsen flame. Calcium gives a brick red, strontium a crimson, and barium a fleeting green color to the flame. These three elements are easily identified by direct observation flame test or by the spectroscope. Calcium, barium, and strontium also give insoluble sulfate precipitates when solutions containing their ions are treated with dilute sulfuric acid.

$$M^{++} + H_2SO_4 + 2H_2O \rightarrow MSO_4 \downarrow + 2OH_3^+$$

Where $M^{++} = Ca^{++}$ or Sr^{++} or Ba^{++}

Magnesium ion and beryllium ion do not form insoluble precipitates with sulfate ion.

Magnesium ion is recognized by the fact that it forms, when it reacts with sodium hydroxide, a white precipitate of magnesium hydroxide.

$$Mg^{++} + 2OH^- \rightarrow Mg(OH)_2$$
$$\text{(white)}$$

The precipitate *does not dissolve* on the addition of excess sodium hydroxide. It *does dissolve* on the addition of ammonium chloride, however.

$$Mg(OH)_2 \downarrow + 2NH_4^+ + 2Cl^- \rightarrow \underbrace{Mg^{++} + 2Cl^-}_{\text{(soluble)}} + 2NH_3 + 2H_2O$$
(precipitate)

These properties serve to identify magnesium ion.

The definite identification of beryllium, which is rather difficult, is beyond the scope of this book. Its reactions are quite similar to those of aluminum, with which it is easily confused in analysis.

KEY WORDS

alkaline earths	deionized water	mortar	stalactites
barium	ion exchanger	plaster of paris	stalagmites
beryl	lime	quicklime	strontium
beryllium	limestone	regeneration	water softener
calcium	magnesium	slaked lime	zeolite

HIGHLIGHTS

The **alkaline earths** include **beryllium, magnesium, calcium, strontium, barium,** and **radium.** All are above hydrogen in the activity series. All form insoluble hydroxides and carbonates. All react with water at appropriate temperatures. The carbonates of all are decomposed by heat.

Beryllium occurs in the mineral **beryl;** magnesium in carnallite; calcium in calcite and gypsum. Barium and strontium occur as carbonates and sulfates. Radium occurs in uranium ores. Dolomite is the double carbonate of calcium and magnesium.

The pure alkaline earth metals are obtained by the electrolysis of their fused salts. Magnesium is obtained partly by "mining the sea." Beryllium and magnesium are widely used in making light alloys for many industrial purposes.

Lime in its various forms is a very important material. **Mortar** and portland cement are lime products. The solubility of **limestone** in carbonic acid accounts for the formation of natural caves.

Hardness in water is caused by the presence of the ions of calcium, magnesium, and iron. Hardness in water is corrected by one of the following methods: (1) by precipitating these ions with lime, washing soda, or phosphates; (2) by ion-exchange zeolites, or resins.

QUESTIONS

1. Why is Group IIa called the alkaline earth group?
2. What electron structure is characteristic of each of the elements of this group?
3. Explain the relation between atomic number and activity with this group.
4. What compounds of the metals of this group are insoluble?
5. What is the largest-known source of magnesium?
6. Explain how magnesium metal is made from the source referred to in question 5.

7. Name six forms of calcium carbonate found in nature.
8. Why is beryllium an expensive metal?
9. What is the principal use for beryllium?
10. What is Dow metal?
11. Why is the extinguishing of a magnesium fire difficult?
12. Give one use for barium metal.
13. What is "milk of magnesia"?
14. Give four industrial uses for limestone.
15. Describe the manufacture of calcium oxide (quicklime).
16. What precautions should be observed in the storage of calcium oxide?
17. In early days, what was the main use of lime?
18. Describe the uses of gypsum.
19. How is plaster of paris made? How is its setting explained?
20. Describe the chemistry of the formation of limestone solution caverns.
21. Explain how a limestone deposit is laid down in the sea.
22. Explain the two types of water hardness.
23. Explain how each type of water hardness may be corrected.
24. Explain the softening of water by the use of zeolite.
25. How is deionized water obtained?
26. Is hard water objectionable for all uses? Explain.

CHAPTER 46

copper, silver, and gold

Copper, silver, and gold are the elements that make up Group I*b*. They are the oldest metals known to man. Relics show that they were in use as early as 3000 BC.

Properties of copper, silver, and gold

Although in the same main group as the alkalis, these metals are quite different from the alkalis. About the only common property of all members of this group, aside from the fact that all are metals, is that all of them show a valence of 1. The properties of copper, silver, and gold are shown in Table 46–1.

TABLE 46–1. Properties of copper, silver, and gold

Property	Copper	Silver	Gold
Symbol	Cu	Ag	Au
Atomic number	29	47	79
Electronic structure	2	2	2
	8	8	8
	18	18	18
	1	18	32
		1	18
			1
Valences	1 and 2	1 (2 very rarely)	1 and 3
Melting point, °C	1083	961	1063
Density, 20°C, g/cm^3	8.92	10.5	19.3
Atomic radius, angstroms	1.27	1.44	1.44
Estimated percentage of earth's crust	0.0001	0.0000001	

588

Because of their low activity, copper, silver, and gold are known as the **noble metals.** This low activity is explained by their electronic structures, which are shown in Table 46–1. Note that although these elements all have one electron in the outer shell, they do not have an inert gas structure underneath this one electron. This is because these elements fall in the middle of the long series in the periodic table. Hence by losing one electron, they do not acquire the very stable electronic structure of an inert gas. Therefore, they do not show the great tendency to lose electrons, which the alkalis show. Note also that these atoms are smaller than the alkalis. This means that their valence electrons are nearer to the nucleus. These two facts cause the noble metals to be among the least active metals known.

Occurrence of copper

Copper is found in the free state in many places on the earth. The largest deposit of native copper ever discovered was on the Keweenaw peninsula in northern Michigan. Most copper is produced from sulfide ores, of which the most important is **chalcopyrite,** $CuFeS_2$, which is found in Arizona, Montana, Utah, Nevada, New Mexico, and Alaska. These states, together with Michigan, are the principal copper-producing regions of the United States. *Chalcocite*, Cu_2S, is mined in large quantities in Butte, Mont., and Alaska. *Cuprite*, Cu_2O, is mined in South America, from where the United States now imports large amounts of copper. Other important copper-producing areas are Africa, Russia, and Japan.

Copper is an essential element in the life of many organisms. The role it plays in human nutrition has been indicated earlier. In lobsters and oysters, the oxygen-carrying compound in the blood is a copper-containing hemoglobin in place of the iron-containing hemoglobin found in man and the other more highly developed organisms. Hence these sea foods are good nutritional sources of copper when included in the diet.

Metallurgy of copper

Native copper is separated by melting the copper and allowing it to drain away from the gangue. A limestone flux may be added if necessary. The treatment of sulfide ores is quite involved. This is because such ores, as mined, contain a very low percentage of copper —sometimes less than 1 percent. The ore is concentrated, first by flotation, then by chemical means, until a product is obtained containing 40 to 45 percent copper, combined with sulfur, along with iron sulfide and silica. This is known as **copper matte.** The copper matte is melted and placed in a copper converter (an apparatus shaped like

A copper converter discharging molten copper. (Anaconda Copper Mining Co.)

a large concrete mixer) where air is blown through it. The following reactions occur:

$$CuS + O_2 \rightarrow Cu + SO_2 \uparrow$$
$$2FeS + 3O_2 \rightarrow 2FeO + 2SO_2 \uparrow$$
$$FeO + SiO_2 \rightarrow \underset{(slag)}{FeSiO_3}$$

At the temperature of the converter, copper oxide is unstable (compare with mercuric oxide) and hence almost none of it is formed. Most of the copper is liberated directly in the free state. The iron oxide and silica react to form a separate layer of molten slag. The sulfur dioxide from copper smelting is commonly used to produce sulfuric acid.

The molten copper is stirred with green-wood poles which supply carbon to reduce any small amount of copper oxide which might be present. The molten copper is then cast into slabs, which are refined electrolytically.

Electrorefining of copper

At the refinery, the crude copper is refined electrolytically to yield a product of 99.98 percent purity. Iron and zinc are removed, as are gold and silver, also. (These metals are practically always present in copper ores.) The silver recovered from the electrolytic refining of copper generally pays for the cost of refining, and this is the largest single source of silver in the United States. Arsenic, for making insecticides, and selenium, for making ruby glass, are also valuable by-products of the refining.

Properties and uses of copper

Although New England produces no primary copper, this area has been famous for its copper fabrication plants for 200 years. It has produced a wide variety of copper articles ranging from copper bottoms for wooden ships to brass works for "dollar" watches. In fact, so much copper is worked in lower New England that the water of Long Island Sound has a copper content higher than that of the sea water in adjacent regions. (For this reason, oysters and lobsters caught in these waters are supposed to be an especially good source of dietary copper.)

Copper is used in the United States in larger quantities than any other metal except iron. Its price per pound is generally six to seven times that of ordinary steel.

Copper has the highest electrical and heat conductivity of any metal except silver. About one-fourth of the copper produced is used in the electrical industry as a conductor—electric power distribution lines, electric wiring of homes, motors, generators, and other uses. For these uses the copper must be extremely pure. As little as 0.03 percent of arsenic lowers the electrical conductivity of copper 14 percent. This is another reason for electrolytic refining.

Because of its good heat conductivity, copper is employed for evaporator coils in mechanical refrigerators, convector-type radiators for house heating, automobile radiators, steam heating coils, hot water tanks, and cooking untensils. The latter are particularly effective for cooking on electric ranges where high heat conductivity is es-

The electrolytic refining of copper. This man is removing a tank load of 31 extra-heavy cathodes from an electrolytic cell. Electrolytic refining produces copper of 99.98 percent purity. This high degree of purity is necessary for copper that is to be used in the electrical industry. (Anaconda Copper Mining Co.)

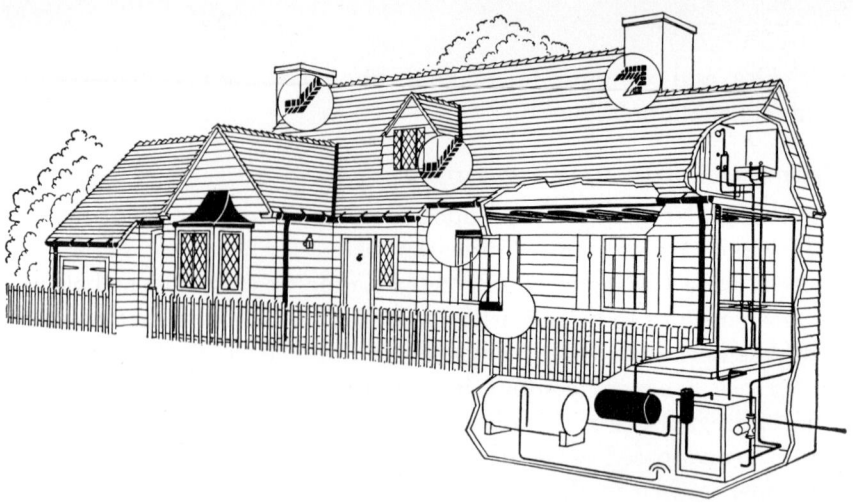

Fig. 46–1. The dark lines show some of the ways in which copper and brass are used in the construction of a home. (Revere Copper and Brass, Inc.)

pecially important. Cooking utensils made of stainless steel but having copper bottoms for more efficient heat transmission and distribution have recently become very popular with the housewife. The heat conductivity of copper is nearly twice that of aluminum and nine times that of steel.

Copper tubing, because it is noncorrodible and more quickly installed, has largely replaced steel for water pipes in many sections of the United States. The same is true for hot-water tanks. Although copper pipe costs more per pound than steel pipe, the total cost of installing copper plumbing is not much greater today than the cost of installing steel pipe. This is partly because the copper tubing used is much thinner (hence uses much less metal per foot of pipe) and also because it is more quickly installed. Copper pipe can be quickly soldered to fittings (elbows, tees, and so forth), whereas steel pipe must be threaded. Also, soft copper tubing can be bent quickly around corners, but steel must be cut and threaded and an elbow must be installed. Copper plumbing has the further advantage that, once installed, it normally lasts for the entire life of the building.

Copper is malleable and ductile, which makes the fabrication of wires and tubes fairly simple.

Copper sheets are used for roofing. When exposed to the atmosphere, they acquire a beautiful gray-green color because of surface corrosion [$Cu_2(OH)_2CO_3$]. The corrosion does not continue beyond the surface, however, and copper roofing lasts almost indefinitely. Best-quality gutters and lead and down pipes are also made of it.

Including the copper used in brass hardware, plumbing fixtures, and other uses, probably 2000 pounds of copper are used in building a modern six-room house.

Alloys

About one-fourth of the copper produced is used in alloys.

Brass is a general term which means almost any alloy containing copper and zinc. Normally brass contains 60 to 85 percent copper. If it also contains tin, the alloy is called **bronze**. *Aluminum bronze* contains copper (about 90 percent) and aluminum (about 10 percent) and may or may not contain a small amount of iron. United States coinage gold contained 90 percent gold and 10 percent copper. The United States "nickel" is 75 percent copper and 25 percent nickel, whereas the Canadian nickel is 100 percent nickel. United States coinage silver is 10 percent copper. During World War II the United States penny was minted of steel because of a copper shortage. *Monel metal* is nickel (about 67 percent) and copper (about 28 percent), with some iron and manganese. It is a noncorrodible metal highly prized for kitchen sinks, counter tops, and food processing machinery.

The Statue of Liberty is made of copper sheets ¼ in. thick. (Anaconda Copper Mining Co.)

A small amount of copper alloyed with steel greatly reduces the tendency of the steel to corrode. Most sheet steel used for roofing is copper-bearing steel.

Chemical properties of copper

Copper is below hydrogen in activity and, therefore, not acted upon by ordinary acids. Nitric acid, because it is a strong oxidizing agent, attacks copper, forming copper nitrate (see Chap. 32, page 360). Hot, concentrated sulfuric acid also attacks copper (see Chap. 29, page 333).

As noted earlier, copper, in the presence of air, forms a surface film of basic cupric carbonate [$Cu_2(OH)_2CO_3$]. Normally the corrosion stops as soon as this surface film is formed. However, in the presence of an acid, even a very dilute one, this coating will dissolve. This exposes the copper underneath to further action by the atmosphere.

$$Cu_2(OH)_2CO_3 + 2H_2SO_4 \rightarrow 2CuSO_4 + 3H_2O + CO_2$$
$$\text{(soluble)}$$

Hence copper in the presence of air and an acid will be dissolved. For this reason copper pipes buried underground sometimes are destroyed by corrosion in a relatively short time whereas in another locality, where the ground water is not acid, a copper pipe buried underground may last many, many years.

Although copper compounds of valences 1 and 2 are known, the cupric compounds are the only ones stable in contact with the oxygen of the air at room temperature. Most cuprous compounds are quickly oxidized, by air, at room temperature, to the cupric state. One exception is the very insoluble cuprous oxide (Cu_2O) which is found in nature as the mineral *cuprite*.

Copper compounds

The cupric ion in water solution has a characteristic blue color. This color is due to the hydrated cupric ion [$Cu(H_2O)_x^{++}$] since anhydrous copper sulfate and copper chloride are colorless, although the compound copper sulfate pentahydrate ($CuSO_4 \cdot 5H_2O$ or blue vitriol) is, of course, blue.

With ammonia, solutions of cupric salts form an intensely blue solution due to the formation of a cupric ammonia complex ion.

$$Cu(H_2O)_x^{++} + 4NH_3 \rightarrow Cu(NH_3)_4^{++} + xH_2O$$
(light blue)   (intensely blue)

In this ion the cupric ion shares four pairs of electrons with four ammonia molecules.

$$\begin{array}{ccccc}
 & & H & & \\
 & & \cdot\cdot & & \\
 & H : & N : & H & \\
H & & \cdot\cdot & & H \\
\cdot\cdot & & & & \cdot\cdot \\
H : N & : & Cu & : & N : H \\
\cdot\cdot & & & & \cdot\cdot \\
H & & \cdot\cdot & & H \\
 & H : & N : & H & \\
 & & \cdot\cdot & & \\
 & & H & &
\end{array}$$

The copper atom thereby has the use of eight electrons in an outer orbit, giving it an electron structure much like that of argon. Because the electron structure of copper is made more stable by sharing electrons, copper forms similar **complex ions** with a large number of other substances which can share one or more pairs of electrons with it. The reaction with ammonia is sometimes used as a test for copper.

The most important use of copper compounds is based on the fact that they are fungicides. Copper compounds are widely employed in sprays to control fungus diseases, such as black spot mildew, and other

Copper compounds are often used to control fungus diseases of plants. Here a spray from a 600-gal mechanical sprayer is applied to fruit trees. (Caterpillar Tractor Co.)

diseases on roses, grapes, apples, melons, and potatoes. The two forms in which the copper is most commonly employed are **Bordeaux mixture** and *cuprous oxide*. The latter is a yellow powder used in fungicide dusts. Bordeaux mixture, named after the region of France where it was developed to control fungus on grapes, consists of a mixture of copper sulfate pentahydrate and lime. When water is added, insoluble copper hydroxide is formed. This precipitate, mechanically suspended in water, is sprayed on the plant.

The soluble copper sulfate is used to prevent the growth of algae[1] in swimming pools and municipal reservoirs. Since, in large amounts, copper sulfate is toxic to man, the quantities used must be regulated carefully.

Test for copper

The blue color of the hydrated cupric ion $[Cu(H_2O)_x^{++}]$ and its reaction with ammonia are characteristic of copper.

Cupric ion reacts with iron, such as that of a common nail, to plate out red copper metal.

$$Fe^0 + Cu^{++} \rightarrow Cu^0 + Fe^{++}$$

This is sometimes used as a test for copper.

Occurrence and production of silver

The occurrence of silver as an impurity of copper ores has been mentioned. Silver occurs in lead ores and is produced regularly as a byproduct of lead metallurgy. Silver also occurs free in nature, generally mixed with quartz. Silver chloride (AgCl), known as *horn silver*, and silver sulfide (Ag_2S), *argentite*, are also found in nature.

[1] Algae are microscopic plants. They form the scum on pools and ponds.

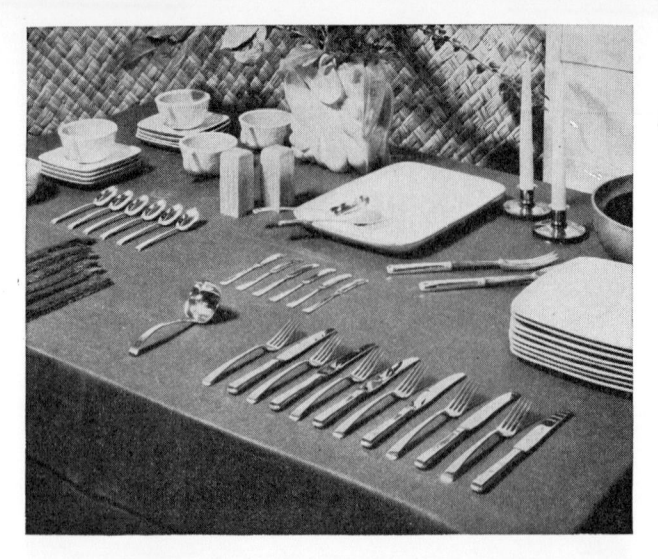

The production of table silver is one of the uses for the element silver. Such table services are very beautiful and long wearing. Two types of silver table service are common, sterling silverware and the silver-plated variety. (Towle Manufacturing Co.)

Mexico and the Rocky Mountain states, including Idaho, Utah, Colorado, Arizona, Nevada, and California, are the main silver-producing areas of the world.

Although most of the industrial silver production is a by-product in the refining of copper and lead, some ore is worked entirely for its silver content. This is generally native silver ore. The most modern method of silver metallurgy involves *leaching with sodium cyanide solution*. In the presence of water and cyanide ion, oxygen of the air will oxidize silver, converting it to a soluble silver cyanide complex ion.

$$4Ag^0 + 8Na^+ + 8CN^- + O_2 + 2H_2O \rightarrow 4Na^+ + \underbrace{4Ag(CN)_2^- + 4Na^+}_{\text{or} \atop 4NaAg(CN)_2} + 4OH^-$$

An explanation for this surprising fact is beyond the scope of this book.[1] Sodium cyanide solution is allowed to percolate over the crushed ore, and the resulting solution is collected and treated with zinc, which replaces the silver.

$$2Na^+ + 2Ag(CN)_2^- + Zn^0 \rightarrow \underbrace{2Na^+ + Zn(CN)_4^=}_{\text{or} \atop Na_2Zn(CN)_4} + 2Ag^0 \text{ silver metal}$$

The annual world production of silver is about 285 million ounces (=about 9000 tons), which at the price of $1.29 per ounce, has a value of about $368 million. (The United States government issues treasury certificates against its silver at the rate of $1.29 per ounce.)

It is estimated that the total amount of silver produced since the beginning of history is 18 billion ounces. Of this amount, about one-third has been lost, one-third is in hoards, and most of the remainder is in the form of coins, jewelry, and table silver.

[1] The interested reader is referred to L. B. Richardson and A. J. Scarlett, *General College Chemistry*, Henry Holt and Co., Inc., New York, 1947, p. 554.

Properties and uses of silver

Silver has the highest electrical and heat conductivity of any metal known. Its density (10.5 g/cm³) is higher than that of copper. Silver is very ductile and is easily drawn into extremely thin wires. Its high luster and reflecting power give rise to the term *silvery white*. This property is employed in making common mirrors, most of which are coated with silver.

Unlike copper, silver does not **tarnish** appreciably in ordinary moist air. Its chemical activity is less than that of copper. Silver does tarnish in the presence of hydrogen sulfide.

$$H_2S + 2Ag \rightarrow \underset{\text{(silver tarnish)}}{Ag_2S} \downarrow + H_2 \uparrow$$

The reaction appears to be contradictory to the activity series since silver is below hydrogen in activity. The explanation is found in the fact that all replacement reactions, such as this, are really reversible. The activity series gives the direction in which the reaction will go *when all reacting ions and ionic products are present in equal concentration*. However, as you have seen, the direction in which a reversible reaction occurs can be changed by changing the concentration of reactants or products (see Chap. 26, pages 285 to 287). In this case silver sulfide is so extremely insoluble as to reverse the direction which this reaction would otherwise take. That is to say, this reaction would not occur except for the extreme insolubility of silver sulfide. Copper and mercury, which are also below hydrogen in the activity series, are also tarnished by hydrogen sulfide and for the same reason—namely, the extreme insolubility of their sulfides.

Silver and oxygen do not combine directly. In fact the oxide, when made indirectly, is quite unstable, decomposing, when warmed, into silver and oxygen.

$$2Ag_2O \xrightarrow{300°C} 4Ag + O_2$$

Because of its lack of a tendency to oxidize and its high electrical conductivity, silver is ideally suited for making special electrical switches and contacts, as in aircraft ignition systems. At high altitudes, ignition systems tend to arc badly, and if made of copper or brass, become badly corroded. Silver is extensively employed in making contacts in telephones and telephone equipment.

During World War II when copper became exceedingly scarce because of the great demand for it, silver was sometimes used as a substitute. In at least one of the plants used for making magnesium, the bars which carried the large amount of electric energy that the plant used were constructed of silver borrowed from the United States government hoard at Fort Knox! As soon as conditions permitted, this silver was replaced with copper and returned to the government.

Much of the silver which does not find its way into hoards is used in coinage and jewelry. As mentioned earlier, United States silver coins are 90 percent silver and 10 percent copper. **Sterling silver** is 92.5 percent silver and 7.5 percent copper, as are also British silver coins—minted before 1920—from which comes the term *sterling silver*. British coins minted since 1920 are 50 percent silver. The function of the copper is to harden the silver which, when pure, is too soft for most uses. Flat table silver may be either sterling or silver plate. For silver plate, silver is electrolytically plated onto a brass object, and, of course, silver plate is much less expensive than sterling. Dental amalgams consume small amounts of silver.

Compounds of silver

Silver has a valence of $+1$ in all its important compounds. Most of them are insoluble. This includes the halides, silver chloride (AgCl), silver bromide (AgBr), and silver iodide (AgI), and silver sulfate (Ag_2SO_4). The only common soluble silver salt is silver nitrate ($AgNO_3$). Silver nitrate is made by the action of nitric acid on the metal.

$$3Ag + 4HNO_3 \text{ (dilute)} \rightarrow 3AgNO_3 + NO \uparrow + 2H_2O$$

Solutions of silver nitrate are easily decomposed into free silver and oxides of nitrogen. Even sunlight will cause the decomposition, hence the practice of storing this substance in dark brown bottles. Organic matter, such as that in the skin, will cause reduction of the silver ion to metallic silver. For this reason, silver nitrate which gets on the fingers accidentally produces black stains. These stains consist of finely divided silver deposited into the pores of the skin. Some indelible inks are based on this principle.

Silver ion has certain ability to destroy bacteria—hence the practice of painting a sore throat with silver nitrate solution. **Argyrol** is a solution of a silver-protein compound which owes its bactericidal effect to the presence of the silver ion. It is used in medicine as an antiseptic for treating eyes, nose, or throat. It is standard medical practice to treat the eyes of newborn babies with a silver nitrate solution. This is to destroy venereal infection which the child may have contracted at birth and which, if not so treated, can cause blindness.

It should be noted that silver compounds are highly toxic and should be used medically only by trained persons.

The young lady can see her face in the mirror because of the thin film of metallic silver on the back of the glass plate. This silver film reflects almost all the light that strikes it. (Lever Brothers Co.)

You have read in an earlier chapter that a test for the chloride ion is based upon the formation of a silver chloride precipitate. This precipitate is soluble in ammonia.

$$Ag^+ + Cl^- \rightarrow AgCl \downarrow$$
$$\underset{\text{(insoluble)}}{AgCl} + 2NH_3 \rightarrow \underset{\text{(soluble)}}{Ag(NH_3)_2{}^+} + Cl^-$$

The reason for the latter fact is that silver ion forms a complex with ammonia similar to that of copper. The silver-ammonia complex is colorless.

Silver mirrors

Mirrors are formed by reducing a silver ion solution. If a piece of *carefully cleaned* glass is present, the silver deposits as a thin metallic film on the glass. If the glass is improperly cleaned, the silver will not deposit on the glass but instead will precipitate as a fine black powder. A suitable reducing agent is glucose or formaldehyde. The silver solution used is silver nitrate to which ammonia has been added until the precipitate which first forms has dissolved. In such solutions the silver is present as the silver-ammonia complex ion, $Ag(NH_3)_2{}^+$. When this is mixed with a solution of glucose or formaldehyde and warmed, the silver is reduced to the metallic state. As stated, the glass to be plated should be carefully cleaned. If the glass is washed in a solution of stannous chloride ($SnCl_2$) and then thoroughly rinsed with water just before plating, the chance of obtaining a good silver film is improved. Why the stannous chloride is helpful is not known.

Commercially mirrors are made by separately spraying the two solutions from twin nozzles onto the cleaned glass. The resulting silver deposit is dried, backed with copper, and shellacked.

Silver polish

Since tarnish on silver is due to silver sulfide, the object of silver polishing is to remove the sulfide. Sodium cyanide dissolves silver sulfide almost instantly because it forms a very stable complex ion with silver ion.

$$\underset{\text{(insoluble)}}{Ag_2S} + 4Na^+ + 4CN^- \rightarrow \underset{\text{(soluble)}}{2Na^+ + 2Ag(CN)_2^-} + 2Na^+ + S^=$$

However, because cyanides are extremely toxic, they should never be used for cleaning silver except by an expert. Because of this, the housewife must content herself with a less efficient but safer polish. Most commercial silver polishes depend upon the presence of:

1. Ammonia and/or sodium thiosulfate, which have a slight ability to dissolve silver sulfide by forming complex ions with silver. (If the sulfide were as soluble as silver chloride or iodide, the reagent would dissolve it readily. But we have seen that if the sulfide were as soluble as the chloride, it would not form in the first place.)

2. A mild abrasive such as very fine silica or clay to remove mechanically the tarnish film.

Test for silver

Silver is easily recognized by the same test as that for chloride ion. The unknown is treated with dilute hydrochloric acid. A white precipitate, soluble in ammonia, is evidence for silver ion.

$$Ag^+ + Cl^- \rightarrow \underset{\text{(white)}}{AgCl \downarrow}$$

$$\underset{\text{(insoluble)}}{AgCl \downarrow} + 2NH_3 \rightarrow \underset{\text{(soluble)}}{Ag(NH_3)_2^+} + Cl^-$$

History of photography

The effect of light upon the silver halides has long been known. **Daguerre** first applied this knowledge to the photographic process in 1839. He exposed to light a plate coated with silver iodide and developed it by exposure to mercury vapor. A *positive* image was obtained by this process. The modern type of dry plate was first used in the 1880s and originally consisted of fine crystals of silver halide dispersed in gelatin and spread on glass. Later celluloid film was substituted for glass. Modern film bases are cellulose nitrate (which is inflammable) or cellulose acetate which is the base used in safety film (see Chap. 38, pages 464 to 466). The substitution of the flexible film base for glass made for greater convenience in photography and made possible the development of motion pictures.

The photographic process

If any of the silver halides is allowed to stand in strong light, it slowly decomposes into silver and the halogen.

$$2AgI \xrightarrow{\text{sunlight}} 2Ag + I_2 \uparrow$$

When exposed to light for a short time, about one second or less, no decomposition of the halide can be observed. However, *a short exposure changes the halide in some way so that it is more easily reduced to metallic silver after exposure than before.* Also, the greater the amount of light striking the halide, the more readily is it later reduced to silver and the halogen. Modern photography is all based on this effect. It is a strange fact that an industry as large as the photographic industry is based upon a principle which is so poorly understood.

1. *Preparation of the films.* Modern film consists of finely divided crystals of silver bromide and silver iodide dispersed in gelatin and spread evenly on the film base. The emulsion is prepared by mixing solutions of silver nitrate, gelatin, and sodium iodide and bromide. Just before the gelatin hardens, it is poured over the film base. The **film speed**[1] depends on the halides present and the size of the silver halide particles in the film. Silver iodide is more light-sensitive than the bromide, and larger silver halide particles are more rapidly affected by light than the smaller ones. Fast film has a larger proportion of silver iodide and larger-sized particles than slow film.

2. *Exposure.* The brief exposure of the film in the camera to the image of the object being photographed produces no visible effect on the film as noted earlier. However, this exposure affects the silver halides, so that the silver ion is more readily reduced to the metal. This effect is in proportion to the intensity of the light striking various parts of the plate.

3. *Development.* **Development** consists of soaking the film in a solution of a mild reducing agent consisting of an organic compound. The reducing agent is selected so that it has no effect on the silver halide which has not been illuminated but is able to reduce the silver halide which has been exposed to light. Thus an image of the object is produced by the deposit of finely divided metallic silver in the gelatin in proportion to the intensity of light reaching various parts of the film.

$$\text{Unexposed silver halide} \xrightarrow{\text{development}} \text{no reaction}$$

$$\text{Exposed silver halide} \xrightarrow{\text{development}} \text{silver deposited}$$

[1] Speed of a film refers to the length of exposure required to produce an image. Fast films are more sensitive, hence require shorter exposures.

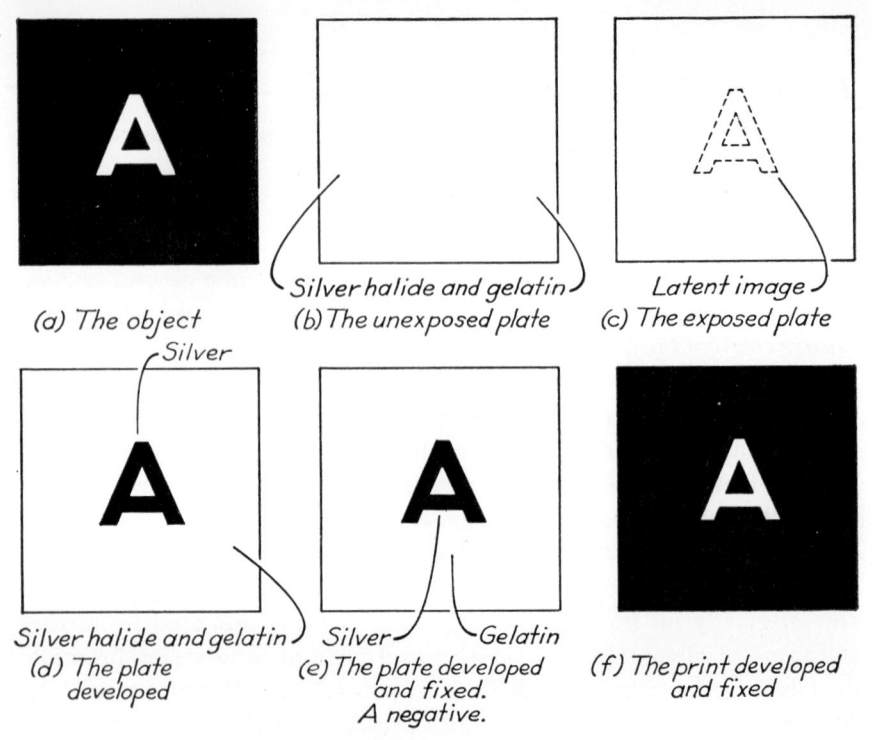

(a) The object
(b) The unexposed plate — Silver halide and gelatin
(c) The exposed plate — Latent image
(d) The plate developed — Silver
(e) The plate developed and fixed. A negative. — Silver, Gelatin
(f) The print developed and fixed

Fig. 46–2. The stages in the photographic process.

4. Fixing. The image produced by development must be fixed to make it permanent. **Fixing** consists of soaking the film in photographer's **hypo,** which is a solution of sodium thiosulfate ($Na_2S_2O_3$). This compound dissolves the unreduced silver halide and removes it from the film. It does so by forming a complex ion with silver ion.

$$\underset{\text{(precipitate)}}{AgI \downarrow} + 2Na^+ + S_2O_3^= \rightarrow \underset{\text{(soluble)}}{Na^+ + Ag(S_2O_3)^-} + I^- + Na^+$$

If the film is not fixed, it becomes completely black on exposure to light because the light decomposes the remaining unreduced silver halide. After fixing, the film is washed and dried.

5. Printing. The process described above produces an image of the object which is dark where the object was light and light where the object was dark (see Fig. 46–2). It is, therefore, called a **negative. Positive** prints are made by illuminating a piece of paper, surfaced with a silver halide emulsion, through the negative. The paper is then developed and fixed as described for the film. The denser parts of the negative protect the paper below them and leave these parts least affected. The print is thus a positive of the original object. That is, it is dark where the object was dark and light where the object was light. The light-sensitive agents in printing paper are silver chloride and bromide.

Occurrence and production of gold

Although a gold telluride (AuTe$_2$) is known, gold occurs in nature almost exclusively as the free metal. It is produced as a by-product of the refining of copper and, less commonly, of lead and zinc. In addition to being found associated with the above metals, gold is sometimes found distributed through quartz veins. Erosion of some of these materials in the past has washed out the gold and deposited it in stream beds.

In mining an ore of the latter type, the less dense sand is washed away by a stream of water, a modern version of the *gold panning* of earlier days. Gold in quartz is generally separated by leaching the ore with sodium cyanide in the presence of air as described for silver.

There are about seven hundred ounces of gold in every cubic mile of sea water, but as yet there is no profitable way of removing it.

Properties and uses of gold

Gold has a density of 19.3 g/cm^3 and is one of the two metallic elements which are not white in color. Its great ductility and malleability have been mentioned earlier. The metal is soft and, therefore, not very durable physically. Its principal uses are in making jewelry and for hoarding. The metal has few properties which recommend it for practical uses. It is a tribute to the peculiarity of human nature that from prehistoric times man has treasured gold and been willing to give up useful, durable, productive possessions to acquire it. All the gold mined since the beginning of history would make a cube about forty feet on edge.

Since 1932 the United States government has made a set policy of buying gold from all offerers at a fixed price of $35 per ounce. This practice has indirectly fixed the value of the American dollar in terms of gold. The gold so purchased is kept in vaults at Fort Knox, Ky., and now represents a value of about $24 billion.

For jewelry, gold is alloyed with copper to harden it. Gold that is 100 percent pure is called 24-carat gold; 18-carat gold is then $18/24$ gold. This 18-carat gold is generally considered too soft to be practical for jewelry. Therefore, 14-carat jewelry is more common.

White gold is an alloy of gold with nickel and zinc, or with palladium, or with silver; *green gold* is an alloy of silver or cadmium with gold. Because of its malleability and resistance to corrosion, gold is well suited for dental work.

Chemically, gold is the least active metal. It is not attacked by any single acid, but aqua regia (see Chap. 32, page 361) or any of the halogens attack it. Gold compounds are of minor importance.

KEY WORDS

argyrol	Daguerre	negative
Bordeaux mixture	development (of film)	noble metals
brass	electrorefining	photography
bronze	film speed	positive
chalcopyrite	fixing (of film)	sterling silver
complex ions	hypo	tarnish
copper matte	mirror	

HIGHLIGHTS

Because of their low degree of chemical activity, copper, silver, and gold are known as **noble metals.** All are relatively soft metals and have a high density. All are highly malleable and ductile. These metals are the best-known conductors of heat and electricity and in this respect rank in this order: silver, copper, gold. Copper may be dissolved by hot, concentrated sulfuric acid or by nitric acid. Silver may be dissolved by nitric acid. Gold is soluble only in aqua regia, a mixture of nitric and hydrochloric acids.

Next to iron, copper is the most widely used metal in the United States. Because of its electrical conductivity, copper is used in electric power lines, for house wiring, and for numerous electric and electronic devices, such as motors and generators. Because of its heat conductivity, copper is used for refrigerator coils and cooking utensils. The chemical stability of copper accounts for its use in water pipes, storage tanks, and plumbing fixtures. Copper compounds, such as copper sulfate pentahydrate and cuprous oxide, are excellent fungicides. They are used to control fungus diseases, such as black spot mildew, on fruits, vegetables, and flowers.

The intense blue color of the cupric ammonia **complex ion** is the basis of the test for the metal.

Silver is obtained as the by-product in refining lead and copper ores. Silver is easily **tarnished** by the sulfur compounds of the atmosphere. Silver is used in jewelry and coinage. It is also the basis of the photographic industry, in which silver halides are dispersed in gelatin on glass plates or plastic films. The steps in the photographic process are: exposure, **development, fixing,** washing, and printing.

Gold is usually alloyed with copper and other metals in jewelry and coinage and for use in dentistry. White and green gold are such alloys.

QUESTIONS

1. Why are the metals of Group Ib much less active than those of Ia?
2. What regions of the Western Hemisphere are important copper producers?
3. In what forms is copper found in nature?
4. Describe the metallurgy of native copper.
5. Describe the treatment of copper sulfide ores to obtain the metal.
6. What products are obtained as by-products in the electrolytic refining of copper?
7. List all the objects that you know of in your home which are made wholly or in part of copper metal.
8. Upon what properties of copper do the uses listed in question 7 depend?
9. Why are copper pipes for plumbing preferred to steel pipes?
10. What is monel metal?
11. Explain why copper pipes buried underground sometimes are rapidly corroded.
12. Explain how one could tell in advance whether a copper pipe would be corroded when buried in a certain location.
13. What is the principal use of copper compounds?
14. Describe the reaction of cupric ion and ammonia. Would you expect the ammonium ion to give this reaction? Explain.
15. What is the greatest source of silver in the United States?
16. Give two industrial uses for silver.
17. What is sterling silver?
18. Explain why it is necessary to "fix" a film after development.
19. What types of ingredients are present in silver polish?
20. Describe the test for silver ion.

CHAPTER 47

aluminum

Judged by the amount produced, aluminum is the most important light metal and the third most important of all metals. Among metals, only steel and copper are used in the United States in larger quantities than aluminum. The production of aluminum in 1956 in the United States was about 1,300,000 tons.

Occurrence of aluminum

Aluminum is the third most abundant element and the most abundant metal in the earth's crust. Aluminum is estimated to make up 8.13 percent of the earth's crust. Because of its high activity, aluminum is never found free in nature. The metal always occurs combined with oxygen and generally also with silicon. The common occurrence of feldspar ($KAlSi_3O_8$), its weathering into clay [$H_2Al_2(SiO_4)_2 \cdot H_2O$], and the widespread occurrence of other aluminum silicate minerals such as the micas, have already been mentioned (see Chap. 41, pages 509 and 523, and Chap. 44, page 554).

Although these aluminum silicates are very common and available almost anywhere on the earth's surface, none of them are of any value at present as an ore of aluminum. This is because the extraction of aluminum from the aluminum silicates is too difficult and expensive to be profitable financially. It is to be hoped that a practical method for obtaining the metal from clay will be developed. If so, it would mean that future generations of mankind would have an inexhaustible supply of this useful and versatile metal.

Bauxite, $Al_2O_3 \cdot xH_2O$,[1] is the only mineral from which aluminum is made at present. It is a white-to-reddish earthy-looking material.

---

[1] The x means that the amount of water present varies from one sample to another.

Arc-type furnaces in which aluminum oxide, corundum, is produced. (Carborundum Co.)

Bauxite is found in Arkansas, Alabama, Georgia, and Tennessee, but the greater part of the ore used in the United States is imported from British and French Guiana, South America.

Cryolite, $3NaF \cdot AlF_3$, is found in Greenland, and is used in aluminum metallurgy. **Corundum** (Al_2O_3) is a very hard mineral. It is number 9 on the Mohs' hardness scale of minerals. The name should not be confused with *Carborundum*, a synthetic silicon carbide. Transparent crystals of corundum are among the most valuable gem stones. **Sapphire** is corundum colored blue by the presence of a small amount of an impurity, probably cobalt or titanium. **Rubies** are similar except their red color is probably due to chromium.

Bauxite is the most important ore of aluminum because it is the only one from which the metal is made at present. Aluminum also occurs very widely in clays; however, no practical method of extracting aluminum from clay is yet known. (American Museum of Natural History)

Left, Paul Héroult. Right, Charles Martin Hall. (Aluminum Company of America)

Early processes for aluminum metallurgy

Liberation of aluminum from its compounds is difficult because of the high activity of the metal. Because of this, metallic aluminum has been known for only about 130 years. It was first prepared in 1824 by a Danish physician, Hans Christian Oersted. He used potassium to reduce aluminum chloride:

$$AlCl_3 + 3K \rightarrow Al + 3KCl$$

Later sodium was substituted for potassium, but since the preparation of even sodium was, in those days, also an expensive procedure, aluminum was a precious metal. The public first became aware of aluminum in 1855 when a bar of the metal was exhibited at the International Fair at Paris where it attracted much attention because of its low density. By that time the price of aluminum had dropped to $90 per pound because of economies developed in the manufacture of metallic sodium. First public interest in aluminum in America was aroused in 1876 when the Washington monument was capped with that metal. By 1886 the price of aluminum had dropped to $12 per pound and about five thousand pounds were being made yearly. By way of contrast, the production of aluminum in the United States during World War II exceeded two billion pounds (or about fourteen pounds for every man, woman, and child in the United States), and the price was around 15 cents per pound. For this we are indebted to **Charles Martin Hall** and **Paul Héroult**.

Charles Martin Hall was a student at Oberlin College, Ohio, from 1881 to 1885. One day, in a chemistry class, Hall's professor, Frank F.

Jewett, remarked that the person to discover a cheap method for making aluminum would thereby not only make himself a large fortune but also become a great benefactor to mankind. Hall became interested in the problem and conducted experiments in his family's woodshed. In 1886 when he was twenty-two years old and a year after graduation from Oberlin, he developed the method of aluminum metallurgy which is still used, essentially unchanged, today. In the same year a Frenchman, Paul Héroult, also twenty-two years old, independently developed the same process.

When Héroult applied for a United States patent on his process, he found that Hall had already applied for a patent on the same process. Eventually the conflicting claims were settled by Hall's getting the American patent rights while Héroult got the French rights to the process. In 1888 a small plant operating on the Hall process was producing aluminum at New Kensington, Pa. From the Hall patents grew the Aluminum Company of America, one of the larger American corporations, and until World War II, the only producer of virgin aluminum in the United States.

Aluminum metallurgy: the Hall process

Because of its great stability, aluminum oxide can be cheaply reduced only by electrolytic methods. Carbon, hydrogen, and other cheap reducing agents are unable to reduce it. Moreover, the electrolytic reduction cannot take place in water solution because hydrogen, which is less active than aluminum, is always obtained instead. Since aluminum oxide melts above 2000°C it cannot be directly melted and electrolyzed. Hall's real discovery consisted of finding that *cryolite* ($3NaF \cdot AlF_3$), which melts at 1000°C, *dissolves aluminum oxide, and the resulting solution can be electrolyzed to yield aluminum.*

$$2Al_2O_3 \underset{\substack{\text{(dissolved in} \\ \text{cryolite)}}}{\xrightarrow{\text{electrolysis}}} 4Al + 3O_2 \uparrow$$

The process is carried out in large cells shown in Fig. 47–1. The cell is made of steel and given a lining of carbon which serves also as the negative electrode. Carbon rods serve as the anodes. Purified aluminum oxide (see page 611) is added to the molten cryolite, where it dissolves. On electrolysis, the aluminum oxide yields molten aluminum which collects at the bottom of the cell. The oxygen liberated at the carbon electrode combines vigorously with this carbon at the high temperature of the cell, so that

$$\underset{\substack{\text{(positive} \\ \text{electrode)}}}{C} + O_2 \rightarrow CO_2 \uparrow$$

these electrodes are actually consumed in the process and must be replaced regularly.

The production of 1 lb of aluminum requires:

>3 to 4 lb of crude bauxite ore
>$\frac{3}{4}$ lb carbon
>12 kilowatthours of electrical energy

Because of the large amount of electrical energy consumed, aluminum plants are always located near large electric generating stations—particularly hydroelectric stations. That is, it is cheaper to transport the ore than to transmit the electrical energy long distances. The aluminum industry is one of the largest consumers of electrical energy in the entire United States.

Purification of the ore

Although the bauxite ore used at present is largely hydrated aluminum oxide, it is necessary to purify it before electrolysis. The removal of iron from the ore is particularly important. The purification is based on the fact that aluminum oxide, which is amphoteric (see page 615), is soluble in concentrated sodium hydroxide solution. Iron oxide, which is not amphoteric, is not soluble in this solution. Thus the finely crushed ore is heated under pressure with sodium hydroxide solution.

$$Al_2O_3 + 2NaOH \xrightarrow{heat} 2NaAlO_2 + H_2O$$
$$\text{(soluble)}$$

$$Fe_2O_3 + NaOH \rightarrow \text{no reaction}$$

The iron oxide is then removed by filtering the solution. From the sodium aluminate solution, aluminum hydroxide is precipitated by cooling.

$$NaAlO_2 + 2H_2O \xrightarrow{cooling} Al(OH)_3 \downarrow + NaOH$$
$$\text{aluminum hydroxide}$$

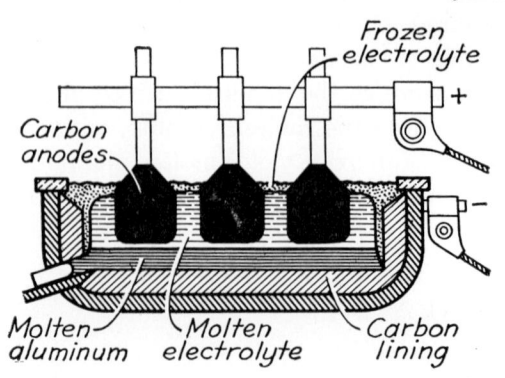

Fig. 47–1. The electrolysis of aluminum oxide dissolved in molten cryolite takes place in a carbon-lined steel cell. The molten metal is withdrawn from the bottom at intervals.

An aluminum reduction plant of the Aluminum Company of America. Plants such as this can produce billions of pounds of aluminum every year at a price as low as 15 cents per pound. Note that the plant is located near a river which probably has a hydroelectric station. (Aluminum Company of America)

The resulting precipitate of purified aluminum hydroxide is converted to the oxide by heating,

$$2\text{Al(OH)}_3 \xrightarrow{\text{heat}} \text{Al}_2\text{O}_3 + 3\text{H}_2\text{O}$$

yielding purified aluminum oxide (alumina) which is used in the electrolysis cell.

Properties and uses of aluminum

Table 47-1 gives some of the properties of aluminum. Aluminum is a light, soft, silvery metal which is a good conductor of heat and electricity and which resists corrosion in contact with normal air or fresh water.

TABLE 47-1. Properties of aluminum, Al

Atomic number	13
Electron structure	2, 8, 3
Valence	3
Melting point, °C	660
Boiling point, °C	2057
Density, g/cm^3	2.7

At temperatures of 100 to 150°C aluminum is quite ductile and may be easily rolled and drawn in sheets, wire, and tubing. At temperatures near its melting point aluminum becomes brittle. At its melting point the metal is too viscous to make good castings, but by alloying with a small amount of copper or magnesium, its fluidity is increased so that castings can be made of these alloys.

Magnalium is an alloy containing 10 to 30 percent magnesium, the rest aluminum. An alloy of aluminum and copper containing 5 to 12

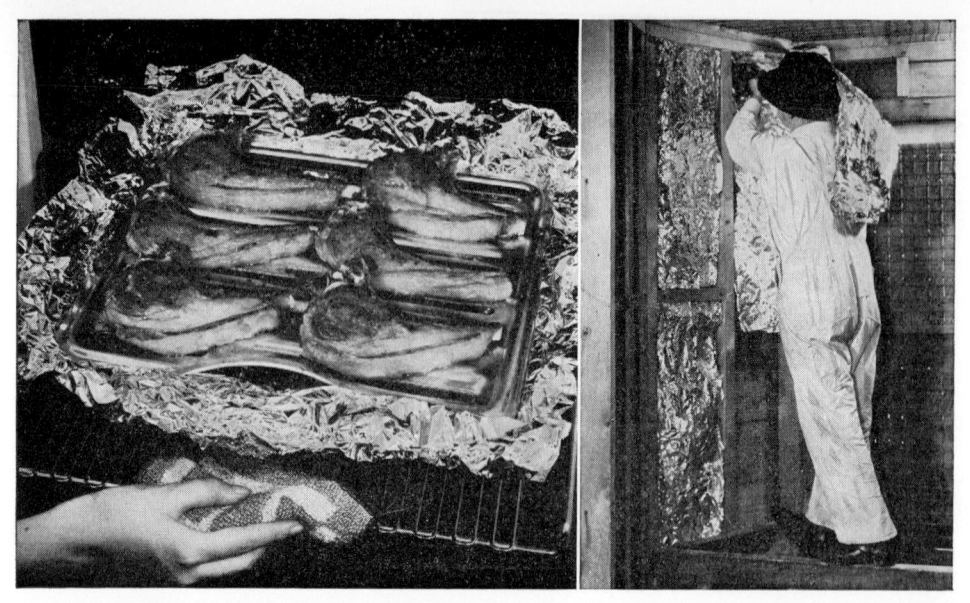

Left, aluminum is used as a kitchen aid to reflect heat evenly on the chops. Right, aluminum is used to insulate a house. (Aluminum Company of America)

percent aluminum is known as *aluminum bronze*. It resembles gold in appearance and is used for letters on store fronts, jewelry, and when powdered, for gilt paint. It is more resistant to corrosion than bronze. *Duralium* contains mainly aluminum with copper (about 4 percent), magnesium (1 percent), manganese (1 percent), and silicon (1 percent). An alloy of aluminum with nickel, cobalt, and iron, known as *alnico*, is used for making small, powerful magnets essential for speakers in modern radio and television sets.

Aluminum and its alloys are widely used to make cameras, cooking utensils, airplanes, railway coaches, truck and house trailers, storm windows, venetian blinds, pistons and connecting rods for automobiles, and many other items where strength and low density and/or corrosion resistance are required.

A wire made of aluminum has 65 percent the electrical conductivity of a copper wire of the same size. However, because its density is only 30 percent that of copper, aluminum is a better electrical conductor than copper, *pound for pound* (Fig. 47–2). Since a pound of aluminum

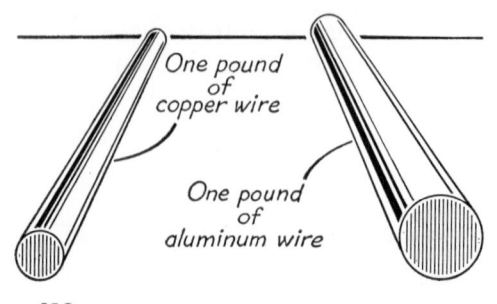

Fig. 47–2. A wire made from a pound of aluminum will have a diameter 1.8 times larger than a wire of the same length made from a pound of copper. The resistance of the larger aluminum wire is about one-half that of the copper.

Aluminum is used to paint gas-storage tanks because the aluminum reflects the light and heat of the sun. (Aluminum Company of America)

is somewhat cheaper than a pound of copper, you can see why aluminum has largely replaced copper for high-tension electric cable. The greatest disadvantage of aluminum cable is its lower tensile strength. This has been offset by making a cable with a core of iron wire to give it strength to stand ice storms. This core is surrounded by aluminum wires which carry most of the electric current. Aluminum foil has almost entirely replaced tin foil. Tin foil is almost never encountered now because of the high cost of tin. Butter, cheese, and candy as well as frozen foods are frequently wrapped in aluminum foil. The foil has the advantage over paper of being completely impermeable to odors as well as to moisture vapor.

The reflecting power of aluminum

Polished aluminum reflects 95 percent of the radiant heat which strikes it, which is much greater than the percentage reflected by any other common metal. This fact is the basis for using thin aluminum foil as an insulator in walls and ceilings of houses. Such foils are very efficient insulators against loss of heat by radiation. Sheet aluminum used for roofs and siding of buildings serves the same purpose. It has been shown that a building roofed with aluminum is cooler in summer and warmer in winter than one roofed with sheet steel, but otherwise the same. Of course, aluminum is a good heat conductor and gives no insulating effect against heat transfer by conduction. For best results, a building should be insulated with aluminum foil and also with a material of low heat conductivity, such as rock wool, glass wool, or

A view of the 200-in. mirror of the Hale telescope. This mirror is aluminum-coated, as are most mirrors of modern astronomical telescopes, because aluminum is capable of reflecting ultraviolet rays as well as visible light. (California Institute of Technology)

foam glass. A very efficient insulating board consisting of several sheets of aluminum foil with sealed air spaces between them serves the same purpose.

Aluminum paint, made by suspending finely divided metallic aluminum in a varnish, produces nearly as good a reflecting surface as aluminum metal itself. Thus there is a real advantage in painting a roof or gasoline storage tank with aluminum paint. However, painting a steam or hot water radiator with aluminum paint accomplishes a result *exactly opposite* to the desired one. This is because the aluminum paint reflects and thereby decreases the amount of radiant heat given off by the radiator.

Aluminum also has the ability to reflect ultraviolet rays; hence astronomical telescope mirrors and other mirrors for reflecting ultraviolet light are coated with aluminum. Since aluminum is very soft, such mirrors must be treated with great care as the surface can easily be damaged.

Aluminum and corrosion

Although high in the activity series, aluminum is valued because of its resistance to corrosion. This is because, as soon as it is exposed to air, aluminum acquires a surface coating of aluminum oxide by reaction with the components of the atmosphere. This oxide surface film is fine-grained and sticks closely to the metal beneath it. The metal below is thus protected from corrosion. The durability of aluminum is not due to its lack of tendency to corrode, but rather to the unusual properties of the corrosion film which protects the metal underneath it.

The corrosion film of aluminum is so thin and fine-grained that its presence is hardly noticed unless one is looking for it. It can be observed by rubbing an aluminum article with fine sandpaper, which exposes the uncorroded metal underneath.

Anything which is able to dissolve this oxide film will cause the aluminum to be rapidly corroded away. Thus because chloride ion solutions have the ability to dissolve the oxide film, aluminum is not resistant to sea water or the salt spray atmosphere of the seacoast. When tomatoes are cooked in an aluminum kettle, the inside of the kettle is made bright and shiny. This is because tomatoes contain organic acids which dissolve the oxide film. (This does not harm the food because all the evidence indicates that aluminum compounds are nonpoisonous.)

Chemical properties of aluminum

Aluminum metal is dissolved rapidly by hydrochloric acid.

$$6HCl + 2Al \rightarrow 2AlCl_3 + 3H_2 \uparrow$$

Nitric acid has no effect on aluminum because it is unable to dissolve the oxide coating and thus cannot get at the metal.[1] In fact concentrated nitric acid is shipped in aluminum containers.

Aluminum reacts with sodium hydroxide.

$$2NaOH + 2Al + 2H_2O \rightarrow 2NaAlO_2 + 3H_2 \uparrow$$

Hence articles made of aluminum should never be subjected to caustic soda or other strongly alkaline solutions. This includes cooking utensils.

As noted earlier, aluminum hydroxide is **amphoteric.** This means that it forms salts with both acids and bases. Thus a precipitate of aluminum hydroxide dissolves in acids:

$$Al(OH)_3 + 3HCl \rightarrow \underbrace{Al^{+++} + 3Cl^-}_{\text{(soluble)}} + 3H_2O$$
(precipitate)

(base) + (acid) → (salt) + (water)

This shows aluminum hydroxide acting as a base.

Aluminum hydroxide also dissolves in bases:

$$Al(OH)_3 \text{ or } HAlO_2 \cdot H_2O + NaOH \rightarrow \underset{\text{(soluble)}}{NaAlO_2} + 2H_2O$$

(acid) + (base) → (salt) + (water)

This shows aluminum hydroxide acting as an acid.

[1] This probably is due to the fact that nitric acid dissolves the oxide only very, very slowly.

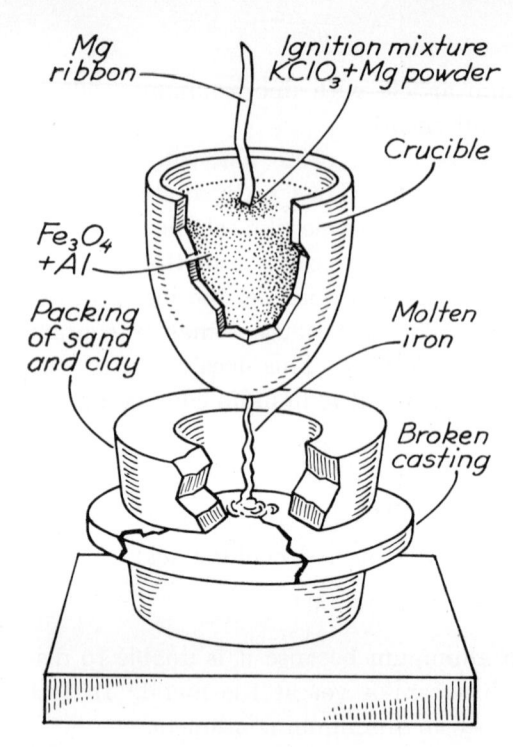

Fig. 47-3. Thermite welding. The reaction takes place as follows: $3Fe_3O_4 + 8Al \rightarrow 4Al_2O_3 + 9Fe$. When this reaction occurs, the heat of reaction is so great that the iron becomes liquid. If the reaction vessel is held over a broken casting, as shown in the drawing, the melted iron will run into the break. When the molten iron hardens upon cooling, the break will be sealed.

Thermite

The affinity of aluminum for oxygen is very great. Thus the metal burns violently when finely divided and suspended in oxygen (see Chap. 7, page 56). Aluminum will reduce other metal oxides.

$$3Fe_3O_4 + 8Al \rightarrow 4Al_2O_3 + 9Fe$$

The heat of this reaction is such that temperatures as high as 3000°C are obtained in this way. To start the reaction, an ignition powder, generally barium peroxide and aluminum, is used. This reaction mixture of magnetic iron oxide (Fe_3O_4) and aluminum is known as **thermite.** It was used in incendiary bombs during World War II. The thermite mixture ignited the magnesium bomb casing. The reaction of aluminum with metal oxides has two peacetime uses:

1. *To weld heavy machinery.* The thermite mixture is ignited over the place to be welded, for example, a broken propeller shaft on a ship. The iron liberated in the molten state flows into the area to be welded, where it solidifies (Fig. 47-3).

2. *To reduce other metal oxides* which otherwise are difficult to reduce. This is known as the **Goldschmidt process.** Manganese, chromium, molybdenum, and tungsten are reduced in this manner.

$$Cr_2O_3 + 2Al \rightarrow Al_2O_3 + 2Cr$$

Since metal oxides and molten metal are, like oil and water, immiscible, the aluminum oxide floats to the top after the reaction.

Aluminum compounds

1. *Aluminum oxide.* The hardness of aluminum oxide makes it one of the best metal cutting abrasives available (this is, *alundum*). It is incorporated into grinding wheels and also made into metal and paper coated abrasives. **Emery** is a naturally occurring material containing aluminum oxide mixed with magnetic oxide of iron (Fe_3O_4).

By blowing powdered aluminum oxide, mixed with traces of other metal oxides, into an oxyacetylene flame, the oxides are fused and collect as a globule (known as a **boule**) at the tip of the flame. The result is a synthetic sapphire or ruby which is, in every respect except cost, the equivalent of the natural gem. In general, the synthetic stones are somewhat freer of flaws than the natural gems. In this way a synthetic sapphire ½ in. across can be made for a dollar or so. Because of their hardness, synthetic rubies and sapphires are widely employed in industry for watch jewels and for bearings on delicate machines.

2. *Aluminum hydroxide.* The use of aluminum hydroxide for clarifying water has been mentioned earlier (see Chap. 13, page 135). Here its action is to entangle solid particles suspended in the water. A somewhat similar principle is involved in certain types of textile dyeing. In this process aluminum hydroxide is precipitated in the fibers of the textile which is then passed through a solution of the dyestuff. The aluminum hydroxide adsorbs the dye, thereby binding it firmly to the textile. Cotton, which otherwise is difficult to dye, is commonly dyed in this way. When so used, the aluminum hydroxide is known as a **mordant,** and the color formed by adsorbing the dye on the aluminum hydroxide is known as a **lake**. Other metallic hydroxides may be used in the same way.

3. *Alum.* If a solution containing aluminum sulfate and potassium sulfate is allowed to evaporate slowly, large, well-formed crystals result. These crystals are known as common **alum.** The formula is $KAl(SO_4)_2 \cdot 12H_2O$ [This is sometimes written $K_2SO_4 \cdot Al_2(SO_4)_3 \cdot 24H_2O$].

Crystals of similar form may be grown by using any other univalent sulfate or any other trivalent sulfate. Thus, for example, sodium chrome alum is $NaCr(SO_4)_2 \cdot 12H_2O$.

One alum will grow on a crystal of another. In this way a crystal made up of layers of different colors may be obtained.

Papermakers' alum, $Al_2(SO_4)_3 \cdot 18H_2O$, used in the paper industry, is not a true alum.

Alum and aluminum sulfate are used in baking powder (see Chap. 35, page 405), water purification (see Chap. 13, page 135), papermaking (see Chap. 38, page 463), and in tanning white leather (see Chap. 42, page 534).

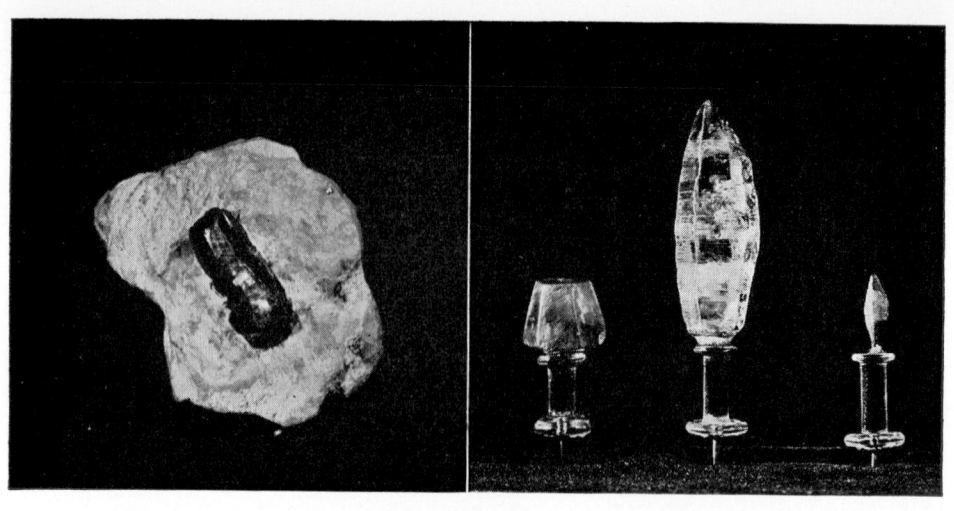

Left, a natural ruby crystal embedded in its matrix. Right, a group of three sapphire gem crystals. (American Museum of Natural History)

Pottery, china, and porcelain

Terra cotta, pottery, tile, and other such materials, are made from clay. After shaping, the article is fired. The result, known as *bisque*, is porous and must be covered with a glaze to make it waterproof. A glaze may be formed by adding sodium chloride near the end of the firing process. The salt reacts with the clay (a hydrogen aluminum silicate) to form a fusible sodium aluminum silicate, which forms the glaze. Hydrogen chloride is liberated. The red color of such articles is due to the iron oxide present.

China and porcelain are made from pure white china clay to which some ground feldspar is added. After the first firing, the product is coated with a glazing mixture, for example, a paste of water, feldspar, limestone, silica, lead oxide, and boric acid. Then it is fired again, this time at a higher temperature. Various metal oxides are used in the glaze to produce certain colors. Bone china is made in a similar manner from a mix high in calcium phosphate, which is one of the mineral constituents of bones.

Portland cement

Portland cement, which is the kind used in concrete, is made by heating a mixture of calcium carbonate and clay. Some rocks naturally contain the materials in the desired ratio. The crushed rock is fed into a gas-fired cylindrical furnace where it is heated until the particles fuse just enough to stick together in lumps. This material (known as sinter) is finely ground, mixed with 1 to 2 percent gypsum, and sold as portland cement.

When a mixture of portland cement with sand, gravel, and water, is allowed to stand, it hardens into **concrete**—one of our very important building materials. Unlike lime mortar, portland cement will set under water.

The reason for the setting of concrete is not clearly known. It is known that, like plaster of paris, the setting is due to the reaction between portland cement and water, but the exact products formed by the setting are not known with certainty. Here is a case of a large industry, based upon the manufacture and use of portland cement, in which the scientific facts underlying the basis of the industry are incompletely known.

Test for aluminum

The aluminum ion is colorless. The precipitation of colorless, gelatinous aluminum hydroxide by the addition of ammonia and ammonium chloride to the aluminum ion solution is used as a test. (The ammonium chloride is used to prevent the excess ammonia from dissolving aluminum hydroxide to form ammonium aluminate.) Since the precipitated aluminum hydroxide resembles silicic acid, it is necessary to make a further test. If a solution of aluminon reagent[1] is added to the precipitated aluminum hydroxide, a bright red lake is formed. The red lake is definite evidence of aluminum. The formation of the lake is based on the same principle as that mentioned earlier for dyeing textiles.

KEY WORDS

alum	concrete	Hall	portland cement
amphoteric	corundum	Héroult	ruby
bauxite	emery	lake	sapphire
boule	Goldschmidt process	mordant	thermite

HIGHLIGHTS

Next to steel and copper, aluminum is the most widely used metal in the United States. It is also the most abundant metal in the earth's crust, being a constituent of feldspar, clay, **bauxite,** cryolite, and **corundum.**

The modern metallurgy of aluminum was discovered independently in 1886 by **Charles M. Hall** and **Paul Héroult.** In this process aluminum is prepared by the electrolysis of a solution of aluminum oxide in molten cryolite.

---

[1] Aluminon reagent is the ammonium salt of aurin tricarboxylic acid. Formula: $(NH_4)_3C_{22}H_{11}O_9$.

Aluminum has low density and is a good conductor of heat and electricity. It is, therefore, used to construct airplanes, railroad coaches, and highway busses. Among its alloys are magnalium, aluminum bronze, duralium, and alnico. Because of its ability to reflect heat and ultraviolet rays, aluminum is widely used as an insulating material.

The thin coating of insoluble aluminum oxide on all aluminum surfaces exposed to the atmosphere prevents the further corrosion of these surfaces. Aluminum reacts with both acids and bases to evolve hydrogen. It is also attacked by sea water.

The strong affinity of aluminum for oxygen is made use of in the **thermite** process, used in welding heavy machinery and in reducing certain metallic ores. Synthetic **rubies** and **sapphires** are forms of aluminum oxide with traces of other elements. In the dye industry aluminum hydroxide is the **mordant** which adsorbs the dye and with it forms the **lake**. Clay—an aluminum-containing material—is the basis of the ceramic industry. Clay is also one of the basic materials of the **portland cement** industry.

QUESTIONS

1. What three metals are produced in the largest quantities in the United States?
2. From what mineral is aluminum metal produced at present?
3. Why is it desirable to develop a cheap method for producing aluminum from clay?
4. Describe the Hall process for aluminum manufacture.
5. How is the crude aluminum ore purified?
6. What besides aluminum ore is consumed in the manufacture of aluminum?
7. What is aluminum bronze? For what is it used?
8. What is magnalium?
9. Explain why aluminum is used in high-tension electric cables.
10. What advantages are gained by having a building covered with an aluminum roof or side walls?
11. Discuss the insulating value of aluminum.
12. How is the apparent resistance of aluminum to corrosion explained?
13. What is meant by the term amphoteric hydroxide? Write reactions which illustrate your answer.
14. What is thermite? For what is it used?
15. Explain how artificial sapphires and rubies are made. For what are they used?
16. Describe the manufacture of portland cement.

CHAPTER **48**

zinc, cadmium,

and mercury

Zinc, cadmium, and mercury make up Group IIb in the periodic table. These elements all have two valence electrons (Table 48–1) but do not have a rare gas electron structure underneath their valence electrons. Consequently these elements differ from the alkaline earths in much the same way as Group Ib differs from the alkali metals.

TABLE 48–1. The elements zinc, cadmium, and mercury

Property	Zinc	Cadmium	Mercury
Symbol	Zn	Cd	Hg
Atomic number	30	48	80
Electronic structure	2	2	2
	8	8	8
	18	18	18
	2	18	32
		2	18
			2
Melting point, °C	419	321	−38.9
Boiling point, °C	907	767	357
Density, 20°C, g/cm³	7.14	8.64	13.55
Atomic radius, angstroms	1.33	1.49	1.46
Activity	Decreases........................→		

Like the alkaline earths, zinc, cadmium and mercury all show a valence of +2 only.[1] Thus Group II is the only group in the periodic table in which there are *no elements with variable valence.*

[1] The case of mercury, which may appear to be contradictory to this, is explained on page 629.

Some of the properties of these elements are given in Table 48–1.

Zinc and cadmium are above hydrogen in activity and mercury is below it.

Occurrence of zinc

Zinc occurs in nature as zinc sulfide (ZnS), known as *sphalerite* or *zinc blende;* as zinc oxide (ZnO), *zincite;* as zinc carbonate (ZnCO$_3$), *smithsonite;* as *franklinite*, a complex mixture of oxides of zinc, iron, and manganese; and also as zinc silicate (Zn$_2$SiO$_4$·H$_2$O) known as *calamine*. The most important zinc ore deposits in the United States are the sulfide ores of Missouri, Oklahoma, and Kansas. Franklinite ore is mined in New Jersey.

Metallurgy of zinc

The production of zinc metal from the sulfide or carbonate ores is carried on as described in Chap. 43, pages 547 and 548, where the general method for the treatment of ores was given. The ore, after concentration, is roasted, thereby converting it to the oxide.

$$2ZnS + 3O_2 \xrightarrow{\text{heat}} 2ZnO + 2SO_2 \uparrow$$

$$ZnCO_3 \xrightarrow{\text{heat}} ZnO + CO_2 \uparrow$$

The resulting zinc oxide is mixed with powdered coal and heated to about 1000°C.

$$ZnO + C \xrightarrow{1000°C} Zn \uparrow + CO \uparrow$$

Sphalerite is the most important ore of zinc. It is processed by roasting to form the oxide and then reducing the oxide with carbon. Powdered coal is usually used to supply the carbon. (American Museum of Natural History)

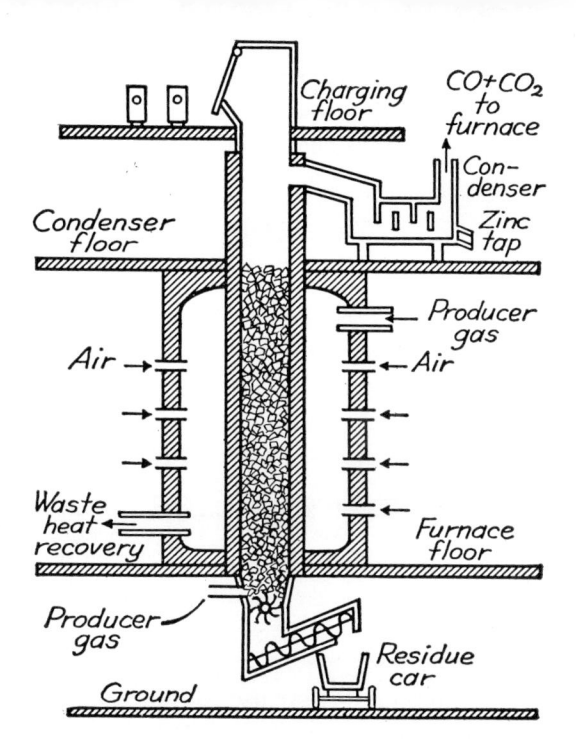

Fig. 48–1. A cross section of a modern zinc smelter. The zinc vaporizes at the temperature at which the zinc oxide is reduced. Note the condenser at the top of the smelter where the zinc is collected. (This drawing is not made to scale.)

At this temperature, the liberated zinc boils off. Outside the furnace the zinc vapor is cooled and condensed to a liquid which is cast into ingots. In a modern zinc smelter, the reduction chamber is a vertical cylinder (Fig. 48–1), heated from the outside with a gas flame. The smelter is charged from the top with roasted ore and coal. The zinc vapor distills off and passes out through the condensers. The ash and gangue are removed from the bottom of the smelter.

The crude zinc obtained in this way (known as **spelter zinc**) is then purified by distillation. More recently, electrolytic processes for zinc metallurgy have been developed. In these the zinc ore is leached with acid and the resulting aqueous solution of zinc sulfate is electroplated. Zinc deposits at the negative electrode. The zinc obtained from this process is very pure (better than 99.9 percent).[1]

Properties of zinc

Zinc is a bluish-white metal, soft and malleable at 150°C but becoming brittle just below its melting point. Mossy zinc, used in the chemical laboratory, is made by pouring the molten metal into water.

When exposed to moist air, zinc forms basic zinc carbonate

[1] Since zinc is more active than hydrogen, electrolysis of aqueous solutions of zinc salts would normally yield hydrogen instead of zinc metal. It has been found that zinc rather than hydrogen can be deposited by keeping the hydronium ion concentration of the solution low and by using a strip of very pure zinc as a cathode. If you are interested, you should consult more advanced textbooks for an explanation of this fact.

[Zn$_2$(OH)$_2$CO$_3$], a fine white surface coating which protects the metal underneath from corrosion.

Zinc reacts with acids to liberate hydrogen.

$$Zn^0 + 2OH_3^+ \rightarrow Zn^{++} + H_2 \uparrow + 2H_2O$$

Slight impurities of less active metals catalyze this reaction. *Very* pure zinc reacts with acids only slowly. Thus in the generation of hydrogen in the laboratory, adding a few drops of copper sulfate solution to the generator will speed up the reaction. This is because the zinc liberates metallic copper which catalyzes the reaction that releases hydrogen.

Zinc reacts with sodium hydroxide solution to liberate hydrogen.

$$Zn^0 + 2Na^+ + 2OH^- \rightarrow 2Na^+ + ZnO_2^= + H_2 \uparrow$$

Consequently, like aluminum, articles made of zinc should never be subjected to strongly alkaline solutions.

Uses of zinc

The most important use for zinc is in plating iron and steel to protect them from corrosion. **Galvanized** iron is made by dipping iron, which has been carefully cleaned of oxide film, into molten zinc. **Sherardized** iron, which is about the same, is made by coating the steel with powdered zinc and placing the metal in an oven where the zinc is melted. The zinc then forms a continuous coating over the steel. More recently, electrolytic methods have been developed for plating zinc onto iron.

It seems surprising, at first glance, that zinc is used to protect a less active metal, iron, from corrosion. The explanation lies in the nature of the corrosion film which zinc forms. The zinc corrosion film is like the corrosion film formed by aluminum in that it effectively seals the surface and thus prevents further corrosion. On the other hand when iron corrodes, it forms a flaky, horny rust which is porous and full of cracks and so allows moisture and air to get through it and to the metal underneath. Hence if iron is subjected to corrosion, the process continues until the iron is completely consumed.

Galvanized iron is used to make roofing and siding for buildings, garbage cans, fencing, gutters and pipes, water pipes, tanks, and a host of other articles. It must be noted, however, that because of the high activity of zinc anything which removes the corrosion film will cause the entire zinc coating to be consumed. This happens because removing the film exposes the active metal underneath. Even when exposed to ordinary air, the zinc corrosion film is slowly dissolved. Hence galvanized articles eventually rust because of the removal of the zinc coating unless they are painted periodically. In hot, moist climates,

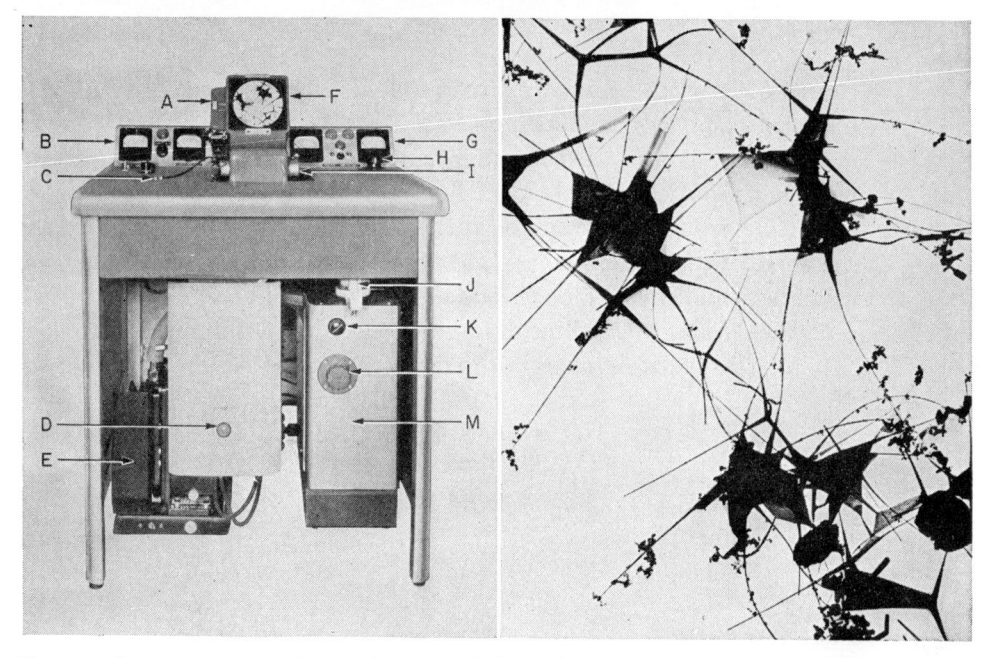

Electron microscopes are used to study metals. Left, electron microscope: *A*, camera and plate holder; *B*, vacuum gauges; *C*, camera cable release; *D*, diffusion pump indicator light; *E*, forepump; *F*, viewing screen; *G*, high-voltage meter; *H*, power supply controls; *I*, pumping valves; *J*, desiccator; *K*, electron gun bias; *L*, magnification control; *M*, high-voltage power supply. Right, a picture of zinc smoke. Note that the same picture appears on the viewing screen of the electron microscope. (Farrand Corp.)

the zinc corrosion film is removed much more rapidly than in the temperate climate. This probably explains why tin-coated steel roofing (that is, tin roof) is more commonly employed in warm climates than is galvanized roofing. The zinc corrosion film is also readily soluble in even dilute acids. This explains why galvanized iron is never used for storing or canning food (tin cans are tin-coated steel) including milk. But here the factor to be considered is not only the durability of the containers but also the fact that zinc compounds are highly toxic.

The next most important use for zinc is in making brass (see Chap. 46, page 593) and certain other zinc-containing alloys. *Dry cells* (for flashlights and other purposes) use a zinc cup as a container. This zinc is not only a container but also one of the reactants in the chemical reaction which produces the electric energy. The construction and operation of dry cells is discussed in Chap. 52.

Zinc compounds

1. *Zinc oxide.* Zinc oxide is made by burning zinc vapor. When formed in this way, it is a fine powder. The compound is yellow when hot and white when cold. Zinc oxide is used as a white paint pigment because it has the advantage over white lead (a lead hydroxycarbon-

ate) of not darkening when exposed to hydrogen sulfide. Lead sulfide is black and zinc sulfide is white.

Zinc oxide is also used in reinforcing rubber and in making certain mildly antiseptic medical ointments.

2. *Zinc sulfide.* Zinc sulfide is the only common white sulfide. It is a component of a common white paint pigment known as *lithopone*, which is a mixture of zinc sulfide and barium sulfate.

3. *Zinc hydroxide.* Zinc hydroxide is, like aluminum hydroxide, amphoteric. It dissolves in both acids and bases.

$$Zn(OH)_2 + 2OH_3^+ + 2Cl^- \rightarrow \underbrace{Zn^{++} + 2Cl^-}_{\text{zinc chloride}} + 4H_2O$$

$$Zn(OH)_2 + 2Na^+ + 2OH^- \rightarrow \underbrace{2Na^+ + ZnO_2^=}_{\text{sodium zincate}} + 2H_2O$$

or
H₂ZnO₂

Test for zinc

The zinc ion is colorless. The formation of a white zinc sulfide precipitate on the addition of ammonium sulfide to a solution of a zinc salt is used to identify zinc. The presence of other heavy metals which form dark-colored sulfides interferes with the test; hence they must be removed before applying this test.

Cadmium

Cadmium is found in nature as cadmium sulfide (CdS), *greenockite*. Most commercial cadmium is produced as a by-product of zinc metallurgy. It is separated from the crude zinc in the distillation of the latter.

Cadmium metal is white and soft, with a lower melting point than zinc. It is above hydrogen in activity, but unlike zinc the hydroxide is not amphoteric.

The main use for the metal is, like zinc, for the protection of steel from corrosion. Cadmium adheres to steel better than zinc and hence is not so readily peeled off. Thus it is more suitable for rustproofing nuts and bolts, screws, pliers, and wrenches. Since cadmium hydroxide is not amphoteric, the metal is not attacked by alkaline solutions as is zinc. Consequently cadmium-plated steel is more durable than galvanized steel when the metal is subjected to alkaline solutions. Thus cadmium-plated steel is preferred over galvanized steel where the object is in contact with concrete, since concrete gives an alkaline reaction.

Cadmium sulfide is canary yellow in color. It is used as a pigment. The formation of cadmium sulfide on passing hydrogen sulfide into a cadmium solution (about 0.3M in hydrochloric acid) is used as a *test* for the metal.

Cadmium ion is toxic and the metal should not come in contact with food or even drinking water. During World War II cadmium-plated steel was used to make ice-cube trays because of the scarcity of aluminum for civilian use. Several deaths due to cadmium poisoning were reported as being traced to the trays.

Occurrence and metallurgy of mercury

Mercury was one of the metals known to the ancients. The Latin name for the element means *silver water*. It is from the Latin name that we get the symbol Hg.

Mercury is found free in nature and also as mercury sulfide (HgS), *cinnabar*. On roasting, the sulfide is converted into sulfur dioxide and free mercury rather than mercuric oxide, which is unstable at high temperatures.

$$HgS + O_2 \rightarrow Hg \uparrow + SO_2 \uparrow$$

The resulting crude mercury is purified by distillation.

In the laboratory the metal may be purified by allowing it to drip through a column of dilute nitric acid. Foreign matter mechanically mixed with it can be removed by straining the metal through a chamois skin or even a piece of cotton or linen cloth.

Spain, Italy, and California are the principal sources of mercury.

Properties and uses of mercury

Mercury is the only common metal which is liquid at room temperatures. The fact makes it useful for *thermometers* and *electrical switches*. A mercury switch is silent, does not present a fire hazard, and easily lends itself to automatic control. Mercury switches are widely used in thermostats for hot water boilers, constant temperature water baths, and so on. The high density of the metal (13.6 g/cm^3) makes it useful for constructing barometers and for confining gases and measuring the pressure of gases (see Chap. 9, pages 79 and 80).

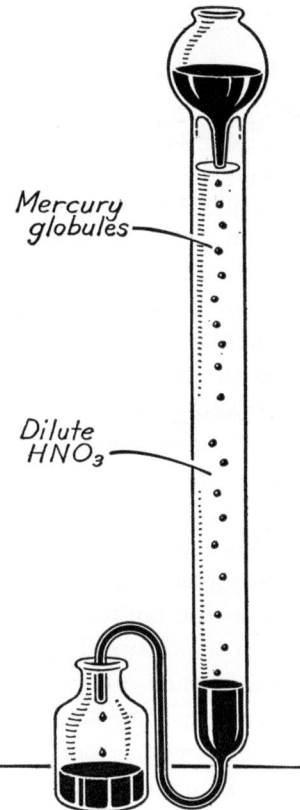

Fig. 48–2. Mercury can be purified by dropping it, as fine globules, through nitric acid.

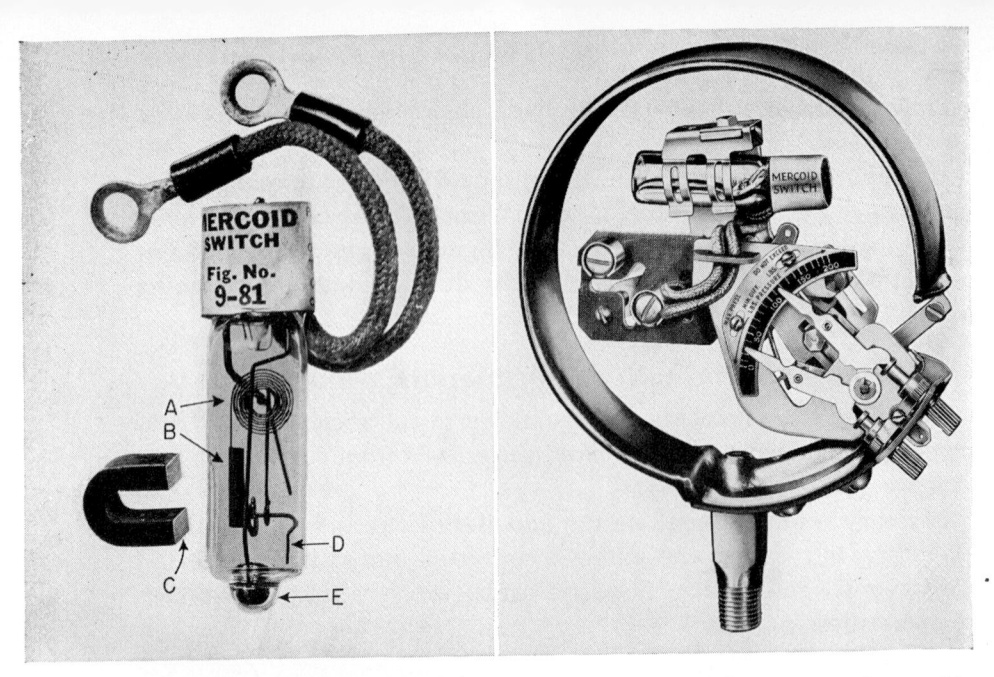

Left, mercury switch: A, return spring; B, armature; C, permanent magnet; D, movable electrode; E, mercury. Right, the mercury switch in place in a thermostat. (Mercoid Co.)

1. Fluorescent lights. When a beam of electrons passes through mercury vapor, ultraviolet rays are produced. This fact is the basis of sun lamps and also of the modern fluorescent lamp. In the latter the inside of the tube is coated with a powder which is capable of emitting visible light when struck by ultraviolet rays. (This is known as **fluorescence.**) Hence in a lamp of this type the visible light actually is emitted by the fluorescent powder in the tube. Fluorescent lamps are favored over incandescent lamps because (1) the light source is more diffuse, hence these lamps do not cast as many shadows; and (2) fluorescent lamps are more efficient in transmitting electric energy into visible light.

Since these lamps depend upon mercury vapor for the source of ultraviolet, the tube contains a small globule of metallic mercury. When the lamp is turned on, the mercury must vaporize before the lamp lights up. This explains why such lamps do not light up the instant they are switched on and the further fact that they will not operate in very cold air.

2. Mercury vapor engines. By substituting a higher boiling liquid, such as mercury, for the water normally used in an external combustion engine (that is, a steam engine or steam turbine), the efficiency of the engine can be increased. Certain heat engines using mercury vapor instead of steam have been built. Although more efficient than steam engines, mercury vapor engines have two serious disadvantages:

(1) the high initial cost of the mercury, and (2) the toxic effect of the mercury vapor if any of it escapes into the atmosphere.

3. *Amalgams.* Alloys containing mercury are known as **amalgams.** Mercury forms alloys with all common metals (except iron) as well as with gold and silver. (Hence mercury should never be placed in a copper, brass, or aluminum container.) Some of the mercury alloys are liquid; others are solid at room temperature. Amalgams of tin, silver, and gold are employed in dentistry for filling teeth. Such alloys are made by mixing the metals just before use. When immediately placed in the cavity, they harden within a few hours.

Chemical properties of mercury

Mercury is closest to the noble metals in activity. It is not attacked by hydrochloric acid, but nitric (or hot concentrated sulfuric) acid will dissolve it.

$$Hg + 4HNO_3 \text{ (concentrated)} \rightarrow Hg(NO_3)_2 + 2NO_2 \uparrow + 2H_2O$$

Mercuric compounds are those in which the valence of mercury is clearly 2. For example,

$Hg(NO_3)_2$ mercuric nitrate
$HgCl_2$ mercuric chloride (or corrosive sublimate, or bichloride of mercury)

Mercurous compounds always contain two atoms of mercury per molecule. For example,

$Hg_2(NO_3)_2$ mercurous nitrate
Hg_2Cl_2 mercurous chloride (or calomel)

The General Electric Company has a mercury-unit power plant to produce steam for a 25,000-kilowatt steam-turbine generator. These engines are more efficient than steam engines; however, the high cost of the mercury needed to run them and the toxicity of the mercury are serious disadvantages. (General Electric Co.)

These compounds give, in solution, the ion Hg_2^{++}, *not* $2Hg^+$.

$$Hg_2Cl_2 \rightarrow Hg_2^{++} + 2Cl^-$$

The mercurous ion is actually a mercuric (Hg^{++}) ion combined with an atom of mercury by a pair of electrons shared between them.

$$Hg_2^{++} = Hg^{++} : Hg$$

Mercurous compounds are formed by reducing mercuric compounds with metallic mercury.

$$Hg^{++} + Hg^0 \rightarrow Hg_2^{++}$$

Another important mercury compound is **mercuric fulminate** [$Hg(ONC)_2$]. This compound is made from mercury, nitric acid, and alcohol. Mercuric fulminate is used in percussion caps as a **detonator**, that is, a highly unstable substance that can easily be exploded with such violence as to set off the main charge of dynamite.

Toxicity of mercury

All mercury compounds are toxic if they get into the system. Some, such as mercuric chloride, are more toxic than others because they are more soluble; hence they are more completely absorbed from the digestive tract. Salts of mercury increase the flow of various body fluids; hence one symptom of mercury poisoning is the increased flow of saliva.

Calomel, Hg_2Cl_2, has been used as a medicine. The fact that it does not cause death when taken internally is due to its low solubility. The low solubility causes only slight absorption from the digestive tract to take place. Its use as a medicine is declining.

The toxicity of mercury vapor has already been mentioned. Although mercury metal has only a very low vapor pressure at room temperature, *continued* exposure to the vapor is dangerous and should be avoided. Hence the practice of discarding small amounts of mercury in the laboratory sink is dangerous, since the metal is retained in the drain pipe trap and may continue to supply mercury vapor into the laboratory. Besides, the practice is destructive of the plumbing if other than iron because the mercury amalgamates it.

Dilute solutions of mercuric chloride (1 part to 1000 parts of water) are used as medical antiseptics. Although an efficient antiseptic, the use of mercuric chloride solutions in homes is highly dangerous because children or others may unintentionally get an overdose.

Mercurochrome is a mercury compound of an organic dye. It is used as a mild local antiseptic and is relatively nontoxic.

Test for mercury

A copper wire, dipped into a solution of a mercurous or mercuric salt, becomes coated with a gray or silvery deposit of metallic mercury.

Mercurous chloride (Hg_2Cl_2), like silver chloride (AgCl), is a white insoluble compound formed by adding chloride to a solution of mercurous ion. When ammonia is added to the mercurous chloride precipitate, it turns black because of the formation of finely divided metallic mercury.

$$Hg_2^{++} + 2Cl^- \rightarrow Hg_2Cl_2 \downarrow$$
$$\underset{\text{(white)}}{Hg_2Cl_2 \downarrow} + 2NH_3 \rightarrow HgNH_2Cl \downarrow + \underset{\text{(black)}}{Hg^0 \downarrow} + NH_4Cl$$

Mercurous chloride is thus easily distinguished from silver chloride.

KEY WORDS

amalgam	detonator	mercuric fulminate	sherardized iron
cadmium	fluorescence	mercurochrome	spelter zinc
calomel	galvanized iron	mercury	zinc

HIGHLIGHTS

Zinc, cadmium, and **mercury** all have a valence of +2 only. Zinc occurs as the sulfide, oxide, carbonate, and silicate. The metallurgy of zinc consists mainly of roasting the sulfide and carbonate ores.

Zinc is a soft metal with a bluish-white luster. On exposure to moist air, it acquires a thin protective layer of basic zinc carbonate which prevents further corrosion. Zinc reacts with both acids and bases to liberate hydrogen. Its hydroxide is amphoteric.

Zinc is used in **galvanizing** and **sherardizing** sheet iron products in order to protect them from corrosion. Zinc is a constituent of brass and other alloys. Both the oxide and the sulfide are used as white pigments in paint.

Cadmium is a by-product of zinc metallurgy. It forms a better protective coating for iron than zinc does. It is, therefore, widely used for coating nuts, bolts, screws, and other small objects. The sulfide of cadmium is yellow and is used as a pigment in paint.

Mercury occurs free and as cinnabar, the sulfide, which when roasted yields the free metal. Mercury is the most common metal which is liquid at room temperature. Mercury is used in making thermometers, switches for automatic devices, and in vapor form in fluorescent lights. It is also used in mercury vapor engines. An alloy containing mercury is called an **amalgam.**

QUESTIONS

1. How does the activity of the alkaline earth elements compare with those of Group IIb?
2. What are the main ores of zinc?
3. Describe the metallurgy of zinc sulfide ores.
4. How can the rate of reaction of zinc and an acid be increased?
5. Explain how zinc is used to protect iron from corrosion.
6. What is galvanized iron? Sherardized iron?
7. Why is zinc-coated steel never used for food containers?
8. What use is made of zinc oxide?
9. What is the color of zinc sulfide?
10. What is lithopone? For what is it used?
11. What is the principal use of cadmium?
12. Describe two ways of purifying mercury.
13. Give five uses for mercury metal.
14. Explain why mercuric chloride is more poisonous than mercurous chloride. Is either nontoxic?
15. What is an amalgam?
16. Describe a test for a soluble mercury compound.
17. How is the mercurous ion distinguished from silver ion?

CHAPTER 49

iron, cobalt, and nickel

Iron, cobalt, and nickel all have similar electron structures. Since they closely resemble each other and since they fall between manganese (which belongs in Group VII) and copper (which belongs in Group Ib), they are placed together as the first triad in Group VIII. In Group VIII, the resemblance between the elements of the same triad is much closer than the resemblance between the elements which fall in the same vertical column.

Element	Symbol	Atomic number	Electron structure	Melting point, °C
Iron	Fe	26	2, 8, 14, 2	1535
Cobalt	Co	27	2, 8, 15, 2	1495
Nickel	Ni	28	2, 8, 16, 2	1455

Although it is true that some members of Group VIII show a maximum valence of 8, for example, OsF_8, the only important valences of iron, cobalt, and nickel are $+2$ and $+3$.

Iron, cobalt, and *nickel* are the only elements that are *magnetic*.

Iron and steel

The ancients and the alchemists of the Middle Ages called gold the king of metals. Today, gold counts for little and the undisputed king of metals is **iron.** The story of the development of the iron and steel industries is in large measure the story of the development of the industrial age. The story begins long before history when some savage happened to heat a lump of iron ore in an especially hot fire. He found a chunk of strange metal in the coals and may have noticed that it could be shaped by beating with stones when red hot. From that day on, iron has played an ever-increasingly important role in the life of

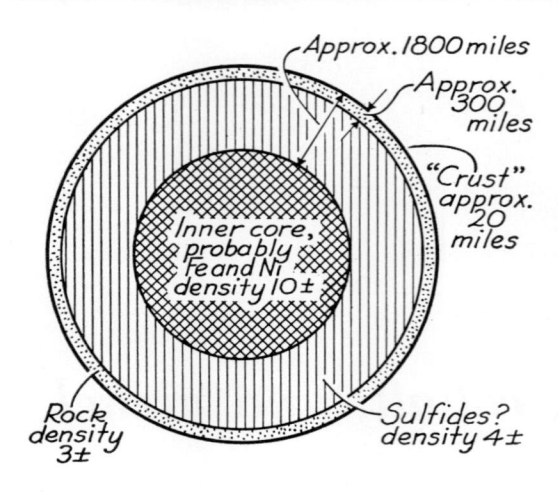

Fig. 49-1. Schematic diagram showing the probable make-up of the earth. All the evidence available at present suggests that the earth's core is made up of iron and nickel.

man until today, in the United States, we consume every year almost a ton of the metal for every man, woman, and child in the country.[1]

The present-day manufacture of iron and steel requires three primary raw materials: (1) iron ore, (2) coal which will make the proper grade of coke, and (3) limestone. There are several places in the world where these three resources occur close to each other. They are (1) the region between Pittsburgh and Chicago, (2) the area around Birmingham, Ala., (3) the region known as the Midlands in England, and (4) the Ruhr valley in central Europe.[2]

These regions have produced most of the world's steel. It is no accident that the countries which control these regions have been the centers of the world's industry and technology.

Occurrence of iron

Iron is the fourth most plentiful element on the earth's surface and the second most common metal. It is estimated that the earth's crust is 5.1 percent iron. Except for meteorites, many of which are largely metallic iron, the metal is never found free in nature.

The average density of the entire earth is about 5.5 g/cm^3. The average density of the rocks on or near the surface of the earth is about 2.7 g/cm^3. This fact, together with the fact that the earth is magnetic and other evidence, suggests that the earth's core is free iron and/or cobalt and nickel (see Chap. 18, page 205). However, there is no reason to believe that this metal at the earth's core will ever be tapped for man's use. It is too far below the earth's surface. Iron occurs in all the higher forms of animal and plant life. In higher animals iron forms part of the oxygen-carrying hemoglobin of the red blood cells.

[1] This includes scrap which is reconverted into new steel.

[2] There may be other, as yet undeveloped, regions of this type. One such is believed to exist in Manchuria.

Although iron is widespread in nature, ores suitable for making steel are not. To be usable for steel, an ore must contain a high percentage of iron and a low percentage of phosphorus, sulfur, and silica. The principal iron ore of the United States is **hematite** (Fe_2O_3). It is mined in the Lake Superior region (see below), in the Birmingham, Ala., district, and also in France and Germany. **Magnetite** ($Fe_3O_4 = FeO \cdot Fe_2O_3$) is magnetic oxide of iron. It is mined in the Adirondacks of New York State, the Soviet Union, Norway, and Sweden. *Limonite* ($2Fe_2O_3 \cdot 3H_2O$) is of less importance. *Pyrite* (FeS_2) or fool's gold is a common mineral, but it cannot be used for steelmaking because of its high sulfur content.

The **Mesabi** district at the head of Lake Superior was the greatest deposit of iron ore the world has ever known. Originally this consisted largely of nearly pure red hematite, so soft that it could be scooped out of the ground with giant power shovels. Dumped into waiting freight cars, the ore was hauled to lake steamers which carried it to the lower lake ports. From there the ore was shipped to the waiting blast furnaces of Pittsburgh, Chicago, Gary, and other cities.

The changing pattern

The great Mesabi iron mines, which in the past have supplied 85 percent of America's iron ore, have furnished most of the bone and sinew that made the American industrial giant. These mines have furnished the steel which has carried us triumphantly through two world wars and has given us the world's highest standard of living.

But now, there is a saying: Mesabi would not stand another world war. The greatest quantity of high grade ore has already been mined from this deposit. Although it will continue to supply some ore for years to come, probably it will never again supply ore at World War II rate. Hence America must seek other iron ore supplies.

Two other ore sources are already in sight. The United States Steel Corp., the largest steel company in the world, has purchased large iron ore deposits in Venezuela. The company plans to ship this ore to Atlantic coast ports where new blast furnaces and steel mills have been built to process it. In 1951, a new steel plant to utilize Venezuelan ore was opened on the Delaware River near Trenton, N.J. Labrador has large deposits of iron ore which are also being developed. Transportation of this ore depends upon shipping it by rail to the St. Lawrence River.[1] From there the ore is shipped by boat either (1) to Atlantic coast ports where, for the most part, new blast furnaces and steel mills must be built to process it, or (2) down the St. Lawrence River into the

---

[1] The Canadian government in recent years has operated a railroad from the ore deposits to the coast.

An open-pit iron mine in the Mesabi range. (American Iron and Steel Institute)

lower lake ports to supply the already existing mills. The second route will require the deepening of the St. Lawrence River to provide a channel 27 ft deep all the way from its mouth to the Great Lake ports. This is one of the main considerations in the matter which is commonly known as the "Development of the St. Lawrence Seaway," a project of great economic importance to both Canada and the United States.

However the matter of future iron ore supplies turns out, two things are certain. First, steel mills will become more widely scattered throughout the United States than formerly. Second, ores will be used which are not so rich as those formerly mined from Mesabi, and the ores will have to be transported greater distances and probably purchased abroad. This means the price of steel will tend to increase.

In order to appreciate the problems of obtaining supplies of iron ore and transporting it to the mills, you should remember that the world consumes more iron ore than any other mineral except coal and oil. At the present United States rate of steel production of over 150 million tons yearly, we are consuming approximately 600 billion pounds of iron ore per year.

The metallurgy of iron

Important as iron is, few people have ever seen pure iron. Iron is difficult to obtain in the highly purified state and industry has almost no use for pure iron.

Iron is a silvery-white, soft, tough metal. When alloyed with a few tenths of one percent carbon the result, known as *steel*, is hard, strong, and elastic. Larger amounts of carbon make the metal harder and brittle—these alloys are known as **cast iron**. Sulfur and phosphorus when present with the iron make it very brittle. Hence sulfur and phosphorus are undesirable in steel and, if present in the ore, must be removed during the steelmaking. Almost all the iron used in the world is used either (1) as cast iron, (2) as carbon steels, or (3) as special alloy steels which contain a small percentage of carbon plus other special alloying ingredients.

Steelmaking involves two main steps: (1) the production of pig iron, which is carried out in a blast furnace, and (2) the conversion of pig iron into the desired type of steel.

The blast furnace

The first step in iron metallurgy is the reduction of the oxide ore in the blast furnace. This is a large tapered shell 25 to 35 ft in diameter and 90 to 100 ft high, lined with fire-resistant brick (Fig. 49-2). The charge consists of iron ore, lumps of coke, and limestone. Heated air is blown into the furnace near its bottom. Here the oxygen from the air blast combines with the coke, forming carbon dioxide. As the hot carbon dioxide travels up through the charge, it comes in contact with hot, unburned carbon, where it is reduced to carbon monoxide. The resulting carbon monoxide reduces the iron oxide. While the reactions occurring in the blast furnace are quite complex, the principal ones in the reduction of the ore are

Near bottom $\quad C + O_2 \rightarrow CO_2$
Higher up $\quad C + CO_2 \rightarrow 2CO$
$\quad Fe_2O_3 + 3CO \rightleftarrows 2Fe + 3CO_2$
or $\quad Fe_3O_4 + 4CO \rightleftarrows 3Fe + 4CO_2$

At the temperature of the furnace the iron is melted, and as it is liberated, the metal drips down into the crucible at the bottom of the furnace, from which it is removed periodically.

But since the iron ore is never pure iron oxide, there are other reactions. Silica is always present and must be removed. That is why limestone, used as a flux, is added with the ore (see Chap. 33, pages 369 and 370). Thus at the temperature of the furnace, the limestone is converted into calcium oxide.

$$CaCO_3 \xrightarrow{\text{heat}} CaO + CO_2$$

which reacts with the infusible silica to form a fusible slag

$$\underset{\text{(flux)}}{CaO} + \underset{\text{(gangue)}}{SiO_2} \rightarrow \underset{\text{(slag)}}{CaSiO_3}$$

This molten slag also drips down into the bottom of the furnace where it collects as a separate layer on top of the molten iron.

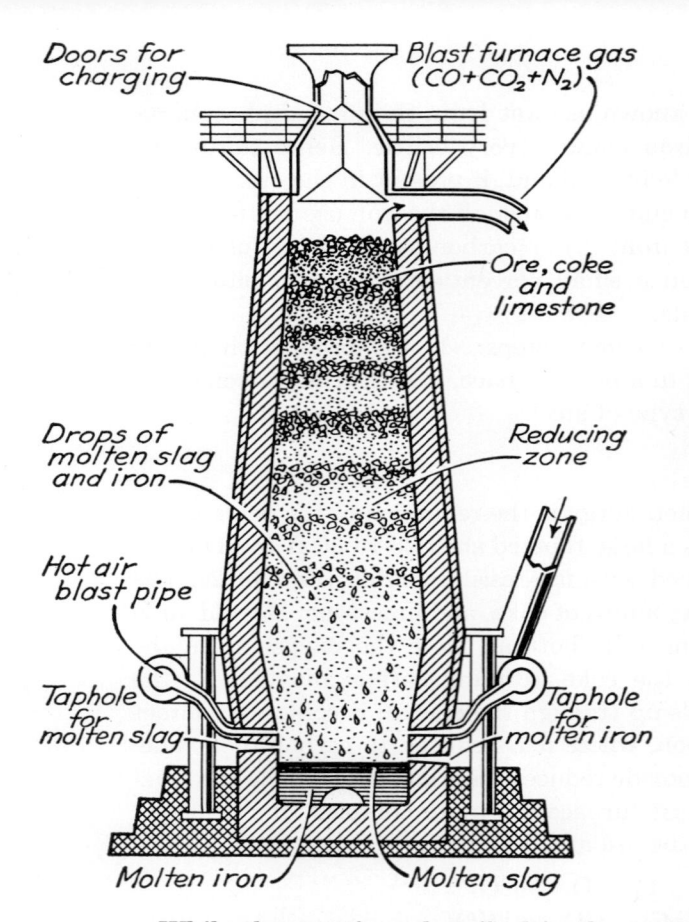

Fig. 49–2. A blast furnace. The blast furnace is essentially a tapered shell lined with fire-resistant brick. In the blast furnace iron ore is reduced to the free metal with coke. Limestone is used as the flux. The product of the blast furnace is called *pig iron*.

While the reactions described in the preceding paragraphs are the main reactions which occur in the blast furnace, there are other changes which must be considered.

Some silica is reduced to free silicon and this dissolves in the molten iron. Manganese oxide and phosphates, if present in the ore as they generally are, are reduced to free manganese and phosphorus and dissolve in the molten iron. Also, the molten iron, in dripping down through the furnace, becomes saturated with carbon. The solubility of carbon in molten iron is about 4.2 percent.

The product of the blast furnace is known as **pig iron** or cast iron and it has the following approximate composition:

Element	*Percent*
Carbon	4.2
Silicon	1.5
Manganese	1.0
Phosphorus	0.5
Sulfur	0.05
Iron	The remainder

This molten product may be sent directly to the steel mill for conversion into steel; or it may be cast in blocks of about 100 to 150 lb each, called *pigs*.

The other products of the blast furnace are (1) slag, most of which is crushed and used as a substitute for stone in road building, or for railroad ballast, or converted into *rock wool* for insulation, and (2) combustible furnace gases. Since the reduction of iron oxide by carbon monoxide is a reversible reaction, the reaction does not go to completion. The exhaust gases contain carbon monoxide—hence their fuel value. They are retained and used to preheat the air blown into the bottom of the furnace.

Except for strikes and shutdowns to repair or reline the furnace, operation of a blast furnace is continuous. The furnace is charged from the top through a double-door arrangement which prevents the escape of hot gases. On the average, a furnace produces about one thousand tons of pig iron daily. This requires the following raw materials:

	Tons
Iron ore	2000
Coke	1000
Limestone	500

Cast iron

Iron castings, such as steam radiators, sewer pipe, and boilers for furnaces, are made by remelting pig iron and pouring the liquid into prepared sand molds. Cast iron is always harder and more brittle than steel. These properties are due to the presence of the other elements along with the iron, particularly to the high percentage of carbon. Although the hardness of cast iron is sometimes desirable, as, for example, in making a plow point, its brittleness is generally undesirable, since it makes the article non-elastic and liable to break from slight shocks.

Pig iron is suited for making castings largely for two reasons:

1. Because of its high carbon content, the melting point of pig iron is about 1130°C as compared with 1535°C which is the melting point of pure iron. (Recall the effect of impurities on melting point, Chap. 15, page 164.) Hence it is possible to get pig iron into a highly fluid state so that it flows into all the crevices of the mold.

2. Pig iron expands on solidification, thereby also tending to give a good, sharp reproduction of the mold.

To some extent the physical properties of cast iron can be varied by heat treatment. Thus there are two common kinds of cast iron:

1. *White cast iron*, produced by rapid cooling of the molten metal.

The carbon of white cast iron is all in the form of **cementite** (Fe$_3$C) which is uniformly dispersed throughout the iron (that is, in solid solution). White cast iron is exceedingly hard but very brittle. These properties are caused by the cementite present.

2. *Gray cast iron*, formed by cooling the casting slowly. Under these conditions, some of the cementite has time to decompose

$$Fe_3C \xrightarrow{\text{cool slowly}} 3Fe + \underset{\text{graphite}}{C}$$

and fairly large crystals of graphite are deposited throughout the mass of metal. Gray cast iron, therefore, is grayish in color because of the graphite crystals. Since there is less carbon in solution in the iron, gray cast iron is not quite so hard and brittle as white cast iron.

The principal advantage of cast iron, other than its hardness, is that casting is a relatively cheap way of getting a metal into a desired form, such as a pipe. Cast iron is used, therefore, where its brittleness is not objectionable.

The major part of the pig iron from the blast furnace is taken directly from the furnace to the steel mill, while still molten.

Making steel

Steel is almost free of phosphorus, sulfur, and silicon,[1] and contains from 1.5 percent to 0.05 percent carbon. Hence the conversion of pig iron into steel is largely a matter of removing the undesirable impurities. Two principal methods are used: (1) the Bessemer process and (2) the open-hearth process.

[1] Except where silicon is desired for special uses.

An open-hearth furnace receiving a charge of molten iron. This process employs iron ore or rusty scrap iron to remove carbon from pig iron. The open-hearth process produces, in general, a better grade of steel than the Bessemer process. (American Iron and Steel Institute)

In the Bessemer process, air is blown through molten pig iron to remove the impurities from it. Silicon and manganese burn first; but when the carbon starts to ignite, the flame changes color, becomes brighter, and is accompanied by a shower of sparks as shown. (American Iron and Steel Institute)

1. The Bessemer process. The **Bessemer process** was discovered independently by a Kentuckian, William Kelley, in 1847, and by an Englishman, Sir Harry Bessemer, a few years later. In this process the carbon is burned out by blowing air through the molten pig iron. A large container shaped like a concrete mixer is used. This is known as a *Bessemer converter*. In the United States the converters are lined with silica firebrick. Air is blown through an opening in the bottom of the converter. The oxidation of the impurities liberates enough energy to keep the metal molten. Carbon, silicon, and manganese burn to the oxides and either escape as gases or collect on the top of the molten metal. The silicon and manganese burn first, producing an orange-yellow flame, tinted blue. As the carbon starts to burn, the flame becomes brighter and is accompanied by a shower of sparks. Then as the carbon is burned out, the flame dies down, and the melting point of the iron rises. The charge must now be poured, since there is no source of heat to keep it molten and if not poured it will solidify in the converter. Just before pouring, the desired amount of carbon (and other elements if desired) is added to give the steel the final desired composition. A **scavenger** is also added to combine with the oxygen and nitrogen in the bubbles dispersed through the steel; otherwise the steel would be full of flaws due to these air bubbles. Various scavengers are used. A common one is aluminum. An alloy of iron and titanium (ferrotitanium) is also used. The entire process takes about fifteen minutes,

Top, a modern spectrograph. Bottom, a plate from the spectrograph. This plate shows an analysis of crude petroleum oil. Iron ore, steel, and many other materials may be analyzed in this manner. (Bausch & Lomb Optical Co.)

after which the steel is poured into molds to give ingots of steel. The ingots then go to the rolling mill to be rolled into rails, sheets, and strips as desired.

The Bessemer process is the cheapest method for making steel, but it does not produce as good quality steel as the open-hearth process. This is because the Bessemer process does not remove the phosphorus from the metal and because the steel is apt to contain flaws due to the presence of air bubbles when it solidified. The open-hearth process is preferred in the United States.

2. *The open-hearth process.* The **open-hearth process** employs iron ore or rusty scrap iron to combine with the unwanted carbon in pig iron. The charge consists of pig iron, rusty scrap or iron ore, and sometimes limestone. These are heated in large saucer-shaped depres-

sions known as open-hearth furnaces. The furnace is heated by a gas flame that passes over the top of the charge. Oxygen from the iron ore or rusty scrap combines with the phosphorus and silicon to form nonmetallic oxides which combine with the lining of the furnace [which is $MgCO_3$ or $CaMg(CO_3)_2$] or with the limestone to form slag.

$$6P + 5Fe_2O_3 \rightarrow 3P_2O_5 + 10Fe$$
$$3Si + 2Fe_2O_3 \rightarrow 3SiO_2 + 4Fe$$
$$P_2O_5 + 3MgCO_3 \rightarrow Mg_3(PO_4)_2 + 3CO_2 \uparrow$$
$$SiO_2 + MgCO_3 \rightarrow MgSiO_3 + CO_2 \uparrow$$

Carbon is oxidized to carbon dioxide and escapes.

$$3C + 2Fe_2O_3 \rightarrow 3CO_2 \uparrow + 4Fe$$

Manganese is converted to manganese silicate.

As the heating continues, samples of the melt are taken to the laboratory for analysis. When the analysis shows that the impurities have been removed and the carbon content reduced to the desired amount, a scavenger is added and the melt cast into ingots. The process generally takes 10 to 12 hr.

The open-hearth process is favored over the Bessemer process in the United States for several reasons: (1) The composition of the steel can be more exactly controlled, (2) phosphorus can be removed, and (3) the process allows the use of scrap iron, thereby reducing the amount of pig iron and conserving the iron ore resources.

Crucible steel is steel made in small batches by hand control in crucibles holding about one hundred pounds. By more accurate control of conditions a high-grade steel for special uses, such as tools, watch springs, and razor blades, is produced. In the United States this method has now been largely replaced by *electric furnace* steel. In this case the heat is produced by electricity; hence the temperature can be very closely controlled.

About 90 percent of the United States steel production is by the open-hearth process.

Types of steel

In general, the lower the carbon content, the softer and more ductile is the steel.

1. *Mild* steels used for bridges, automobiles, ships, wire, and nails contain from 0.05 to 0.20 percent carbon.

2. *Medium* steels used for railroad rails and wheels as well as structural steel for buildings contain from 0.2 to 0.6 percent carbon.

3. *High-carbon* steel used for tools, springs, and cutting instruments contains from 0.6 to 1.5 percent carbon.

Although the carbon content of a steel in general determines its hardness and elasticity, the properties of the steel can be greatly influenced by *heat-treatment*. This is one of the reasons why steel is so useful. Although heat-treatment is a complex subject which is outside the scope of this book, a few facts deserve mention. Steel heated to about 900°C and cooled quickly by quenching in water is harder and more elastic than if cooled slowly. By reheating a quenched steel to 300°C or higher, the hardness may be reduced by an amount depending on the length and temperature of the reheating. Thus if it is desired to make a penknife, the steel should have a carbon content of around 1 to 1.5 percent. When heated to about 900°C, then plunged into water, and then reheated to about 225°C, the steel will be found to have the desired hardness, elasticity, and toughness. Steel intended to withstand both shock and wear, as in an auto axle, is made with a tough core and hard surface by **case hardening.** In this process the article is heated in a coke or sodium cyanide (NaCN) bath. Under these conditions, carbon enters the surface, thereby hardening it, and the core remains tough and strong.

Alloy steels, as the term is used in industry, are those which contain elements other than carbon. These elements are added to produce certain special properties. A great many alloy steels are known and doubtless many others can and will be discovered. A few are shown in Table 49–1.

TABLE 49–1. Alloy steels

Name of steel	Composition	Special properties	Uses
Silicon (duriron)	12–14% Si	Acid-resistant	Acid-carrying pipes, tanks
Copper	0.2–1% Cu	Resistant to corrosion	Roofing, culverts
Stainless	18% Ni 8% Cr	Rustproof	Cutlery, cooking utensils, kitchen tops, trailers, railroad cars
Nickel	2–4% Ni	Hard, elastic, and resistant to corrosion	Gears, driveshafts, and other automobile parts
Manganese	12–15% Mn	Extremely hard and wear-resistant	Safes, rock crushers
Chromium-vanadium	5–10% Cr variable amount V	High strength and shock resistance	Automobile axles
Tungsten (wolfram)	10–20% W 3–10% Cr	Retain hardness at high temperatures	High-speed cutting tools
Molybdenum	5–6% Mo	Retain hardness at high temperatures	High-speed cutting tools

The reactions of iron

Iron is above hydrogen in activity and liberates hydrogen from acids. It rusts in moist air, a complex process which is still poorly understood. At high temperatures iron combines with oxygen to form magnetic oxide of iron (Fe_3O_4).

$$3Fe + 2O_2 \xrightarrow{heat} Fe_3O_4$$

Iron forms two series of compounds, those in which it has a valence of $+2$, known as *ferrous compounds*, and those in which it has a valence of $+3$, known as *ferric compounds*.

Ferrous compounds are formed by the action of iron on hydrochloric or dilute sulfuric acid

$$Fe^0 + 2OH_3^+ \rightarrow Fe^{++} + H_2 \uparrow + 2H_2O$$

or by reduction of ferric ion with the metal

$$2Fe^{+++} + Fe^0 \rightarrow 3Fe^{++}$$

The ferrous compounds are oxidized by oxygen of the air in the presence of water to the ferric state; hence they are unstable in solutions which are in contact with air. Ferrous salt solutions are best kept in the laboratory by putting a few iron nails into the solution. This free iron serves to reduce any ferric iron formed by reaction with the oxygen of the atmosphere. The ferrous ion is nearly colorless. In concentrated solutions it gives a pale green color.

Ferric ion is also nearly colorless in solution, but solutions of ferric salts are generally rusty brown in color because of hydrolysis.

$$\underset{\text{(colorless)}}{Fe^{+++}} + 2H_2O \rightleftarrows \underset{\text{(brown)}}{Fe(OH)^{++}} + OH_3^+$$

Since this reaction is reversible, the color present in solutions of ferric chloride or nitrate can be made to disappear by adding a strong acid such as nitric. This reverses the above reaction.

Ferric ion may be recognized by adding ammonium thiocyanate (NH_4SCN) solution, which produces an intense blood-red color.

$$Fe^{+++} + SCN^- \rightarrow \underset{\text{(intensely red)}}{Fe(SCN)^{++}}$$

Occurrence and metallurgy of nickel and cobalt

Nickel and **cobalt** occur in nature mainly as sulfides and arsenides, commonly associated with copper and silver. About 90 percent of the nickel consumed in the United States comes from Ontario, Canada, and most of this is produced by the International Nickel Co. Low-grade nickel ores occur in Cuba, but apparently these deposits cannot be

Several forms of iron are used in the manufacture of a modern toaster. For example, the body is made of chromium-plated steel. The heating elements are made of nichrome, which is an alloy of nickel, iron, and other elements. Nichrome has high electric resistance, a high melting point, and does not burn up at red heat. (General Electric Co.)

worked profitably except when the price of nickel is high and there is great demand for it. During World War II, the Cuban deposits were worked, but operations ceased shortly after the war. Now these deposits are again being opened up. There are no known nickel deposits of value inside the United States. Important nickel deposits occur in Finland and New Caledonia. Cobalt is produced as a by-product from the nickel ores of Ontario. Most of the remaining amount of cobalt consumed in the United States comes from the Belgian Congo.

The smelting of nickel and cobalt ores is complex. The ores are roasted to remove sulfur and arsenic, then reduced with carbon. One of the biggest problems is the separation of nickel and cobalt. In one process this separation depends upon the fact that nickel forms a gaseous nickel carbonyl [$Ni(CO)_4$] when heated with carbon monoxide, whereas cobalt does not. The resulting nickel carbonyl is decomposed into nickel and carbon monoxide by heating it to a higher temperature.

Properties and uses of nickel and cobalt

Nickel is a hard, white, magnetic metal. Although above hydrogen in activity, it does not corrode in ordinary air; hence for many years it was used to plate copper and brass objects such as bathroom fixtures. In this connection it has been, of late, largely replaced by chromium. Nickel is used as a catalyst in the hydrogenation of fats (see Chap. 37, page 446). Its principal use is in making heat-resisting and corrosion-resisting alloys such as monel metal, stainless steel, nichrome, and Invar steel. *Nichrome* is widely used as electric heating elements for stoves, toasters, and other electric heaters. Nichrome is an alloy of nickel plus iron (12 percent), chromium (11 percent), manganese (2 percent), and carbon (about 0.1 percent). Its high electrical resistance, high melting point, and the fact that it does not burn up at red heat make it suitable for this use. *Invar steel* contains nickel (36 percent), iron (63.8 percent), carbon (0.2 percent). Invar steel expands only very slightly with temperature increases, hence its use for precision measuring scales and surveyors' tapes.

Cobalt is a hard, silvery-white metal. It is above hydrogen in activity but very resistant to corrosion. The demand for this metal for making special alloys exceeds the supply at present. Its use in permanent magnets (*alnico*) has been mentioned earlier. At present the other principal use for cobalt is for making heat-resisting alloys necessary for jet engines and the *stellite* alloys (containing cobalt and one or more of the metals chromium, molybdenum, iron, nickel, tungsten) which are essential for certain high-speed tools.

Chemical properties of nickel and cobalt

Both cobalt and nickel form compounds in which they have valences of $+2$ and $+3$. Unlike iron, the $+2$ valence compounds of these two elements are much more stable than the $+3$ valence compounds, and the latter are rarely encountered. The hydrated nickel ion $[Ni(H_2O)_x^{++}]$ is apple-green color in solution. The hydrated cobalt ion $[Co(H_2O)_x^{++}]$ is light pink but the anhydrous cobalt ion (Co^{++}) is deep blue. This is the basis of the sympathetic ink experiment (see Chap. 13, page 140), and also the indicator used in drying agents such as silica gel. When the silica gel can absorb no more water, cobalt chloride mixed with it changes from blue to pink.

KEY WORDS

alloy steels	cast iron	hematite	nickel
Bessemer process	cementite	iron	open-hearth process
blast furnace	cobalt	magnetite	pig iron
case hardening	crucible steel	Mesabi	scavenger

HIGHLIGHTS

Iron, cobalt, and **nickel** all have valences of $+2$ and $+3$. Iron is the most widely used metal in America.

The chief ores of iron are **hematite, magnetite,** and limonite. In the **blast furnace,** ore, coke, and limestone react to produce **pig iron** or **cast iron** which contains about 4 percent carbon and other impurities.

Molten iron from the blast furnace may be taken directly to the steel mill. The steelmaking processes are the **Bessemer,** the **open-hearth,** and the electric furnace. The open-hearth process is the most widely used because it may be controlled more accurately than the Bessemer process. The electric furnace process produces steel of high quality. The hardness of steel is determined by the carbon content, by tempering, and by the addition of appropriate alloying metals. Steel is classified as mild (0.05 to 0.20 percent carbon), medium (0.20 to 0.60 percent carbon), and high carbon (0.60 to 1.50 percent carbon). Among the more important elements used in making alloy steel are silicon, copper, nickel, chromium, manganese, vanadium, tungsten, and molybdenum.

Most of our nickel and cobalt comes from Canada. Carbon monoxide is used to separate nickel from cobalt in the refining process. Monel and nichrome are important nickel alloys. Stellite is an alloy of cobalt and is very important in high-speed tools.

QUESTIONS

1. What raw materials are necessary to make iron and steel?
2. Name four areas in the world where these raw materials are found close together.
3. What are the requirements of an iron ore to be used for making steel?
4. What are the principal iron ores mined in the United States?
5. What future sources of iron ore outside the United States are now known?
6. Compare the properties of pure iron, steel, and cast iron.
7. What are the two main steps in steelmaking?
8. What are the products of the blast furnace?
9. Why does pig iron contain so much carbon?
10. What properties of pig iron make it suitable for castings?
11. How is white cast iron different from gray cast iron?
12. Describe the Bessemer process for steelmaking.
13. Give two reasons why the open-hearth process is preferred for steelmaking in the United States.
14. How does the carbon content influence the properties of steel?
15. What is stainless steel?
16. What properties does manganese impart to steel?
17. Describe a test for ferric ion.
18. What is the source of most of the nickel consumed in the United States?
19. What is nichrome? For what is it used?
20. Why is cobalt a "strategic" metal?

CHAPTER **50**

tin, lead, and titanium

The important metals, tin, lead, and titanium are members of Group IV. Tin and lead are the last members of Group IV*b* of which carbon and silicon are the first two members. Tin and lead are metallic in physical properties. This subgroup is a good illustration of the way in which metallic properties become more pronounced as the atomic number increases within any subgroup.

Titanium is the first member of Group IV*a*; hence it does not closely resemble tin and lead.

Occurrence and metallurgy of tin

Tin is not an abundant element. The earth's crust is estimated to contain 0.000001 percent tin. However, there are a few places on the earth where concentrated tin ore exists, and because of this, tin has been known and used by man for several thousand years. The only tin ore of importance is **cassiterite,** SnO_2. Deposits of cassiterite at Cornwall, England, were worked as early as 1000 BC by the Phoenicians. These mines are still yielding some tin. Most of the world's tin now comes from the Malay states, Indonesia, and Bolivia. The United States has no known tin deposits of economic value.

The metallurgy is simple. The ore is concentrated, roasted to remove any arsenic or sulfur which may be present, then reduced with carbon. The crude metal is separated from any iron which it may contain by melting the tin (mp 232°C) and allowing it to drain away from the impurities. If necessary, tin may be further purified by electrolytic methods.

Properties and uses of tin

Tin exists in two allotropic forms. Common **white tin** is a soft, malleable white metal. If cooled below 18°C, this variety becomes unstable and changes into a gray, brittle, semimetallic looking mass which is readily powdered. This material is still elementary tin but has a different crystal structure and hence different physical properties than white tin. It is known as **gray tin**. (Compare this with the behavior of sulfur, Chap. 28, pages 317 and 318.)

$$\underset{\text{(gray)}}{\text{Sn}} \underset{18°C}{\rightleftarrows} \underset{\text{(white)}}{\text{Sn}}$$

Although the transformation point is 18°C, the change from white tin to gray tin is slow. The metal must be held below 18°C for many days before the change is noticeable. It is most rapid at about $-50°C$. Therefore, tin articles in cold climates will slowly undergo change into gray tin. It is recorded that tin organ pipes in Zeitz, Germany, were ruined as a result of the cold winter of 1850. It was also early noticed that medals made of tin which were stored in cold museums sometimes became covered with patches of gray powder. For this reason the change became known as **tin disease**. It was not until much later that this "disease" was shown to be due to a change in physical form of the metal.

TABLE 50-1. Properties of tin, Sn

Atomic number	50
Electron structure	2, 8, 18, 18, 4
Valences	2, 4
Melting point, °C	232
Boiling point, °C	2270
Density, g/cm^3, 20°C	7.30

White tin is very malleable; hence it was one of the first metals used in foil form. Its use as tin foil has been largely replaced by aluminum.

Tin is above hydrogen in activity but does not corrode in air—probably because of a thin oxide film which protects the metal as in the case of aluminum. Its main use, which is based on this fact, is for making tin-plated steel for use as roofing, tin cans, milk cans, and other food-processing equipment. The tin coating may be applied by dipping the cleaned steel into molten tin or by the newer method of electroplating. The latter gives a more uniform coating and consumes less tin. Tin-coated steel resists corrosion as long as the steel is not exposed. However, if a scratch exposes the steel underneath, the steel will start to rust, since it is more active than the tin. Hence most

The most important ore of lead is galena. To produce the free metal, galena is roasted to give lead oxide (PbO) and then the lead oxide is reduced with carbon. (American Museum of Natural History)

commercial tin plate which carries only a thin coating of tin is not very durable.

Other uses for tin are in making alloys, especially bronze, solder, babbitt metal, and type metal.

Chemical properties of tin

When acted upon by hydrochloric acid, tin is converted to *stannous chloride*.

$$Sn^0 + 2OH_3^+ + 2Cl^- \rightarrow H_2 \uparrow + Sn^{++} + 2Cl^- + 2H_2O$$

Tin also shows a valence of 4. Tetravalent tin compounds resemble in some respects those of carbon and silicon.

Thus chlorine acts upon tin to form tin tetrachloride, a *volatile liquid* suggestive of carbon tetrachloride.

$$2Cl_2 + Sn \rightarrow SnCl_4$$

In the tetravalent tin compounds the atoms are held together by covalence.

The reaction of tin with chlorine is used for de-tinning scrap, a process for reclaiming tin from scrap metal. In this process the scrap is treated with chlorine; the resulting liquid tin tetrachloride is collected and converted back into metallic tin.

Occurrence and metallurgy of lead

Lead is more common in nature than tin, and the United States is fairly well supplied with lead ores. The principal ore is *galena* (PbS), although *cerussite* (PbCO$_3$) and *anglesite* (PbSO$_4$) are known. Important lead deposits are found in Missouri, Idaho, Colorado, Utah, Mexico, Germany, and Canada.

In the production of the metal, the ore is roasted, then reduced with carbon.

$$2PbS + 3O_2 \rightarrow 2SO_2 \uparrow + 2PbO$$
$$PbO + C \rightarrow Pb + CO$$

Other methods are also used.

The crude lead almost always contains silver. This is removed by the **Park's process.** This process is based on the fact that molten lead and zinc are, like oil and water, insoluble in each other, and the further fact that silver is much more soluble in zinc than in lead. Hence to remove the silver, the crude molten lead is stirred with molten zinc. The molten zinc dissolves most of the silver, and on standing, the zinc layer rises to the top, where it is skimmed off, carrying the silver in solution. The zinc (bp 907°C) is separated from the silver by distillation, the silver remaining behind as a nonvolatile residue.

Properties and uses of lead

Lead is a very soft, grayish metal with very low tensile strength. Its high density is well known.

TABLE 50-2. Properties of lead, Pb

Atomic number	82
Electron structure	2, 8, 18, 32, 18, 4
Valences	2, 4
Melting point, °C	327
Boiling point, °C	1620
Density, g/cm³, 20°C	11.34

When exposed to air, lead acquires a surface corrosion film but the corrosion stops at this point. Hence the metal is very durable in contact with air and most solutions, and many of its uses depend upon this fact.

Lead pipe is used for plumbing.[1] The pipe is formed by squeezing the lead through a die with hydraulic pressure. Since lead pipe is soft and easily bent, it is easy to install. The metal is not, however, strong enough to be threaded. Therefore, the joints must be soldered together using molten lead or a tin-lead alloy. The soldering process is known to plumbers as *wiping*, since the molten solder is applied to the joint with a wool rag. Because of the danger of lead poisoning, lead pipes probably should never be used for carrying drinking water. Buried underground where subsurface waters are acid, lead is generally more durable than copper (see Chap. 46, page 593).

[1] The very word *plumbing* is derived from the Latin for lead!

Lead has the greatest ability of any of the common elements to absorb radiation. For this reason, lead cases are used to store and ship radioactive elements. (Brookhaven National Laboratories)

Electric cables that are to be buried underground are sometimes sheathed with lead. This use for lead is decreasing because of the development of synthetic resins which are suitable for this purpose and which are cheaper. Telephone cables are commonly sheathed with lead. A great deal of lead is used in making storage batteries and some is used for making solder. Lead for making shot for shotgun shells and bullets is hardened by the addition of 0.5 percent arsenic.

In 1950 about 275 million pounds of lead were used in making tetraethyllead $[Pb(C_2H_5)_4]$ which is added to motor fuels to increase their octane rating.

White lead $[Pb_2(OH)_2CO_3]$ is the second most extensively used white paint pigment. (Titanium dioxide is first.) It is present in most oil paints. Although white lead has good covering power, it has two disadvantages: (1) The pigment blackens on exposure to hydrogen sulfide because of the formation of black lead sulfide and (2) it is poisonous. Consequently lead paints should never be used for baby furniture if there is any possibility that the baby might lick or chew the painted surface. Neither should lead paints be used where cattle or other livestock can lick or chew the painted surface. Cattle seem to be particularly sensitive to lead poisoning.[1] Special nontoxic white paints are available.

[1] This may have some bearing on the fact that barns are traditionally painted red. Ordinary red barn paint is red iron oxide (Fe_2O_3) and oil. It is nontoxic.

Lead has the highest atomic weight of all common metals. Since the ability of an element to absorb radiation is proportional to its atomic weight, this explains its widespread use for shielding x-ray equipment and radioactive samples.

Chemical properties of lead

Although above hydrogen in activity, lead is not acted upon by either hydrochloric or dilute sulfuric acid. This is because both lead chloride and lead sulfate are insoluble and precipitate out as a protective film on the surface of the metal. Hence lead sheets are sometimes used to cover chemical laboratory tables and to line laboratory sinks.

Lead commonly has a valence of +2. The nitrate [$Pb(NO_3)_2$] and the acetate [$Pb(C_2H_3O_2)_2$] are the only common lead salts which are soluble.

Lead dioxide, PbO_2, a dull red powder, is a powerful oxidizing agent. It is used in the lead storage battery.

Litharge, PbO, mixed with glycerin, hardens into a stonelike material. It is useful for cementing drainpipes into a concrete or ceramic sink.

Minium is Pb_3O_4 (Pb_2PbO_4). It is a bright red powder. Mixed with oil it makes a good rustproofing paint for steel and is frequently used on bridge girders, roofs, fences, and other materials that need protection.

TABLE 50-3. Alloys containing tin or lead

Name	Lead, %	Tin, %	Other metals, %
Standard type metal	58	26	Antimony 15; copper 1
Solder, common, soft	50	50	
Babbitt		90	Antimony 7; copper 3
Pewter		85	Antimony 1.7; copper 6.8; bismuth 6
Fusible alloy (mp 145°C)	32	50	Cadmium 18

Lead poisoning

Lead compounds are quite toxic and particularly dangerous because their toxic effect is cumulative. That is, minute amounts of lead taken at intervals into the body are not excreted but accumulate in the body and may eventually cause trouble. The lead ion tends to accumulate in the bones, particularly the joints. (This is probably because the carbonates and phosphates of lead, like those of calcium, are insoluble.) Mild cases of lead poisoning have been observed which involved stiffness and lameness in the joints not unlike rheumatism or arthritis. Intake of large amounts of lead results in death.

The surface of a 2-ton ingot of titanium is being prepared for milling by the worker in the photograph above. (E. I. du Pont de Nemours & Co.)

Because of the wide use of lead compounds in paint, painters should be particularly careful to avoid the intake of even minute amounts of paint. The use of lead pipes for drinking water also presents the hazard of lead poisoning. Pure water or water containing dissolved carbon dioxide or ammonia slowly dissolves lead as it passes through the pipe. Hence drinking such water that has run through lead pipes will cause the accumulation of lead in the body. On the other hand it is claimed that if the water contains sulfate ion, this will precipitate the insoluble lead sulfate ($PbSO_4$) on the inside surface of the pipe. This prevents solution of the pipe, and hence the water will not become contaminated. For the average person, who is unable to decide whether his own water supply contains enough sulfate ion to protect him from lead poisoning, the safest course is to use pipes of iron, copper, or brass. Doubtless there are many people who suffer from lead poisoning who are not aware that lead is the cause of their difficulty.

Occurrence of titanium

Although generally unfamiliar to the layman, titanium compounds have for the last 20 years become increasingly important as pigments. The recent development of commercial production of the metal, which has very interesting properties, has aroused new interest in the element.

Titanium is the *ninth* most common element in the earth's crust, which contains approximately 23 times as much titanium as carbon. The amount of titanium is 5 to 10 times the amount of phosphorus and sulfur found in nature. It is estimated that 0.63 percent of the earth's crust is made up of titanium.

This element is never found free in nature but always combined with oxygen. Its important minerals are **rutile** (TiO_2) and **ilmenite** ($FeTiO_3$). These minerals are found in large amounts in Virginia, Florida, and North Carolina. Large deposits of ilmenite exist in the Adirondack Mountains of New York, the Scandinavian Peninsula, and the Ural Mountains of Russia.

Preparation of titanium

The preparation of pure titanium metal is difficult because its oxide is an infusible and highly stable compound. The present process (known as the **Kroll process**) involves (1) conversion of titanium dioxide (TiO_2) to titanium tetrachloride ($TiCl_4$) and (2) reduction of titanium tetrachloride to the metal. Thus titanium dioxide is heated with chlorine and carbon

$$TiO_2 + 2C + 2Cl_2 \rightarrow TiCl_4 + 2CO$$

forming titanium tetrachloride, a volatile liquid boiling at 136°C (compare with carbon tetrachloride). This is then reduced with metallic magnesium in a closed bomb at 800°C in an atmosphere of helium or argon.

$$TiCl_4 + 2Mg \xrightarrow{800°C} 2MgCl_2 + Ti$$

After cooling, the reaction products are broken up, and the magnesium chloride is leached out, leaving a *sponge* of titanium metal. This sponge is cold-rolled and worked to eliminate the pores and form the massive metal.

Properties and uses of titanium

Titanium metal is silver-white. Its tensile strength is nearly twice that of iron and its resistance to corrosion about as good as stainless steel. But its density ($= 4.5 \text{ g/cm}^3$) is scarcely more than half that of stainless steel. Hence it seems to combine the good properties of aluminum with those of steel. Titanium is known to form promising alloys with other metals. In view of these facts and the vast amount of titanium ore available, there is reason to believe that titanium will become one of the important structural metals of the future. This idea is quite encouraging. Two world wars plus increasing civilian demand for structural metals have left the United States as well as other parts of the world with seriously diminished mineral resources. But here is a metal, abundant in nature, which may well replace many of those formerly used and now becoming scarce.

Commercial production of titanium was not started until 1948. Because of the difficulties in preparing the metal by the above process, its present price is high—$5 to $10 per pound. Uses are just being developed and are limited by the availability of the metal and its high cost. Therefore, a cheaper method for the manufacture of titanium is badly needed. It is hoped such a method will be developed soon. The metallurgy of titanium is today in about the state of development that the metallurgy of aluminum was before Hall developed the present electrolytic method for its manufacture in 1886.

Although remarkably resistant to corrosion under atmospheric conditions, titanium combines with both oxygen and nitrogen at high temperatures. Because of this and its high melting point (= 1725°C), the metal cannot be cast but must be shaped by cold-working or machining. **Ferrotitanium,** an alloy of iron and titanium, made by reduction of the mixed oxides with carbon, is used as a scavenger in steelmaking (see Chap. 49, page 641).

Chemical properties and compounds of titanium

As noted earlier, titanium becomes quite active at high temperatures. It is above hydrogen in activity and reacts with concentrated sulfuric, or hydrochloric, acid, although nitric acid does not affect it.

$$Ti + 2H_2SO_4 \rightarrow Ti(SO_4)_2 + 2H_2 \uparrow$$

A great deal of planning went into the production of titanium on a commercial scale. Here two chemists and an engineer are shown working on the pilot plant design. (E. I. du Pont de Nemours & Co.)

Titanium dioxide is one of the best white pigments known. It has great covering power and is not toxic. It also has the advantage that it does not darken on exposure to hydrogen sulfide. Most good white paints, such as the one used to paint these buildings, employ titanium dioxide as the white pigment. (Library of Congress)

Finely divided titanium dioxide is white and has the best covering power of any white pigment known. It is now the leading white pigment and is used for paints, lacquers, refrigerator enamel, papermaking, white shoe cleaner, face powder, and white rubber goods. Not only does the compound have excellent covering power but it is nontoxic and does not darken on exposure to hydrogen sulfide as do lead pigments.

Titanium dioxide pigment is made by dissolving crushed ilmenite ($FeTiO_3$) ore (which is black) in sulfuric acid. This solution is then diluted with water and boiled to precipitate gelatinous titanium hydroxide, which is heated to form the oxide pigment. The ferrous sulfate ($FeSO_4$) stays in solution and is unchanged by the boiling.

$$\underset{\text{(mineral)}}{FeTiO_3} + 3H_2SO_4 \rightarrow \underset{\text{(soluble)}}{Ti(SO_4)_2} + 3H_2O + FeSO_4$$

$$Ti(SO_4)_2 + 2H_2O \xrightarrow{\text{boil}} Ti(OH)_4 \downarrow + 2H_2SO_4$$

$$Ti(OH)_4 \xrightarrow{\text{heat}} \underset{\substack{\text{(white and} \\ \text{finely di-} \\ \text{vided)}}}{TiO_2} + 2H_2O$$

TABLE 50-4. Properties of titanium, Ti

Atomic number	22
Electron structure	2, 8, 8, 4
Valences	2, 3, 4
Melting point, °C	1800
Boiling point, °C	Above 3000
Density, g/cm^3, 20°C	4.5

Although titanium compounds having a valence of 2 and 3 are known, the only compounds stable in contact with air are those in which the titanium has a valence of 4.

KEY WORDS

cassiterite	Kroll process	minium	tin disease
ferrotitanium	lead	Park's process	titanium
gray tin	lead poisoning	rutile	white lead
ilmenite	litharge	tin	white tin

HIGHLIGHTS

Common **tin** is a soft white malleable metal. **Cassiterite** (SnO_2), its chief ore, is readily reduced with carbon. At very low temperatures tin becomes gray in color and very brittle, a different allotropic form.

Tin, like aluminum, on exposure to air acquires a protective film. Tin-plated steel is used for roofing and for the construction of milk cans and food-processing equipment. Alloys of tin include bronze, solder, babbitt metal, and type metal.

Tin reacts with hydrochloric acid to form stannous chloride and with chlorine to form tin tetrachloride, a volatile liquid. This latter reaction is the basis of the process for recovering scrap tin.

Galena (PbS), the principal ore of **lead,** is roasted and reduced with carbon. The silver in crude lead is recovered by melting lead and zinc together **(Park's process).** The silver is more soluble in the molten zinc than in the lead and is recovered from the zinc by distillation of the zinc.

Lead, too, acquires a corrosion-stopping film, making it suitable for certain plumbing fixtures and for sheathing electric cables underground. Among the more important compounds of lead are **white lead,** a pigment; lead dioxide, a good oxidizing agent; **litharge,** a cementing material; and **minium.** The toxicity of lead compounds is cumulative.

Titanium is relatively abundant in the earth's crust but its metallurgy is not sufficiently perfected to provide large quantities of the metal at a reasonable cost. Titanium has about twice the tensile strength of iron and only about half the density. Its chief ore is **rutile** (TiO_2) which is an excellent pigment. Briefly it may be said that the industrial use of titanium today is probably in the same stage that of aluminum was one hundred years ago.

QUESTIONS

1. Which of the three elements, titanium, tin, or lead, is most abundant in nature? Which is least abundant?
2. What parts of the world supply most of the world's tin?
3. What is meant by the term *tin disease?* Explain.
4. What are the main uses for tin?
5. How is tin reclaimed from scrap metal?
6. Describe Park's process for removing silver from crude lead.
7. What parts of the United States are the major lead producers?
8. What metal has now largely replaced tin for foil?
9. What are the advantages of using lead for plumbing?
10. What are the disadvantages of using lead for plumbing?
11. What are the disadvantages of white lead as a paint pigment?
12. How is titanium metal produced?
13. Compare the properties of titanium with those of aluminum and stainless steel.
14. What are the uses for titanium dioxide?
15. What reasons are there for thinking that titanium may become one of the principal structural materials of the future?

Suggested Projects for Unit Eleven

1. Determine what elements and products we obtain from the sea and what others we may have to obtain from this source in the future.
2. Consider the vocational possibilities of metallurgy as a career. It has many challenges for the careful student.
3. Place a cent in a small quantity of ammonium hydroxide overnight. Observe the result and work out an equation for the reaction. You may not find it in any common textbook.
4. Find out why the degree of purity of gold is measured in carats.
5. Think up some laboratory uses for aluminum foil which is now readily available.
6. Find out how to prepare ammonium amalgam. Better talk it over with your teacher before you make some.
7. Hall and Héroult made the same discovery the same year independently. Find some other cases where great discoveries or inventions were made simultaneously and independently by two or more people.
8. Look up the current prices of the metals studied in this unit.

UNIT TWELVE: Electrochemistry

CHAPTER 51

oxidation-reduction

reactions

The basic process in all matters involving electrochemistry is **electron transfer**. This process frequently occurs in chemical reactions—but does not occur in all chemical reactions. For example, consider the combination of copper and oxygen.

$$2Cu^0 + O_2 \rightarrow 2Cu^{++}O^=$$

The fundamental change is the *transfer* of two electrons from a copper atom to an oxygen atom. This causes the copper to become doubly positive (Cu^{++}) and the oxygen to become doubly negative ($O^=$). Very early in the development of the science of chemistry and before anything about the electron transfer was known, this kind of process became known as **oxidation** for the very good reason that it involved combining oxygen with copper. That is, the early chemists said: The copper has been oxidized.

Now consider the combination of copper with sulfur, and with chlorine:

$$Cu^0 + S^0 \rightarrow Cu^{++}S^=$$
$$Cu^0 + Cl_2 \rightarrow Cu^{++}(Cl^-)_2$$

In each case the copper atom has suffered the same fate as in the first reaction. That is, *it has lost two electrons*. Hence as the nature of valence and atomic structure became more clearly known, the term *oxidation*, originally used only for reactions involving the addition of oxygen, was broadened to include reactions like the two just described.

Today the term oxidation means loss of electrons. Oxidation does not necessarily involve oxygen.

Reduction is the name given to the opposite process. **That is, reduction means the gain of electrons.** Oxygen, sulfur, and chlorine have been reduced in the preceding equations to oxide, sulfide, and chloride ions. An **oxidizing agent** is an agent capable of causing an oxidation; hence it is an agent capable of being reduced. Examples of oxidizing agents are nitric acid, chlorine, ferric ion (Fe^{+++}), and oxygen (O_2). Note in each case that elements concerned can have lower valences than those shown. A **reducing agent** is an agent capable of causing a reduction; hence itself is capable of being oxidized. Examples are sodium metal (Na^0) but not sodium ion (Na^+), ferrous ion (Fe^{++}), hydrogen (H_2), and hydrogen sulfide (H_2S).

Examples of oxidation-reduction reactions

An oxidation-reduction reaction, therefore, is a reaction involving a transfer of electrons. Each of the reactions mentioned thus far in this chapter is an oxidation-reduction reaction. Other familiar examples are

$$Zn^0 + 2H^{+*} + 2Cl^- \rightarrow Zn^{++} + H_2 \uparrow + 2Cl^- \tag{1}$$

*H^+ is written instead of OH_3^+ for convenience. Actually the latter is the one present in solutions of acids.

Or omitting the unchanged Cl^-,

$$Zn^0 + 2H^+ \rightarrow Zn^{++} + H_2 \uparrow$$
(oxidation; reduction)

$$3Cu^0 + 8HNO_3 \rightarrow 3Cu^{++} + 6NO_3^- + 2NO + 4H_2O \tag{2}$$
(dilute)

Or omitting the $6NO_3^-$ which are unchanged,

$$3Cu^0 + 8H^+ + 2NO_3^- \rightarrow 3Cu^{++} + 2NO + 4H_2O$$
(oxidation; reduction)

Oxidation-reduction reactions always involve a change in valence. Thus in the cases above the valence changes are

Eq. (1). Oxidation —valence of zinc changed from zero in Zn^0 to $+2$ in Zn^{++}

Reduction—valence of hydrogen changed from $+1$ in H^+ to zero in H_2

Eq. (2). Oxidation —valence of copper changed from zero in Cu^0 to $+2$ in Cu^{++}

Reduction—valence of nitrogen changed from $+5$ in NO_3^- to $+2$ in $NO*$

* This is the valence you must use for nitrogen if oxygen is assumed to be -2. It does not mean that nitrogen ions exist with these charges.

The following reaction is *not* an oxidation-reduction reaction because no electron transfer occurs.

$$Ag^+ + NO_3^- + Na^+ + Cl^- \rightarrow AgCl \downarrow + Na^+ + NO_3^-$$

Or omitting the unchanged Na^+ and NO_3^-,

$$Ag^+ + Cl^- \rightarrow AgCl \downarrow$$

That no electron transfer occurs is indicated by the fact that the valence of every element concerned is the same on both sides of the equation.

How to balance oxidation-reduction equations

Oxidation-reduction reactions sometimes involve several reactants and products. Therefore, balancing oxidation-reduction equations by the trial-and-error method is sometimes a tedious and time-consuming procedure. Many different schemes have been developed for balancing these types of equations. The most useful method is the one called the **ion-partial method** which is described in the following paragraphs. Not only is this the best method for balancing oxidation-reduction equations, but it serves at the same time to introduce some basic principles of cells and batteries.

To balance an oxidation-reduction equation by the ion-partial method, the equation is split up into two parts (known as *partials*). One partial shows the oxidation process; the other shows the reduction process. These simple partials are easily balanced and then added together. This procedure produces a completely balanced equation. The method will first be illustrated with a simple equation:

$$Al^0 + H^+ \rightarrow Al^{+++} + H_2 \quad \text{(unbalanced)}$$

To balance by the ion-partial method:

Step 1: Write and balance the oxidation process.

$$Al^0 \rightarrow Al^{+++} + 3e^- \quad \text{This is the oxidation partial.}$$

Step 2: Write and balance the reduction process.

$$2H^+ + 2e^- \rightarrow H_2 \quad \text{This is the reduction partial.}$$

You must remember that neither of the processes can occur without the other. Some substance must gain any electrons lost and another one must lose any electrons gained. Furthermore, in any such equation the total number of electrons lost must equal the total gained.

Step 3: Multiply each partial by the number necessary to make the number of electrons lost in the oxidation equal the number gained in the reduction. Thus

$$2(Al^0 \rightarrow Al^{+++} + 3e^-)$$
$$\underline{3(2H^+ + 2e^- \rightarrow H_2)}$$

Step 4: Add the resulting partials.

$$2Al^0 + 6H^+ \rightarrow 2Al^{+++} + 3H_2 \quad \text{This is the balanced equation.}$$

If each of the steps listed is correctly carried out, a correctly balanced equation is always obtained. Of course, this simple equation could have been balanced by inspection, but other more complex equations can also be balanced by this treatment.

PROBLEM: Balance the reaction

$$Cu^0 + HNO_3 \rightarrow Cu^{++} + NO + H_2O$$
$$\text{or}$$
$$H^+ + NO_3^-$$

Step 1: The oxidation is:
$$Cu^0 \rightarrow Cu^{++} + 2e^-$$
The reduction is:
$$NO_3^- \rightarrow NO$$

But the reduction equation is incomplete. **Whenever an ion loses oxygen in being reduced, this oxygen is converted to water by reaction with hydrogen ion.**[1] Hence

$$NO_3^- + 4H^+ \rightarrow NO + 2H_2O$$

But, where do the electrons go? And how many? In the preceding cases it has been easy to see where the electrons went in the partial and how many were involved. By following a simple rule, you can easily decide where to put the electrons in any partial. The rule is: Add the proper number of electrons to the side necessary to make the total charge the same on both sides of the partial. Thus the foregoing equation shows a net charge of +3 on the left and zero on the right.

	$NO_3^- + 4H^+ \rightarrow NO + 2H_2O$	
Charge	−1 + +4	
Net charge	+3	zero

[1] In the reverse case of an ion gaining oxygen, the exactly opposite process occurs. That is, the oxygen comes from water, and hydrogen ion is formed.

Therefore, if three electrons are added to the left, both sides have the same net charge. In this equation this happens to be zero, but this is not always the case.

Hence Step 2: The reduction partial:

$$3e^- + NO_3^- + 4H^+ \rightarrow NO + 2H_2O$$

Step 3:
$$3(Cu^0 \rightarrow Cu^{++} + 2e^-)$$
$$2(3e^- + NO_3^- + 4H^+ \rightarrow NO + 2H_2O)$$

Step 4: $3Cu^0 + 2NO_3^- + 8H^+ \rightarrow 3Cu^{++} + 2NO + 4H_2O$

The final equation should always be checked to make sure it balances chemically as well as electrically. That is, there should be the same number and kinds of atoms on both sides, and the net charge should be the same (but not necessarily zero) on both sides. Thus in the foregoing case, the net charge is

On left side -2 and $+8 = +6$
On right side $3(+2)$ $= +6$

Hence the equation balances electrically.

If you want to write an equation showing only molecules but no ions (which you generally do not), then in the preceding equation introduce six extra nitrate ions (NO_3^-) on the left and right. This would make the net charges on both sides zero [that is, $+6 + (-6) = 0$].

$3Cu^0 + 8H^+ + 2NO_3^- + 6NO_3^- \rightarrow 3Cu^{++} + 6NO_3^- + 2NO + 4H_2O$
                    (the extra   (the extra
                     ones)   ones)

or $3Cu + 8HNO_3 \rightarrow 3Cu(NO_3)_2 + 2NO + 4H_2O$

However, since the products are soluble and ionized, the six *extra* nitrate ions are not changed; they appear on both sides and preferably are omitted.

With practice you will soon become familiar with this very useful procedure. A few more illustrations follow.

Balance:
$$Cu^0 + HNO_3 \rightarrow Cu^{++} + NO_2 + H_2O$$
$$\text{(concentrated)}$$

Step 1:
$$Cu^0 \rightarrow Cu^{++} + 2e^-$$

Step 2:
$$1e^- + NO_3^- + 2H^+ \rightarrow NO_2 + H_2O$$

Step 3:
$$Cu^0 \rightarrow Cu^{++} + 2e^-$$
$$\underline{2(1e^- + NO_3^- + 2H^+ \rightarrow NO_2 + H_2O)}$$

Step 4:
$$Cu^0 + 2NO_3^- + 4H^+ \rightarrow Cu^{++} + 2NO_2 + 2H_2O$$

This equation balances chemically and electrically. Check it!

Balance:
$$Ag^0 + HNO_3 \text{ (concentrated)} \rightarrow Ag^+ + NO_2 + H_2O)$$

Step 1:
$$Ag^0 \rightarrow Ag^+ + 1e^-$$

Steps 2 and 3:
$$\underline{1e^- + NO_3^- + 2H^+ \rightarrow NO_2 + H_2O}$$

Step 4:
$$Ag^0 + NO_3^- + 2H^+ \rightarrow Ag^+ + NO_2 + H_2O$$

Balance:
$$Hg^0 + HNO_3 \text{ (concentrated)} \rightarrow Hg^{++} + NO_2 + H_2O$$

Step 1:
$$Hg^0 \rightarrow Hg^{++} + 2e^-$$

Steps 2 and 3:
$$\underline{2(1e^- + NO_3^- + 2H^+ \rightarrow NO_2 + H_2O)}$$

Step 4:
$$Hg^0 + 2NO_3^- + 4H^+ \rightarrow Hg^{++} + 2NO_2 + 2H_2O$$

Note that the partial for the reduction of concentrated nitric acid is the same for each of the preceding reactions. This is also true of most other oxidizing and reducing agents. Hence by this method you need to learn only one partial for each such reactant. Then this partial added to the partial for the other reactant gives the desired final equation. Thus in oxidation-reduction, the chemist is somewhat like the painter, who, instead of carrying all the innumerable colors which he uses on his canvas, carries only the primary colors. Then by combination of these he can produce any desired color.

Balance:
$$Pb^0 + PbO_2 + H^+ \rightarrow Pb^{++} + H_2O$$

Step 1:
$$Pb^0 \rightarrow Pb^{++} + 2e^-$$

Steps 2 and 3:
$$\underline{2e^- + PbO_2 + 4H^+ \rightarrow Pb^{++} + 2H_2O}$$

Step 4:
$$PbO_2 + Pb^0 + 4H^+ \rightarrow 2Pb^{++} + 2H_2O$$

Balance:

$$Cu^0 + H_2SO_4 \text{ (concentrated)} \xrightarrow{\text{heat}} SO_2 + Cu^{++} + H_2O$$

Step 1:
$$Cu^0 \to Cu^{++} + 2e^-$$

Steps 2 and 3:
$$2e^- + SO_4^= + 4H^+ \to SO_2 + 2H_2O$$

Step 4:
$$Cu^0 + SO_4^= + 4H^+ \to Cu^{++} + SO_2 + 2H_2O$$

Balance:
$$HCl + KMnO_4 \to Mn^{++} + Cl_2 \uparrow + K^+ + H_2O$$

Note: $KMnO_4$ ionizes into K^+ and MnO_4^-.

Step 1:
$$2Cl^- \to Cl_2 \uparrow + 2e^-$$

Step 2:
$$5e^- + MnO_4^- + 8H^+ \to Mn^{++} + 4H_2O$$

Step 3:
$$5(2Cl^- \to Cl_2 \uparrow + 2e^-)$$
$$2(5e^- + MnO_4^- + 8H^+ \to Mn^{++} + 4H_2O)$$

Step 4:
$$10Cl^- + 2MnO_4^- + 16H^+ \to 2Mn^{++} + 8H_2O + 5Cl_2 \uparrow$$

KEY WORDS

electron transfer oxidation reduction
ion-partial method oxidizing agent reducing agent
oxidation-reduction reaction

HIGHLIGHTS

Oxidation, in the broad sense, is any chemical reaction in which an element loses one or more electrons and thereby has its valence numerically increased.

Reduction, the reverse process, is any chemical reaction in which an element gains one or more electrons and thereby has its valence numerically decreased.

A substance which causes an oxidation is an **oxidizing agent** and one which causes a reduction is a **reducing agent.** In an **oxidation-reduction reaction** the total number of electrons lost by the substance oxidized always equals the total number gained by the substance reduced.

Balancing equations by inspection is unsatisfactory for all but the simplest cases. The most satisfactory method of balancing equations is by the **ion-partial system.** This method always works and its use helps you understand the real nature of reactions.

QUESTIONS

1. What is meant by the term oxidation?
2. What is meant by the term reduction?
3. What is involved in all oxidation-reduction reactions?
4. Write an example of an oxidation-reduction reaction.
5. Give an example of a reaction which is not an oxidation-reduction type.
6. List the four steps to be performed in balancing an oxidation-reduction reaction.
7. Complete and balance:
$$Hg^0 + HNO_3 \underset{\text{(dilute)}}{\rightarrow} Hg^{++} + NO + H_2O$$
8. Complete and balance:
$$Ag^0 + HNO_3 \underset{\text{(concentrated)}}{\rightarrow} Ag^+ + NO_2 + H_2O$$
9. Complete and balance:
$$Ag^0 + H_2SO_4 \underset{\text{(concentrated)}}{\overset{\text{heat}}{\longrightarrow}} Ag^+ + SO_2 + H_2O$$
10. Complete and balance:
$$H_2S + I_2 \rightarrow S^0 + I^- + H^+$$

CHAPTER **52**

cells and batteries

The method given in Chap. 51 for balancing ionic oxidation-reduction equations is not just a scheme for obtaining the correct numbers for balancing the equations. This method also shows just how these reactions occur; that is, it shows the loss of electrons by one reactant and the gain of electrons by another reactant. This same process is the basis of cells and **batteries**[1]—such as the ones used in flashlights, automobiles, portable radios, and so on. In this chapter you will learn about the construction and operation of cells and their relation to oxidation-reduction reactions.

The sources of electric energy

There are two important methods known to man for producing practical quantities of electric energy: (1) the dynamo and (2) chemical cells. The dynamo (or generator) is a device for transforming mechanical energy such as energy from water power, or a steam engine, into electric energy. We shall not consider the dynamo further. A **cell** is a device for transforming chemical energy into electric energy; that is, the electric energy released by a cell is the result of a *chemical reaction* taking place within the cell. This chemical reaction is always an ionic oxidation-reduction reaction.

A cell is an electron pump

Figure 52-1 shows a schematic diagram of a cell being used to operate a light bulb. Electrons are pumped out of the negative electrode of the cell. These electrons circulate through the copper wire, the lamp filament (*L*), and back into the cell at its positive electrode. The important thing to note is that the cell does not *make* electrons; it merely causes electrons to circulate in the metallic circuit. That is, the cell serves as an electron pump.

[1] A battery is two or more cells operating together.

The operation of a simple cell

Consider the reaction of copper sulfate solution and zinc metal.

$$Zn^0 + Cu^{++} (+ SO_4^=) \rightarrow Zn^{++} + Cu^0 (+ SO_4^=)$$

or

$$Zn^0 \rightarrow Zn^{++} + 2e^-$$
$$\underline{Cu^{++} + 2e^- \rightarrow Cu^0}$$
$$Zn^0 + Cu^{++} \rightarrow Zn^{++} + Cu^0$$

Now as we have seen already, the fundamental process in this reaction is the *transfer of two electrons from a zinc atom to a copper ion*. When zinc and copper sulfate are mixed in a beaker, the cupric ion (Cu^{++}) diffuses up to the zinc granule and picks off the two electrons from an atom of zinc [Fig. 52–2(a)]. That is, the electron transfer is *directly from zinc to copper*. In this case the energy of the reaction is released as heat.

Now these same substances can be caused to react *without ever coming into contact!* In this case the electron transfer takes place through a copper wire [as in Fig. 52–2(b)]. The energy in this case is released as electric energy. Except for these differences the reaction is just the same as the one occurring when copper sulfate and zinc metal are mixed in a beaker.

Figure 52–2 (b) shows a cell based on the copper sulfate–zinc metal reaction. It consists of a battery jar nearly full of a solution of sodium chloride. The exact concentration of the sodium chloride solution is not important. Near the bottom of the jar is a copper plate to which is connected a metal wire that serves as one of the terminals. A zinc plate is immersed in the solution near its surface. Crystals of copper sulfate, dropped into the jar, fall to the bottom and dissolve. This forms a concentrated solution of copper sulfate which, being more dense than water, remains at the bottom if the solution is not shaken or stirred. A galvanometer connected to the two terminals will show that electrons flow in the direction indicated in the drawing. If the

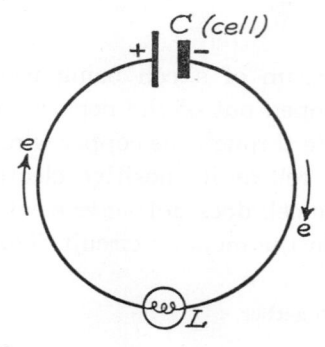

Fig. 52–1. A simple electric circuit. The cell (C) acts as an electron pump, causing electrons (e) to move in the circuit in the direction shown.

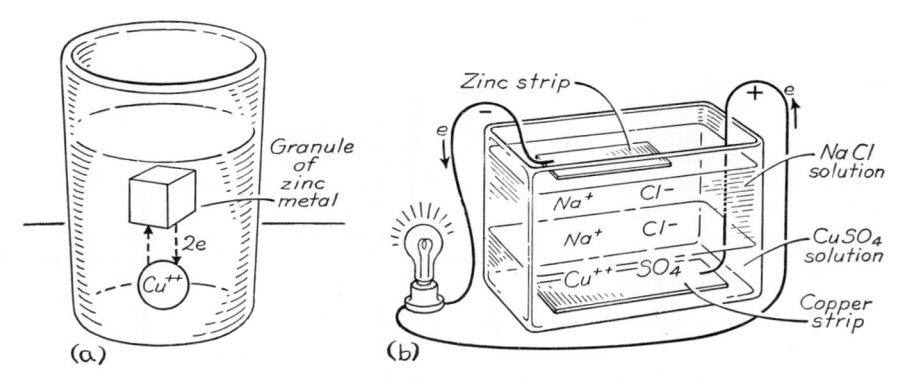

Fig. 52–2. When a solution containing copper ions is mixed with zinc metal, electrons are transferred directly from the zinc atoms to the copper ions (a). The process of obtaining electric energy by the reaction of zinc metal with copper ions is shown in (b).

exposed area of the zinc and copper plates is large enough, this cell will liberate sufficient energy to light an ordinary flashlight bulb.

When the cell operates, the ionic partials shown in the equation on page 670 occur at the two electrodes. That is, at the zinc plate the reaction

$$Zn^0 \rightarrow Zn^{++} + 2e^- \quad \text{(the negative electrode)}$$

occurs. These electrons move from the zinc plate through the wire connected to it and enter the copper plate. There the reaction

$$Cu^{++} + 2e^- \rightarrow Cu^0 \quad \text{(the positive electrode)}$$

occurs. Metallic copper thereby plates out on the copper electrode. The total reaction is thus the sum of these two reactions occurring at the separate electrodes

$$\begin{array}{ll} Zn^0 \rightarrow Zn^{++} + 2e^- & \text{at the negative electrode} \\ \underline{Cu^{++} + 2e^- \rightarrow Cu^0} & \text{at the positive electrode} \\ Cu^{++} + Zn^0 \rightarrow Cu^0 + Zn^{++} & \end{array}$$

That is, this is the same reaction as occurs when these reactants are mixed in a beaker, the only difference being the form in which the energy is liberated. This cell is sometimes known as a **gravity cell** because it depends upon the force of gravity to prevent the mixing of the copper sulfate with the other reactant, zinc. A special form of this cell, which employs a piece of zinc shaped like a large bird's foot (to increase the exposed surface area), is called a *crow's foot* cell.

Why is the sodium chloride necessary?

If the crow-foot or gravity cell is made up, omitting the sodium chloride, it will not operate. It is always necessary to have sodium chloride, or some other electrolyte which does not react with the materials at either electrode, present between the electrodes. This is

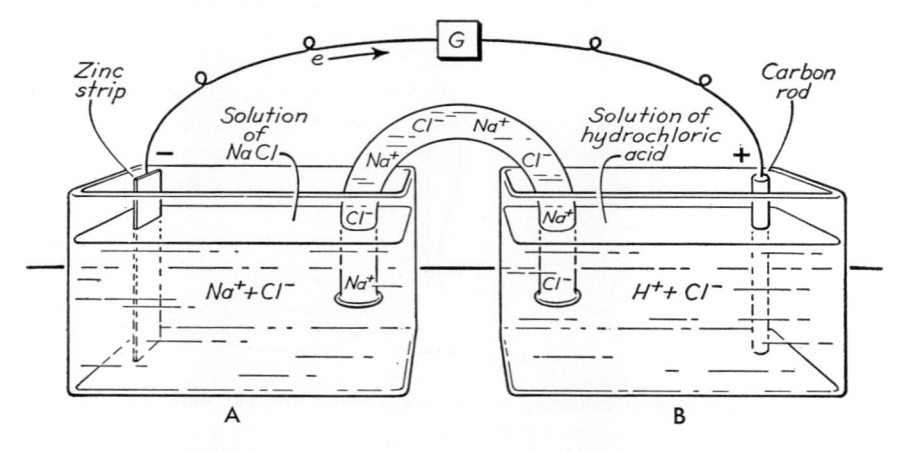

Fig. 52–3. Production of electric energy by the reaction of zinc and hydrochloric acid.

for the following reason: As the zinc ions go into solution around the zinc electrode, it is necessary to have some negative ions to maintain electrical neutrality. If the negative ions are not present, the solution will become positive around the zinc electrode and the reaction will tend to stop. This is because this positively charged solution will repel the positive zinc ions which must enter the solution. At the same time that a zinc ion enters the solution, one cupric ion from the copper sulfate leaves the solution around the copper electrode. This leaves an extra sulfate ion, which must be paired off to maintain electric neutrality around the copper electrode. Thus the sodium chloride furnishes chloride ions to pair off with the zinc ions and at the same time a corresponding number of sodium ions to take the place of the copper ions which have left the solution. Hence the sodium chloride maintains electric neutrality throughout the solution. For this reason, a cell must always contain some inert electrolyte solution between the electrodes, although it does not have to be sodium chloride.

Another familiar reaction

The reaction

$$Zn^0 + 2H^+ \rightarrow Zn^{++} + H_2$$

is easily made to furnish electric energy. A convenient setup for observing the electric energy released by this reaction is shown in Fig. 52–3. This setup is equivalent to that shown in Fig. 52–2(*b*) but is preferred for laboratory study of cells because it is an easy way of preventing the two reactants from mixing. Jar *A* contains a zinc strip, which serves as a reactant and also as its own electrode. This jar contains a solution of sodium chloride. Jar *B* contains the other reactant, hydrochloric acid, and a carbon rod which serves as an electrode. The two containers are connected by means of a U-shaped tube filled with sodium chloride solution. Electrolytic connection between the two electrodes is thereby provided.

The operation of the cell consists of

$$Zn^0 \rightarrow Zn^{++} + 2e^- \quad \text{in jar } A$$
$$2H^+ + 2e \rightarrow H_2 \quad \text{in jar } B$$

After the cell has operated for a few minutes it is generally possible to observe the hydrogen bubbles formed on the carbon electrode.

The total reaction is thus the same as that involved when zinc and hydrochloric acid are directly mixed in a single beaker.

$$Zn^0 + 2H^+ \rightarrow Zn^{++} + H_2 \uparrow$$

Cells are based on ionic oxidation-reduction reactions

Any ionic oxidation-reduction reaction can be set up in a similar manner to produce electric energy. And all cells are based on ionic oxidation-reduction reactions set up in such a fashion as to yield electric rather than heat energy. This is done in all cases by allowing the electron transfer from reducing agent to oxidizing agent to take place indirectly through an outside metal circuit as was done in the preceding cases.

You will now read about the two most important cells in everyday use.

The dry cell

The so-called **dry cell** is incorrectly named because when dry it will not operate. It is actually a zinc-hydrogen cell involving the same reaction as the cell described on page 672. Figure 52–4 shows a diagram of the dry cell. It consists of a zinc cup which serves as: (1) container, (2) reactant, and (3) negative electrode. The positive electrode is a carbon rod. The space around the carbon electrode is filled with a paste of ammonium chloride, water, zinc chloride, and manganese dioxide. The paste also contains flour or clay to stiffen it. The ammonium chloride, as a result of hydrolysis, produces a dilute solution of hydrochloric acid which is one of the reactants.

$$Cl^- + NH_4^+ + H_2O \rightleftharpoons NH_3 + OH_3^+ + Cl^-$$

When the cell operates, the following reactions occur:

$$Zn^0 \rightarrow Zn^{++} + 2e^- \quad \text{at zinc cup (negative electrode)}$$
$$\underline{2H^+ + 2e^- \rightarrow H_2} \quad \text{at carbon rod (positive electrode)}$$
$$Zn^0 + 2H^+ \rightarrow Zn^{++} + H_2$$

If the hydrogen gas accumulated on the carbon rod, it would act as an insulator, thereby tending to stop the reaction. Manganese dioxide is added to prevent the formation of hydrogen gas. It does so by reacting with the liberated hydrogen.

$$2MnO_2 + H_2 \rightarrow Mn_2O_3 + H_2O$$

Zinc chloride serves to combine with ammonia to form the zinc ammonia complex $[Zn(NH_3)_4^{++}]$. This reaction prevents the liberation of noxious ammonia gas.

The cell is sealed at the top with pitch or wax.

As the cell operates, the zinc cup is consumed; hence a run-down cell frequently shows a badly corroded cup. The zinc cup is lined on its inside with porous paper to reduce the contact between the ammonium chloride solution and the zinc cup. When these two substances come in direct contact, they react directly. This produces an internal short circuit which destroys the cell. At best, however, the paper liner serves only to slow down the direct reaction between the zinc and the ammonium chloride solution. Hence dry cells do not keep indefinitely and, therefore, should be used as soon as possible after manufacture. This is why the practice by the manufacturers of dating the cells was adopted.

A single dry cell produces about 1.5 volts. Higher voltages are produced by connecting two or more cells *in series*. In this way 22.5 volt B batteries are made.

The current which a dry cell can produce depends on the rate of the reaction occurring within the cell. The current (usually measured in amperes) flowing in the circuit is a measure of the rate at which electrons are flowing through the circuit. Hence the more rapid the reaction at the electrode the greater the current flowing from the cell. Since *surface area* influences reaction rate (see Chap. 25,

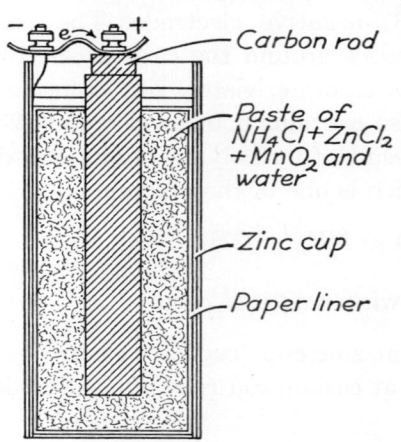

Fig. 52–4. The composition of a dry cell. The current produced by a dry cell depends on the rate of reaction. Therefore, a large dry cell will give more current than a small dry cell. The voltage produced by a dry cell, however, does not vary.

A glass model of a commercial-type lead storage battery cut away to show how it is made.

pages 278 and 279), electrodes having larger surfaces give greater current. Thus a large dry cell gives more current than a dry cell for a pen-sized flashlight. The current from small cells can be increased by connecting two or more small cells *in parallel*. This, of course, has the effect of increasing the surface area of the electrodes.

The **voltage** of a cell is independent of the size of the electrodes and depends only on the *reaction* which is occurring, the *concentration of reactants*, and the *temperature*. Thus all sizes of common dry cells give about 1.5 volts.

The lead storage battery

The most important use for the lead storage battery is in automobiles. Here it serves to operate not only the starter, but also the multitude of other electric gadgets which the modern automobile contains.

A storage cell, or accumulator, differs from the dry cell in that the storage cell can be recharged, after it has become run down, by passing electric energy back into it. Therefore, it can be re-used. A dry cell, once run down, cannot be recharged.

A diagram of a charged lead storage cell is shown in Fig. 52–5. The positive electrode consists of a grid of lead. The openings in this grid contain a paste of finely powdered lead dioxide (PbO_2). The negative electrode is also a grid of lead, but here the active ingredient, which is in the grid openings, is finely divided metallic lead. The electrolyte consists of a 38 percent solution of sulfuric acid. The specific gravity of this solution is 1.28. The operation of the storage cell depends upon the fact that lead dioxide will oxidize metallic lead. Both of the reactants are thereby converted to the intermediate valence of $+2$. The electrode reactions are as follows:

$$Pb^0 \rightarrow Pb^{++} + 2e^- \quad \text{at the negative electrode}$$
$$2e^- + PbO_2 + 4H^+ \rightarrow Pb^{++} + 2H_2O \quad \text{at the positive electrode}$$

(This partial shows why the electrolyte is an *acid*.)

$$Pb^0 + PbO_2 + 4H^+ \rightarrow 2Pb^{++} + 2H_2O$$

But the sulfate ion forms insoluble lead sulfate ($PbSO_4$) with the lead ions; hence the total reaction is

$$Pb^0 + PbO_2 + 4H^+ + 2SO_4^= \underset{\text{charge}}{\overset{\text{discharge}}{\rightleftarrows}} 2PbSO_4 \downarrow + 2H_2O$$

Thus as the battery is discharged, lead sulfate forms at both electrodes, and the sulfuric acid in the electrolyte is used up. When the battery is discharged, it can be connected with an outside source of electric energy (such as a generator) and electrons forced through the battery in the opposite direction. This recharges the battery. The charging reaction is exactly the reverse of the discharge reaction. Lead and lead dioxide are formed at the proper electrodes, and sulfuric acid is regenerated in the electrolyte solution. Whereas ideally the battery could be charged and discharged an unlimited number of times, mechanical wear and tear on the plates as well as reactions of impurities in the lead eventually produce conditions such that the

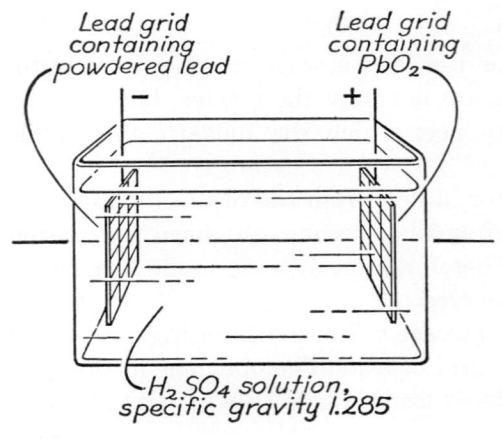

Fig. 52–5. A single, charged lead storage cell. Lead storage batteries are made up of a group of single cells. A 6-volt battery contains three cells; a 12-volt battery contains six cells.

battery can no longer be recharged. In the past the average life of an automobile battery has been about two years, but individual batteries vary greatly in life according to the care they receive and their quality.

For a long time a small amount of antimony was added to the lead grids in order to harden them. It has recently been discovered that this antimony is one of the main causes of battery failure and that, if the lead is hardened by alloying with calcium instead of antimony, the life of the battery is increased two- or threefold.

A single lead cell gives about 2 volts. Automobile batteries usually consist of three such cells, connected in series, giving thereby 6 volts. Twelve volt batteries, consisting of six 2 volt cells, are now also becoming common. The **amperage** of the battery depends upon the rate of the reaction and, therefore, is determined by the surface area of the reactants. In order to get the necessary amperage, several similar plates are connected together, thereby producing the effect of one large plate. It is done for both the positive and negative electrodes. This is why the number of plates in a battery should be considered in making a purchase. For example, a battery may contain 39 standard size plates, giving a total plate area of 2084 in.^{2} Another battery may contain 45 plates, giving a total area of 2405 in.^{2} Other factors being equal, the battery with 45 plates will give about one-fourth more current and will last longer.

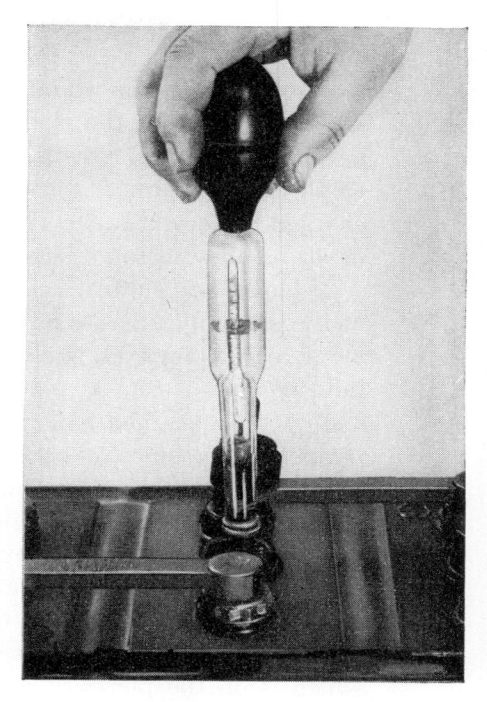

A special hydrometer for measuring the specific gravity of electrolyte in a storage battery.

Some practical points about using a lead storage battery

Everyone who drives an automobile makes use of a storage battery and, therefore, has some responsibility for its maintenance. With proper care the life of a storage battery can be considerably increased. Knowledge of a few important facts will help in increasing the life of the storage battery.

1. As the cell is discharged, the sulfuric acid is used up. Since sulfuric acid is more dense than water, the specific gravity of the electrolyte is reduced as the cell is discharged. Charging regenerates the sulfuric acid (see equation, page 676); hence the specific gravity of the elec-

trolyte increases as the battery is recharged. By measuring the specific gravity of the electrolyte, it is possible to tell whether the battery is charged. This is the method used by the garage man who employs a hydrometer for this purpose. The specific gravity of a fully charged battery is 1.285. The specific gravity of the electrolyte should never be allowed to go below 1.15.

2. Never add sulfuric acid to a battery unless it is known that some of the electrolyte has been accidentally spilled. There are rarely any other reasons for adding electrolyte. Too much acid is harmful to the battery.

3. A fully charged battery will almost never freeze at atmospheric temperatures, since it contains 38 percent sulfuric acid (fp about $-75°C$). However, an uncharged battery may freeze at a few degrees below $0°C$ because it contains very little sulfuric acid. Freezing, as a result of the accompanying expansion, will ruin the battery. Hence you should never expose a discharged battery to low temperatures.

4. A battery should not be allowed to stand discharged for any great length of time. On standing, the finely divided lead sulfate which is on the plates is converted into larger cystals. These larger crystals have less surface area. Therefore, they dissolve so slowly that the battery may, for all practical purposes, become un-rechargeable. This condition of formation of large lead sulfate crystals is known as **sulfating**.

5. Once the battery becomes fully charged, continued passing of electricity through the cell electrolyzes the water in the electrolyte (see Chap. 6, pages 48 and 49).

$$H_2O \xrightarrow{H_2SO_4} H_2 \uparrow + O_2 \uparrow$$

(electrolysis) (at negative electrode) (at positive electrode)

Thus, ideally, overcharging should do no harm other than make necessary the replacement of the water decomposed thereby. Actually the evolution of these gases around the plates together with the heat generated may seriously damage the plates by causing them to buckle and break. Hence overcharging should be avoided. Almost all modern automobiles are equipped with an automatic device on their generator (known as a voltage regulator) which reduces the electric energy going into the battery as the battery becomes fully charged.

6. Always keep the plates covered with electrolyte by adding distilled water as necessary. Although tap water is frequently added to batteries, it practically always results in shortening the life of the battery. Almost any impurity in the water used will harm the battery, particularly those impurities found in hard water. Although it may

sometimes be inconvenient to obtain, the use of distilled (or rain) water will be repaid in longer battery life. A substitute for distilled water may be obtained in most households by collecting in a clean container the water which drips off the freezing unit when the family refrigerator is defrosted.

KEY WORDS

| amperage | cell | gravity cell | sulfating |
| battery | dry cell | lead storage battery | voltage |

HIGHLIGHTS

A **battery** is made up of two or more **cells**. Batteries are the only practical source of electricity where the dynamo or generator is not suitable. A cell, which is in reality an electron pump, is a system of chemical reactions in which there is an oxidation and a corresponding reduction. In other words a cell is a device for supplying a flow of electrons which can be put to practical use. Simple cells are illustrated by the **gravity cell** and the **dry cell**.

The **lead storage battery** is a more complicated device. It, too, is based upon oxidation-reduction reactions. A storage battery differs from a simple battery in that it may be recharged from time to time. Care must be taken to see that the plates of a storage battery are always covered by adding distilled water from time to time as needed. A discharged battery must not be exposed to low temperatures.

QUESTIONS

1. What kinds of chemical reactions can be made to yield electric energy?
2. Does a cell or battery make electrons? Explain.
3. What is the difference between a cell and a battery?
4. Draw a diagram to explain how the following reaction could be used to obtain electric energy:

$$2Ag^+ + 2NO_3^- + Zn^0 \rightarrow 2Ag^0 + 2NO_3^- + Zn^{++}$$

5. What are the reactions at each electrode in the cell mentioned in question 4?
6. Why is moisture necessary in the so-called dry cell?
7. What is the reaction in a dry cell which supplies the electric energy?

8. Describe the construction of a dry cell.
9. What factor determines the current which a cell will furnish?
10. Draw a diagram of a charged lead storage cell.
11. Write the electrode reactions which occur when the lead cell is discharged.
12. Why should a discharged lead cell never be exposed to freezing temperature?
13. How does overcharging damage a lead cell?
14. What effect would you expect to be produced by adding hard water, containing calcium ion, to a lead storage battery? [Look up the solubility of calcium sulfate ($CaSO_4$).]

Suggested Projects for Unit Twelve

1. Construct a gravity cell from material you may obtain from the home, the garage or a junk shop.
2. Make a list of uses for the dry cell. Do the same for the gravity cell and the storage battery.
3. Find examples of complex oxidation-reduction reactions and try to balance them by the ion-partial method.

APPENDIX

The metric system—definitions

1. *The meter.* The unit of length in the metric system is the meter. It is the distance between two lines on a platinum-iridium bar kept in the International Bureau of Weights and Measures in France. Copies of this bar have been made for use in laboratories (such as the U.S. Bureau of Standards) which require them for extreme accuracy. The meter is approximately $1/10{,}000{,}000$ of the distance from the equator to the pole. If the standard meter bar should be destroyed, it could be reproduced because its length has been established in terms of the wave length of the lines in the spectrum of cadmium.

2. *The gram.* The unit of mass in the metric system is the international kilogram. It is the mass of a standard platinum-iridium cylinder kept in the International Bureau of Weights and Measures in France. The gram is $1/1000$ the mass of the standard kilogram.

3. *The liter.* The unit of volume in the metric system is the liter. By definition, the liter is the volume occupied by one kilogram of pure water at four degrees centigrade. It was originally intended that this should be the volume of a cube 10 cm on edge ($= 1000$ cm^3). Actually because the water used for establishing the standard kilogram mass was not pure (it contained dissolved gases), the standard mass proved to be somewhat heavier than that of 1000 cm^3 of pure water at 4°C. For this reason the liter is somewhat larger than 1000 cm^3. Actually

$$1 \text{ liter} = 1000.28 \text{ cm}^3$$

One milliliter is $1/1000$ of a liter and

$$1 \text{ ml} = 1.00028 \text{ cm}^3$$

The difference between the liter and 1000 cm^3 is so slight that it can be neglected for all except the most accurate work.

4. *The second.* The unit of time in the metric system is the second, which is $1/86{,}400$ part of the mean solar day.

TABLES
ATOMIC WEIGHTS[a]

Name	Symbol	Atomic number	International atomic weight
Actinium	Ac	89	227
Aluminum	Al	13	26.98
Americium	Am	95	(243)[b]
Antimony, stibium	Sb	51	121.76
Argon	A	18	39.944
Arsenic	As	33	74.91
Astatine	At	85	(210)[b]
Barium	Ba	56	137.36
Berkelium	Bk	97	(249)[b]
Beryllium, glucinum	Be	4	9.013
Bismuth	Bi	83	209.00
Boron	B	5	10.82
Bromine	Br	35	79.916
Cadmium	Cd	48	112.41
Calcium	Ca	20	40.08
Californium	Cf	98	(249)[b]
Carbon	C	6	12.011
Cerium	Ce	58	140.13
Cesium	Cs	55	132.91
Chlorine	Cl	17	35.457
Chromium	Cr	24	52.01
Cobalt	Co	27	58.94
Columbium, see *Niobium*			
Copper	Cu	29	63.54
Curium	Cm	96	(245)[b]
Dysprosium	Dy	66	162.51
Einsteinium	E	99	(254)[b]
Erbium	Er	68	167.27
Europium	Eu	63	152.0
Fermium	Fm	100	(252)[b]
Fluorine	F	9	19.00
Francium	Fr	87	(223)[b]
Gadolinium	Gd	64	157.26
Gallium	Ga	31	69.72
Germanium	Ge	32	72.60

ATOMIC WEIGHTS[a] (Continued)

Name	Symbol	Atomic number	International atomic weight
Gold, aurum	Au	79	197.0
Hafnium, celtium	Hf	72	178.58
Helium	He	2	4.003
Holmium	Ho	67	164.94
Hydrogen	H	1	1.0080
Indium	In	49	114.82
Iodine	I	53	126.92
Iridium	Ir	77	192.2
Iron, ferrum	Fe	26	55.85
Krypton	Kr	36	83.8
Lanthanum	La	57	138.92
Lead, plumbum	Pb	82	207.21
Lithium	Li	3	6.940
Lutetium, cassiopeium	Lu	71	174.99
Magnesium	Mg	12	24.32
Manganese	Mn	25	54.94
Mendelevium	Mv	101	(256)[b]
Mercury, hydrargyrum	Hg	80	200.61
Molybdenum	Mo	42	95.95
Neodymium	Nd	60	144.27
Neon	Ne	10	20.183
Neptunium	Np	93	(237)[b]
Nickel	Ni	28	58.71
Niobium, columbium	Nb	41	92.91
Nitrogen	N	7	14.008
Nobelium	No	102	(257)[b]
Osmium	Os	76	190.2
Oxygen	O	8	16.000
Palladium	Pd	46	106.7
Phosphorus	P	15	30.975
Platinum	Pt	78	195.09
Plutonium	Pu	94	(242)[b]
Polonium	Po	84	210
Potassium, kalium	K	19	39.100
Praseodymium	Pr	59	140.92
Promethium	Pm	61	(145)[b]
Protactinium	Pa	91	231

ATOMIC WEIGHTS[a] (Continued)

Name	Symbol	Atomic number	International atomic weight
Radium	Ra	88	226.05
Radon	Rn	86	222
Rhenium	Re	75	186.22
Rhodium	Rh	45	102.91
Rubidium	Rb	37	85.48
Ruthenium	Ru	44	101.1
Samarium	Sm, Sa	62	150.35
Scandium	Sc	21	44.96
Selenium	Se	34	78.96
Silicon	Si	14	28.06
Silver, argentum	Ag	47	107.880
Sodium, natrium	Na	11	22.991
Strontium	Sr	38	87.63
Sulfur	S	16	32.066[c]
Tantalum	Ta	73	180.95
Technetium	Tc	43	(99)[b]
Tellurium	Te	52	127.61
Terbium	Tb	65	158.93
Thallium	Tl	81	204.39
Thorium	Th	90	232.05
Thulium	Tm	69	168.94
Tin, stannum	Sn	50	118.70
Titanium	Ti	22	47.90
Tungsten, wolfram	W	74	183.86
Uranium	U	92	238.07
Vanadium	V	23	50.95
Xenon	Xe	54	131.30
Ytterbium	Yb	70	173.04
Yttrium	Y	39	88.92
Zinc	Zn	30	65.38
Zirconium	Zr	40	91.22

[a] Data in this table are from *Handbook of Chemistry and Physics,* 39th ed., Chemical Rubber Publishing Co., Cleveland, Ohio, 1957–1958.

[b] Atomic weights given in parentheses are the mass number of the most stable isotope of that element.

[c] Because of natural variations in the relative abundances of the isotopes of sulfur, the atomic weight of this element has a range of ± 0.003.

PROPERTIES OF SOME INORGANIC SUBSTANCES[a]

Formula	Melting point, °C	Boiling point, °C	Solubility in water, g/liter
AlBr$_3$	97.5	263.3[747mm]	Soluble
AlCl$_3$	190[2.5atm][b]	Subl[c] 182.7	699 (15°C)[d]
Al(NO$_3$)$_3$·9H$_2$O	70	Dec[e] 150	637 (25°C)
Al(OH)$_3$	Dec		Insoluble
NH$_4$Cl (sal ammoniac)	Subl 335		297 (0°C)
(NH$_4$)$_2$CrO$_4$	Dec		405 (30°C)
NH$_4$NO$_3$	169.6	Dec 210	1183 (0°C)
(NH$_4$)$_2$SO$_4$	Dec 280		706 (0°C)
BaBr$_2$	847		980 (0°C)
BaCl$_2$	962[f]	1560	310 (0°C)
BaCO$_3$	1740[90atm]	Dec	0.02 (20°C)
BaCrO$_4$			0.0034 (16°C)
BaF$_2$	1280	2137	1.7 (10°C)
Ba(NO$_3$)$_2$	592	Dec	87 (20°C)
Ba(OH)$_2$·8H$_2$O	78	Loses 8H$_2$O at 780	56 (15°C)
BaSO$_4$	1580		0.0022 (18°C)
CaBr$_2$	765	806–812	1250 (0°C)
CaCO$_3$	Dec 825		0.0153 (25°C)
CaF$_2$	1360		0.016 (18°C)
Ca(OH)$_2$	Loses H$_2$O at 580		1.85 (0°C)
CaI$_2$	575	718	660 (10°C)
Ca(NO$_3$)$_2$	561		1020 (0°C)
CaSO$_4$	1450		2.09 (30°C)
CuCl$_2$·2H$_2$O	Loses 2H$_2$O at 110		1104 (0°C)
CuF$_2$·2H$_2$O			Slightly soluble
Cu(OH)$_2$	Loses H$_2$O		Insoluble
CuSO$_4$·5H$_2$O (blue vitriol)	Loses 4H$_2$O at 110	Loses 5H$_2$O at 150	316 (0°C)
FeCl$_3$·6H$_2$O	37	280–285	919 (20°C)
Fe(NO$_3$)$_3$·6H$_2$O	35		Soluble
Fe(OH)$_3$	Dec		Insoluble
Fe$_2$(SO$_4$)$_3$·9H$_2$O	Dec		4400
FeS	1193	Dec	0.0062 (18°C)
PbBr$_2$	373	916	4.554 (0°C)
PbCl$_2$	501	950	6.73 (0°C)
PbF$_2$	855	1290	0.64 (20°C)

PROPERTIES OF SOME INORGANIC SUBSTANCES[a]
(Continued)

Formula	Melting point, °C	Boiling point, °C	Solubility in water, g/liter
Pb(OH)$_2$	Dec 145		0.155 (20°C)
PbI$_2$	402	954	0.44 (0°C)
Pb(NO$_3$)$_2$	Dec 470		376.5 (0°C)
PbO (litharge)	888		0.017 (20°C)
PbO$_2$	Dec 290		Insoluble
Pb$_3$O$_4$ (minium, red lead)	Dec 500		Insoluble
PbSO$_4$	Dec 1000		0.0425 (25°C)
PbS	1114		0.1244 (20°C)
LiBr	547	1265	1427 (0°C)
Li$_2$CO$_3$	618	Dec	15.4 (0°C)
LiCl	613	1353	454 (25°C)
LiF	870	1676	2.7 (18°C)
LiI	446	1190	Soluble
LiNO$_3$	255		522
Li$_2$SO$_4$	860		261 (0°C)
MgBr$_2$·6H$_2$O	Dec 165		3160 (0°C)
MgBr$_2$	700		1015 (20°C)
MgCO$_3$	Dec 350	Loses CO$_2$ at 900	0.106
MgCl$_2$·6H$_2$O	Dec 116–118		1670
MgF$_2$	1396	2239	0.076 (18°C)
Mg(NO$_3$)$_2$·6H$_2$O	95	Loses 5H$_2$O at 330	423.3 (18°C)
MgO	2800		0.0062
MgSO$_4$·7H$_2$O (epsom salts)	Loses 6H$_2$O at 150	Loses 7H$_2$O at 200	710 (20°C)
Hg$_2$Cl$_2$ (calomel)	Subl 400		0.0021 (18°C)
HgCl$_2$ (corrosive sublimate)	276	302	36 (0°C)
NiCl$_2$·6H$_2$O			2540 (20°C)
NiSO$_4$	Loses SO$_3$ at 840		293 (0°C)
KBr	730	1380	534.8 (0°C)
K$_2$CO$_3$	891	Dec	1120 (20°C)
KCl	776	Subl 1500	347 (20°C)
KClO$_3$	368.4	Dec 400	71 (20°C)
KF	880	1500	923 (18°C)
KI	723	1420	1275 (0°C)
KMnO$_4$	Dec below 240		28.3 (0°C)
KNO$_2$	387		2810 (0°C)

PROPERTIES OF SOME INORGANIC SUBSTANCES[a]
(Continued)

Formula	Melting point, °C	Boiling point, °C	Solubility in water, g/liter
KNO_3 (saltpeter)	334[g]	Dec 400	133 (0°C)
KOH	360.4	1320–1324	970 (0°C)
K_2SO_4	1076[h]		68.5 (0°C)
AgBr	434	Dec 700	0.000084
AgCl	455	1550	0.00089 (10°C)
AgI	Dec 552		0.000003
$AgNO_3$	212	Dec 444	1220 (0°C)
NaBr	755	1390	795 (0°C)
Na_2CO_3	851	Dec	71 (0°C)
$NaHCO_3$	Loses CO_2 at 270		69 (0°C)
NaCl	801	1413	357 (0°C)
NaF	980–997	1700	42.2 (18°C)
NaOH	318.4	1390	420 (0°C)
$NaNO_3$	306.8	Dec 380	730 (0°C)
$Na_2SO_4 \cdot 10H_2O$	Dec 32.4		110 (0°C)
$SrCl_2$	873		435 (0°C)
$SrCO_3$	1497 [60 atm][b]	Loses CO_2 at 1340	0.011 (18°C)
$Sr(NO_3)_2$	570		401 (0°C)
$SrSO_4$	Dec 1580		0.113 (0°C)
$ZnCl_2$	262	732	4320 (25°C)
$Zn(OH)_2$	Dec 125		0.0000026 (18°C)
$Zn(NO_3)_2 \cdot 6H_2O$	36.4	Loses $6H_2O$ at 105–131	1843 (20°C)
$ZnSO_4$	Dec 740		865 (80°C)

[a] Data from *Handbook of Chemistry and Physics*, 39th ed., Chemical Rubber Publishing Co., Cleveland, Ohio, 1957–1958.
[b] Atm = atmospheres
[c] Subl = sublimates
[d] Temperature at which solubility was determined is given in parentheses.
[e] Dec = decomposes
[f] Changes to cubic form at 925°C.
[g] Changes to trigonal form at 129°C.
[h] Changes form at 588°C.

ELECTRON STRUCTURE OF ATOMS[a]

Atomic number	Element	1	2	3	4	5	6	7	Atomic number	Element	1	2	3	4	5	6	7
1	H	1							50	Sn	2	8	18	18	4		
2	He	2							51	Sb	2	8	18	18	5		
3	Li	2	1						52	Te	2	8	18	18	6		
4	Be	2	2						53	I	2	8	18	18	7		
5	B	2	3						54	Xe	2	8	18	18	8		
6	C	2	4						55	Cs	2	8	18	18	8	1	
7	N	2	5						56	Ba	2	8	18	18	8	2	
8	O	2	6						57	La	2	8	18	18	9	2	
9	F	2	7						58	Ce	2	8	18	19	9	2	
10	Ne	2	8						59	Pr	2	8	18	20	9	2	
11	Na	2	8	1					60	Nd	2	8	18	21	9	2	
12	Mg	2	8	2					61	Pm	2	8	18	22	9	2	
13	Al	2	8	3					62	Sm	2	8	18	23	9	2	
14	Si	2	8	4					63	Eu	2	8	18	24	9	2	
15	P	2	8	5					64	Gd	2	8	18	25	9	2	
16	S	2	8	6					65	Tb	2	8	18	26	9	2	
17	Cl	2	8	7					66	Dy	2	8	18	27	9	2	
18	A	2	8	8					67	Ho	2	8	18	28	9	2	
19	K	2	8	8	1				68	Er	2	8	18	29	9	2	
20	Ca	2	8	8	2				69	Tm	2	8	18	30	9	2	
21	Sc	2	8	9	2				70	Yb	2	8	18	31	9	2	
22	Ti	2	8	10	2				71	Lu	2	8	18	32	9	2	
23	V	2	8	11	2				72	Hf	2	8	18	32	10	2	
24	Cr	2	8	13	1				73	Ta	2	8	18	32	11	2	
25	Mn	2	8	13	2				74	W	2	8	18	32	12	2	
26	Fe	2	8	14	2				75	Re	2	8	18	32	13	2	
27	Co	2	8	15	2				76	Os	2	8	18	32	14	2	
28	Ni	2	8	16	2				77	Ir	2	8	18	32	15	2	
29	Cu	2	8	18	1				78	Pt	2	8	18	32	16	2	
30	Zn	2	8	18	2				79	Au	2	8	18	32	18	1	
31	Ga	2	8	18	3				80	Hg	2	8	18	32	18	2	
32	Ge	2	8	18	4				81	Tl	2	8	18	32	18	3	
33	As	2	8	18	5				82	Pb	2	8	18	32	18	4	
34	Se	2	8	18	6				83	Bi	2	8	18	32	18	5	
35	Br	2	8	18	7				84	Po	2	8	18	32	18	6	
36	Kr	2	8	18	8				85	At	2	8	18	32	18	7	
37	Rb	2	8	18	8	1			86	Rn	2	8	18	32	18	8	
38	Sr	2	8	18	8	2			87	Fr	2	8	18	32	18	8	1
39	Y	2	8	18	9	2			88	Ra	2	8	18	32	18	8	2
40	Zr	2	8	18	10	2			89	Ac	2	8	18	32	18	9	2
41	Nb	2	8	18	12	1			90	Th	2	8	18	32	18	11	1
42	Mo	2	8	18	13	1			91	Pa	2	8	18	32	18	12	1
43	Tc	2	8	18	14	1			92	U	2	8	18	32	21	10	1
44	Ru	2	8	18	15	1			93	Np	2	8	18	32	22	10	1
45	Rh	2	8	18	16	1			94	Pu	2	8	18	32	23	10	1
46	Pd	2	8	18	18				95	Am	2	8	18	32	24	10	1
47	Ag	2	8	18	18	1			96	Cm	2	8	18	32	25	10	1
48	Cd	2	8	18	18	2			97	Bk	2	8	18	32	26	10	1
49	In	2	8	18	18	3			98	Cf	2	8	18	32	27	10	1

[a] From N. V. Sidgwick, *The Chemical Elements and Their Compounds*, Oxford University Press, London, England, 1950.

MOLARITIES AND NORMALITIES OF COMMERCIAL CONCENTRATED ACIDS AND AMMONIA

Reagent	Specific gravity	Molarity	Normality	Percentage by weight of acid or base
H_2SO_4	1.84	18	36	96
HCl	1.19	11.7	11.7	36
HNO_3	1.40	15.0	15.0	68
$HC_2H_3O_2$	1.06	17.6	17.6	99.5
NH_4OH	0.90	15	15	58.5

VAPOR PRESSURE OF WATER IN MILLIMETERS OF MERCURY

Temperature °F	Temperature °C	Pressure, mm	Temperature °F	Temperature °C	Pressure, mm
32	0	4.6	73.4	23	21.0
41	5	6.5	75.2	24	22.4
46.4	8	8.0	77.0	25	23.7
48.2	9	8.6	78.8	26	25.2
50.0	10	9.2	80.6	27	26.7
51.8	11	9.8	82.4	28	28.3
53.6	12	10.5	84.2	29	30.0
55.4	13	11.2	86.0	30	31.8
57.2	14	12.0	95.0	35	42.2
59.0	15	12.7	104.0	40	55.3
60.8	16	13.6	122.0	50	92.5
62.6	17	14.5	140.0	60	149.4
64.4	18	15.4	158.0	70	233.7
66.2	19	16.4	176.0	80	355.1
68.0	20	17.5	194.0	90	525.8
69.8	21	18.6	212.0	100	760.0
71.6	22	19.8			

WEIGHTS AND MEASURES

Length

10 millimeters (mm) = 1 centimeter (cm) = 0.3937 in.
100 cm = 1 meter (m) = 39.37 in., 3.281 ft, 1.094 yd
1000 m = 1 kilometer (km) = 0.6214 mile

1 in. = 2.54 cm
1 ft = 0.3048 m
1 yd = 0.9144 m

Volume

1 liter = 1000 milliliters (ml) = 1000.028 cubic centimeters (cm^3)
1 liter = 0.0353 ft^3 = 61.03 in.^{3} = 1.057 qt (U.S.)
1 m^3 = 35.32 ft^3
1 ft^3 = 28.32 liters
1 qt = 0.946 liter

Weights

1 gram (g) = 1000 milligrams (mg)
1000 g = wt of 1 liter of water at 4°C = 35.28 oz avoirdupois
1000 g = 1 kilogram (kg) = 2.205 lb avoirdupois
1000 kg = 1 metric ton = 2205 lb avoirdupois

1 oz avoirdupois = 28.35 g
1 lb avoirdupois = 453.6 g   1 oz troy = 31.103 g = 1.097 oz
1 ton avoirdupois = 907.2 kg   avoirdupois

LARGE AND SMALL NUMBERS

In this book, large and small numbers have been expressed as powers of ten. The following conversion chart may be useful:

1,000,000	= 10^6	0.1	= 10^{-1}
100,000	= 10^5	0.01	= 10^{-2}
10,000	= 10^4	0.001	= 10^{-3}
1,000	= 10^3	0.0001	= 10^{-4}
100	= 10^2	0.00001	= 10^{-5}
10	= 10^1	0.000001	= 10^{-6}
1	= 10^0		

A number such as $3.6 \times 10^4 = 3.6 \times 10,000 = 36,000$.

ADDITIONAL QUESTIONS AND PROBLEMS

Chapter 4

1. When a deposit of gold-containing quartz is assayed, it is found to have 2 oz of gold per ton. How many dollars worth of gold at $35 per ounce could be obtained from 1000 tons of this gold ore?

2. If a sterling-silver spoon weighs 180 g and contains 166.5 g of silver and the rest copper, what is the percentage of each of these metals in the spoon?

3. 9.42×10^{22} atoms of element X weigh 14.00 g. The same number of oxygen atoms weigh 2.64 g. Find the atomic weight of element X.

4. An angstrom unit (Å) is a unit of length and is equal to 10^{-8} cm. The radius of an oxygen atom is 0.66Å. What is the diameter of the oxygen atom in centimeters?

5. If the atomic weight of oxygen were 100.0 units, (a) what would be the weight of a bromine atom? (b) an americium atom? (c) a lithium atom? (d) a fluorine atom?

6. If the atomic weight of sulfur were 50 units, what would be the atomic weight of (a) an oxygen atom? (b) a helium atom? (c) a copper atom? (d) a carbon atom? (e) a hydrogen atom?

7. If the ratio of the weight of an X atom to the weight of an oxygen atom were 2.5:1 and the ratio of the weight of a Y atom to the weight of an oxygen atom were 4:1, what would be the ratio of the weight of an atom of X to the weight of an atom of Y?

Chapter 5

1. How many particles are contained in (a) two moles of chlorine molecules; (b) two gram atoms of chlorine atoms; (c) two moles of butane molecules; (d) two moles of argon atoms?

2. What is the weight in grams of: (a) a chlorine atom; (b) a hydrogen molecule; (c) a water molecule; (d) a methane molecule?

3. Five moles of gaseous sulfur molecules weigh 1284 g. How many atoms are in a sulfur molecule?

4. How many sulfur atoms would weigh the same as a sulfur dioxide (SO_2) molecule?

5. A SO_2 molecule weighs the same as how many (a) oxygen atoms? (b) oxygen molecules? (c) helium atoms? (d) hydrogen molecules?

6. How many moles of each of the following substances are represented by: (a) 6.023×10^{23} hydrogen atoms; (b) 1.807×10^{23} oxygen molecules; (c) 3.0115×10^{23} carbon dioxide molecules; (d) 1.506×10^{23} sugar molecules?

7. How many square centimeters are there on a piece of paper which measures $8\frac{1}{2} \times 11$ in.? (1 in. = 2.54 cm)

8. The average weight of a football team is 175 lb/man. (a) What is the average weight in kilograms? (b) What is the total weight of the team? (1 lb = 454 g; 1000 g = 1 kg)

9. Suppose an area of land contained 11,250 ft² and was twice as long as it was wide. What would be the dimensions in meters? (1 m = 39.37 in.)

10. Suppose you are driving your car in Mexico and you wish to fill a cylindrical 20-liter spare gasoline can (1 liter = 1000 cc). If the diameter of the can is 30 cm, to what height in the can will the gasoline reach?

11. Suppose a sample of air contained 3.01×10^{24} molecules of various gases of which 0.00005 percent was hydrogen, how many molecules of hydrogen are present?

12. Here are some symbols for some imaginary elements: O, P, R, Z. In terms of atoms and molecules, what information is given by: RP_2, $Z_6Q_4R_2$, Q_2, Z, P_3?

Chapter 6

1. Suppose in planning a certain chemical reaction, it was found that 62.5 g of pure oxygen was needed. The oxygen that was available was only 95 percent pure by weight. How many grams of this impure oxygen would be needed to just satisfy the requirements of the reaction?

2. Some planes travel at the rate of 1800 miles per hour. How many kilometers does such a plane travel in 15 sec? (39.37 in. = 1 m; 1000 m = 1 km)

3. One of our satellite spheres has the capacity of 114 in.^{3}. What is the diameter of the sphere?

4. Air is roughly one-fifth oxygen and four-fifths nitrogen and is necessary for respiration. Nitrous oxide is roughly one-third oxygen and two-thirds nitrogen and is used as an anesthetic. Explain. Remember that often in cases of pneumonia air more concentrated in oxygen is used for treatment.

5. At the same cost per pound and the method of making oxygen being the same, which would be the cheaper source of oxygen: potassium chlorate or sodium chlorate? Explain.

Chapter 7

1. To burn 1 gal of gasoline in an automobile requires about 12 yd^3 of air. If the density of air is 1.3 oz/ft^3, what weight of air is necessary to burn 15 gal of gasoline?

2. Balance the following equations:

　　a. $C_3H_8 + O_2 \longrightarrow CO_2 + H_2O$
　　b. $C_2H_6 + O_2 \longrightarrow CO_2 + H_2O$
　　c. $C_3H_8O_3 + O_2 \longrightarrow$
　　d. The equation for the burning of benzene (C_6H_6)
　　e. The equation for the burning of octane (C_8H_{18})

3. In the following equations, tell whether anything is wrong with either one. Explain.

$$CH_4 + 2O_2 \longrightarrow CO_2 + 2H_2O$$
$$5CH_4 + 10O_2 \longrightarrow 5CO_2 + 5H_2O$$

4. Give the chemical equations for (*a*) the burning of isopropyl alcohol (C_3H_8O); (*b*) the combustion of kerosene ($C_{12}H_{26}$).

Chapter 8

1. Although the earth's crust contains about 8 percent aluminum and 0.01 percent copper, the latter has been known since ancient times while aluminum was not discovered until 1827. Explain.

2. The specific gravity of concentrated sulfuric acid is 1.84. If a cubic foot of water weighs 62.5 lb, how many cubic feet are there in a ton of acid?

3. Explain why a marble-sized sphere of iron will float in mercury.

4. Some samples of homogenized milk contain 4.5 percent butterfat by weight. The normal daily fat requirement for the body is about 2 oz. Assuming that all the fat that was needed by the body was furnished by milk and that all the fat that was ingested was utilized, how many quarts of milk would have to be drunk in a week to satisfy this body need? The specific gravity of milk is 1.026 and 1 gal of water weighs 8.34 lb.

5. If you are told that the density of a gas is directly proportional to the sum of the atomic weights of the atoms in the gas and that the density of oxygen gas is 1.43 g/liter, what is the density of sulfur dioxide gas (SO_2) under the same condition?

6. A great many household fuel gases contain carbon monoxide and hydrogen, both of which are colorless, odorless, and burn with a blue flame. How could you determine the presence of hydrogen?

7. The formula for sulfuric acid is H_2SO_4. How many grams of hydrogen may be obtained from 5 kg of sulfuric acid?

8. Helium is twice as dense as hydrogen. Why will helium-filled balloons lift about 93 percent as much as those filled with hydrogen?

Chapter 9

1. Explain the difference between mass, weight, and density.

2. The average velocity of a methane molecule is 4×10^5 cm/sec and that of sulfur dioxide is 2×10^5 cm/sec. How many times faster does the methane molecule travel?

3. Using Graham's law of diffusion, calculate the relative rates of diffusion of oxygen and nitrogen.

4. A sample of gas occupies a volume of 300 ml at 90°C and a pressure of 500 mm of mercury. Calculate its volume at standard conditions.

5. A gas that exerts a pressure of 3 atmospheres at 27°C in a volume of 10 ml is transferred to a vessel of 5 ml capacity and cooled to -73°C. What pressure does it exert under these conditions?

6. 4 liters of a gas at 25°C exert a pressure of 1 atmosphere. If the gas is pumped into a container of 500 ml volume at a temperature of 100°C, what pressure does it exert?

Chapter 10

1. Change the following temperatures to absolute scale: 25°C, 65°C, -185°C.

2. A gas collected when the temperature was 25°C and the pressure was 80 cm of mercury measured 500 ml. Find the volume at -30°C and 75 cm of mercury.

3. 2.2 g of a liquid was vaporized and the volume of the gas formed was found to be 450 ml at a temperature of 120°C and 710 mm of mercury. (*a*) Find the volume that this gas would occupy at standard conditions if the gas could be reduced to standard conditions without condensing. (*b*) Find the weight of this substance which would occupy 22.4 liters at standard conditions, if the substance could exist as a gas under these conditions.

4. If an automobile tire is inflated to a pressure of 28 lb/in.^{2}, calculate the force on 1 ft^2 area of the tire.

5. Suppose that a metal can having a total surface area of 5 ft^2 is completely evacuated, calculate the total force of the atmosphere tending to collapse the can.

6. A 1-liter cylinder contains nitrogen at a pressure of 1 atmosphere. A 5-liter cylinder contains hydrogen at a pressure of 3 atmospheres. Both cylinders are at the same temperature. If the hydrogen is pumped into the cylinder containing the nitrogen, what will be the total pressure in the cylinder, assuming the temperature does not change?

7. The average velocity of an oxygen molecule at 0°C is 4.6×10^4 cm/sec. Using Graham's law, calculate the average velocity of the hydrogen molecule at 0°C.

8. If the average velocity of the oxygen molecule at 0°C is 4.6×10^4 cm/sec, what will its velocity be (*a*) at 50°C? (*b*) at 100°C?

9. 1 liter of carbon dioxide at standard conditions weighs 1.98 g. What is the weight of 1 liter of the gas if the pressure is increased by 60 mm of mercury?

10. A gas occupies 2208 ml at 20°C and 500 mm of mercury pressure. Find its volume at standard conditions.

11. 1 liter of a gas weighs 1.2 g at standard conditions. Find the weight of 1 liter of the same gas at 90°C and 500 mm of mercury.

12. 500 ml of a gas is collected over mercury at 27°C and 300-mm pressure. Find its volume at standard conditions.

Chapter 11

1. Inasmuch as steam is invisible, why is it possible to see something escaping from a boiling pot of water?

2. Why does steam cause a more severe burn than dry air at the same temperature?

3. Prove mathematically that −40°C = −40°F.

4. When you try to burn wet wood, it will not burn. When you try to burn damp wood, you do not obtain much heat. When you burn dry wood, the flame is vigorous. Explain.

Chapter 12

1. A certain chemical reaction liberates enough heat to raise the temperature of 229 g of water from 25°C to 70°C. How many calories of heat did the reaction liberate?

2. 50 g of liquid water at 100°C are cooled and then frozen to ice at a temperature of 0°C. How many calories of heat were removed from the water?

3. The specific heat of iron is 1.1 cal/g. How many calories are necessary to raise the temperature of 1 lb of iron from 25°C to 63°C?

4. An object is weighed in air and found to have a weight of 5.5 g. When immersed in water, the same object weighs 2.2 g. Calculate the specific gravity of the object.

5. How many calories of heat are released when 10 lb of steam at 100°C is condensed to water and then cooled to 50°C?

6. Calculate the number of calories required to convert 150 g of ice at −10°C to liquid water at 50°C.

7. Calculate the number of calories required to convert 1 lb of water at 25°C to steam at 100°C.

8. 15 ml of a gas are collected over water at a temperature of 25°C and a pressure equivalent to 700 mm of mercury. Calculate the volume of the dry gas at standard conditions.

9. If a thermometer, known to be accurate, showed the boiling point of pure water to be 99.5°C, what conclusion would you draw?

10. A sample of air, originally at 25°C, was found to have a dew point of 15°C. What is the relative humidity of the air?

11. A sample of air containing moisture at 65°C was cooled to 32°C before condensation of the water occurred. What was the relative humidity of the sample?

12. A sample of a gas saturated with water at 18°C was heated to 45°C. What is the relative humidity of the sample after heating?

13. Change: (a) 77°F to degrees C; (b) 0°F to degrees C; (c) 5°C to degrees F; (d) −13°F to degrees C; (e) −273°C to degrees F.

14. A cubic foot of water weighs 62.5 lb. A cubic foot of iron weighs 462.5 lb. What is the specific gravity of the iron?

15. A cubic foot of alcohol weighs 49.4 lb. A cubic foot of gasoline weighs 42 lb. If you mixed 2 ft³ of alcohol with 3 ft³ of gasoline, what would be the weight of 1 ft³ of this mixture?

Chapter 13

1. It is estimated that there are 2 tons of gold in each cubic mile of sea water. Calculate the number of atoms of gold per cubic centimeter of sea water.

2. Water is 11.1 percent hydrogen and 88.9 percent oxygen. What weights of hydrogen and oxygen will be required to produce 100 g of water?

3. Hydrogen peroxide is 5.88 percent hydrogen and 94.12 percent oxygen. When it is caused to decompose, only one-half of its oxygen is liberated. What weight of hydrogen peroxide will be needed to produce 50 g of oxygen?

4. An electric spark is caused to pass through a mixture of 9 g of oxygen and 5 g of hydrogen. (a) How many grams of water are formed? (b) Will a part of either gas remain uncombined? (c) If so, how much by weight?

5. Sea water contains approximately 4 percent dissolved material, 70 percent of which is common salt. How many pounds of sea water would it require to furnish 5 lb of common salt?

Chapter 14

1. Using the data in the graph on page 150, what quantity of water would be necessary to dissolve 100 g of potassium bromide at a temperature of 70°C?
2. How many grams of ammonium chloride would be necessary to form a saturated solution containing 57 g of water at 40°C?
3. If a saturated solution containing 130 g of sodium nitrate at 60°C is cooled to 30°C, how many grams of sodium nitrate will crystalize from the solution?
4. 20 g of sodium chloride are mixed with 70 g of water and heated to 100°C. Is the solution a saturated one?
5. (a) Explain in detail how you could separate pure potassium nitrate from a mixture of 100 g of potassium nitrate and 40 g of sodium chloride. (b) How would you proceed to obtain pure sodium chloride from such a mixture?
6. 90 g of sodium nitrate is mixed with 100 g of water and the result is heated to 60°C. If all of the sodium nitrate dissolves, is the resulting solution saturated, supersaturated, or unsaturated?
7. Given a mixture of 50 g of sodium chloride and 100 g of sodium nitrate, explain in detail how you would obtain from this (a) pure sodium chloride and (b) pure sodium nitrate.

Chapter 15

1. A solution of methyl alcohol in water is found by experiment to have a freezing point of −1.56°C. Calculate the molality of the solution.
2. A sugar solution is found by experiment to have a boiling point of 100.88°C at 1 atmosphere pressure. Calculate: (a) the molality of the solution; (b) the grams of sugar per 1000 g of water; (c) the freezing point of the solution.
3. If the osmotic pressure of a solution is 20 atmospheres, (a) what is the osmotic pressure in pounds per square inch? (b) What is the height of the column of mercury which this solution will support? (c) What height of a column of water would the solution support?
4. 20 g of a nonvolatile solute are dissolved in 400 g of water. The resulting solution is found to have a boiling point of 100.15°C at 1 atmosphere. (a) What is the molecular weight of the solute? (b) What would be the freezing point of this solution?
5. What quantity of glycerin would you add to 1000 g of water to produce a solution freezing at −5°C?
6. 17 g of an unknown solute is dissolved in 350 g of water. The resulting solution is found to have a freezing point of −0.27°C. What is the molecular weight of the unknown solute?
7. The freezing point of normal human blood plasma is −0.56°C. (a) What would be the molality of a glucose solution ($C_6H_{12}O_6$) which would have the same osmotic pressure as normal blood plasma? (b) How many grams of glucose must be added to 1000 g of water to produce such a solution?
8. What would be the boiling point of the glucose solution referred to in problem 7?

Chapter 16

1. Look up the boiling points of argon, potassium, scandium, and titanium. Plot these boiling points against the atomic numbers of these elements and, from the curve obtained, estimate the boiling point of calcium. Compare your result with the boiling point given in literature.

2. Look up the melting points of lithium, sodium, rubidium, and cesium. Plot these data against the atomic numbers of these elements. From your curve estimate the melting point of potassium. Compare your result with the accepted value.

Chapter 17

Assume that you have two radioactive samples, one containing 50 atoms of uranium, the other 100. Assuming that 10 percent of each sample decomposes per unit time, show that the same length of time will be required for one-half of each sample to be disintegrated.

Chapter 18

Complete the following reactions:

a. $_7N^{14} + {}_2He^4 \longrightarrow ? + {}_1H^1$
b. $_3Li^6 + {}_1H^2 \longrightarrow {}_2He^4 + ?$
c. $_{13}Al^{27} + {}_2He^4 \longrightarrow {}_{15}P^{30} + ?$
d. $_{15}P^{30} \longrightarrow {}_{14}Si^{30} + ?$
e. $_{16}S^{32} \longrightarrow ? + {}_2He^4$
f. $_{11}Na^{23} + {}_1H^2 \longrightarrow ? + {}_1H^1$
g. $_{11}Na^{24} \longrightarrow ? + {}_{-1}e^0$

Chapter 20

1. What is meant by the "critical size" of a reactor?
2. Why is it difficult to separate isotopes?
3. Compare the processes taking place in the nuclear reactor with those in an atomic bomb.
4. Explain the changes by means of which uranium 238 is converted into plutonium.
5. Explain why some reactors employ graphite as one of the essential materials.

Chapter 22

1. Given that there are 70 parts per million of bromine in sea water, calculate the tons of bromine present in a cubic mile of sea water.
2. Sea water contains 2.8 percent sodium chloride. How many tons of sea water would be required to supply 50,000 lb of sodium chloride?
3. The Atlantic Ocean contains 0.0035 parts per million of iodine as iodide ion. Calculate the pounds of iodine present in each cubic mile of the Atlantic Ocean.
4. 20 g of bromine is needed for an experiment. What weight of sodium bromide is required to produce this bromine?
5. What weight of bromine will be needed to make 100 g of phosphorus tribromide?

6. If a municipal water supply contains one part per million of fluoride ion, how much sodium fluoride is added to each one million gallons of the water supply?

7. What weight of fluorine is contained in 100 lb of Freon 12 (CCl_2F_2)?

8. How much hydrogen fluoride is used to manufacture 1 ton of fluorine?

Chapter 24

1. Using the necessary data given in this chapter, calculate the calories of energy liberated when 1 g of carbon burns to carbon dioxide.

2. How much heat in calories is produced when 25 g of calcium are oxidized to calcium oxide?

3. How much energy would be necessary to completely decompose 100 g of mercuric oxide into mercury and oxygen?

4. How much energy is released when 1 lb of hydrogen burns to water?

5. What amount of energy must be supplied to convert 100 g of nitrogen into nitric oxide?

Chapter 25

1. A cube of starch, 1 cm on edge, is ground. Assume that the particles from the grinding are cubic and that each particle has an average edge of 0.00001 cm. What is the surface area of the starch (*a*) before and (*b*) after grinding?

2. If a certain reaction is known to take place in 1 min at 0°C, how long a time would you expect the reaction to require at 100°C?

3. If potatoes can be boiled in an open vessel at 1 atmosphere of pressure in 30 min, how much time would you expect to be required to cook the potatoes in a pressure cooker which is operated at 120°C?

4. How long would it take to boil a "two-minute" egg, if the egg is cooked in an open vessel at an altitude where the boiling point is 70°C?

5. How much faster would you expect a given reaction to go at 100°C than it goes at −100°C?

Chapter 26

1. In the equation representing Deacon's process, page 283, if one starts with 4 moles of hydrogen chloride and 1 mole of oxygen, (*a*) how many moles of chlorine, water, hydrogen chloride, and oxygen exist in equilibrium at 350°C? (*b*) How many moles of chlorine and water will be formed if the reaction could be caused to go to completion?

2. If the reaction for the blast furnace given on page 282 reaches equilibrium, the reaction is 80 percent complete. (*a*) How much carbon dioxide and iron will be formed starting with 1 mole of iron oxide and 3 moles of carbon monoxide? (*b*) How much carbon monoxide will remain unreacted?

3. Using the data given on page 287 for the formation of sulfur trioxide from sulfur dioxide and oxygen, (*a*) how many moles of sulfur trioxide will be formed by mixing 2 moles of sulfur dioxide and 1 mole of oxygen and allowing them to come to equilibrium at 600°C? (*b*) How many grams of sulfur trioxide will be formed? (*c*) How many moles of sulfur dioxide and oxygen will be left unreacted at this temperature?

4. If it takes 1 min for the reaction given on page 287 to reach equilibrium at 400°C, approximately how long would you expect it to take to reach equilibrium in this reaction at 100°C?

Chapter 27

1. (*a*) If one mole of sulfuric acid is dissolved in enough water to make 1 liter of solution, what is the concentration of sulfuric acid? (*b*) Assuming that the sulfuric acid is completely ionized, what is the concentration in moles per liter of hydronium ion? (*c*) How many grams of hydronium ion are present in a liter of such a solution?

2. One molar acetic acid is approximately 1 percent ionized. What is the approximate concentration in moles per liter of hydronium ion in a one-molar solution of acetic acid?

3. Sodium hydroxide is a strong base and completely ionized. What is the concentration in moles per liter of hydroxyl ions in a one-tenth molar solution of sodium hydroxide?

4. What is the concentration of hydroxyl ions in a one-thousandth molar solution of calcium hydroxide? Assume that the calcium hydroxide is completely ionized.

5. (*a*) Compare the concentration of hydronium ion existing in a one-molar solution of hydrochloric acid with that in a one-molar solution of acetic acid. (*b*) How does the base-neutralizing ability of these two solutions compare?

6. What weight of copper chloride must one use in order to prepare a solution from which one could deposit 100 g of metallic copper?

7. What weight of (*a*) sodium hydroxide is produced by the electrolysis of a solution containing 50 g of sodium chloride? Calculate the weights of (*b*) hydrogen and (*c*) chlorine produced at the same time.

8. Write the equation for the hydrolysis of potassium carbonate in water.

9. Write the equation for the hydrolysis of sodium sulfide in water.

10. Write the equation for the hydrolysis of ammonium sulfate in water.

11. In the analysis of an unknown sample of lye by titration with hydrochloric acid, the following results were obtained: the weight of the lye sample was 0.615 g and the volume of 0.500 molar hydrochloric acid used to neutralize the sample was 21.6 ml. Calculate (*a*) the weight of hydrochloric acid used; (*b*) the weight of sodium hydroxide present in the unknown sample; (*c*) the percent of sodium hydroxide in the unknown sample.

12. How many grams of sulfuric acid are present in a liter of one-tenth normal solution?

13. How many grams of calcium hydroxide are present in a liter of 0.001 normal calcium hydroxide solution?

14. It is found that 50.1 cc of one-tenth normal sodium hydroxide are necessary to neutralize 25 cc of an unknown sulfuric acid solution. Calculate (a) the normality of the sulfuric acid; (b) the molarity of the sulfuric acid; (c) the grams of sulfuric acid per liter of solution.

15. 25 cc of one-tenth normal sodium hydroxide are required to neutralize 20 cc of a vinegar solution. Assuming that the only acid present in the vinegar is acetic acid, calculate (a) the normality of the vinegar solution as acetic acid; (b) the grams of acetic acid present per liter of vinegar solution.

16. Indicate whether or not you would expect a reaction to occur when dilute solutions of the following substances are mixed as indicated. Give reasons for each answer. (a) Potassium chloride and sodium nitrate; (b) Potassium chloride and silver nitrate; (c) Sodium chloride and potassium hydroxide; (d) Copper chloride and potassium hydroxide; (e) Sodium carbonate and sulfuric acid.

Chapter 28

1. Calculate the weight in grams of 125 ml of hydrogen sulfide measured at 23°C and 700 mm of mercury pressure.

2. Calculate the percentage of selenium in copper selenide (CuSe).

3. How many pounds of sulfur dioxide will be produced by burning 500 lb of pure sulfur?

4. How many pounds of hydrogen sulfide can be produced from 60 lb of pure sulfur?

Chapter 29

1. What volume of sulfur dioxide, measured at standard temperature and pressure, can be produced by the action of hydrochloric acid on 100 g of sodium sulfite?

2. What weight of sulfur is necessary to produce, on burning, 100 liters of sulfur dioxide measured at 50°C at 1 atmosphere of pressure?

3. One liter of sulfur dioxide gas, measured at standard temperature and pressure, is dissolved in water to form 10 liters of sulfurous acid solution. (a) What is the molarity of the resulting sulfurous acid solution? (b) What is the normality of this solution? (c) How many grams of sulfurous acid are contained in 1 liter of the solution?

4. What weight of sodium hydroxide is required to neutralize 10 cc of the solution referred to in problem 3?

5. The per capita consumption of sulfuric acid in this country is about 181 lb. What weight of sulfur is used to prepare this amount of sulfuric acid?

6. 96 percent commercial concentrated sulfuric acid has a density of 1.86 g/liter. Calculate the molarity of the commercial concentrated acid.

7. (a) How many grams of commercial concentrated acid (see problem 6) must be used to prepare 1 liter of 1 molar sulfuric acid? (b) How many cubic centimeters is this?

8. What weight of sulfur is required to produce 65 g of sodium thiosulfate by reaction with sodium sulfite?

Chapter 30

1. What is the density of helium at standard temperature and pressure in grams per liter?
2. Which of the gases listed in Table 30–2, page 338, have a density less than that of the atmosphere as a whole?
3. Can you suggest any reason why krypton and xenon might be more efficient for filling incandescent lamp bulbs than argon?
4. A steel cylinder contains 5 liters of helium stored at a pressure of 2000 lb/in.^{2} at 25°C. (a) What is the volume of this helium at standard temperature and pressure? (b) What is the weight of the helium contained in the cylinder?

Chapter 31

1. On the average 1 ton of bituminous coal yields 5 lb of ammonia when the coal is coked. How much ammonium sulfate is produced each day from a coke mill that cokes 1000 tons of coal each day?
2. A plant producing ammonia by the Haber process produces 100 tons of ammonia per day. If the hydrogen for this process is produced by passing steam over iron, what weight of iron is required to produce the hydrogen required for one day's operation of the plant?
3. Calcium cyanamide is sometimes used as a plant fertilizer. What percentage nitrogen does it contain?
4. At 0°, 1305 volumes of ammonia will dissolve in 1 volume of water. What is the percentage of ammonia in a saturated water solution at 0°C and 1 atmosphere of pressure?
5. Commercial concentrated ammonium hydroxide has a density of 0.9 g/ml and contains 28 percent by weight ammonia. Calculate the molarity of commercial concentrated ammonium hydroxide.
6. (a) Compare the percentage of nitrogen contained in ammonium nitrate and in ammonium nitrite. (b) Do you think that ammonium nitrite would be suitable for use as a fertilizer? Explain.
7. It is said that a good stand of alfalfa in the course of one season's growth will fix in the soil 150 lb of nitrogen. (a) How much ammonium nitrate would have to be added to an acre of soil in order to supply this amount of nitrogen? (b) What would be the cost of this ammonium nitrate if ammonium nitrate fertilizer grade can be purchased for $95 per ton?

Chapter 32

1. What volume of nitric oxide at standard temperature and pressure is formed by the complete decomposition of 10 g of nitrous acid in solution?
2. What weight of nitric acid is required to produce 100 lb of nitroglycerin?
3. Commercial concentrated nitric acid is about 15 molar. What volume of this acid would you use to make 1 liter of $1/10$ molar nitric acid?
4. What weight of ammonia is required to produce 1 ton of nitric acid by the Ostwald process?

5. What weight of water is produced in question 4?

6. What weight of ammonium nitrate is required to produce 100 g of laughing gas (N_2O)?

7. The solubility of nitrous oxide in water is 60 volumes of nitrous oxide in 100 volumes of water at 20°C. What is the percent concentration of a saturated solution of nitrous oxide at 20°C and one atmosphere?

Chapter 33

1. A certain ore contains 10 percent SiO_2. What weight of calcium oxide is required to convert to fusable calcium silicate the SiO_2 contained in one ton of this ore?

2. Calculate the percentage of hydrogen in orthophosphoric acid.

3. Calculate the percentage of phosphorus in triple superphosphate, $Ca(H_2PO_4)_2$.

4. What volume of gaseous phosphene will be produced by the action of water on 70 g of calcium phosphide?

Chapter 34

1. It is said that the Hope diamond weighs 44.5 carats. What is the weight of the Hope diamond in ounces?

2. Making use of the values given in Table 34–1, page 391, how many Btu can be obtained by burning 1 ton of bituminous coal?

3. Using the data given in Table 34–2, page 392, how many pounds of ammonium sulfate will be produced from the ammonia formed in the destructive distillation of 100 lb of average bituminous coal?

4. (a) Using the data in Table 34–1, page 391, how many calories of heat can be produced from the burning of $1 worth of bituminous coal if the coal is priced at $20 per ton? (b) Compare this figure with the number of calories produced on burning $1 worth of crude oil, assuming that the crude oil is valued at 15 cents per gallon and that 1 gal of oil weighs 6 lb.

Chapter 35

1. Suppose that you were preparing to generate 100 liters of carbon dioxide, measured at standard temperature and pressure, by the use of calcium carbonate and hydrochloric acid in a Kipp generator. What is the minimum weight of calcium carbonate which you should place in the generator?

2. Calculate the density of carbon dioxide at standard temperature and pressure in grams per liter.

3. How does the density of carbon dioxide compare with the density of the atmosphere? What bearing does your answer have on the dangers of going into an old well or cistern?

4. A certain foamite-type fire extinguisher contains 200 g of sodium bicarbonate. What volume of carbon dioxide at standard temperature and pressure will this fire extinguisher produce, assuming that it contains excess acid?

5. 100 g of coke are converted into water gas by the action of steam. What is the total volume of gases produced, measured at standard temperature and pressure?

6. What volume of formic acid (HCO₂H) is necessary to produce 1 liter of carbon monoxide at standard temperature and pressure?

7. Calculate the percentage of nitrogen in urea.

Chapter 37

1. 100 g of glyceryl stearate are converted into glycerin and soap, according to the equation given on page 449. What weight of glycerin and soap is produced?

2. What weight of hydrogen is required to hydrogenate 1 ton of glyceryl oleate to glyceryl stearate, according to the equation given on page 446?

3. What volume of oxygen (measured at standard temperature and pressure) is required to convert a solution containing 450 g of ethyl alcohol to acetic acid?

4. In the manufacture of DDT, the chlorine used comes from sodium chloride. How much salt is necessary to furnish the chlorine needed to manufacture 1 ton of DDT?

Chapter 41

1. What weight of water is necessary to produce 100 liters of hydrogen at 23°C and 700 mm pressure by the reaction of water, silicon, and sodium hydroxide?

2. Calculate the percentage of silicon in SiO_2.

3. What weight of carbon (in pounds) is required to produce 1 ton of silicon from SiO_2?

4. How many grams of sodium silicate can be produced from 1 kg of SiO_2?

5. Calculate the percentage of silicon in feldspar.

Chapter 42

1. In a colloidal dispersion of silver, it is assumed that each silver particle is a cube of 4×10^{-6} cm on an edge. (*a*) How many colloid particles are produced from 0.1 g of silver? (*b*) What is the total area of the silver particles? (*c*) What is the area of a single cube of silver weighing 0.1 g? The density of silver is 10.5 g/cc.

2. A colloidal dispersion of mercury is composed of mercury globules having a diameter of 1×10^{-6} cm. What is the surface area of the particles formed from 1 g of mercury? Assume that the particles are spherical.

Chapter 43

1. Using the data from Table 43–3, page 543, calculate the weight of 1 ft³ of aluminum; 1 ft³ of iron; 1 ft³ of titanium.

2. Using the data in Table 43–3, page 543, (*a*) calculate the weight of an aluminum wire 1 cm in diameter and 1 km in length. (*b*) Calculate the weight of a copper wire of the same dimensions. (*c*) What is the relationship of the answers you have obtained to the construction of high tension electrical cables?

3. From the data in Table 43–3, page 543, do you think lead would be satisfactory for the construction of high-tension cables? Explain your answer.

4. What is the percentage of iron in hematite?
5. Calculate the percentage of copper in chalcopyrite.
6. What weight of carbon is required to reduce 1 kg of cassiterite?
7. Calculate the percentage of zinc in sphalerite.

Chapter 44

1. (a) What weight of sodium hydroxide is necessary to supply, on electrolysis, 1 ton of metallic sodium? (b) What volumes of hydrogen and oxygen (measured at standard temperature and pressure) will be produced at the same time?

2. Assuming that rock salt costs $8 per ton, (a) what will be the cost of the rock salt required to supply 100 lb of metallic sodium on electrolysis? (b) What weight of chlorine will be produced simultaneously?

3. What weight of sodium would be required to produce 100 cc of hydrogen gas (measured at 25°C and 740 mm of mercury pressure) by the reaction of sodium and water?

4. What weight of sodium chloride is necessary to produce 1 ton of sodium bicarbonate by the Solvay process?

5. 1 lb of sodium bicarbonate is heated and converted, thereby, into sodium carbonate. (a) What weight of sodium carbonate is formed? (b) What weight of carbon dioxide is formed simultaneously?

6. What weight of calcium chloride is produced as a by-product in the manufacture of 1 ton of sodium carbonate by the Solvay process?

7. The potassium source in fertilizers is commonly potassium chloride. What weight of potassium chloride must be added per acre of land to replace the potassium used in the growing of a corn crop which yields 80 bu to the acre? Use data in Table 44–4, page 560.

8. What volume of carbon dioxide measured at standard temperature and pressure is formed on heating 1 ton of calcium carbonate?

Chapter 45

1. On the average, sea water contains about 3.5 percent solids. Of this, about 3.5 percent is magnesium ion. What weight of sea water is required to furnish enough magnesium ion to make 1 ton of magnesium metal?

2. Calculate the percentage of water in gypsum.
3. Calculate the percentage of water in plaster of paris.
4. What is the minimum weight of water necessary to convert 100 g of plaster of paris into gypsum?
5. What weight of beryllium chloride would be required to furnish 1 lb of beryllium metal on electrolysis?
6. In obtaining magnesium from the sea, the magnesium is precipitated as magnesium hydroxide, neutralized with hydrochloric acid to form magnesium chloride, which is then electrolyzed to produce metallic magnesium. What weight of hydrochloric acid is required to neutralize enough magnesium hydroxide to form 100 lb of metallic magnesium?
7. Calculate the percentage of magnesium in magnesite ($MgCO_3$).

8. What weight of sodium hydroxide is required to precipitate completely, as magnesium hydroxide, the magnesium contained in 100 g of magnesium chloride?
9. What weight of calcium chloride must be used to make 50 lb of quicklime?
10. What weight of water is necessary to slake completely 1 ton of quicklime?
11. Water hardness is commonly expressed in parts per million. Thus 100 parts per million of calcium ion means 100 parts of calcium ion per million parts of water by weight. What weight of sodium stearate soap would be required to precipitate the calcium from 1 gal of water with a hardness of 200 parts per million? (Assume 1 gal of water weighs 8 lb.)
12. A certain natural water contains calcium bicarbonate to a degree of 150 parts per million of calcium. If 1 liter of this water is boiled, what weight of calcium carbonate would precipitate?

Chapter 46

1. Suppose you were offered a cubic foot of gold if you could lift it. (*a*) Do you think you could do so? Explain your answer. (*b*) At a value of $35/oz, what would the gold be worth?
2. It is said that the United States government has stored about $24,000,000 worth of gold in Fort Knox. If this gold were converted into a single cube, what would be its dimensions? (Value of gold, $35/oz.)
3. What weight of sodium cyanide is required to dissolve the silver in 1 ton of ore which contains 0.001 percent silver?
4. What weight of ammonia is required to dissolve 1 g of silver chloride?
5. Calculate the percentage of copper in (*a*) chalcocite; (*b*) cuprite.
6. What weight of iron is required to deposit all of the copper from a liter of a solution of 1-molar copper sulfate?
7. 1 g of silver is to be dissolved in nitric acid. What is the minimum volume of 3-molar nitric acid that must be used?

Chapter 47

1. What weight of potassium would be required to produce 100 g of aluminum from aluminum chloride?
2. What weight of purified aluminum oxide (Al_2O_3) is required to produce 1 ton of aluminum on electrolysis by the Hall process?
3. In problem 2, if we assume that all of the oxygen liberated combines with the carbon electrode to form carbon dioxide, what weight of carbon is consumed in the manufacture of 1 ton of aluminum?
4. In the purification of aluminum ore, as indicated on page 610, what weight of sodium hydroxide is required to dissolve completely the aluminum oxide contained in 1 ton of bauxite ore that is 55 percent Al_2O_3?
5. (*a*) What length of wire 0.1 cm in diameter can be made from 1 lb of aluminum? (*b*) What length of wire 0.1 cm in diameter can be made from 1 lb of copper?

6. What volume of hydrogen (measured at standard temperature and pressure) will be produced by the action of 1 lb of aluminum on an excess of sodium hydroxide?

Chapter 48

1. Calculate the percentage of zinc in (*a*) zinc sulfide; (*b*) zinc oxide; (*c*) zinc carbonate.

2. What weight of carbon is required to reduce 1 lb of zinc oxide to metallic zinc?

3. What weight of zinc is needed to liberate 5 g of hydrogen by reaction with sodium hydroxide?

4. What weight of zinc is needed to liberate 5 g of hydrogen by reaction with hydrochloric acid?

5. A certain solution contains 5 g of zinc ions. (*a*) What weight of sodium hydroxide is required to precipitate completely the zinc ions as zinc hydroxide? (*b*) What weight of sodium hydroxide is required to dissolve completely the precipitate initially formed?

6. What is the minimum amount of concentrated nitric acid (assumed to be 15 molar) that is needed to dissolve completely 10 g of mercury?

7. What weight of metallic mercury is required to reduce completely the mercuric ions in 1 liter of a 1-molar solution of mercuric chloride?

Chapter 51

1. Complete and balance:
$$H_2O + H_2S + HNO_3 \text{ (concentrated)} \longrightarrow NO_2 + H_2SO_4$$

2. Complete and balance:
$$H_2SO_3 + HNO_3 \text{ (dilute)} \longrightarrow H_2SO_4 + NO$$

3. Complete and balance:
$$KMnO_4 + HCl \longrightarrow KCl + Cl_2 + MnCl_2$$

4. Complete and balance:
$$Cu + H_2SO_4 \text{ (concentrated)} \longrightarrow Cu^{++} + SO_2 + SO_4^{=}$$

INDEX

Abrasives, 400, 617
Absolute alcohol, 436
Absolute temperature scale, 84
Absolute zero, 85–86, 95
Acetaldehyde, 439
Acetanilide, 144
Acetate rayon, 464–465, 484
Acetates, solubility of, 157
Acetic acid, 65, 304, 441, 442, 689
   pH of $1M$ solution, 304
Acetone, 440
Acetylene (ethyne), 417–418, 478, 486
Acheson process, 384
Acid anhydride, 141, 142
Acid salts, 293–294
Acidic oxides, 141, 142
Acids, formation from oxides, 141
  liberation of hydrogen from, 67, 68
  molarity and normality of commercial concentrated, 689
  naming of, 42
  properties of, 65, 292, 295–296, 298
Acrylic polymers, 480–481
Acrylonitrile, polymerization of, 485
Actinide series, 173–175
Actinium, 174, 682, 688
Active metals, reaction, with acids, 67–68
  with alkalis, 68
  with hydrogen, 71
  with water, 65, 66
Activity in terms of electronic structure, of alkali metals, 553–554
  of alkaline earth metals, 566, 567
  of metals, 231–232
  of nonmetals, 233
Activity series, 73–75
Adipic acid in synthesis of nylon, 483
Adsorption, by charcoal and bone black, 389–390
  by silica gel, 516

Agate, 512
Agene, 365
Agricultural applications of chemistry, care and feeding of livestock, 324, 443, 452, 495–496, 504, 555
  "blind staggers," as due to silenium in vegetation, 324
  halogeton hazard, as due to oxalic acid, 443
  importance of vitamin D, 504
  protein requirements, 495–496
  roughage utilization, 452
  salt-craving of herbivorous animals, 555
  conservation problems, 108, 354, 377, 560–561
  control, of brush and weeds, 455–456
  of fungi, 321, 594–595
  of insect pests, 453–454
  erosion, 560
  fertilizers as source, of nitrogen, 346, 348, 351, 352–353
  of phosphates, 376–377
  of potassium, 560–561
  lime, agricultural uses of, 304, 576
  plant metabolism, photosynthesis in, 270, 338
  potassium requirement in, 555, 560–561
  protein formation in, 495
  sulfur in, 321
  soil, acidity of, importance to individual crops, 304–305
  quality of, relation of clay to, 523
  relation of sand to, 513–514
Air, composition of, 337
  density of, 259
Air blast damage from atomic explosion, 213–214
Air conditioning, 125–126
Air-slaked lime, 576
Airplane fuel, 426
Alabaster, 570

707

Alamogordo, N.M., 213
Alchemists, 26, 41, 181–182
Alcohol baths, 115
Alcohols, 432–438
  high-molecular-weight, in detergents, 449–450
  in waxes, 445
  (*See also* names of alcohols)
Aldehydes, 439
Algae, control of, 595
Aliphatic, 418
"Alkali disease," 324
Alkali metals, 552–564
  electron structure and properties, 552–554
  occurrence in nature, 554–555
  preparation, 556
  properties and uses, 556, 557
  reaction with nitrogen, 345
  tests for, 562–564
Alkaline earth metals, 566–585
  compounds of, 567–568
  electronic structure and properties, 566–567
  occurrence in nature, 568–570
  preparation, 570–573
  reaction with nitrogen, 345
  tests for, 585
  uses of, 573–574
  (*See also* names of metals)
Alkalis, definition, 68
  preparation of hydrogen from, 68
Allotropic modifications, 50
  of carbon (*see* Diamonds; Graphite)
  of oxygen, 49–50
  of phosphorus, 370–371
  of sulfur, 317–320
  of tin, 650
Alloy steels, 644
Alloys, 549
  (*See also* names of metals and alloys)
Almonds, 505
Alnico, 612, 647
Alpha (α) particles or rays, 186, 188–190, 196, 235
Alum, 617
Aluminon reagent, 619
Aluminum, 606–619
  chemical properties, 56, 68, 75, 345, 615–616
  compounds, 617–619
  metallurgy, 608–611
  occurrence and abundance in nature, 606–607

Aluminum, ore, 545, 548, 606–607, 610–611
  physical properties and uses, 542, 543, 611–615
  test for, 619
Aluminum alloys, 593, 611–612
Aluminum bronze, 593, 611–612
Aluminum foil, 613
Aluminum hydroxide, 615, 617
Aluminum oxide, 609–611, 617
  heat of formation, 268
Aluminum paint, 614
Alundum, 617
Amalgams, 629
Americium, 175, 682, 688
Amethyst, 511, 527
Amino acids, 467–468
  fate in body, 494
  nutritionally essential, 494–495
Ammonia, 72, 127, 296, 346–351, 428
  chemical properties, 350–352
  complex ion formation, with copper, 594
  with silver, 599
  critical constants, 98
  laboratory preparation, 349
  manufacture, from coal, 346–347, 392
  by cyanamide process, 348
  by Haber process, 347–348
  physical properties, 349–350
  test for, 352
  uses, 135, 352–353
"Ammonia fountain," 350
Ammonium chloride "dust" experiment, 87–88
Ammonium hydroxide, 351–352
  commercial, concentration of, 689
Ammonium ion, 296
Ammonium phosphate, use in matches, 374
Ammonium salts, 351–352
  solubility of, 157
Ammunition, use of acetone in, 440
Amperage of battery, factors affecting, 674–675, 677
Amphoteric behavior, of aluminum hydroxide, 615
  of zinc hydroxide, 626
Amyl acetate, 445
Amyl butyrate, 445
Analysis, 17, 18
Anemia, 499
Anesthesia, by diethyl ether, 450
  by ethylene, 416
  by nitrous oxide, 363

Anglesite, 651
Angstrom unit, 20–21
Animal charcoal, 388
Annual production (consumption),
    of aluminum, 606, 608
  of chlorine, 241
  of copper, 591
  of iron and steel, 633–634
  of petroleum, 427
  of sulfur, 314
  of sulfuric acid, 334
Anode, 8
  reactions occurring at, 298, 302
Anthracite coal, 391
Antifreeze, 162–163, 434, 436, 438
"Antiknock" gasoline, 244, 425–426, 653
Antimony (stibium), 175, 238, 543, 654, 682, 688
Antimony sulfide, 323
Antimony trisulfide, use in matches, 374
Antirachitic vitamin (vitamin D), 493, 504
ANTU, 457
Apatite, 248, 367, 368, 513, 570
Appetite, relation to thiamine, 501
Apples, malic acid in, 443
  nutrients in, 505
  storage of, use of carbon dioxide in, 277–278
Apricots, odor of, 445
Aqua fortis, 357
Aqua regia, 361, 603
Aquadag, 384
Aquamarine, 568
Arachidonic acid, 492
Aralac, 470
Arc process for nitric acid manufacture, 362–363
Archimedes' principle, 69, 110–111
Arcing under water to produce colloids, 529
Argentite, 595
Argon, 226, 227, 338, 340–341, 682
Argyrol, 598
Aromatic hydrocarbons, 418–419
Arsenic, 175, 590–591, 682, 688
Artificial radioactivity, 185
Asbestos, 58, 59, 475, 569
Ascorbic acid (vitamin C), 489, 493, 503, 505
Astatine, 175, 235, 682, 688
Aston, F. W., 198–199
Astronomy as "mother of physics," 12

Atmosphere, composition of, 337, 338
  pressure of, 79–80
  as unit of pressure, 80
Atom(s), analogy to solar system, 196–197, 224
  building blocks of, 195–196
  definition of, 22
  in gram-atomic weight, 27–28
Atomic (nuclear) bomb, 208–214
Atomic (nuclear) energy, 219–220
  as ultimate source of other more familiar forms, 270
Atomic (nuclear) explosions, description of, 214
  injuries from, 213–214
Atomic number, 196–197, 224, 233
  table of, 682–684
Atomic ratio, 31–32
Atomic size, 20–21
Atomic theory, Dalton's, 16–19
  modifications from recent findings, 23
Atomic (nuclear) transmutations, 205–206, 208, 209
Atomic weights, actual, 20, 28
  conventional scale of, 20
  relation to mass number, isotopes, and energy, 200–204
  table of, 682–684
Automobile antifreeze, 162–163, 434, 436, 438
Automobile engine, 424, 427
  efficiency of, 271
Avogadro's law, 257
  applications of, 257–260, 263–264
Avogadro's number, 28, 31
Azote, 343

B battery, 674
Babbitt metal, 549, 651, 654
Bacon, 505
Bacteria, in drinking water, 134–136
  nitrogen-fixing, 354
Bacterial fermentation as source, of acetic acid, 442
  of acetone, 440
Bacterium aceti, 442
Baekeland, Leo, 474
Bakelite, 439, 474, 475
Baking, carbon dioxide in, 404–405
Baking powders, 404–406, 558
Baking soda (sodium hydrogen carbonate), 406, 558
  pH of solution of, 304

709

Balancing of equations, 34–35
   of oxidation-reduction reactions, 663–667
Balata, 470
Balloons, filled with helium, 259, 339
   filled with hydrogen, 69, 73, 259
Bananas, nutrients in, 505
   odor of, 445
Barite, 545
Barium, electron structure and properties, 567
   occurrence, 568
   ores, 545
   physical constants, 543
   test for, 585
   uses, 574
Barium chloride as test for sulfate, 334
Barium salts, solubility of, 157
Barometer, 79–80
Bases, distinguishing characteristics of, 142
   naming of, 42
   properties of, 292, 296, 298–299
Basic cupric carbonate, 592, 593
Basic oxides, 141–142
Basic zinc carbonate, 623–624
Battery, dry cell, 673–675
   lead storage, 675–679
Battery plates, importance of number of, 677
Bauxite, 545, 606–607, 610
Beans, 503, 505
Becquerel, Henri, 182–183
Bee analogy to kinetic molecular theory, 91, 99, 101
Beef, 505
Beehive oven for coking, 391
Beer, 304, 435
Beeswax, 438
Beet greens, 443, 498
Beet sugar, 450–451
Beetle, 476
"Bends," 155–156
Benzene, 157, 418
Benzine, 418, 421
Benzyl bromide as tear gas, 245
Bergius process, 429
Beriberi, 501
Berkelium, 175, 682, 688
Beryl, 545, 568–569
Beryllium, occurrence, 568–569
   ore, 545, 548
   physical constants, 543
   preparation, 570–571

Beryllium, properties, 567
   uses, 573
Beryllium alloys, 573
Beryllium compounds, 575
Berzelius, 26
Bessemer process, 641–642
Beta (β) rays (beta particles, electrons), 186, 195, 205, 206
Bicarbonate hardness of water, 582
Bichloride of mercury, 629, 630
Binary compounds, naming of, 40
Binding energies, 204, 205
Biotin, 321
Bird feathers, silica in, 509
Bismuth, 175, 682, 688
   in alloys, 654
   conversion to astatine, 235
   physical constants, 543
   radioactive, in uranium 238 series, 205, 206
Bisque, 618
Bituminous coal, 391
Black gunpowder, potassium nitrate in, 561
Blast furnace for pig iron manufacture, 637–639
Bleaching, by hydrogen peroxide, 144
   by hypochlorous acid, 240
   by ozone, 50
   by sulfur dioxide, 327
"Blind staggers" of livestock, 324
Blood, gases dissolved in, 147, 155–156
   osmotic relations in, 165–166
   pH of, 304
Blood plasma, freezing point of, 166
Blue vitriol, 138
Body, human adult, amount of calcium in, 497
   amount of iron in, 499
   amount of phosphorus in, 368, 496
Body oxidation processes, 58–60
Boiled linseed oil, 448
Boiler scale, 581
Boiling, 118–122
Boiling point, definition, 118
   of halogens, 253
   of inert gases, 338
   of metals, 543, 544
   of paraffin hydrocarbons, 413, 421
   relation to atmospheric pressure, 118–120
   of salts, 685–687
   of solutions, 160–162, 311

Boiling-point increase, 160–162
  of electrolytes, 311
Bomb, atomic, 208–214
  hydrogen, 203
  plutonium, 213, 218–219
  uranium, 208–214
Bond, electrovalent versus covalent, 228–231
Bone black, 388
Bone china, 618
Bones and teeth, mineral elements in, 367–368, 491, 496
  relation to vitamin A, 500
  relation to vitamin D, 504
Booth, James Curtis, 420
Bordeaux mixture, 595
Boric oxide in glass, 519, 520
Boron, 174, 682, 688
  as absorber of neutrons, 212, 217
  reaction with nitrogen, 345
Boron carbide, 400
Borosilicate glass, 519, 520
Boule, 617
Boyle, Robert, 372
Boyle's law, 82–83, 93
Boys, recommended dietary allowances for, 493
Brand, H., 367, 368
Brass, 148, 549, 593
Bread, enriched, 502, 505
  whole-wheat, 502, 505
Bricks, 59
British coinage silver, 598
British thermal unit (Btu), 109
Broccoli, 498, 505
Bromide, test for, 247, 252
Bromine, 241–245, 253
  comparison with other halogens, 253
  occurrence, 241
  preparation, 242–243
  properties, 243
  test for, 243, 246
  uses, 244–245
Bronze, 593
Brown, Robert, 530
"Brown ring" test for nitrate, 364–365
Brownian movement, 530–531
Brush, chemical control of, 455–456
Btu (British thermal unit), 109
Building board, gypsum, 578–579
Bulletproof glass, 519
Bully tree, 470
Buna S (GRS) rubber, 485–487
Buoyancy of gases, 259

Burette, 80, 81
Butadiene in formation of synthetic rubbers, 485, 486
Butane, 413, 415
Butter and butterfat, 446, 447, 505
Butyl (GRI) rubber, 486, 487
Butyric acid (and butyrates), 442, 446, 447
By-product oven for coking, 391

Cabbage, 498, 503, 505
Cadmium, 543, 621, 626–627, 654
Cadmium-coated steel, 626
Cadmium ores, 545, 548
Cadmium sulfide, 323, 626–627
Caisson disease, 155–156
Caissons, use of helium in, 340
Calamine, 622
Calcite, 513, 545, 570
Calcium, activity, 75
  electron structure and properties, 566–567
  in foods and nutrition, 493, 497–498, 505
  metabolism, relation to oxalic acid in food, 442–443
  occurrence, 568, 570
  physical constants, 543
  test, 585
  use, 574
Calcium carbide, 348, 417, 578
Calcium carbonate and calcium hydrogen carbonate, 575–576, 579–582
  (See also Calcite; Iceland spar; Limestone)
Calcium chloride as drying agent, 140
Calcium cyanamide as fertilizer, 348
Calcium hydrogen sulfite in manufacture of pulp, 462
Calcium hydroxide (slaked lime, hydrated lime), 576, 578
Calcium oxide, heat of formation, 268
  use as flux, 369–370
Calcium salts in water supply, 133, 581–584
Calcium sulfate, 578–579
Calculation, of empirical formula, 31–32
  of molecular formula, 33
  of percentage composition, 260–261
  of yields, 256, 262–263
Calgon, 583

711

Caliche as source of iodine, 245
Californium, 175, 682, 688
Calomel, 629, 630
Calorie, definition of, 109
Calories in food, 492, 493, 505
Calx, 54
Cancer control, by artificial radioisotopes, 220–221
   by radiation, 193
Cane sugar, 450–451
Canned heat, 436
Carat as measure, of gem stones, 382
   of gold content, 603
Carbohydrates, 270, 450–452, 491
   combustion of, 58
   oxidation in body, 58
   reaction with concentrated sulfuric acid, 332–333
Carbon, as neutron moderator, 217
   occurrence in nature, 380
   reaction, with concentrated sulfuric acid, 333
     with fluorine, 249
     with steam, 67
     with sulfur, 320, 397–398
   as reducing agent, in pig iron manufacture, 637, 639
     in preparation of phosphorus, 368–369
   valence of, 396–397
Carbon black, 392–393
   for reinforcing rubber, 471
Carbon-to-carbon distance, in diamond, 387
   in graphite, 387
Carbon content as affecting properties of iron and steel, 636–637, 643
Carbon dioxide, 401–406
   chemical properties, 406
   as component of air, 337
   critical constants, 98
   density of, 259
   for extinguishing fires, 403–404
   heat of formation, 268
   importance in baking, 404–405
   physical properties, 402
   preparation of, 401
   role in photosynthesis, 338
   solid (*see* Dry ice)
   use as refrigerant, 127
Carbon disulfide, 157, 268, 320, 397–399, 464
Carbon monoxide, 57, 98, 406–409
Carbon tetrachloride, 157, 399–400

Carbonate ores, metallurgy of, 547–548
Carbonated beverages, 155
Carbonates, solubility of, 157
Carbonyls, metal, 408, 646
Carborundum, 400, 401
Carboxyl group, 442
Carburetor, 424
Carlsbad, N.M., salt mines, 555, 560
Carnallite, 570
Carnauba wax, 438, 445
Carnotite, 184
Carotenes, 500
Carothers, W. H., 481
Carrots, 500
Case hardening of steel, 644
Casein, 470, 534
Cassiopeium (lutetium), 175, 683, 688
Cassiterite, 545, 649
Cast iron, 637–640
Catalysis and catalysts, 279–280
   (*See also* individual reactions and processes)
Cathode, 8
   reactions occurring at, 298–299, 302–303
Cattle, ability to utilize cellulose, 452
   ability to utilize urea, 495–496
Caustic soda (*see* Sodium hydroxide)
Cavendish, Lord Henry, 63
Caverns, limestone, 579–580
Celanese rayon (acetate rayon), 464–465
Cellophane, 463–464
Cells, electrical, 669–676
Celluloid, 466
Cellulose and its derivatives, 451–452, 460–466
Cellulose acetate, 464–465
Cellulose nitrate, 360–361, 465–466
Cementite (iron carbide), 549, 640
Centigrade temperature scale, 84, 111
Ceramics, 618
Cerium, 174, 682, 688
Cerotic acid, 445
Cerussite, 545, 651
Ceryl alcohol, 445
Cesium, 544, 552–555, 557, 562
Cesium hydride, 71, 72
Chain reaction, 208–213, 216–217
Chalcocite, 545, 589
Chalcopyrite, 545, 589
Chamber process, 331–332

Change, chemical, 8–9
  physical, 8
Charcoal, 388–391
Chard, 498, 505
Charles's law, 85–86, 93–94
Cheese, free fatty acids in, 442
  nutrients in, 498, 505
Chemical combination in terms of planetary electrons, 228–231
Chemical energy, 269
Chemical equilibrium, 282–290
Chemical pulp, 462
Chemical reactions, rate of, 273–280
  types of, 36
Chemical warfare, 235
Chemistry, definition of, 1
  early practice of, 12
  object of studying, 10
  organic, origin of name, 395
    number of compounds in, 411, 415
  qualitative and quantitative compared, 80, 256
Chemurgic Council, 437
Children, recommended dietary allowances for, 493
Chilean nitrate (saltpeter), 343, 358
China, 618
China clay, 523, 618
Chlorates, metal, solubility of, 157
Chlordan, 454
Chloride, test for, 247
Chlorides, metal, solubility of, 157
Chlorination of drinking water, 135
Chlorine, 235–241, 253
  chemical properties, 70, 238–240, 321
  critical constants, 98
  essential to nutrition, 496
  isotopes of, 198, 201
  occurrence in nature, 236–237
  physical properties, 238
  preparation, 236–238
  test, 240–241, 246
  use, in gas warfare, 235
    in industry, 241, 651
    in water purification, 135
Chlorine dioxide, 365
Chlorine water, 239
Chlorophyll, 270
Chloroplatinate test for potassium, 562
Chloroprene, polymerization to neoprene, 486
Chromium, 175, 543, 616, 682, 688
Chromium-vanadium steel, 644

Cinnabar, 545, 627
Citric acid, 65, 300, 442, 443
Citrus fruits, 503
Clay, 46, 59, 523, 618–619
Climate, relation to heat of vaporization of water, 115–116
  relation to specific heats of water and rock, 109–110
Cloud formation, 528–529
Coagulation of latex, 534
Coal, conversion to liquid fuel, 429
  destructive distillation of, 391–392
  formation of, 390–391
  fuel value of, 391
  size of potential supply, 392
Coal gas, 391, 392
Coal tar, 391–392
Coated abrasives, 400
Coated lenses, 520
Cobalt, 543, 612, 633, 645–647
  nucleus, stability of, 204, 205
  role in nutrition, 496, 502–503
Cobalt chloride or cobaltous ion as test for moisture, 140, 647
Cobaltinitrite test for potassium, 562
Codfish, 505
Coinage (U.S.), gold, 593
  nickel, 593
  silver, 593
Coke, 391–392
  in pig iron manufacture, 637, 639
  in preparation of hydrogen and water gas, 67
  in reduction of phosphate rock, 368–369
Cola beverage, pH of, 304
"Cold flame" experiment, 372, 373
"Cold light" emission, 372, 373
"Cold rubber," 486
Colloid mill, 528
Colloids, 526–536
  charge on, 531–532
  classification of, 527
  color of, 535–536
  contrasted with solutions and coarse suspensions, 526–527
  definition of, 526–527
  preparation of, 528–529
  reasons for permanence, 530–532
  ways to break up, 532–534
Color of metals, 542
Colored glass, 519
Columbium (niobium), 175, 683, 688

713

Combination reactions, 36
Combustion, 54–55, 364
   without oxygen, 70
Complex ions, of copper, 594
   of silver, 596, 599, 600, 602
"Compound 1080," 457
Compounds, in alloys, 549
   covalent versus electrovalent, 228–231
   definition of, 9
Compressibility, of gases, 79
   of liquids, 99
Compression ratio of gasoline engine, 424
Concentration, of commercial concentrated acids and ammonia, 689
   of ore, 546
   of reactants, effect on equilibrium point of reversible reactions, 285–287, 290
     effect on reaction rate, 277–278
   of solutions, 159–160, 309
Concrete, 618–619
Condensation, 114–116
Conduction of heat, 94–95
Conductivity, electrical, of graphite, 385
   of metals, 543, 545
   of molten salts, 297
   of solutions of electrolytes, 294–295, 297–299
Congressional committee on petroleum resources, 428
Conservation, of energy, 203–204
   of mass, 203–204
   of natural resources, nitrogen, 354
     petroleum, 427–428
     phosphorus, 377
     potassium, 560–561
     water, 108
Contact process, 330–331
   as illustrating van't Hoff's law, 287
Conversion, of temperature scales, 111
   of units of measure, 690
Cooking, loss of vitamin C in, 503
Copper, 588–595
   chemical properties, 75, 333, 360, 593–594
   crystal structure, 17
   electronic structure and properties, 588–589, 591–592
   metallurgy, 589–591
   occurrence, 545, 588, 589

Copper, physical properties, 542, 543, 588
   role in nutrition, 496, 499, 589
   test for, 594, 595
   uses of, 591–593
Copper alloys, 593, 611–612, 654
Copper compounds, 593–595
Copper converter, 589–590
Copper matte, 589–590
Copper steel, 593, 644
Copper sulfate as test for moisture, 140
Copper-zinc cell, 670–671
Coral, 570
Cordite, 440
Corn sirup, 451
Cornwall, England, tin mines, history of, 649
Corrosion, of aluminum, 614–615
   of copper, 592
   of iron, 624
   of lead, 652
   of tin, 650
   of zinc, 623–624
Corrosion inhibitors, 163
Corrosive sublimate, 629–630
Corundum, 513, 607
Cosmic rays, 212, 338
Cottage cheese, 505, 534
Cottonseed oil, 446, 447
Cottrell precipitator, 532, 533
Covalence and covalent compounds, 229–231
Cracking of petroleum, 422–423
"Crepe rubber," 471
Critical pressure, 98
Critical size of sample for atomic chain reaction, 212–213
Critical temperature, 49, 98
   relation to kinetic molecular theory and van der Waals' forces, 100–101
Crucible steel, 643
Crude oil (see Petroleum)
Cryolite, 248, 607, 609, 610
Crystal structure, determination of, 385–387
   of diamond, 385–387
   of graphite, 387–388
   of metals, 542
   relation to properties, 387, 388
   of salts, 297
   of silica (quartz), 514–515
Crystallization, 151–153
   fractional, 149–151
Crystallography, x-ray, 385–387

Cubic centimeter, 79
Cullinan diamond, 382–383
Cupric ammonia complex ion, 594
Cuprite, 545, 589, 594
Curie, Marie Sklodowska, 183–185, 193
Curium, 175, 682, 688
Curling of hair, 469
Current from battery, factors affecting, 674–675, 677
Cutting, of diamonds, 381–382
  of steel, 61
Cyanamide process, 348
Cyclotron, 208, 235

2,4-D, 455–456
Daguerre, L. J. M., 600
Dalton, John, 12, 16, 18, 182
Dalton's atomic theory, 16–19, 23
Dalton's law, 93
Da Vinci, Leonardo, 45
Davy, Humphry, 235, 363, 381, 556
DDT, 453–454
Deacon's process, 283
De Boisbaudran, Lecoq, 178
Decay of teeth, relation to fluorides, 249–250
  relation to vitamin D, 504
De Chancourtois, A. E. B., 170
Deficiency diseases, 489
  (See also Beriberi; Pellagra; Rickets; Scurvy; Xerophthalmia)
Definite composition, law of, 17
Dehydrate, 139
Dehydrating agents, calcium chloride, 140
  silica gel, 516
  sulfuric acid, 332, 333
Deionized water, 584–585
Deltas, explanation of, 532–533
Denatured alcohol, 437
Denier, 484
Density, 4
  of alkali metals, 553
  of alkaline earth metals, 567
  of aluminum, 611
  of copper, silver, and gold, 588
  of gases, 79, 338
    calculation of, 258–259
  of lead, 654
  of tin, 650
  of titanium, 658
  of zinc, cadmium, and mercury, 621
Dentrifrices, magnesium hydroxide in, 575

Dentistry, use of amalgams in, 629
Dephlogisticated air, 55
Desiccator, 140–141
Destruction (oxidative) of vitamin C, 503
Destructive distillation, of coal, 391–392
  of wood, 388
Detergents, 438, 449–450, 584
Detinning of scrap metal, 651
Detonator, use of mercuric fulminate, 630
Deuterium, 142, 143, 200
Development of photographic film, 601
Dextrin, 451
Diamond saw, 383
Diamonds, 380–384, 386–387
  artificial, 383–384
  crystal structure, 386–387
  cutting of, 381–382
  famous, 382–383
  hardness on Mohs' scale, 513
  occurrence and mining of, 381
  properties, 382
  use in industry, 383–384
Diatomaceous earth, 509
Dibasic acids, 293–294
Diet, essential components of, 491, 494–495, 496, 499–504
  recommended dietary allowances, 492, 493
  relation to, bones and teeth, 367–368, 496, 499–500, 504
    deficiency diseases (see Beriberi, Pellagra, Rickets, Scurvy, Xerophthalmia)
    emotional stability, 501
    eyes, 500, 502
    growth and development, 489, 494–495, 497, 495–500, 501, 502
    healing of wounds, 503
    resistance to infection, 500, 502
    tooth decay, 249–250, 504
  sources, of calcium, 498, 505
    of calories, 505
    of phosphorus, 368, 497
    of protein, 495, 505
    of vitamins, 500, 502–506
Diethyl ether, 450
Diffusion of gases, 79, 92
  rates of, 86–88
Dimethyl dichlorosilane, polymerization of, 521
  use for waterproofing, 522–523

715

Distillate, 136
Distillation, 136–138
　destructive (see Destructive distillation)
　fractional, 137
　of liquid air, 46–47
　of petroleum, 421–422
Divers, occupational disease of, 155–156
Diving bells, use of helium in, 340
Dolomite, 380, 569, 570, 576
Double-acting baking powders, 405
Double bond, 387
Double replacement reactions, 36
Dow metals, 573
Downs' process, 556
Drainpipes, unplugging of, by chemical means, 68
Dried fruit, use of sulfur dioxide in processing, 328
Driers used in paints, 448
Drills, diamond-tipped, 383
Drinking water, 133–136, 584
Dry cell, 673–675
Dry ice, 120–121, 152, 402–403
Drying oil, 447–448
Ductility of metals, 543–544
Duralium, 612
Duriron (silicon steel), 511, 644
Dust, as cause of spontaneous combustion, 278–279
　useful role in atmosphere, 338
Dyeing, 617
Dynamic equilibrium, distinguishing characteristics of, 123
Dysprosium, 174, 682, 688

e^- (see Electron)
e^+ (positron), 196
Earth, age of, computed from radioactivity data, 191
Earth's core, probable composition, 205, 634
Earth's crust (including oceans and atmosphere), alkali metals in, 554
　alkaline earth metals in, 568
　aluminum in, 606
　bromine in, 241
　carbon in, 380
　chlorine in, 236
　copper and silver in, 588
　figure illustrating composition of, 10
　fluorine in, 248
　iron in, 634

Earth's crust, silicon in, 509
　tin in, 649
　titanium in, 656
Economic poisons, 452–457
Efficiency, of chain reaction, 210, 216–217
　of gasoline engine in relation to compression ratio, 424
Efflorescence, 139
Egg shells, 570
Eggs, 498, 502, 504, 505
Einstein, Albert, 202
Einsteinium, 173
"Eka-aluminum," 178
"Eka-silicon" (germanium), 171
Electric discharge in formation of nitric acid, 362–363
Electric furnace in manufacture, of carbon disulfide, 398
　of graphite, 384
　of phosphorus, 369
　of silicon carbide, 400
　of steel, 643
Electrical charge on colloids, 531–532
Electrical conductivity, of graphite, 385
　of metals, 543, 545
　of molten salts, 297
　of solutions of electrolytes, 294–295, 297–299
Electrical energy, from chemical reactions, 669–676
　in chemical reactions, 271
Electrical heating elements, nichrome for, 646–647
Electrical industry, use of copper in, 591
　use of silver in, 597
Electrical switches, mercury, 627, 628
Electrodes, 8, 294–295
　use of graphite for, 385
Electrolysis, 8, 9, 271, 295–299, 302
　in industrial production, of alkali metals, 556
　　of alkaline earth metals, 570–573
　　of aluminum, 609–610
　　of chlorine, 237
　　of fluorine, 248
　　of hydrogen, 237
　　of sodium hydroxide, 237
　　of zinc, 623
　　of water, 48–49, 65

Electrolytes, 292–311
  break-up of colloids by, 532–534
  classes of, 292–294
  effect on boiling point, freezing point, and osmotic pressure, 311
  electrical conductivity of, 294–295
  electrolysis of, 297–299, 302–303
  inert, role in cell, 671–672
  ionization of, 295–297, 299–302
  reactions between, 310–311
Electron(s), emission in radioactivity, 186, 188, 189, 195, 205, 206
  mass of, 186
  planetary, 224–233
    arrangement in orbits, 224–227
    relation to activity, of metals, 231–232
      of nonmetals, 233
    relation to covalence, 229–231
    relation to electrovalence, 228–229
Electron-pair bond, 229–231
Electron transfer, 661–662
Electronic structure, of all elements, 688
  of first 20 elements, 227
  relation to properties, of alkali metals, 553
    of alkaline earth metals, 566–567
    of carbon, 396–397
    of Group I*b* elements, 588
    of Group II*b* elements, 621
    of halogens, 233
    of inert gases, 226, 338
    of metals, 540–541
    of sulfur, 319–320
Electronic tube filaments, barium in, 574
Electroplating, 385
Electrorefining of copper, 590–591
Electroscope in detection of radioactivity, 183–184, 187
Electrotyping, 385
Electrovalence and electrovalent compounds, 228–229
Elements, abundance in nature, 10
  atomic weights of, 682–684
  definition of, 10
  magnetic, 633
  prediction of, 171, 178
  symbols for, 25–27
  transition, 177
  (*See also* Earth's crust; Periodic table)

Embalming fluid, 439
Emerald, 568
Emery, 617
Emotional stability in relation to thiamine, 501
Empirical formula, 32
Emulsifier, 534, 535
Emulsions, 534–535
End point, 308
Endothermic process, 154
Endothermic reaction, 267
Energy, calories in foods and nutrition, 492, 493, 505
  as constituent of atom, 201–204
  as having mass, 202–204
Energy change, in chemical reactions, 266–271
  forms of energy involved, 270–271, 372, 373
  in nuclear reactions, 192, 202–203
  uranium reactor as means of utilizing, 219–220
Energy-mass relationship, 201–204
Engine, internal-combustion, 424, 427
  mercury vapor, 628–629
Enriched bread, flour, and cereals, 502
Enzymes, 280, 501
Epsom salts, 138, 575
Equations, 33–35
  how to write and balance, 34–35
  for oxidation-reduction reactions, 663–667
Equilibrium, 122–124
  chemical, 282–290
  physical, 288, 289
  in saturated solution, 153
Equilibrium point of reversible reaction, effect of concentration of reactants on, 285–287
  effect of pressure on, 288–289
  effect of temperature on, 287–288, 290
Erbium, 174, 682, 688
Erosion, soil, and potassium problem, 560
Escherichia coli, 134
Essential amino acids, 494–495
Essential fatty acids, 492
Esters, 445–449
Etching of glass by hydrogen fluoride, 250, 251
Ethane, 412, 413
Ethanol (*see* Ethyl alcohol)
Ethene (*see* Ethylene)

717

Ethers, 450
Ethyl alcohol (ethanol), 98, 162–163, 432, 435–437
Ethyl chloride as local anesthetic, 115
Ethyl gasoline, 244, 425–426, 653
Ethylene (ethene), 416, 417
　polymerization of, 476–477
Ethylene dibromide, 244
Ethylene glycol, 162–163, 438
Ethyne (*see* Acetylene)
Evaporation, 114–124
　as affected by fanning, 124
　heat absorbed in, 114–116
　relation to kinetic molecular theory, 116
　relation to temperature, 117
　as reversible change, 122–124
Excess, chemical use of term, 17
Exothermic process, 154
Exothermic reaction, 266
Explosive shells, white phosphorus in, 373
Explosives, nitrogen compounds as, 343, 351, 463
Exposure of photographic films, 601
External-combustion engine, mercury, 628–629
Eyes, affected by vitamin A deficiency, 500
　affected by riboflavin deficiency, 502

Fact, definition of, 13
Fahrenheit temperature scale, 84, 111
Farming (*see* Agricultural applications of chemistry)
Fats, 444–449, 491, 492
　oxidation of, 58
　solubility of, 157
Fatty acids, 442
　in aging of cheese, 442
　nutritionally essential, 492
Federal Food and Drug Law regulation on baking powders, 406
Feldspars, 513, 523, 554, 561, 606
Fermium, 173
Ferric chloride, heat of formation, 268
Ferric hydroxide colloid, 528, 529
Ferrosilicon, 511
Ferrotitanium, 641, 657
Ferrous and ferric compounds, 645
Ferrous nitroso ion, 362, 365

Fertilizers, nitrogen compounds as, 346
　ammonia, 352–353, 355
　ammonium nitrate, 351
　calcium cyanamide, 348
　calcium nitrate, 363
　phosphate, 376–377
　　use of sulfuric acid in manufacture of, 332, 334
　potassium in, 560–561
"Filling" of paper, 463
Film speed, 601
Films, photographic, 600, 601
Filtrate, 5
Filtration, 5
Fire extinguishers, foamite type, 404
　using carbon tetrachloride (Pyrene type), 399–400
　using liquid carbon dioxide, 403
Fireproof substances, 58–59
Fischer-Tropsch process, 429
Fish liver oils, 500, 504
Fission, nuclear, 209, 211–212
Fixation of nitrogen (*see* Nitrogen fixation)
Fixing of photographic film, 602
Flame tests, 562–564, 585
Flash burns from atomic explosions, 213–214
Flavorings, use of esters in, 444–445
Flint, 512
Flint glass, 518–520
Flotation, 546
Flowers of sulfur, 318
Fluoracetate, sodium, as rat poison, 457
Fluorescence, 628
Fluorescent light bulbs, 628
　beryllium compounds in, 575
Fluoride, in making nonreflecting glass, 520
　test for, 251
Fluoridization of public water supplies, 249–250
Fluorine, 248–250, 253
　compared with other halogens, 253
　occurrence, 248
　preparation, 248
　properties, 249
　relation to teeth, 249–250
　uses, 249–250, 477–478
Fluorite, 248, 513, 570
Fluorocarbons, 249
Flux, 369–370, 546, 637
Foam glass, 519

Foamite type fire extinguisher, 404
Fog light, 536
Folic acid, 503
Foods, functions of, 490–491
   oxidation in body, 58–60
   as sources, of calcium, 498, 505
      of Calories, 505
      of niacin, 502, 505
      of phosphorus, 368, 497
      of protein, 495, 505
      of riboflavin, 502, 505
      of thiamine, 502, 505
      of vitamin A, 500, 505
      of vitamin C, 503, 505
      of vitamin D, 504
      of vitamin E, 506
      of vitamin K, 504
Forces, van der Waals', 99–101
Formaldehyde, 439
Formalin, 439
Formic acid, 407, 440–441
Formulas, 29–33
   determination of, 31–33
   empirical, 32
   information contained in, 29–30
   molecular, 33
   prediction from valence, 38–40
Fossils, 512
Four "elements" of Greeks, 181
Fractional crystallization, 149–151
Fractional distillation, 137
Francium, 174, 552, 553, 555, 682, 688
Franklinite, 622
Frasch, Herman, 316
Frasch process for mining sulfur, 316, 317
Freezing point, 152
   of inert gases, 338
   of solutions, 162–163, 311
   (*See also* Melting points)
Freezing-point depression, 162–163
   of electrolytes, 311
Freons, 98, 127, 249, 256
Frosting of electric light bulbs, 251
Fructose, 450–451
Fruits, artificial ripening of, with ethylene, 416
   esters in, 445
   organic acids in, 443
Fuel oil, 421, 423
Fuels, common, fuel value of, 391
   as ultimately derived from solar energy, 270
Fuming nitric acid, 359
Fuming sulfuric acid, 330, 331

Fungicides, copper compounds, 594–595
   sulfur, 321
Furnace, coal, 406–407
Fusible alloy, 654
Fusion, nuclear, 203, 205

Gadolinium, 175, 682, 688
Galactose, 451
Galena, 316, 545, 651
Gallium, 174, 178, 544, 682, 688
Galvanized iron, 624–625
Gamma (γ) rays (x rays), 186–187, 189
Gangue, 546
Gas, municipal city, 407
   natural, 421–422
Gas ions in atmosphere, 338
Gas-in-liquid solutions, 155–156
Gas masks, charcoal-containing, 389
   for protection against carbon monoxide, 389, 408
Gas warfare, 235
Gas-washing bottle, 333
Gases, adsorption by charcoal, 389–390
   distinguishing properties, 78–79
   kinetic molecular theory, 90–94
   liquefaction of, 97–105
   pressure-volume relation, 82–83
   temperature effects, 83–86
Gasoline, 421–427
   airplane, 426
   antiknock, 244, 425–426, 653
   boiling point, 421
   combustion in automobile engine, 57, 424
   jet, 426
   octane rating, 425–426
   tetraethyllead in, 425
   yield from crude oil, 422
      shifted by cracking and polymerization, 423–424
Gasoline engine, 424–427
Gastric juice, hydrochloric acid in, 241
Gay-Lussac's law, of combining volumes, 264
   of temperature effect, 83–84, 93–94
Geon, 478–479
Germanium, 172, 174, 178, 380, 682, 688
Giant molecules, 460–486
Gilt paint, 611–612
Girls, recommended dietary allowances for, 493

719

Glass, etching with hydrogen fluoride, 250, 251
  history of, 516–517, 557–558
  kinds of, 518–520
  manufacture of, 518–520
  not entirely insoluble, 149
Glass electrode, 305
Glauber's salt, 138
Glazing of china, 618
Glow of phosphorus, 367, 372–373
Glucose, 450–452
Glycerides, 445–449
Glycerin (glycerol), 162–163, 438–439, 449
  reaction with nitric acid, 360
Glyceryl butyrate, 446, 447
Glyceryl linoleate, 446, 447
Glyceryl linolenate, 447
Glyceryl oleate, 446, 447
Glyceryl palmitate, 446, 447
Glyceryl stearate, 445–447, 449
Goiter, simple, relation to iodine deficiency, 247
Gold, 75, 133, 542, 543, 588, 603
  colloidal, 529
Gold alloys, 593, 603, 629
Gold telluride, 603
Goldschmidt process, 616
Goodyear, Charles, 321
Graduated cylinder, 80, 81
Graham, Thomas, 530
Graham's law, 86–88
Gram, 690
Gram atom, 27
Gram-atomic weight, 27–28
Gram-molecular weight, 30–31
Granite, 5
Grapefruit, 505
Graphite, crystal structure, 387–388
  in gray cast iron, 640
  manufacture, 384
  occurrence, 384
  properties, 384–385
  uses, 217, 384–385, 528
Gravity cell, 671
Gray cast iron, 640
Gray tin, 650
Greases, fats, and oils, solubilities of, 157
Greeks, early, theory of structure of matter, 181
Green gold, 603
Greenockite, 545, 626
GRI (butyl) rubber, 486, 487
Grinding as means to prepare colloids, 528

GRM rubber (neoprene), 486–487
Groups of periodic table, 173–177
Group Ib elements, 588–603
Group IIb elements, 621–631
GRS (buna S) rubber, 485–487
Guayule, 470
Guinea pig in vitamin C studies, 503
Guncotton, 463
Gutta-percha, 470
Gypsum, 316, 513, 570, 578–579, 618
Gypsum board, 578–579

Haber, Fritz, 347
Haber process, 347–348
Hafnium, 174, 683, 688
Hahn, Otto, 209
Hair, 467–469
Hales, S., 45
Half-life, 190–191
Halides, silver, in photography, 600–602
Halite, 236, 545
Hall, Charles Martin, 608–609
Hall process, 609–610
Halogen compounds of nitrogen, 365
Halogens, 235–253
  origin of name, 235
  reaction, with acetylene, 417
    with gold, 603
    with olefin hydrocarbons, 416
    with phosphorus, 371
  tabular comparison of properties, 253
  (*See also* names of halogens)
Halogeton, 443
Ham, 505
Hanford, Wash., plant of Atomic Energy Commission, 219, 220
Hard glass, 518
Hard water, 133, 581–584
Hardness, of metals, 542, 543, 552, 553, 566, 567
  Mohs' scale of, 513
Hay, incompletely cured, as cause of fire, 276
Healing of wounds in relation to vitamin C, 503
Heat, 94–95
  of formation, 267–268
  of fusion, 113–114
  of solution, 154–155
  of vaporization, 114–116
Heat conductivity of metals, 543, 545
Heat pump, 128–129
Heat-resisting glass, 519

Heat treatment of steel, 644
Heating, plumbing, and refrigeration, copper for, 591–592
Heavy water, 142–143, 217
Helium, 226, 227, 338–340
   critical constants of, 98
   density of, 259
   as illustrating mass-energy relationship, 201–203
   liquefaction of, 105
Hematite, 1, 545, 635
Hemoglobin, 59–60, 408, 499
Henry's law, 155–156
Heptane, 413
Herbicides, 455–456
Herbivorous animals, salt craving of, 555
Héroult, Paul, 608–609
Hershey, J. W., 384
Herty, Charles, 462
Hevea, 470–471
Hevea rubber, 471
Hexachlorobenzene (666), 454
Hexamethylene diamine in synthesis of nylon, 483
Hexane, 413
High altitudes, problems of cooking at, 119
High-carbon steel, 643
High polymers, 460
   inorganic, 476
   (*See also* Polymerization, and names of substances)
High-tension wire, aluminum for, 612–613
Hindenburg disaster, 53
Hiroshima atomic explosion, 213
Holmium, 174, 683, 688
Homogeneous forms of matter, 4
Homogenization of milk, 535
Hope diamond, 383
Horn silver, 595
Household ammonia, pH of, 304
Household applications of chemistry, air conditioning, 125–126
   controlling, insects, 452–455
      rats and mice, 372, 398–399, 457
   cooking and food preparation, 119–120, 152, 160, 404–406, 444–445, 449, 503, 534–535
   (*See also* Diet)
   fire prevention, by fire extinguishers, 399–400, 403, 404
      by preventing spontaneous combustion, 275–276

Household applications of chemistry, heating, 97, 115, 128–129, 391, 406–407, 421–422, 436, 581
   home construction, 577–579, 591–592, 613–614, 618–619, 624–625, 639, 653, 655
   laundering, cleansing, dry cleaning, 50, 144, 240, 327, 351, 399, 449–450, 468–469, 535, 581–584
   light bulbs, 251, 340–341, 575, 628
   matches, 373
   permanent waving, 469
   quick freezing, 275
   refrigeration, 126–127, 274–275
   silverware, plated and sterling, 110–111, 323, 597, 600
   textiles, 463–470, 481–485
   water, purification for drinking, 134–136
      softening for laundry and boiler supply, 482–484
Humidity, 124–126
Hydrated lime (calcium hydroxide), 576, 578
Hydrates, 138–140
Hydrides, metal, 71–72
Hydriodic acid and hydrogen iodide, 253
Hydrobromic acid and hydrogen bromide, 252–253
Hydrocarbons, 412–419
   burning of, 57
   (*See also* Petroleum and names of hydrocarbons)
Hydrochloric acid and hydrogen chloride, 98, 241, 251–252, 295, 304
Hydrofluoric acid and hydrogen fluoride, 248–251
Hydrogen, 63–75
   buoyant action of, 69
   chemical properties, 56–57, 63, 69–72, 239, 249
   density of, 258, 259
   discovery, 64
   isotopes of, 200
   liquefaction of, 105
   occurrence, 64–65
   physical properties, 68–69, 98
   preparation, 65–68, 237, 302–303
      in field with silicon and sodium hydroxide, 511
   uses of, 72–73
Hydrogen bomb, 203

Hydrogen bromide and hydrobromic acid, 252–253
Hydrogen chloride and hydrochloric acid, 98, 241, 251–252, 304
Hydrogen fluoride and hydrofluoric acid, 248–251
Hydrogen halides, 250–253
Hydrogen iodide and hydriodic acid, 253
Hydrogen peroxide, 143–144
Hydrogen-phosphorus compounds, 374
Hydrogen sulfide and hydrosulfuric acid, 98, 322–323
Hydrogenation, of coal, 73, 429
of oils, 72, 446
Hydrolysis, of esters, 449
of salts, 306–307
Hydronium ion, 295–296, 298–303, 306–307, 310–311
Hydroxides, naming of, 42
solubility of, 157
Hydroxyl ion, 296, 302
Hypo (sodium thiosulfate), 334–335, 602
Hypochlorous acid and hypochlorites, 136, 239–240

Ice, heat of fusion of, 113–114
melting of, by pressure, 289
Ice cream, 505
Iceland spar, 570
Igneous rock associated with diamonds, 381
Ilmenite, 656
Improvability of normal nutrition, 489–490, 497–498, 502
Incandescent bulbs, 340–341, 628
Incendiaries, use of magnesium in, 574
use of thermite in, 616
use of white phosphorus in, 373
Indicators for determination of pH, 292, 305–306
Indium, 174, 683, 688
Inert gases, 226, 337–341
(*See also* names of gases)
Infants, recommended dietary allowances for, 493
Infection, resistance to, relation to riboflavin, 502
relation to vitamin A, 500
"Inflammable air," 64
Inoculation of supersaturated solutions, 151–152
Insecticides, 452–455

Insulation, aluminum, 613–614
rock wool, 639
Insulators, silicone resins as, 522
Internal-combustion engine, 424, 427
Invar steel, 647
Invert sugar, 450–451
Iodides, 240, 246, 247
Iodine, 245–247, 253
in nutrition, 247, 496, 499
tincture of, 247
Iodine pentoxide in test for carbon monoxide, 409
Iodized salt, 247
Ion exchangers, 583–585
Ion-partial method of balancing oxidation-reduction equations, 663–667
Ionization, 295–303
Ionization potential, 553
Ions, 295–303, 306, 310–311
in breaking up colloids, 532–534
Iridium, 175, 683, 688
Iron, 633–647
in foods and nutrition, 493, 496, 499, 505
metallurgy, 636–643
occurrence in nature, 634–635
ores, 2, 545, 547, 635–636
physical properties, 542, 543, 636
reactions of, 56, 66, 67, 75, 645
stability of nucleus, 204, 205
uses of (*see* Cast iron; Steel)
Iron carbide (Fe_3C) in steel and cast iron, 549, 640
Iron carbonyl, 408
Iron salts in water supply, 133, 581–584
Iron sulfide, 323
Irradiation, ultraviolet, in formation of vitamin D, 504
Isoamyl acetate, 445
Isobutane, 414, 415
Isobutylene in formation of synthetic rubbers, 486
Isomers, structural, 414–415
Isotopes, 23, 178, 197–201, 233
definition, 197–198
detection and measurement, 198–201
relation to periodic table, 178, 233
symbols for, 198

Jet engines, 426
Joints, stiffness in, from lead poisoning, 654
Joule-Thomson effect, 104, 402–403

Kale, 443, 498, 502, 505
Kerosene, 420–423
Ketones, 440
Keweenaw Peninsula, 589
Kilogram (kg), 113, 690
Kimberley diamond mines, 381
Kinetic molecular theory, 91–95
  applied to liquids, 99–101
  confirmed by Brownian movement, 530–531
  as explaining, effect of concentration of reactants on reaction rate, 277
    effect of temperature on reaction rate, 277
    heat and temperature, 94–95
    properties of gases, 92–94
  in relation, to evaporation, 116
    to liquefaction of gases, 99–101
King, C. G., 503
Kingston and Newburgh, N.Y., test on fluoridization of drinking water, 249–250
Kipp generator, 322, 401
Kohinoor diamond, 382, 383
Koroseal, 478–479
Kraft paper, 462
Kroll process, 656
Krypton, 226, 338, 341

Lacquer solvents, esters as, 445
Lacquers, 445, 447, 465
Lactose, 451
Lake (in dyeing), 617
Laminated safety glass, 520
Lamps, fluorescent, 628
  incandescent, 340–341, 628
Langmuir, Irving, 152, 340–341
Lanthanide series, 172, 174–175
Lanthanum, 174, 683, 688
Latent heat, of fusion, 113–114
  of vaporization, 114–116
Latex, 470, 534
Laue, M. von, 385
Laughing gas, 363–364
Lauryl alcohol, 438
Lauryl sulfate, sodium salt, 449
Lavoisier, Antoine Laurent, 54–55, 343
Law, 13
  of conservation of energy, 203–204
  of conservation of mass, 203–204
  of definite composition, 17
  of mass action, 285–287

Law, of multiple proportions, 18–19
  (*See also* under proposer's name, as Henry's law)
Lead, 651–655
  chemical properties and compounds, 653–654
  occurrence and metallurgy, 545, 547, 651–652
  properties and uses, 331, 519, 542, 543, 652–654
  radioactive, in uranium 238 series, 205, 206
  toxicity, 653, 654–655
Lead alloys, 654
Lead chloride, heat of formation, 268
Lead pencils, 385
Lead storage battery, care of, 675–679
Lead sulfide, 323
Lead tetraethyl (tetraethyllead), 244, 425, 556, 653
Le Blanc, Nicholas, 557–558
Le Châtelier, Henri, 288
Le Châtelier's law, 288–290
  applied in Haber process, 347–348
Legal standard, for acetic acid in vinegar, 442
  for baking powders, 406
Legumes, nitrogen-fixing bacteria on, 354
Lemon juice, pH of, 304
Lettuce, 498, 505
Life, length of, increase by superior nutrition, 490, 497, 500, 502
Light, velocity of, 202
Light meters, use of selenium in, 324
Light scattering by colloids, 535–536
Light-sensitive substances, 72
Lightning in nitrogen fixation, 354, 362–363
Lignin, 461, 463
Lignite, 391
Lime, 576–577
Lime kiln, 576, 577
Lime-sulfur, 321
Limestone, 570, 575–577
  agricultural use of, 304, 576
  as starting material for organic syntheses, 578
  use in pig iron manufacture, 637, 639
Limestone solution caverns, 579–580
Limonite, 635
Linde machine, 104–105

723

Linoleic acid and linoleates, 445–447
   as essential food factor, 492
Linolenic acid and linolenates, 447
Linseed oil, 447–448
   rags soaked with, as cause of spontaneous combustion, 275–276
Liquefaction of gases, 97–105
Liquid air, as industrial source, of inert gases, 339
   of nitrogen, 101–102, 344
   of oxygen, 46–47, 100–101
   production of, 103–105
   properties of, 101–102
Liquids, distinguishing characteristics of, 99
   relation to kinetic molecular theory and van der Waals' forces, 99–101
Liter, 79, 690
Litharge, 654
Lithium, 543, 552–555, 557, 562
Lithopone, 334, 626
Liver, 502, 504, 505
Livestock, importance of salt for, 555
   importance of vitamin D for, 504
   poisoning, by oxalic-acid-containing weed halogeton, 443
   by selenium-containing vegetation, 324
   protein requirements of, 495–496
Los Alamos bomb assembly plant, 219
Low-temperature carbonization, 392
Lubricants, graphite suspensions, 384
   silicone oils, 521
Lubricating oil, 421
Lucite, 480–481
Lung damage, relief with pure oxygen, 60
Luster of metals, 542
Lutetium, 175, 683, 688
Lye (see Sodium hydroxide)

Macromolecules, 387
Magnalium, 573, 611
Magnesia (magnesium oxide), 575
Magnesite, 545, 569, 573
Magnesium, electron structure and properties, 75, 543, 567
   as nutritionally essential, 491, 496
   occurrence, 545, 548, 568–570
   preparation, 571–573

Magnesium, test for, 585
   uses, 573–574
Magnesium alloys, 573–574, 611, 612
Magnesium citrate, 575
Magnesium compounds, 575
Magnesium deficiency in soils, 576
Magnesium hydroxide, 575
Magnesium nitride, 345
Magnesium oxide (magnesia), 575
Magnesium salts in water supply, 133, 581–584
Magnetic elements, 633
Magnetic oxide of iron, 66
Magnetite, 635
Magnets, use of silicon in, 511
Malaria control, DDT in, 454, 455
Malic acid, 442, 443
Malleability of metals, 542–543
Maltose, 435
Manganese, 75, 543, 593
   in amethyst, 511
   as nutritionally essential, 496
Manganese steel, 644
Marble, 575–576
Margarine (oleomargarine), 448, 505
Mass, of electron, 195
   of proton, neutron, and helium nucleus, 201
Mass action effect, 285–287, 290
Mass-energy relationship, 201–204
Mass number, 198
Mass spectrograph, 198–200
Mass spectrometer, 199
Matches, 373–374
Matter, definition of, 1
Mayonnaise, 535
Mayow, J., 45
Meats, 368, 497, 502
   (See also names of meats)
Mechanical energy from chemical reactions, 270, 271
Medicine and allied fields, applications of chemistry in, 134–136, 220–222, 489–507
   anesthesia, general, by diethyl ether, 450
   by ethylene, 416
   by nitrous oxide, 363
   local, by ethyl chloride, 115
   blood, gases dissolved in, 147, 155–156
   osmotic relations in, 165–166
   pH of, 304
   control, of cancer, by artificial radioisotopes, 220–221

Medicine, control, of cancer, by radiation, 193
   of malaria, 454, 455
   of typhus fever, 453
   of water-borne diseases, 134
   disinfectant, argyrol as, 598
      bichloride of mercury, 629, 630
      mercurochrome, 630
      silver nitrate, 498
      tincture of iodine, 247
   fluoridization of public water supplies, 249–250
   healing of wounds, 503
   laxative action of magnesium compounds, 575
   oxygen tent, in lung damage, 60
   physiological effects, of alcohol, 437
      of radiations, 187, 193, 214, 220–222
   poisoning, by beryllium compounds, 575
      by cadmium, 627
      by carbon disulfide, 398–399
      by carbon monoxide, 57, 408
      by carbon tetrachloride, 400
      by DDT, 454
      by hydrogen sulfide, 322
      by lead compounds, 654–655
      by mercury compounds, 630
      by methyl alcohol, 435
      by selenium compounds, 324
      by white phosphorus, 370
   prevention and cure, of beriberi, 501
      of pellagra, 502
      of rickets, 504
      of scurvy, 502
      of simple goiter, 247
      of xerophthalmia, 500
   resistance to infection, effect of nutrition on, 500, 502
   tracer studies, 221, 222
   water purification, 134–136
Medium steel, 643
Melamine, 476
Melting points, of alkali metals, 553
   of alkaline earth metals, 567
   of glycerides (fats and oils), 446
   of inorganic salts, 685–687
   of metals, 543, 544
   of paraffin hydrocarbons, 413
   as test of purity, 164
Men, recommended dietary allowances for, 493

Mendeléeff, D. I., 171–172, 178–179
Mendelevium, 173, 683
Mercerized cotton, 466
Mercuric compounds, 629
Mercuric fulminate, 630
Mercuric oxide, 46, 47, 268
Mercurochrome, 630
Mercurous compounds, 629–630
Mercury, 627–630
   chemical properties, 75, 629–630
   occurrence and metallurgy, 545, 627
   properties and uses, 543, 621, 627–629
   test for, 631
   toxicity, 630
Mercury alloys, 629
Mercury vapor engine, 628–629
Mesabi iron mines, 635
Metabolism, 247
Metal carbonyls, 408, 646
Metal hydrides, 71–72
Metal oxides, reaction with ammonia, 350
   reaction with water, 141–142
   reduction by aluminum, 616
Metallic bond, 541
Metallic properties and periodic table, 176–177, 541
Metallurgy, 546–550
   carbon (coke) in, 368–369, 547, 637, 639
   fluxes in, 369–370
   sulfuric acid in, 334
Metals, 539–550
   active, reaction with ammonia, 350
      reaction with carbon dioxide, 404, 406
   activity of, 75
      electronic explanation, 231–232
   compared with nonmetals, 540
   crystal structure of, 541, 542
   distinguishing characteristics of, 540–541
   history of man's use of, 75, 539
   natural forms of, 545, 546
   occurrence, 545–546
   physical properties, 542–545
   reaction, with chlorine, 238–239
      with nitric acid, 360
      with phosphorus, 372
      with sulfur, 320
   (*See also* names of metals)
Metaphosphoric acid and metaphosphates, 375, 376

Meteorites, 634
Meter, 690
Methane, 259, 412, 413
Methanol (*see* Methyl alcohol)
Methoxychlor, 454–455
Methyl alcohol (methanol), 73, 162–163, 432, 434–435
Methyl butyrate, 445
Methyl chloride, 98, 127
Methyl methacrylate, polymerization of, 480–481
Methyl trichlorosilane, 521
Micas, 554
Midgley, T., 256, 425
Midland, Mich., brine wells, 570
Mild steel, 643
Milk, citric acid in, 443
 as colloid, 535
 nutritive value of, 368, 497, 502, 504, 505
Milk of magnesia, 575
Milk sugar, 451
Milliliter, 79, 690
"Mineral" elements of food and nutrition, 491, 495
 (*See also* names of elements)
Mining, of diamonds, 381
 of sulfur, 316, 317
"Mining the sea," 572
Minium, 654
Mirrors, manufacture of, 599
Miscibility, 156–157
Mixed crystal alloys, 549
Mixtures, 5–7
Models, scale, of atoms and molecules, 20–22, 29, 413, 414
Moderators (for slowing neutrons), 217
Mohs' scale of hardness, 513
Moissan, Henri, 248, 383
Moisture, adsorption by silica gel, 516
Moisture indicators, 140, 647
Molal freezing point depression, 162
Molal increase of boiling point, 161
Molal osmotic pressure, 165
Molality, 160
Molar volume of gases, 257–258
Molarities of commercial concentrated acids and ammonia, 689
Molarity, 159–160
Molasses, fermentation of, 435
Mole, 30–31
Molecular distillation, 137–138
Molecular formula, 33

Molecular models, 20–22, 29, 413, 414
Molecular weight, 30
 of gases, determination, 260
 of solutes, determination, 161, 164
Molecules, 21
 polar, 433–434
Molybdenum, 175, 543, 550, 616, 683, 688
Molybdenum steel, 644
Monobasic acids, 293
Monoclinic sulfur, 318, 319
Monel metal, 593
Mordant, 617
Mortar, 577–578
Mossy zinc, 623
Motor fuels, substitute, 392
Mottled enamel, 249
Multiple proportions, law of, 18–19
Muriatic acid (*see* Hydrochloric acid)
Muscovite, 554
Mutations produced by radiations, 187

n (*see* Neutrons)
Nagasaki atomic explosion, 213
Naphthalene, 419
National Research Council's "Recommended Daily Dietary Allowances," 492, 493
National resources, of coal, 392
 of iron, 635–636
 of petroleum, 428
Native metal, 545
 metallurgy of, 546
Natural gas, 67
Natural rubber, 470–472
Negative (photographic), 602
Negative electrode (cathode), reactions occurring at, 298–299, 302–303
Neodymium, 174, 683, 688
Neon, 98, 226, 227, 338, 340
Neoprene, 486–487
Neptunium, 175, 218, 683, 688
Nerves as affected by thiamine deficiency, 501
Neutralization, 293–294
Neutrons, 195–196, 209–213
Newburgh and Kingston, N.Y., test on fluoridization of drinking water, 249–250
Newlands, J. A. R., 170–172
Niacin, 493, 502, 505
Nichrome, 647

Nickel, 75, 204, 205, 543, 545, 633, 645–647
Nickel (coin), 549, 593
Nickel alloys, 549, 593, 612, 646–647
Nickel carbonyl, 408, 646
Nickel steel, 644
Nicotinic acid (*see* Niacin)
Night blindness, 500
Niobium, 175, 683, 688
Niter, 343
Niton (*see* Radon)
Nitrates, brown ring test for, 364–365
  solubility of, 157
Nitric acid, chemical properties, 360–361
  commercial manufacture, 346, 358–359, 362–363
  heat of formation, 268
  laboratory preparation, 357–358
  physical properties, 359
  uses, 357
Nitric oxide, 268, 362
Nitrocellulose, 360
Nitrogen, discovery of, 343
  occurrence, 337, 343–344
  preparation, 101–102, 344
  properties, 98, 259, 345–346
  uses, 340–341, 346
Nitrogen cycle in nature, 353, 354
Nitrogen dioxide and nitrogen tetroxide, 361–362
Nitrogen fixation, definition, 348
  by bacteria, 354
  industrial, in arc process, 362–363
    in cyanamide process, 348
    in Haber process, 347–348
  by lightning, 354
  military and economic importance of, 348–349
Nitrogen-fixing bacteria, 354
Nitrogen halides, 365
Nitroglycerin, 360
Nitrous acid and nitrites, 364
Nitrous oxide, 363–364
Nobel, Alfred, 193
Nobel prizes, 193
Nobelium, 173, 178, 683
Noble gases, 339
  (*See also* Inert gases)
Noble metals, 238, 588–603
Nomenclature, 40–42
  tungsten versus wolfram, 71
Nonadecane, 413
Noncombustible substances, 58–59

Nonmetal oxides, reaction with water, 141
Nonmetallic properties and periodic table, 176–177
Nonmetals, activity of, electronic explanation, 233
  compared with metals, 540
  reaction, with chlorine, 239
    with nitric acid, 361
Nonreflecting glass, 520
Normal boiling point, 118
  (*See also* Boiling point)
Normal salts, 294
Normalities of commercial concentrated acids; ammonia, 689
Normality, 309
Nuclear bomb, 208–214
Nuclear energy, 208, 219–220, 270
Nuclear fission, 209, 211–212
Nuclear-fission bomb, 213, 223
Nuclear fusion, 203, 205
Nuclear power plant, 210–212
Nuclear transformations, 205–206
Nucleus of atom, 195–206
  charge on, 196–197
  density of, 197
  radius of, 197
  volume of, 197
Number of atoms in gram-atomic weight, 27
Number of molecules in gram-molecular weight, 30–31
Numbers, expressed as powers of ten, 690
Nutrition, 489–506
  essential amino acids, 494–495
  essential fatty acids, 492
  essential "mineral elements," 496–499
  importance to human welfare, 489–490
  improvements in, 489–490, 497–498, 502
  and length of life, 490, 497, 500
  standards of, 491–493
Nylon, 481–484

Oak Ridge, Tenn., plant of Atomic Energy Commission, 212, 219
Oatmeal, 505
Octadecane, 413
Octane, 413
Octane rating, 425–426
Octyl acetate, 445
Odors and flavors due to esters, 444
Oersted, Hans Christian, 608

Oildag, 384
Oil shales, 428
Oil of vitriol (*see* Sulfuric acid)
Oils, 445–449
  solubility of, 157
Oily rags as cause of spontaneous combustion, 275–276
Olefin hydrocarbons, 415–417
Oleic acid and oleates, 445–447
Oleomargarine, 448, 505
Oleum, 330–332
Olive oil, 446, 447
Olivine, 381
Onyx, 512
Opal, 512
Open-hearth process, 640, 642–643
Optical glass, 518–520
Oranges, 304, 445, 505
Orbit number, 225
Orbits, electron, 224–227
  maximum capacities, 225–226
Ores, 545–548
Organic acids, 440–443
Organic chemistry, origin of name, 395
Organic compounds, reason for large number of, 411, 415
Orlon, 485
Orthophosphoric acid and orthophosphates, 375–376
Osmium, 175, 542, 683, 688
Osmosis, 164–167
"Osmotic flower garden," 166–167
Osmotic pressure, 165–166
  of solutions of electrolytes, 311
Ostwald process, 358–359
Overcharging of storage battery, detrimental effect of, 678
Oxalic acid and oxalates, 442–443, 498
Oxidation, 661–662
  of oil paints, 447–448
Oxidation-reduction reactions, 661–667
Oxide ores, 545
  metallurgy of, 547
Oxides, of metals and nonmetals compared, 141–142
  solubility of, 157
Oxidizing agent, 662
Oxyacetylene torch, 57, 60–61, 417
Oxygas flame, 60, 61
Oxygen, 45–50, 53–61
  abundance in earth's crust and atmosphere, 46, 337
  allotropic modifications, 49–50

Oxygen, discovery, 45–46
  origin of name, 55
  physical properties, 49, 98, 259
  preparation, 46–49, 100–101
  reaction, with compounds, 57–58
    with elements, 56–57
  role in body, 59–60
  test for, 59
  uses, 59–61
Oxygen tent, 60
Oxyhydrogen torch, 56, 60–61
Oyster shell, 570
Ozone, 49–51

p (proton), 195
Paint rags as cause of spontaneous combustion, 275–276
Paints, oil, drying of, 447–448
  pigments in, cadmium sulfide, 626
    carbon black, 393
    ferric oxide, 653
    lithopone, 334
    titanium dioxide, 658
    white lead, 653
    zinc compounds, 625–626
Palladium, 175, 543, 683, 688
Palmitic acid and palmitates, 445–447
Pantothenic acid, 503
Paper, manufacture from paper stock, 463
  and wood pulp, 461–462
Paper stock, 462
Papermakers' alum, 617
Paraffin hydrocarbons, 412–415
Paraffin wax, 414, 421, 422
Park's process, 652
Particle size, effect on reaction rate, 278–279
Peanuts, 503, 505
  protein of, synthetic wool from, 470
Pearl, 570
Pears, odor of, 445
Peas, 503, 505
Peat, 391
Pellagra, 502
Pencils, 385
Pentane, 413
Pentlandite, 545
Peppers, green, 503, 505
Pepsin, 280
Percentage composition, calculation from formula, 260–261
Perchlorate test for potassium, 562
Perey, M., 555

Perfumes, use of esters in, 444
Periodic table, 169–179
  actual table, 174–175
  defects of, 178–179
  groups of, 173–177
  history of, 169–171
  periods of, 172–175
  relation, to atomic number, 233
    to metallic and nonmetallic properties, 176–177, 541
    to valence, 173, 176
  significance of, 169, 179
  subgroups of, 177
  subperiods of, 172, 177
  use in prediction of new elements, 171, 178
Permanent hardness of water, 582
Permanent waves, 469
Permeability of gases, 79
Peroxides, 143–144
Perspiration in control of body temperature, 114
Petrified wood, 512
Petroleum, 419–429
  cracking of, 422–423
  distillation of, 421–422
  distribution and size of resources, 419, 427–428
  history of, 419–421
  polymerization of low-boiling fractions, 423–424
  products from, 421–422, 427, 486
    (*See also* names of products, as Gasoline)
  relation, to explosives, 427
    to synthetic rubber, 427
  substitutes for, 392, 428–429
Petroleum ether, 421, 422
Petroleum jelly, 421, 422
Pewter, 654
pH, 303–307
Phlogiston theory, 54
Phoenicians, as supposed discoverers of glass, 516
  use of Cornwall tin mines, 649
Phosphate baking powders, 405
Phosphate rock, 367, 368, 376–377
Phosphates, 375–377
  as essential to soil fertility, 368, 376–377
Phosphene, 374
Phosphides, 372
Phosphorescence, 270, 372
Phosphoric acids and phosphates, 375–377
Phosphorous acids, 375

Phosphorus, 367–377
  chemical properties, 56, 276, 371–372
  in foods and nutrition, 368, 496–497
  forms (white, red, violet), 370–371
  glow of, 372–373
  history, 367, 368
  manufacture of, 368–370
  occurrence of, 367–368
  physical properties, 370–371
  uses, 373–374
Phosphorus halides, 371
Phosphorus-hydrogen compounds, 374
Phosphorus sesquisulfide (P_4S_3), use in matches, 374
Phosphorus tribromide in preparation of hydrogen bromide, 252–253
Phosphorus triiodide in preparation of hydrogen iodide, 253
Photochemical reaction in formation of vitamin D, 504
Photoelectric cells using cesium, 72, 557
Photoflash bulbs, 56
Photographers' hypo, 138
Photographic film, cellulose derivatives as base, 466
Photographic plate or film in detection of radioactivity, 182–183, 185–186
Photography, 600–602
Photosynthesis, 270, 338
Physical change, 8
Physical properties, 4
Physiological effects, of alcohol, 437
  of radiations, 187, 193, 214
Physiological salt solution, 166
Pig iron, 637–640
Pineapple, odor of, 445
Pipette, 80, 81
Pitchblende, 184
Planetary electrons (*see* Electrons, planetary)
Plants, assimilation of selenium by, 324
  as converters of solar energy, 270
  formation of proteins in, 495
  importance of potassium to, 555, 560–561
  relation, to calcium of soil, 498
    to pH of soil, 304–305
    to phosphorus in soil, 368, 479

Plants, silicon in, 509
  sulfur metabolism of, 321
Plaster of paris, 578
Plastic sulfur, 318, 320
Plasticizers, 479
Plastics, synthetic, 473–487
  basic structure, 474–475
  classification, 475–476
  (*See also* names of plastics)
Plate glass, 519
Platinum, 75, 175, 543, 683, 688
Plexiglas, 480–481
Plumbing, lead pipe for, 653, 655
  uses of copper in, 591, 592
Plutonium, 175, 683, 688
  production of, 217–218
Plutonium bomb, 213, 218, 219
Poison gas warfare, 235
Poisons, useful, 398–399, 452–457
Poke, 443
Polar molecules, 433–434
Polishes, silicone-containing, 522
Polonium, 175, 184–185, 188, 205, 206, 683, 688
Polyethylene (polythene), 476–477
Polyhydric alcohols, 438–439
Polymerization, 417
  of acrylonitrile, 485
  of adipic acid and hexamethylene diamine, 481–484
  of butadiene and isobutylene, 486
  of butadiene and styrene, 485–486
  of chloroprene, 486–487
  of dimethyl dichlorosilane, 521
  of dimethyl dichlorosilane and methyl trichlorosilane, 521
  of ethylene, 476–477
  of low-boiling petroleum fractions, 425–426
  of methyl methacrylate, 480–481
  of oil paints, 447–448
  of styrene, 479–480
  of tetrafluoroethylene, 477–478
  of vinyl chloride, 478–479
Polystyrene (styron), 479–480
Polythene (polyethylene), 476–477
Polyvinyl chloride plastics, 478–479
Porcelain, 618
Pork, 503, 505
Pork fat, hardness as related to diet, 446–447
Portland cement, 59, 578, 618–619
Positive (photographic), 602
Positive electrode (anode), reactions occurring at, 298, 302
Positron, 196

Potability of water, 134
Potash alum, 139
Potassium, compounds and uses, 560–561
  electron structure and physical properties, 543, 553
  as essential to nutrition, 496
  occurrence and sources, 545, 554–555
  in soil, importance to plant growth, 560
  relation to weathering of feldspar, 523
  use of fertilizers to restore, 560–561
  test for, 562, 563
Potassium chlorate, 47–48, 373–374, 561
Potassium chloride, 268
Potassium salts, solubility of, 157
Potato crop, effect of DDT on, 454
Potatoes, 505
Pottery, china, and porcelain, 618
Powder metallurgy, 550
Praseodymium, 174, 683, 688
Precipitate, 36
Prediction of elements, 171, 178
Pressed glass, 519
Pressure, defined, 92
  effect, on equilibrium point of reversible reactions, 288–289
    on solubility of gas in liquid, 155–156
  of gas, effect of temperature, 83–84
    effect of volume, 82–83
    explained by kinetic molecular theory, 92, 93–94
    how measured, 79–80
  vapor (*see* Vapor pressure)
Pressure cookers, 119–120
Prestone, 438
Priestley, Joseph, 46, 363, 470
Printers' ink, use of carbon black in, 393
Printing of photographs, 602
Producer gas, 407
Promethium, 175, 683, 688
"Proof" of alcohol solutions, 437
Propane, 412, 413
Propanol (propyl alcohol), 433
Propene (propylene), 416
Properties, defined, 1
  metallic and nonmetallic, 176–177, 541
Propionic acid, 441

Propylene (propene), 416
Propyne, 417
Protactinium, 174, 683, 688
   in uranium 238 series, 205
Proteins, 466–470
   in foods and nutrition, 491–496
   in nitrogen cycle in nature, 353, 354
   test for, 361
Protium, 200
Proton, 195
Provitamin A, 500
Prunes, 505
Ptyalin, 280
Purslane, 443
Pyrene fire extinguisher, 399–400
Pyrethrum, 455
Pyrex, 519, 520
Pyrite, 316, 635
Pyrophosphoric acid and pyrophosphates, 375, 376
Pyrosulfuric acid, 330, 331

Qualitative and quantitative chemistry compared, 80, 256
Quantitative, definition of, 20
Quartz, 511, 513–515
Quick freezing, 275
Quicklime (calcium oxide), 141, 576

Radiant energy in chemical reactions, 270
Radiation injury, 187, 214
Radiations, absorption by lead, 653, 654
Radical, 36
Radio tubes, use of magnesium in final evacuation of, 345–346
Radioactive disintegration rate, 189–191
Radioactive elements, properties of, 185–187
Radioactive isotopes, man-made, 153, 220–222
   naturally occurring, of potassium and rubidium, 555
Radioactivity, 181–193
   characteristics of, 185–187
   discovery of, 182–183
      importance of, 193
   explanation of, 187–189
   as modifying Dalton's theory, 23
   relation to discovery of radium and polonium, 183–185
   significance of, 193
Radiocobalt, 220

Radioiodine, 220–221
Radiophosphorus, 221, 222
Radiozinc, 221
Radium, 185–193, 205, 206, 567, 568, 570
   course of radioactive disintegration, 188
   discovery of, 185
   scarcity in nature, 192
   types of rays emitted by, 186–187
Radius of free atom, of alkali metals, 553
   of alkaline earth metals, 567
   of copper, silver, and gold, 588
   of halogens, 253
   of zinc, cadmium, and mercury, 621
Radon, 188, 205, 206, 226, 338, 341
Raindrops and snowflakes, dust as condensation nuclei for, 338
Rainmaking, 152
Rancidification of fats, 449
Rare earths, 172, 174–175
Rat poisons, 372, 398–399, 457
Rayleigh, Lord, 535–536
Rayon, 463–466
Rays, types of, produced by radioactivity, 186–187
Reactant, 33
Reaction rates, 273–280
   effect, of catalysts, 279–280
   of concentration of reactants, 277–278
   of surface area, 278–279
   of temperature, 274–277
Reagent, 274
Red phosphorus, 371, 374
Reducing agent, 329, 662
Reduction, 70–71, 662
Refractive index of diamond, 382
Refrigeration, mechanical, 126–127
   liquids used in, 127, 328, 346
   role in food preservation, 274–275
Regent diamond, 382, 383
Relative humidity, 125
Relativity, theory of, 202
Reproduction in relation to vitamin E, 506
Residue, 5
Resins for ion exchange, 584–585
Resistance, to DDT, 454
   to infection in relation to nutrition, 500, 502
Resources, of coal, 392
   of iron, 635–636
   of petroleum, 427–428

Respiration, 59–60
Reversals in Mendeléeff table, reason for, 178, 233
Reversible reactions, 282–290
Rhenium, 175, 684, 688
Rhombic sulfur, 317–319
Rhubarb, 443
Riboflavin, 493, 502, 505
Rickets, 504
Ring hydrocarbons, 418–419
Roasting of ores, 547–548
Rock, ground, as source of soil potassium, 561
"Rock oil," 420
Rock salt (sodium chloride), deposits of, 236
Rock wool insulation from slag, 639
Rockets, high-altitude, fuel requirements of, 60, 61
Roentgen, W. K., 187
Roll sulfur, 318
Roofing, use of copper for, 592
Rose quartz, 511
Rosin for sizing of paper, 463
Roughage utilization by ruminants, 452
Rubber, natural, 470–472
  silicone, 522
  synthetic, 485–487
    compared with natural rubber, 487
    resistance of, to temperature and other factors, 487
    vulcanization of, 320, 321, 470–472
Rubidium, 544, 552–555, 557, 562
Ruby, 607, 617, 618
Rum, 435
Ruminants, protein requirements of, 485–496
  as utilizing cellulose, 452
Rust, 8
Rutherford, Daniel, 343
Rutherford, Lord, 196–197
Rutile, 545, 656

Safety glass, 520
Sal ammoniac, 346
Salad dressing, 535
Saltpeter, Chilean, 343, 358
Salts, 292–293, 297, 306–307
  solubilities of, 157, 685–687
Samarium, 175, 684, 688
Sand, 59, 511
  relation to soil quality, 513–514
Sandpaper, 513

Sandstone, 514
Sapphire, 607, 617, 618
Saturated organic compounds, 446
Saturated solution, 148, 153
Sawdust, utilization of, 435, 452
Scandium, 174, 684, 688
Scavenger, 641, 643
Schaefer, Vincent, 152
Scheele, K. W., 45, 46, 235
Scientific method, 12–15
Scurvy, 502
Sea water, bromides in, 241
  chlorides in, 236
  conversion to drinking water, 585
  gold in, 603
  iodides in, 245
  as source, of bromine, 242–243
    of magnesium, 569–570
    of sodium chloride, 236–237
Searles Lake, Calif., 555, 560
Seaweed and sponges as source of iodine, 245
Second, 690
Selenium, 175, 324, 684, 688
  as by-product of copper refining, 591
Semipermeable membrane, 164–165
Separation, of mixtures, 149–151
  of uranium isotopes, 211, 212
Shale, oil from, 428
Shatterproof glass, use of polystyrene in, 480
Sheep, 452
Shellac, 447
Shellfish, copper in, 589, 591
Shells and bullets, use of lead for, 653
Sherardized iron, 624
Sherman, H. C., 490, 497
Shields against radiation, 653, 654
Shrink-fitting of metal parts, 403
Shrinkage of wool, 468–469
Siderite, 545
Signal flares, 56
Silane, 509
Silica (see Silicon dioxide)
Silica gel, 516
Silicate minerals, 523
Silicates, demonstration of osmosis using, 166–167
Silicon, 509–523
  comparison with carbon, 509–510, 514
  occurrence, 509
  preparation, 510

Silicon, properties, 511
  uses, 511
Silicon carbide (carborundum), 400
Silicon dioxide (silica), 511-516
  crystal structure, 514–515
  importance to soil quality, 513–514
  occurrence, 511–512
  properties, 512–513
  uses, 369–370, 512–513
Silicon steel (duriron), 644
Silicones, 520–523
Silk, 466–467
  tensile strength of, 484
Silliman, Benjamin, 421
Silver, 588, 595–602
  annual production of, 596
  compounds of, 598–599
    in photography, 601–602
  electron structure and physical properties, 542, 543, 588
  occurrence and metallurgy, 590, 595–596, 652
  properties and uses, 75, 597–599
  tarnishing of, 323
Silver alloys, 593, 598, 629
Silver colloids, 529
Silver iodide, 152
Silver ion, test for, 600
Silver nitrate, 598
Silver oxide, 268
Silver polish, 600
Silverfish, ability to digest cellulose, 452
Silverware, plated or sterling, 110–111
Simple decomposition (simple replacement) reactions, 36
Sinter, 618
Sizing agents in papermaking, 463
Skeleton, mineral elements in, 491, 496
Skin as affected by vitamin A, 500
Slag, 369–370, 639
Slaked lime (calcium hydroxide), 141, 576, 578
Slaking of lime, 141
Smelting of zinc, 623
Smithsonite, 545, 622
Smoke, Brownian movement in, 530–531
Smoke nuisance, control by Cottrell precipitator, 532, 533
Smoke screens, use of phosphorus to make, 371, 373

"Smoked sheet rubber," 471
Snow, dust in formation of, 338
  photograph of crystals, 113
Soap, action of, 535
  making of, 449
"Soapless soap," 449–450, 584
Soapstone, 569
Soda alum, 138
Soda ash (sodium carbonate), 557–559
Soda-lime glass, 518, 520
Soda pulp, 462
Sodium, electron structure and physical properties, 543, 553
  essential to nutrition, 496
  percentage of earth's crust, 554
  preparation of free metal, 556
  sources of, 545, 554
  test for, 562
  uses of, 556
Sodium acetate, 151
Sodium bicarbonate (sodium hydrogen carbonate), 558
Sodium carbonate (soda ash), 557–559
Sodium chloride, heat of formation, 268
  as industrial starting material, 557–559
  sources, 236–237, 554
  uses, 557
Sodium cyanide in electroplating and mining, 559, 596
Sodium fluoracetate, 457
Sodium fluoride, 248
Sodium hydride, 71–72
Sodium hydrogen carbonate (sodium bicarbonate), 558
Sodium hydroxide, industrial uses of, 557
  preparation by electrolysis of salt, 237, 302–303
Sodium iodate, 245
Sodium nitrate as fertilizer, 559
Sodium salts, solubility of, 157
Sodium silicate (waterglass), 515–516
Sodium sulfate in paper manufacture, 559
Sodium thiosulfate, 151
Sodium tripolyphosphate, 583
Sodium vapor lamps, 536, 556
Softening of water, 582–584
Soft glass, 518
"Soft" pork problem, 446–447

733

Soil, clay in, 523
  erosion of, relation to potassium problem, 560
  pH of, 304–305
  silica in, 513–514
Solar atom, 196–197, 224
Solar energy, 203
Solder, 654
Solid solution alloys, 549
Solubility, 5–7, 148–150
  effect of temperature on, 149–151, 288
  of gas in liquid, 155–156
  general rules of, 157
  of liquid in liquid, 156–157
  measurement of, 149
Solute, 147
Solution, energy change of, 154–155
Solutions, 146–157, 292–311
  classification of, 147–148
  definition of, 146
  of electrolytes, 292–311
  of gases in liquids, 155–156
  of inorganic substances, 685–687
  of liquids in liquids, 156, 157
  saturated, 151–152
  supersaturated, 151–152
Solvay process, 558–559
Solvent, 147
Sörensen, S. P. L., 303
Souring of milk, colloid change in, 534
Southern pine, pulp from, 462
Soybean oil, 447
Soybean protein, synthetic wool from, 470
Soybeans, 505
Specific gravity, 110–111
  of diamond, 382
  of metals, 542, 543
Specific heat, 109–110
  of ice, 113
Spectroscope, 563–564
Spectroscopic analysis, 563–564
Spectrum, 563
Speed, of light, 202
  of photographic film, 601
Spelter zinc, 623
Sphalerite, 316, 545, 622
Spinach, 443, 498, 505
Spinnerets, 463, 464, 484
"Spirits of hartshorn," 346
Sponges, 245, 509
Spontaneous combustion, 275–276
Stability, of compounds, relation to activity series, 74–75

Stability, relation to heat of formation, 268
  of elements, relation to binding energy, 205
Stainless steel, 644
Stalactites, 579, 580
Stalagmites, 579, 580
Standard solution, 308
Standard temperature and pressure (STP), 86
Stannous chloride, 651
Staple rayon, 464
Starch, 451
  reaction with iodine, 246
Starch-iodide paper, 246–247
Stars of enormous density, nucleonic explanation of, 197
Steam engine, 271
Steam heating, 115
Stearic acid and stearates, 441, 445–447, 449
Steel, 633–634, 640–643
  cutting and welding of, 61
  manufacture of, 640–643
    Bessemer process, 641–642
    future prospects, 635–636
    open-hearth process, 640, 642–643
  principal sites of, 634
  raw materials of, 634
  types of, 643–644
Stellite alloys, 647
Sterling silver, 598
Sterno, 436
Storage batteries, 653, 675–679
Strassfurt, Germany, salt mines, 555, 570
Strassmann, F., 209
Strawberries, 503
Strong versus weak acids, 299–301
Strong versus weak bases, 301–302
Strontianite, 545
Strontium, electron structure and properties, 543, 566
  occurrence, 545, 568
  test for, 585
Structural formulas, 414–415
  of wool fibers, 468
  (*See also* individual compounds)
Structural isomers, 414–415
  number possible, 415
Structural metal, titanium as potential, 656–657
Structure, of crystals (*see* Crystal structure)
  of matter, early ideas of, 181–182

Styrene, in formation of synthetic rubber, 485
 polymerization of, 479
Styron (polystyrene), 479
Subgroups of periodic table, 177
Sublimation, 114
Subperiods, 172, 177
Substance, definition of, 4
Sucrose, 450–451, 505
Sugars, 450–451
 refining of, 7, 390
 solubilities of, 157
Sulfate hardness of water, 582
Sulfate process of making kraft paper, 462
Sulfates, 333, 334
 solubility of, 157
"Sulfating" in lead storage cells, 678
Sulfide ores, metallurgy of, 547
Sulfides, reaction with oxygen, 58
 use for identifying metal ions, 323
Sulfites and sulfurous acid, 326, 328–329
Sulfur, 314–323, 326–335
 chemical properties of, 70, 320–321, 333
 essential to nutrition, 321, 496
 mining by Frasch process, 316, 317
 new method for extraction from volcanic rock, 317
 occurrence, 314, 316, 317
 physical forms of, 317–320
 uses of, 305, 321, 471
Sulfur cross links, between protein chains in hair, 469
 in vulcanized rubber, 472
Sulfur dioxide, 98, 326–328, 331
Sulfur lambda (Sλ), 318–320
Sulfur monochloride, 321, 339
Sulfur mu (Sμ), 318–320
Sulfur trioxide, 326, 329–331
Sulfuric acid, manufacture of, 330–332
 properties, of concentrated, 332–333
 of dilute, 333–334
 uses of, 334, 376–377
Sulfurous acid and sulfites, 326, 328–329
Sun, energy of, 203
 ultraviolet radiation of, 50
Sunset, color of, 536
Sunshine and vitamin D, 504

Superchlorination of drinking water, 135
Supercooled liquid(s), 152, 318, 320
 glass as, 513, 518
 plastic sulfur as, 318, 320
 silica as, 512–513
Superphosphate, 376–377
Supersaturated solutions, 151–152
Surface area, of battery plates, effect on amperage, 674–675, 677
 effect on reaction rates, 278–279
Sweet potatoes, 500, 505
Swiss chard, 443, 498, 505
Sylvite, 545
Symbols for elements, 25–27
Sympathetic ink, 140
Synthesis, 17–18, 36
Synthetic, meaning of, in two senses, 395
Synthetic diamonds, 383–384
Synthetic fibers, 481–485
Synthetic graphite, 384
Synthetic rubbers, 485–487
Synthetic sapphires and rubies, 617

2,4,5-T, 456
Talc, 513, 569
Tallow, 445–447
Tanning of hides, 533–534
Tantalum, 175, 684, 688
Tar, 421, 422
Tarnishing of silver, copper, and mercury, 323, 597
Tartaric acid, 443
Tartrate baking powders, 405
Tax on alcohol, 437
Tear gas, benzyl bromide as, 245
Technetium, 175, 684, 688
Teeth, relation to fluorides, 249–250
 relation to vitamin D, 504
Teflon, 148, 477–478
Telephone filters from quartz, 513
Tellurium and its compounds, 324
Temperature, 94–95
 effect on equilibrium point of reversible reactions, 287–288, 290
 demonstration of, 361–362
 effect on reaction rates, 274–277
 effect on solubility, 149–151, 155, 156, 288
 effect on volume and pressure of gases, 83–86
Temperature scales, 84, 111
Temporary hardness of water, 582

Tensile strength, 460
  of metals, 542
  of textile fibers, 484
Terbium, 174, 684, 688
Termites, ability to digest cellulose, 452
Ternary compounds, naming of, 42
Terra cotta, 618
Tetraethyllead, 244, 425, 556, 653
Tetrafluoroethylene, polymerization of, 477
Tetrahedral structure of diamond crystal, 386–387
Texas City explosion, 351, 352
Textile dyeing, use of aluminum hydroxide in, 617
Thallium, 174, 684, 688
Theory, 13
  of relativity, 202
Thermal contact, 94
Thermite, 616
Thermochemical equations, 266–267
Thermometers, use of mercury for, 627
Thermonuclear bomb, 203
Thermoplastic polymers, 475–476
Thermosetting polymers, 476
Thermostats, use of mercury for, 627, 628
Thiamine (vitamin B_1), 321, 493, 501–502, 505
Thiocyanate, reaction with ferric ion, 645
Thiosulfates, 334–335
  complex ion formation with silver, 602
Thorium, 174, 684, 688
  in uranium 238 series, 205
Thorium nitrate in experiment to demonstrate radioactivity, 182–183
Thulium, 175, 684, 688
Thyroid gland and thyroxine, 247
Tile, 618
Tin, 543, 545, 547, 649–651
Tin alloys, 593, 629, 651, 654
"Tin disease," 650
Tin foil, 650
Tin-plating of steel, 625, 650–651
Tin tetrachloride, 651
Tincture of iodine, 247
Titanium, 543, 545, 655–658
  in rose quartz, 511
Titanium dioxide, 463, 464, 656, 658
Titanium tetrachloride, 656

Titration, 307–309
Tobacco in relation to potassium fertilizers, 560
Toluene, 418, 427
Tomatoes, 304, 503, 505
  marked by radiozinc, 221
Topaz, 513
Toxicity, of beryllium compounds, 575
  of cadmium, 627
  of carbon disulfide, 398–399
  of carbon monoxide, 57, 408
  of carbon tetrachloride, 400
  of DDT, 454
  of hydrogen sulfide, 322
  of lead compounds, 654–655
  of mercury compounds, 630
  of methanol, 435
  of selenium compounds, 324
  of white phosphorus, 370
Tracer studies, 221, 222
Transition elements, 177
Transmutations, atomic, 205–206, 208, 209
Transuranium elements, 173
Tribasic acids, 294
Triple superphosphate, 377
Trisodium phosphate as water softener, 583
Tritium, 200
Tung oil, 448
Tungsten (wolfram), 175, 543, 550, 616, 684, 688
  for filament of light bulbs, 340–341
    use of diamond dies for drawing, 383
Tungsten steel, 644
Turpentine, 448
Type metal, 651, 654
Typhus fever control by DDT, 453

Ultraviolet radiation, 50
  in formation of vitamin D, 504
  of sun, changed to heat by ozone layer of atmosphere, 50
Unsaturated hydrocarbons, 416
Uranium, in discovery of radioactivity, 182–184
  in estimating age of earth, 191
  isotopes, relative proportions in nature, 212
  purification of, 212
Uranium 235, fission of, 209, 211–213

Uranium 238, conversion to plutonium, 218
  radioactive disintegration of, 205
Uranium bomb, 208–214
Uranium reactor, 216–222
  to produce energy, 219–220
  to produce plutonium, 217–219
  to produce radioactive isotopes, 220–222
Urea, as first organic compound to be synthesized, 395
  as source of protein for ruminants, 495–496

Vacuum, 79
Vacuum distillation, 137–138
Valence, 37–40, 228–231
  of common elements and radicals, 38–40
  electronic explanation of, 228–231
  meaning of, 37–38
  relation to periodic table, 173, 176–177, 179
  two types of, 228–231
  variable, 39, 41–42
Valence orbit, 228
Vanadium, 175, 644, 684, 688
Van der Waals' forces, 99–101, 387–388
Van't Hoff's law, 287–288, 290
Vapor pressure, 117–124
  how measured, 117
  relation to boiling point, 118–120
  variation with temperature, 117–118, 123, 288
  table showing (for water), 689
Vargas diamond, 382
Vegetable oils, hardening (hydrogenation) of, 72, 446
Vegetables, organic acids in, 443
Velocity of light as factor in Einstein equation, 202
Vinegar, 442
  pH of, 304
Vinyl chloride, polymerization of, 478–479
Violet phosphorus, 371
Viscose cellophane, 463–464
Viscose rayon, 463–464
  tensile strength of, 484
Vitamin A and its precursors, 493, 499–501, 505
Vitamin A value, 500, 501
Vitamin B$_1$ (thiamine), 493, 501–502, 505
Vitamin B$_6$, 502

Vitamin B$_{12}$, 496, 502–503
Vitamin C (ascorbic acid), 489, 493, 503, 505
Vitamin D, 493, 504
Vitamin D milk, 504
Vitamin E, 506
Vitamin K, 504
Vitamins, 491
Voltage, of B battery, 674
  factors determining, 675
  of lead storage batteries, 677
  of single dry cell, 674
Volume of gas, effect of pressure, 82–83
  effect of temperature, 85–86
  how measured, 80–82
Volume change of reaction, calculation of, 263–264
Von Laue, M., 385
Vulcanization of rubber, 320, 321, 470–472
Vycor, 519, 520

Warfarin, 457
Washing soda, 138, 304, 559, 582
Water, 107–126, 133–143
  as basis of units of measure, 109–111
  boiling of, 118–122
  chemical properties of, 65–67, 138–142, 239, 249
  critical constants of, 98
  density of, 110, 112–113
  electrolysis of, 48–49, 65
  evaporation of, 117, 122–124
  hard, 581–584
  heat of formation of, 268
  heat of fusion of, 113–114
  heat of vaporization of, 114–116
  of hydration, 138–140
  importance of, 107–108
  impurities in, 132–134, 581
  ionization of, 302–303
  natural, 132–136
  purification for chemical use, 136–137, 584–585
  test for, 140
  treatment for household use and drinking, 134–136, 582–584
Water-borne diseases, 134
Water gas, 67, 407
Waterglass, 515–516
Waterproofing with dimethyl dichlorosilane, 522–523
Waxes, 445
Weak versus strong acids, 299–301

737

Weak versus strong bases, 301–302
Weed killers, 455–456
Weight calculations, 262–263
Weizmann, C., 440
Welding, 61
   with thermite, 616
   use of helium atmosphere in, 340
Wells, Horace, 363
Wheat germ, 502
Whisky, 435
White cast iron, 639–640
White gold, 603
White lead as paint pigment, 653
White phosphorus, 370–371, 373–374
White tin, 650
Whole-grain cereals, 497, 502
Whole wheat, 502, 505
Williams, R. R., 501
Window glass, 518, 520
Wine, 435
Winkler, C., 171, 178
Wöhler, F., 395
Wolfram, status of name, 71
   (*See also* Tungsten)
Women, recommended dietary allowances for, 493
Wood, composition of, 461
   destructive distillation of, 388
   fuel value of, 391
   manufacture of paper from, 461–463
Wood alcohol (*see* Methyl alcohol)
Wood waste products as source of glucose, 435, 452
Wool, 466–469, 484
Wounds, healing of, in relation to vitamin C, 503

X-ray studies of crystal structure, 385–387

X-ray tube, 187
   use of beryllium in, 573
X rays, 186–187, 189
Xanthoproteic acid test, 361
Xenon, 226, 338, 341
Xerophthalmia, 500

Yeast, 280
Yields, calculation of, 256, 262–263
   of gasoline from crude oil, 422–424
   of reversible reactions, ways to increase, 285–290
Ytterbium, 175, 684, 688
Yttrium, 174, 684, 688

Zeolites for water softening, 583–584
Zinc, 621–626
   chemical properties, 68, 75, 333, 623–624
   compounds, 625–626
   metallurgy, 622–623
   as nutritionally essential, 496
   occurrence, 545, 622
   physical properties and electron structure, 542, 543, 621, 623–624
   test for, 626
   uses, 624–625, 652
Zinc alloys, 593, 625
Zinc blende (sphalerite), 622
Zinc-hydrochloric acid cell, 672–673
Zinc oxide, 268, 471, 625–626
Zinc phosphide as rodent poison, 372
Zinc sulfide, 323, 626
Zincite, 545, 622
Zirconium, 174, 684, 688
Zymase, 280

THE PERIODIC TABLE

GROUPS

	Ia	IIa	IIIa	IVa	Va	VIa	VIIa	VIII
Hydride / Oxide	RH / R$_2$O	RH$_2$ / RO	R$_2$O$_3$	RO$_2$	R$_2$O$_5$	RO$_3$	R$_2$O$_7$	RO$_4$

ATOMIC NUMBERS ABOVE SYMBOLS

PERIODS

Period	Ia	IIa	IIIa	IVa	Va	VIa	VIIa	VIII		
1	1 H 1.0080									
2	3 Li 6.940	4 Be 9.013								
3	11 Na 22.991	12 Mg 24.32								
4	19 K 39.100	20 Ca 40.08	21 Sc 44.96	22 Ti 47.90	23 V 50.95	24 Cr 52.01	25 Mn 54.94	26 Fe 55.85	27 Co 58.94	28 Ni 58.71
5	37 Rb 85.48	38 Sr 87.63	39 Y 88.92	40 Zr 91.22	41 Nb 92.91	42 Mo 95.95	43 Tc (99)	44 Ru 101.1	45 Rh 102.91	46 Pd 106.7
6	55 Cs 132.91	56 Ba 137.36	57 La 138.92	58* to 71	72 Hf 178.58	73 Ta 180.95	74 W 183.86	75 Re 186.22	76 Os 190.2	77 Ir 192.2	78 Pt 195.09
7	87 Fr [223]	88 Ra 226.05	89 Ac 227	90† to 103						

RARE EARTH

*Group IIIa Lanthanide Series	58 Ce 140.13	59 Pr 140.92	60 Nd 144.27	61 Pm [145]
†Group IIIa Actinide Series	90 Th 232.05	91 Pa 231	92 U 238.07	93 Np [237]